THE GREAT ICE AGE

THE
GREAT ICE AGE

And its Relation to the Antiquity of Man

By JAMES GEIKIE, LL.D., F.R.S., ETC. LU

OF H. M. GEOLOGICAL SURVEY OF SCOTLAND

SECOND EDITION, REVISED

1877

Maps and Illustrations

LONDON:

EDWARD STANFORD, 55, CHARING CROSS, S.W.

DJU

g

TO

ANDREW CROMBIE RAMSAY, LL.D., F.R.S.

DIRECTOR-GENERAL OF THE GEOLOGICAL SURVEYS OF THE UNITED KINGDOM.

MY DEAR RAMSAY,

There is no one from whom in the course of my geological studies I have received more help and encouragement than you. Not only have your scientific writings been of essential service to me, but I have gathered much also in conversation from your wide experience, and feel that I have gained a great deal by having come in contact with one possessed of such originality of conception and independence of thought as yourself. The lessons that stand us most in stead are not always got out of books, and I am glad of this opportunity to acknowledge my indebtedness to you for many such lessons. It gives me much pleasure to inscribe this volume with your name, in token of my regard and affection for you as my teacher and friend.

Believe me,

My dear RAMSAY,

Very sincerely yours,

JAMES GEIKIE.

EDINBURGH : *December*, 1873.

PREFACE TO FIRST EDITION.

————◆————

IN the following pages I have endeavoured to give a systematic account of the Glacial Epoch, with special reference to its changes of climate. My intention at first was to restrict myself to a brief description of British glacial and postglacial deposits, for the purpose of pointing out the general succession established, or in process of being established, by geologists in this country; and, thereafter, of drawing some conclusions as to the position in the series of the palæolithic gravels, &c., of southern England. But I eventually found, that in order to make my argument intelligible to non-specialists, it would be necessary to describe in detail some sufficiently large area, in which glacial deposits might be considered as typically developed. It is for this reason that I have entered so fully into the geological history of glacial and postglacial Scotland. In delineating the post-tertiary geology of that country, I have been enabled to discuss many elementary matters, which are, no doubt, sufficiently familiar to my fellow-hammerers, but which a general reader could hardly be expected to know. In short, while treating of the Scottish deposits, I have endeavoured to explain the mode of investigating, and the principles of interpreting glacial phenomena. I also thought that by confining detailed sketching to the glacial history of a well-defined region, it would be possible to convey to the reader's mind a more vivid impression of what the Glacial Epoch really was, than if I ventured to take a wider canvas. But my chief aim throughout has been to indicate the succession of climatic changes that obtained during the Glacial Epoch—not in Scotland alone, but in every glaciated region which has been carefully studied by geologists. For I have long been of opinion that until this has been done, until we clearly understand what the succession of changes during the Ice Age was, it is premature to speculate upon the geological age of those deposits which yield the earliest traces of man in Britain. The great difference that obtains between the fauna of undoubted postglacial and recent beds in Scotland, north of England, Wales, and Ireland, on the one hand, and the cave-deposits and palæolithic gravels of southern England on the other, has long been a puzzle to me, as it has, no doubt, been to other geologists. But it was not until years had been spent in the study of the glacial deposits that what I conceive to be the true explanation of the difficulty dawned upon me.

Geologists are aware that the postglacial age of the cave-deposits has not infrequently been called in question. Dr. Buckland, Mr. Godwin-Austen, and Professor Ramsay, have each expressed a belief that some of our cave-deposits may date back to preglacial times ; and Mr. Godwin-Austen long ago pointed out that the " sub-aerial beds " of the English Channel districts were the equivalents of the glacial deposits elsewhere ; and that the broad alluvia of our more southerly rivers, such as the Severn, the Fal, the Dart, and the Thames, belong to a period prior to the great submergence, during which the high-level marine drifts of Wales were accumulated. In other words he showed that these river-gravels could not be referred to postglacial times. Within more recent years a modification of Mr. Godwin-Austen's view has been energetically put forward by Mr. W. Boyd Dawkins, who is of opinion that our palæolithic deposits belong to a time subsequent to the great submergence just referred to. He holds that man and the extinct mammalia lived in the south of England at a period when Scotland, Wales, and the northern districts of England were covered with ice and snow, and when our summers were warm and our winters very severe. Other geologists, however, as Mr. Prest-

wich, have contended that we have no evidence of warm summers having obtained during palæolithic times; while, yet
others have, on the contrary, thought the evidence pointed to a
considerably warmer climate than we now enjoy. Sir C. Lyell
gives two explanations of the facts, and thinks the commingling
of arctic and southern forms of animal life, may point either to
a period of strongly-contrasted summers and winters, or to
fluctuations of climate; but he is clearly of opinion that all the
palæolithic gravels belong to postglacial times. The Rev. O.
Fisher has described a deposit, called by him "trail," which he
believes to be the product of land-ice; as it overlies in places
palæolithic deposits, he considers that a glacial period has
intervened since the disappearance of palæolithic man. Mr. J.
Croll has referred to the apparently conflicting evidence of the
mammaliferous deposits, as an indication of former changes of
climate, and this is the view which Sir J. Lubbock inclines to
support, and which is advocated in these pages. I have, however, ventured an explanation of the peculiar distribution of
palæolithic gravels, differing from any previously advanced.
None of these gravels in my opinion are postglacial, but all
must be relegated to preglacial and interglacial times. Their
absence from the northern districts I account for by showing
that they have been swept out of these regions by confluen.
glaciers, and by the sea during the period of great submergencet

These views I first broached during the discussion that followed upon the reading of an interesting paper by Mr. W.
Boyd Dawkins, at the Edinburgh meeting of the British Association in 1871. But as the time allowed for discussion at
these meetings is necessarily short, I was unable to do justice
to my views; believing them, however, to be worth attention, I
gave an outline of them in a series of monthly articles in the
Geological Magazine, the first of which appeared in the number
for December, 1871. These articles I subsequently collected,
and re-issued with some additions and rearrangements in the
summer of the year following.

As far as I know, these papers were the first attempt to

prove, by correlating glacial deposits, that the palæolithic gravels of southern England could not be of postglacial age, but ought to be referred to interglacial and preglacial times. They also bring forward, for the first time, reason to show that a wide land-surface existed in the British area after the disappearance of the ice-sheets, and before the period of great submergence had commenced.

The recent discovery of human remains in the Victoria Cave, where, as Mr. Tiddeman has shown, the deposits are overlaid by a glacial accumulation, is direct evidence in corroboration of the conclusions which I had previously arrived at and published.

In the preparation of this volume I have availed myself of a number of papers, communicated from time to time to various scientific societies and publications, and in fact these chapters may be considered as only an expansion of the articles "On Changes of Climate during the Glacial Epoch," which first appeared in the pages of the *Geological Magazine.*

It would be unbecoming in me, if I did not here acknowledge the obligations I am under to the writings of those who have preceded me in describing the glacial deposits of Scotland, more especially to the successive publications of Messrs. Maclaren, Chambers, Jamieson, and A. Geikie. I had hoped to be able to append a list of works by these and other authors, relating to the glacial and postglacial geology of the British Islands, together with such foreign papers as I had come across in the course of my reading; but after making some progress, I was reluctantly compelled to abandon my design, as the list threatened to form quite a volume of itself.

To my colleagues on the Geological Survey of Scotland, I am indebted for much valuable assistance, willingly rendered. Of these, my old friend, Mr. B. N. Peach, supplied me with the highly characteristic sketches of striated stones, and the beautiful views of Loch Doon, and the Carse of Stirling; while from the facile pencil of Mr. H. M. Skae, I received the fine drawing of the Coolin Mountains, and the illustrations of

Alpine, Arctic, and Antarctic scenery which adorn these pages. Mr. R. L. Jack also kindly furnished me with the map and sections of Loch Lomond, and with the chart showing the physiography of western Scotland that would appear upon an elevation of 600 feet. To the same obliging friend I am likewise indebted for many practical hints and suggestions during the progress of my work through the press. Mr. R. Etheridge, Jun., has enhanced the value of these pages by the long list of organic remains which is given in the Appendix; and has, moreover, laid me under many obligations by the trouble he has taken to verify references and consult libraries, of which my absence from town on official duty would otherwise, in many cases, have prevented me availing myself. Mr. J. Croll, Mr. J. Horne, and Mr. D. R. Irvine, have also obliged me with a number of glacial notes.

To several of my colleagues on the English Geological Survey, I have likewise to render my acknowledgments. Mr. A. H. Green furnished me with a long series of notes relating to the glacial deposits of England, which, however, the limits I had set for myself have not allowed me to make use of. But I hope my friend may himself be induced to give some general account of the post-tertiary deposits of England—a work which would be of essential service to the students of glacial geology. Mr. Green was also good enough to read over the proofs of Chapter IX., and to suggest a number of improvements and additions which I have gladly incorporated with the text. Mr. Etheridge examined for me several lists of shells from the "pliocene sands" of northern Italy, and his opinions and advice have been of great assistance. I am also indebted to Mr. Whitaker for a diagram-section and notes, relating to the gravels of the Thames valley.

* * * * * * *

PREFACE TO SECOND EDITION.

THE three years which have elapsed since the publication of this work have added considerably to our knowledge of the Glacial Epoch, and it has been gratifying to me to find that the new facts disclosed have very materially strengthened my general argument. It becomes increasingly evident that the Epoch in question was not one continuous Age of Ice, but consisted rather of a series of alternate cold (glacial) and warm or genial (interglacial) periods; and the facts as they multiply make it clearer than ever that the ancient ossiferous and palæolithic gravels and cave-deposits of England cannot be assigned to a later date than the last genial interval of the Ice Age, while some portion of them certainly belongs to earlier interglacial and even perhaps to preglacial times. The recent most important and interesting discovery by Mr. S. B. J. Skertchly of palæolithic brick-earth underlying the chalky boulder-clay near Brandon, puts it beyond doubt that man lived in Britain as early at least as that interglacial mild period which preceded the climax of glacial cold.

In the first issue of this work many points of interest connected with the glacial accumulations themselves were purposely left untouched, attention having been directed chiefly to those facts which served to illustrate the general climatic conditions that obtained during glacial and postglacial ages. Some of the points in question, however, appear to me now to have a more direct bearing upon the general argument of these pages than I formerly supposed, and the opportunity of the present re-issue has therefore been taken to discuss these in such detail as seemed desirable. For the convenience of those who have perused the first edition, and who may wish to see what novelties appear in the present volume, I may note here some of the chief additions and alterations.

Considerable changes have been made in several of the chapters relating to Scotland. The account of the till has been revised, and such details added as appeared to illustrate more fully the mode in which that deposit has been accumulated. I formerly attempted to restrict the term *boulder-clay* to morainic deposits in which indications of marine action were more or less well-marked; while the term *till* was applied exclusively to masses of stony clay in which traces of sea-work were wholly wanting. But although care was taken to state that the one kind of deposit frequently passes or shades into the other, and that both had evidently been formed by the grinding-action of land-ice, yet I find that my attempt to modify our terminology has only led to misapprehension. I have, therefore, given it up, and now use the words *till* and *boulder-clay* as strictly synonymous, and signifying merely a deposit which owes its origin more or less directly to the grinding-action of glaciers. Further descriptions of the Scotch interglacial beds have been given, and the shelly tills or boulder-clays have been treated at some considerable length. The origin suggested for most of these deposits is in the main the same as that which Dr. Croll was the first to advance in regard to the shelly till of Caithness; but personal observations in the Outer Hebrides and the north-west of Scotland have enabled me to bring forward certain evidence in connection with the subject which seems to throw not a little light on the conditions that obtained in Scotland prior to the advance of the last ice-sheet.

I formerly maintained that the gravel and sand of the "kame series" was undoubtedly of fluviatile and torrential origin; but I also held, in common with many geologists, that these deposits were subsequently modified during a period of considerable submergence of the land. I now advance a step

further, however, and agree with Mr. Jamieson that the sea
has not had any share in the formation of the kames. Detailed
work in the valleys of the Tweed and the Tay, and explorations
in the maritime districts of the north-west Highlands, have
convinced me that Mr. Jamieson is right in concluding that no
great submergence has overtaken Scotland since the close of
the Glacial Epoch. It will be seen that this modification of my
views in regard to Scotland has enabled me to bring the glacial
deposits of that country into much closer relationship with
those of England, and to present a classification which is altogether more satisfactory.

The account of the glacial deposits of England has been
almost entirely re-written, and embraces the results of recent
personal observations in the eastern and north-eastern counties.
In the former edition I sought to show that all the evidence led
up to only one conclusion : to this, namely—that while the
ossiferous and palæolithic gravels, &c., clearly rested upon and
were therefore younger than the early glacial deposits of the
eastern counties, they were, nevertheless, overlapped by, and
consequently belonged to, an older date than those younger
accumulations of glacial origin which cover such wide areas in
the north of England, in Wales, and in Scotland. It is true
I could point to no actual section in England where this
inferred overlap was visible ; and however cogent and
unanswerable my argument might appear to be, I was yet well
aware that to certain minds nothing short of such an actual
section would suffice for a demonstration. From what I had
already seen of the drifts of the north-eastern counties, I certainly hoped that a section of the kind desiderated would ere
long be discovered, and I have not been disappointed. During
a recent visit to the south-east of Yorkshire, I found that
certain gravel-beds which have yielded mammalian remains
and myriads of *Cyrena fluminalis* and other shells, and which
are acknowledged to be of more recent date than the great
chalky boulder-clay of the eastern counties, are covered by a
mass of unstratified till or boulder-clay in such a way as to

show that the till in question is a true *moraine profonde*. In other words, this section demonstrates that after the deposition of the ossiferous gravels and *Cyrena*-beds a great ice-sheet stretched south as far at least as the valley of the Humber, where its bottom-moraine may now be seen overlapping upon deposits which are clearly representative of the *Cyrena*-beds and palæolithic gravels that occur farther to the south.

Mr. Hardman's investigations in Ireland have enabled me to add something to the account of the interglacial and late glacial deposits of that country.

The chapter relating to the Swedish glacial deposits has been revised and brought up to date, the chief additions being some references to the occurrence of interglacial freshwater deposits and an account of Mr. D. Hummel's theory of the origin of the åsar.

The principal item of interest mentioned in the revised description of the glacial deposits of Switzerland is the recent discovery of traces of man in the Dürnten interglacial beds.

The account of the Italian glacial deposits has been transferred from the Appendix to the text, and some details have been added. These latter refer chiefly to the very remarkable exposure near Como of deposits containing characteristic "pliocene" shells commingled with striated stones.

The glacial deposits of North America are discussed in much greater detail than before, attention being specially directed to the evidence bearing upon the former existence of interglacial periods. For a number of MS. notes relating to the Northwestern States, my thanks are due to Professor N. H. Winchell, State Geologist of Minnesota,

The concluding chapters, treating of the ossiferous and palæolithic deposits, the climatic conditions of pleistocene times, &c., remain much as they were originally written ; but they now include an account of the glacial and interglacial deposits of the Fenland, for which I am greatly indebted to my friend and colleague, Mr. Sydney B. J. Skertchly, and to which I would direct the special notice of English geologists.

This account, I should mention here, is merely an outline-sketch of the results obtained by my colleague during his survey of the Fenland; the full details of his work being given in the official memoir, " The Geology of the Fenland."

The foregoing are among the more important additions and changes, but I have altered and added freely wherever it seemed advisable to do so, in order either to elucidate the line of argument pursued or to present a more complete picture of the physical and climatic conditions of glacial and postglacial times.

A number of new woodcut illustrations have been inserted : I have also borrowed from Dr. Croll's " Climate and Time," a chart illustrative of the direction of ocean currents and winds; and from the " Report of the Geological Survey of Ohio," a sketch map of North America, indicating the main lines of glacial striæ. The map showing the submerged rock-basins of Scotland has been extended so as to embrace the area of the Irish Sea; and the general map of Scotland, showing the direction of the glacial striæ, has been brought up to date, thanks to the assistance of my colleagues in Scotland.

I am much indebted to Mr. R. Etheridge, jun., who has been good enough to revise the valuable list of organic remains occurring in the glacial deposits of Scotland, which he drew up for the first edition. My acknowledgments are also due to several of my English colleagues :—to Mr. Whitaker, who pointed out to me a number of characteristic sections of drift in Suffolk, and readily furnished me with many interesting notes relating to the glacial deposits of the eastern districts of England; and to Mr. H. B. Woodward, for similar assistance in Norfolk. Mr. S. B. J. Skertchly took me over the famous palæolithic districts round Brandon, and pointed out to me the evidence which has led him to conclude that the palæolithic beds which overlie the great clalky boulder-clay cannot be assigned to a later date than the last interglacial period. To the same friend I am much indebted for the excellent account of the chalky till which appears in Chapter XXIX.; he also forwarded

me some notes of his recent great "find" of human implements below that till, immediately after the discovery was made;
but they reached me too late for more than brief notice in a
"postscript." Professor Hull has obliged me with some notes
and a section illustrative of the drift deposits of Ireland : and I
am under many obligations to those foreign geologists who have
been good enough to furnish me with early copies of their
papers, &c., some of which I should not otherwise have been
able to obtain; for even the best of our scientific libraries are
not always "up to date."

GEOLOGICAL SURVEY, PERTH, N.B.,
    August, 1876.

CONTENTS.

———◆———

CHAPTER XIV.

BEDS SUBJACENT TO AND INTERCALATED WITH THE SCOTTISH TILL—*Continued.*

CHAPTER XV.

BEDS SUBJACENT TO AND INTERCALATED WITH THE SCOTTISH TILL—*Continued.*

CHAPTER XVI.

BEDS SUBJACENT TO AND INTERCALATED WITH THE SCOTTISH TILL—*Continued.*

CHAPTER XVII.

INTERGLACIAL DEPOSITS AND SHELLY TILL OF SCOTLAND.—SUMMARY OF RESULTS.

CHAPTER XVIII.

UPPER DRIFT DEPOSITS OF SCOTLAND.

CHAPTER XXV.

POSTGLACIAL AND RECENT DEPOSITS OF SCOTLAND.

CHAPTER XXVI.

POSTGLACIAL AND RECENT DEPOSITS OF SCOTLAND—*Continued.*

CHAPTER XXVII.

POSTGLACIAL AND RECENT DEPOSITS OF SCOTLAND—*Continued.*

CHAPTER XXVIII.

GLACIAL DEPOSITS OF ENGLAND.

CHAPTER XXIX.

GLACIAL DEPOSITS OF ENGLAND—*Continued.*

CHAPTER XXX.

GLACIAL DEPOSITS OF ENGLAND—*Continued.*

CHAPTER XXXI.

GLACIAL DEPOSITS OF IRELAND.—POSTGLACIAL BEDS OF ENGLAND AND IRELAND.

CHAPTER XXXII.

GLACIAL DEPOSITS OF SCANDINAVIA.

CHAPTER XXXIII.

GLACIAL DEPOSITS OF SWITZERLAND.

CHAPTER XXXIV.

GLACIAL DEPOSITS OF NORTHERN ITALY.

CHAPTER XXXV.

GLACIAL DEPOSITS OF NORTH AMERICA.

CHAPTER XXXVI.

GENERAL SUCCESSION OF GLACIAL AND INTERGLACIAL DEPOSITS.

CHAPTER XXXVII.

CAVE-DEPOSITS AND ANCIENT RIVER-GRAVELS OF ENGLAND.

CHAPTER XXXVIII.

CLIMATE OF THE PALÆOLITHIC PERIOD.

CHAPTER XXXIX.

GEOLOGICAL AGE OF THE PALÆOLITHIC DEPOSITS.

PAGE

CHAPTER XL.

GEOLOGICAL AGE OF THE PALÆOLITHIC DEPOSITS—*Continued.*

CHAPTER XLI.

GEOLOGICAL POSITION OF NEOLITHIC, PALÆOLITHIC, AND OSSIFEROUS DEPOSITS OF FOREIGN COUNTRIES.

CHAPTER XLII.

APPENDIX.

THE GREAT ICE AGE

THE
GREAT ICE AGE

And its Relation to the Antiquity of Man

By JAMES GEIKIE, LL.D., F.R.S., ETC. LU

OF H. M. GEOLOGICAL SURVEY OF SCOTLAND

SECOND EDITION, REVISED

1877

Maps and Illustrations

LONDON:

EDWARD STANFORD, 55, CHARING CROSS, S.W.

DJU
G

TO

ANDREW CROMBIE RAMSAY, LL.D., F.R.S.

DIRECTOR-GENERAL OF THE GEOLOGICAL SURVEYS OF THE UNITED KINGDOM.

MY DEAR RAMSAY,

There is no one from whom in the course of my geological studies I have received more help and encouragement than you. Not only have your scientific writings been of essential service to me, but I have gathered much also in conversation from your wide experience, and feel that I have gained a great deal by having come in contact with one possessed of such originality of conception and independence of thought as yourself. The lessons that stand us most in stead are not always got out of books, and I am glad of this opportunity to acknowledge my indebtedness to you for many such lessons. It gives me much pleasure to inscribe this volume with your name, in token of my regard and affection for you as my teacher and friend.

Believe me,

My dear RAMSAY,

Very sincerely yours,

JAMES GEIKIE.

EDINBURGH : *December*, 1873.

PREFACE TO FIRST EDITION.

IN the following pages I have endeavoured to give a systematic account of the Glacial Epoch, with special reference to its changes of climate. My intention at first was to restrict myself to a brief description of British glacial and postglacial deposits, for the purpose of pointing out the general succession established, or in process of being established, by geologists in this country; and, thereafter, of drawing some conclusions as to the position in the series of the palæolithic gravels, &c., of southern England. But I eventually found, that in order to make my argument intelligible to non-specialists, it would be necessary to describe in detail some sufficiently large area, in which glacial deposits might be considered as typically developed. It is for this reason that I have entered so fully into the geological history of glacial and postglacial Scotland. In delineating the post-tertiary geology of that country, I have been enabled to discuss many elementary matters, which are, no doubt, sufficiently familiar to my fellow-hammerers, but which a general reader could hardly be expected to know. In short, while treating of the Scottish deposits, I have endeavoured to explain the mode of investigating, and the principles of interpreting glacial phenomena. I also thought that by confining detailed sketching to the glacial history of a well-defined region, it would be possible to convey to the reader's mind a more vivid impression of what the Glacial Epoch really was, than if I ventured to take a wider canvas. But my chief aim throughout has been to indicate the succession of climatic

a 2

changes that obtained during the Glacial Epoch—not in Scotland alone, but in every glaciated region which has been carefully studied by geologists. For I have long been of opinion that until this has been done, until we clearly understand what the succession of changes during the Ice Age was, it is premature to speculate upon the geological age of those deposits which yield the earliest traces of man in Britain. The great difference that obtains between the fauna of undoubted postglacial and recent beds in Scotland, north of England, Wales, and Ireland, on the one hand, and the cave-deposits and palæolithic gravels of southern England on the other, has long been a puzzle to me, as it has, no doubt, been to other geologists. But it was not until years had been spent in the study of the glacial deposits that what I conceive to be the true explanation of the difficulty dawned upon me.

Geologists are aware that the postglacial age of the cave-deposits has not infrequently been called in question. Dr. Buckland, Mr. Godwin-Austen, and Professor Ramsay, have each expressed a belief that some of our cave-deposits may date back to preglacial times; and Mr. Godwin-Austen long ago pointed out that the " sub-aerial beds" of the English Channel districts were the equivalents of the glacial deposits elsewhere; and that the broad alluvia of our more southerly rivers, such as the Severn, the Fal, the Dart, and the Thames, belong to a period prior to the great submergence, during which the high-level marine drifts of Wales were accumulated. In other words he showed that these river-gravels could not be referred to postglacial times. Within more recent years a modification of Mr. Godwin-Austen's view has been energetically put forward by Mr. W. Boyd Dawkins, who is of opinion that our palæolithic deposits belong to a time subsequent to the great submergence just referred to. He holds that man and the extinct mammalia lived in the south of England at a period when Scotland, Wales, and the northern districts of England were covered with ice and snow, and when our summers were warm and our winters very severe. Other geologists, however, as Mr. Prestwich, have contended that we have no evidence of warm summers having obtained during palæolithic times; while, yet others have, on the contrary, thought the evidence pointed to a considerably warmer climate than we now enjoy. Sir C. Lyell gives two explanations of the facts, and thinks the commingling of arctic and southern forms of animal life, may point either to a period of strongly-contrasted summers and winters, or to fluctuations of climate; but he is clearly of opinion that all the palæolithic gravels belong to postglacial times. The Rev. O. Fisher has described a deposit, called by him "trail," which he believes to be the product of land-ice; as it overlies in places palæolithic deposits, he considers that a glacial period has intervened since the disappearance of palæolithic man. Mr. J. Croll has referred to the apparently conflicting evidence of the mammaliferous deposits, as an indication of former changes of climate, and this is the view which Sir J. Lubbock inclines to support, and which is advocated in these pages. I have, however, ventured an explanation of the peculiar distribution of palæolithic gravels, differing from any previously advanced. None of these gravels in my opinion are postglacial, but all must be relegated to preglacial and interglacial times. Their absence from the northern districts I account for by showing that they have been swept out of these regions by confluen. glaciers, and by the sea during the period of great submergencet

These views I first broached during the discussion that followed upon the reading of an interesting paper by Mr. W. Boyd Dawkins, at the Edinburgh meeting of the British Association in 1871. But as the time allowed for discussion at these meetings is necessarily short, I was unable to do justice to my views; believing them, however, to be worth attention, I gave an outline of them in a series of monthly articles in the *Geological Magazine*, the first of which appeared in the number for December, 1871. These articles I subsequently collected, and re-issued with some additions and rearrangements in the summer of the year following.

As far as I know, these papers were the first attempt to

prove, by correlating glacial deposits, that the palæolithic gravels of southern England could not be of postglacial age, but ought to be referred to interglacial and preglacial times. They also bring forward, for the first time, reason to show that a wide land-surface existed in the British area after the disappearance of the ice-sheets, and before the period of great submergence had commenced.

The recent discovery of human remains in the Victoria Cave, where, as Mr. Tiddeman has shown, the deposits are overlaid by a glacial accumulation, is direct evidence in corroboration of the conclusions which I had previously arrived at and published.

In the preparation of this volume I have availed myself of a number of papers, communicated from time to time to various scientific societies and publications, and in fact these chapters may be considered as only an expansion of the articles "On Changes of Climate during the Glacial Epoch," which first appeared in the pages of the *Geological Magazine*.

It would be unbecoming in me, if I did not here acknowledge the obligations I am under to the writings of those who have preceded me in describing the glacial deposits of Scotland, more especially to the successive publications of Messrs. Maclaren, Chambers, Jamieson, and A. Geikie. I had hoped to be able to append a list of works by these and other authors, relating to the glacial and postglacial geology of the British Islands, together with such foreign papers as I had come across in the course of my reading; but after making some progress, I was reluctantly compelled to abandon my design, as the list threatened to form quite a volume of itself.

To my colleagues on the Geological Survey of Scotland, I am indebted for much valuable assistance, willingly rendered. Of these, my old friend, Mr. B. N. Peach, supplied me with the highly characteristic sketches of striated stones, and the beautiful views of Loch Doon, and the Carse of Stirling; while from the facile pencil of Mr. H. M. Skae, I received the fine drawing of the Coolin Mountains, and the illustrations of

Alpine, Arctic, and Antarctic scenery which adorn these pages. Mr. R. L. Jack also kindly furnished me with the map and sections of Loch Lomond, and with the chart showing the physiography of western Scotland that would appear upon an elevation of 600 feet. To the same obliging friend I am likewise indebted for many practical hints and suggestions during the progress of my work through the press. Mr. R. Etheridge, Jun., has enhanced the value of these pages by the long list of organic remains which is given in the Appendix; and has, moreover, laid me under many obligations by the trouble he has taken to verify references and consult libraries, of which my absence from town on official duty would other- wise, in many cases, have prevented me availing myself. Mr. J. Croll, Mr. J. Horne, and Mr. D. R. Irvine, have also obliged me with a number of glacial notes.

To several of my colleagues on the English Geological Survey, I have likewise to render my acknowledgments. Mr. A. H. Green furnished me with a long series of notes relating to the glacial deposits of England, which, however, the limits I had set for myself have not allowed me to make use of. But I hope my friend may himself be induced to give some general account of the post-tertiary deposits of England—a work which would be of essential service to the students of glacial geology. Mr. Green was also good enough to read over the proofs of Chapter IX., and to suggest a number of improvements and additions which I have gladly incorporated with the text. Mr. Etheridge examined for me several lists of shells from the "pliocene sands" of northern Italy, and his opinions and advice have been of great assistance. I am also indebted to Mr. Whitaker for a diagram-section and notes, relating to the gravels of the Thames valley.

*   *   *   *   *   *   *

PREFACE

PREFACE TO SECOND EDITION.

THE three years which have elapsed since the publication of this work have added considerably to our knowledge of the Glacial Epoch, and it has been gratifying to me to find that the new facts disclosed have very materially strengthened my general argument. It becomes increasingly evident that the Epoch in question was not one continuous Age of Ice, but consisted rather of a series of alternate cold (glacial) and warm or genial (interglacial) periods; and the facts as they multiply make it clearer than ever that the ancient ossiferous and palæolithic gravels and cave-deposits of England cannot be assigned to a later date than the last genial interval of the Ice Age, while some portion of them certainly belongs to earlier interglacial and even perhaps to preglacial times. The recent most important and interesting discovery by Mr. S. B. J. Skertchly of palæolithic brick-earth underlying the chalky boulder-clay near Brandon, puts it beyond doubt that man lived in Britain as early at least as that interglacial mild period which preceded the climax of glacial cold.

In the first issue of this work many points of interest connected with the glacial accumulations themselves were purposely left untouched, attention having been directed chiefly to those facts which served to illustrate the general climatic conditions that obtained during glacial and postglacial ages. Some of the points in question, however, appear to me now to have a more direct bearing upon the general argument of these pages than I formerly supposed, and the opportunity of the present re-issue has therefore been taken to discuss these in such detail as seemed desirable. For the convenience of those who have perused the first edition, and who may wish to see what novelties appear in the present volume, I may note here some of the chief additions and alterations.

Considerable changes have been made in several of the chapters relating to Scotland. The account of the till has been revised, and such details added as appeared to illustrate more fully the mode in which that deposit has been accumulated. I formerly attempted to restrict the term *boulder-clay* to morainic deposits in which indications of marine action were more or less well-marked; while the term *till* was applied exclusively to masses of stony clay in which traces of sea-work were wholly wanting. But although care was taken to state that the one kind of deposit frequently passes or shades into the other, and that both had evidently been formed by the grinding-action of land-ice, yet I find that my attempt to modify our terminology has only led to misapprehension. I have, therefore, given it up, and now use the words *till* and *boulder-clay* as strictly synonymous, and signifying merely a deposit which owes its origin more or less directly to the grinding-action of glaciers. Further descriptions of the Scotch interglacial beds have been given, and the shelly tills or boulder-clays have been treated at some considerable length. The origin suggested for most of these deposits is in the main the same as that which Dr. Croll was the first to advance in regard to the shelly till of Caithness; but personal observations in the Outer Hebrides and the northwest of Scotland have enabled me to bring forward certain evidence in connection with the subject which seems to throw not a little light on the conditions that obtained in Scotland prior to the advance of the last ice-sheet.

I formerly maintained that the gravel and sand of the "kame series" was undoubtedly of fluviatile and torrential origin; but I also held, in common with many geologists, that these deposits were subsequently modified during a period of considerable submergence of the land. I now advance a step

further, however, and agree with Mr. Jamieson that the sea
has not had any share in the formation of the kames. Detailed
work in the valleys of the Tweed and the Tay, and explorations
in the maritime districts of the north-west Highlands, have
convinced me that Mr. Jamieson is right in concluding that no
great submergence has overtaken Scotland since the close of
the Glacial Epoch. It will be seen that this modification of my
views in regard to Scotland has enabled me to bring the glacial
deposits of that country into much closer relationship with
those of England, and to present a classification which is altogether more satisfactory.

The account of the glacial deposits of England has been
almost entirely re-written, and embraces the results of recent
personal observations in the eastern and north-eastern counties.
In the former edition I sought to show that all the evidence led
up to only one conclusion : to this, namely—that while the
ossiferous and palæolithic gravels, &c., clearly rested upon and
were therefore younger than the early glacial deposits of the
eastern counties, they were, nevertheless, overlapped by, and
consequently belonged to, an older date than those younger
accumulations of glacial origin which cover such wide areas in
the north of England, in Wales, and in Scotland. It is true
I could point to no actual section in England where this
inferred overlap was visible ; and however cogent and
unanswerable my argument might appear to be, I was yet well
aware that to certain minds nothing short of such an actual
section would suffice for a demonstration. From what I had
already seen of the drifts of the north-eastern counties, I certainly hoped that a section of the kind desiderated would ere
long be discovered, and I have not been disappointed. During
a recent visit to the south-east of Yorkshire, I found that
certain gravel-beds which have yielded mammalian remains
and myriads of *Cyrena fluminalis* and other shells, and which
are acknowledged to be of more recent date than the great
chalky boulder-clay of the eastern counties, are covered by a
mass of unstratified till or boulder-clay in such a way as to

show that the till in question is a true *moraine profonde*. In other words, this section demonstrates that after the deposition of the ossiferous gravels and *Cyrena*-beds a great ice-sheet stretched south as far at least as the valley of the Humber, where its bottom-moraine may now be seen overlapping upon deposits which are clearly representative of the *Cyrena*-beds and palæolithic gravels that occur farther to the south.

Mr. Hardman's investigations in Ireland have enabled me to add something to the account of the interglacial and late glacial deposits of that country.

The chapter relating to the Swedish glacial deposits has been revised and brought up to date, the chief additions being some references to the occurrence of interglacial freshwater deposits and an account of Mr. D. Hummel's theory of the origin of the åsar.

The principal item of interest mentioned in the revised description of the glacial deposits of Switzerland is the recent discovery of traces of man in the Dürnten interglacial beds.

The account of the Italian glacial deposits has been transferred from the Appendix to the text, and some details have been added. These latter refer chiefly to the very remarkable exposure near Como of deposits containing characteristic "pliocene" shells commingled with striated stones.

The glacial deposits of North America are discussed in much greater detail than before, attention being specially directed to the evidence bearing upon the former existence of interglacial periods. For a number of MS. notes relating to the Northwestern States, my thanks are due to Professor N. H. Winchell, State Geologist of Minnesota,

The concluding chapters, treating of the ossiferous and palæolithic deposits, the climatic conditions of pleistocene times, &c., remain much as they were originally written; but they now include an account of the glacial and interglacial deposits of the Fenland, for which I am greatly indebted to my friend and colleague, Mr. Sydney B. J. Skertchly, and to which I would direct the special notice of English geologists.

This account, I should mention here, is merely an outline-sketch of the results obtained by my colleague during his survey of the Fenland; the full details of his work being given in the official memoir, "The Geology of the Fenland."

The foregoing are among the more important additions and changes, but I have altered and added freely wherever it seemed advisable to do so, in order either to elucidate the line of argument pursued or to present a more complete picture of the physical and climatic conditions of glacial and postglacial times.

A number of new woodcut illustrations have been inserted: I have also borrowed from Dr. Croll's "Climate and Time," a chart illustrative of the direction of ocean currents and winds; and from the "Report of the Geological Survey of Ohio," a sketch map of North America, indicating the main lines of glacial striæ. The map showing the submerged rock-basins of Scotland has been extended so as to embrace the area of the Irish Sea; and the general map of Scotland, showing the direction of the glacial striæ, has been brought up to date, thanks to the assistance of my colleagues in Scotland.

I am much indebted to Mr. R. Etheridge, jun., who has been good enough to revise the valuable list of organic remains occurring in the glacial deposits of Scotland, which he drew up for the first edition. My acknowledgments are also due to several of my English colleagues :—to Mr. Whitaker, who pointed out to me a number of characteristic sections of drift in Suffolk, and readily furnished me with many interesting notes relating to the glacial deposits of the eastern districts of England; and to Mr. H. B. Woodward, for similar assistance in Norfolk. Mr. S. B. J. Skertchly took me over the famous palæolithic districts round Brandon, and pointed out to me the evidence which has led him to conclude that the palæolithic beds which overlie the great clalky boulder-clay cannot be assigned to a later date than the last interglacial period. To the same friend I am much indebted for the excellent account of the chalky till which appears in Chapter XXIX.; he also forwarded

me some notes of his recent great "find" of human implements below that till, immediately after the discovery was made ;
but they reached me too late for more than brief notice in a
"postscript." Professor Hull has obliged me with some notes
and a section illustrative of the drift deposits of Ireland : and I
am under many obligations to those foreign geologists who have
been good enough to furnish me with early copies of their
papers, &c., some of which I should not otherwise have been
able to obtain; for even the best of our scientific libraries are
not always "up to date."

GEOLOGICAL SURVEY, PERTH, N.B.,
   August, 1876.

CONTENTS.

—————

CHAPTER I.

CHAPTER II.

GLACIAL DEPOSITS OF SCOTLAND—THE TILL OR BOULDER-CLAY.

CHAPTER III.

EARLY THEORIES.—CAUSE OF GLACIER MOTION.

CHAPTER IV.

MOLECULAR THEORY OF GLACIER MOTION.—ASPECT OF AN ALPINE
GLACIER.

CHAPTER V.

GREENLAND: ITS GLACIAL ASPECT.

CHAPTER VI.

ORIGIN OF THE TILL AND ROCK STRIATIONS AND GROOVINGS OF SCOTLAND.

CHAPTER VII.

ORIGIN OF THE TILL AND ROCK STRIATIONS AND GROOVINGS OF SCOTLAND—*Continued.*

CHAPTER VIII.

CAUSE OF COSMICAL CHANGES OF CLIMATE.

CHAPTER XIV.

BEDS SUBJACENT TO AND INTERCALATED WITH THE SCOTTISH TILL—*Continued.*

CHAPTER XV.

BEDS SUBJACENT TO AND INTERCALATED WITH THE SCOTTISH TILL—*Continued.*

CHAPTER XVI.

BEDS SUBJACENT TO AND INTERCALATED WITH THE SCOTTISH TILL—*Continued.*

CHAPTER XVII.

INTERGLACIAL DEPOSITS AND SHELLY TILL OF SCOTLAND.—SUMMARY OF RESULTS.

CHAPTER XVIII.

UPPER DRIFT DEPOSITS OF SCOTLAND.

CHAPTER XIX.

UPPER DRIFT DEPOSITS OF SCOTLAND—*Continued.*

PAGE

CHAPTER XX.

UPPER DRIFT DEPOSITS OF SCOTLAND—*Continued.*

CHAPTER XXI.

UPPER DRIFT DEPOSITS OF SCOTLAND—*Continued.*

CHAPTER XXII.

UPPER DRIFT DEPOSITS OF SCOTLAND—*Continued.*

CHAPTER XXIII.

ROCK-BASINS OF SCOTLAND.

CHAPTER XXIV.

ROCK-BASINS OF SCOTLAND—*Continued.*

CHAPTER XXV.

CHAPTER XXVI.

CHAPTER XXVII.

CHAPTER XXVIII.

CHAPTER XXIX.

CHAPTER XXX.

GLACIAL DEPOSITS OF ENGLAND—*Continued.*

CHAPTER XXXI.

GLACIAL DEPOSITS OF IRELAND.—POSTGLACIAL BEDS OF ENGLAND
AND IRELAND.

CHAPTER XXXII.

GLACIAL DEPOSITS OF SCANDINAVIA.

CHAPTER XXXIII.

GLACIAL DEPOSITS OF SWITZERLAND.

CHAPTER XXXIV.

GLACIAL DEPOSITS OF NORTHERN ITALY.

CHAPTER XXXV.

CHAPTER XXXVI.

CHAPTER XXXVII.

CHAPTER XXXVIII.

CHAPTER XXXIX.

GEOLOGICAL AGE OF THE PALÆOLITHIC DEPOSITS.

CHAPTER XL.

GEOLOGICAL AGE OF THE PALÆOLITHIC DEPOSITS—*Continued*.

CHAPTER XLI.

GEOLOGICAL POSITION OF NEOLITHIC, PALÆOLITHIC, AND OSSIFEROUS DEPOSITS OF FOREIGN COUNTRIES.

CHAPTER XLII.

APPENDIX.

LIST OF MAPS, CHARTS, AND FULL-PAGE
ILLUSTRATIONS.

ADDENDUM ET CORRIGENDUM.

———•———

Page 367. In stating that some five species of molluscs found in the Bridlington Crag are not known as living forms, the list of shells given by Mr. Gwyn
Jeffreys in Phillips's "Geology of Yorkshire," Third Edition, p. 274, has been
overlooked. Mr. Jeffreys mentions sixty-seven species, and states that all are
now living and inhabit the arctic and northern seas.

CHAPTER I.

INTRODUCTORY.

THE earlier students of the physical history of our earth considered that a great gap or strongly-defined boundary-line separated the Present from the Past. Some mighty convulsion of nature was believed to have marked the close of the geological ages, and to have preceded the advent of man and the introduction of the plants and animals with which he is associated. It was hardly doubted that the present distribution of land and water over the earth's surface dated back to a time anterior to the coming of our race, and that when man first entered Britain he had to cross seas that still roll between us and the Continent. In short, it was held that within the human period only a few minor changes had been effected in the physical aspect of our country. It was admitted, indeed, that large areas of forest-land had been displenished, that considerable tracts of peat-moss had grown, and that here and there, where the coasts were formed of incoherent materials, the sea had made some inroads; but no one supposed that greater changes than these had come about since the first occupation of Britain.

Subsequent research, however, has overturned many of these opinions, and widened our views in regard to the magnitude of the physical changes of which man has been a witness. Not only have great oscillations of climate happened within the human period, but the distribution of land and sea also has undergone very considerable modifications. Seas have vanished and returned, wide areas of land have appeared and disappeared—broad valleys have been hollowed out of solid rocks by running water. It is from a knowledge of these and similar facts that geologists arrive at their estimate of the antiquity of man, and have

B

assured themselves that no mighty convulsion of nature separates the human period from the earlier ages—the deposits which were at one time looked upon as the sure evidence of such a "break in the succession" being now recognised as only so many links in the chain that binds the present to the past.

The study of these deposits has unfolded a deeply-interesting and almost romantic history. We are introduced to scenes that are in strangest contrast to what now meets the eye in these latitudes : geographical and physical changes of the most stupendous character pass before us ; we see our islands and northern Europe at one time enveloped in snow and ice ; at another time well wooded, and inhabited by rude tribes of men and savage animals ; now the British Islands are united to the Continent—again, the sea prevails, and a large part of Britain is overwhelmed beneath the waters of the ocean, across which ere long float rafts and bergs of ice. To these succeed vast confluent glaciers which overflow a large portion of the British area and usurp the bed of the sea. Yet again, we behold the great ice-fields vanish away, and Britain once more becoming continental, and repeopled. Finally, we follow the working of those physical influences by which at last the present order of things is brought about.

Those who hear of this history for the first time may well be excused if they listen with some incredulity. It seems difficult to understand how the records of such extraordinary events could be preserved ; or how, having been preserved, geologists are able to interpret them. Yet there is really no mystery about the matter. Difficulties undoubtedly do arise, and sometimes problems suggest themselves, for which it is hard or even impossible at present to find a solution. Nevertheless the whole matter resolves itself into a question of circumstantial evidence. The facts are patent to every one who will take the trouble to examine them, and the interpretations adduced by geologists are capable of being attested by an appeal to what is actually taking place in the world around us. In the following pages, therefore, I propose to give an outline-sketch of the evidence, mentioning only such details as may serve to bring the salient points clearly before the mind, and endeavouring at the same time to put the reader, who may chance to be not specially skilled in geology, into a position to judge for himself as to the reasonableness of the explanations advanced.

The earlier pages will be occupied with an account of the later chapters in the geological history of Scotland. We shall trace out the succession of events that marked the origin of certain loose and incoherent materials which overlie the solid rocks of that country, and are represented by similar accumulations covering vast areas throughout the northern regions of our hemisphere. The consideration of the Scottish deposits will naturally lead us to inquire into the principles upon which these and their equivalents in other lands must be interpreted. We shall then describe in succession the superficial accumulations of other portions of the British Islands, of Scandinavia, of Central Europe, and of North America, for the purpose of ascertaining how far the conclusions arrived at by geologists in different countries harmonize with each other. Having traversed this wide field of inquiry, and become aware that the deposits, which were at one time slumped together and vaguely believed to represent a period of wild cataclysms and convulsions, are really the records of a long series of changes, each of which flowed as it were into the other, we shall finally take up the subject of the antiquity of man.

In considering this difficult but important and interesting question, it will be necessary to treat first of the special evidences which have been adduced by archæologists and geologists, to prove the great age of our race. Thereafter we shall endeavour to determine what is the exact position in the geological history of those deposits which contain the very oldest traces of man. Our aim, in short, will be to discover, if possible, at what stage during those great climatic and geographical revolutions, which shall have previously engaged our attention, man certainly occupied Britain. If we are able to determine this point, we shall have paved the way for eventually arriving at some approximately definite estimate of the antiquity of man in Western Europe.

CHAPTER II.

GLACIAL DEPOSITS OF SCOTLAND.—THE TILL OR BOULDER-CLAY.

General distribution of Superficial formations.—Till or boulder-clay, the oldest member of the series.—How this is proved.—Character of the till.—Stones in the till.—Unfossiliferous character of the till.—Till developed chiefly upon the low grounds.—Its aspect in upland valleys.—" Sowbacks " or " drums " of till.—" Crag and tail."—Smoothed and broken rocks below till.—Configuration of mountains and hills.—Lines of stones in till.—Subjacent and intercalated beds.—Character of boulder-clay or till which overlies them.—Résumé.

THROUGHOUT the length and breadth of Scotland occur numerous scattered heaps and ragged sheets of sand, gravel, and coarse débris, and widespread deposits of clay, beneath which in many places, especially in the lowland districts, the solid rocks that form the framework of the country are in great measure concealed. The general character of these superficial heaps and gatherings must be familiar to every one. They appear in the scaurs and bluffs that overhang our streams and rivers, and are often well-exposed by the wash of the waves along certain sections of the sea-coast. The traveller by rail can hardly fail to notice them as he is swept along—here capping the rocks with a few feet of sand and gravel, there thickening out so as to form the whole face of the cutting from top to bottom. In the numerous quarries with which the country is pitted, the rock is commonly crowned with a more or less thick covering of similar materials ; while in sinking for coal and ironstone, and in digging foundations for houses and bridges, superficial accumulations of such débris no less frequently occur. Bricks and tiles are manufactured in large quantities from the beds of clay, and the heaps of sand and gravel, occurring as they often do at a great distance from the sea, are much in request by builders, farmers, and others.

So widely are the superficial deposits distributed that they may be said to be common to every part of the country, for they are met with from Zetland to the Cheviots, and from the Outer Hebrides to the east coast. But while they occur over so wide an area they are at the same time very unequally aggregated. In the highland and upland districts they appear to be for the most part restricted to valleys— the craggy broken mountains of the north and the rounded swelling hills of the south of Scotland, showing but little trace of them at the higher elevations. Over the intervening Lowlands, however, they spread in broad but somewhat ragged sheets, which are often continuous across wide tracts.

The materials of which these deposits are made up consist principally of stony clay, fine brick-clay, silt, sand, gravel, and a kind of loose débris of earthy clay and stones. At first sight these various beds appear to be confusedly intermingled, and to show little order in the mode of their occurrence. Sometimes stony clay, at other times sand or gravel, overlies the solid rocks. Again, these deposits may be absent and a fine brick-clay, or a coarse débris of angular stones and large blocks may cumber the ground instead. But this confusion is only apparent—a regular succession does really exist. It frequently happens that in deep artificial excavations or natural exposures, several of these loose materials occur together. And when this is the case we usually find that the lowest-lying member of the series consists of a more or less tough stony or boulder-filled clay. Above this stony clay (*till* or *boulder-clay* as it is called) come beds of sand and gravel, or, as the case may be in mountain-valleys, a loose earthy débris of stones and large blocks and boulders. But in maritime districts it often happens that the first deposit resting immediately upon the till is a fine brick-clay. Thus whenever the boulder-clay or till appears in the same vertical exposure with any of the other superficial deposits it invariably lies at the bottom. Hence we conclude that of all these accumulations the till or boulder-clay is the oldest, since it must have been laid down in its present position before any of the other heaps of material could have gathered over its surface.

It is only now and then, however, that the lowest-lying or

oldest superficial accumulations are overlaid by later formed deposits. Throughout wide districts stony clay alone occurs, just as in other regions heaps of sand and gravel form the only covering of the solid rocks. Yet we can have no difficulty in deciding as to the relative age of the beds ; for having already satisfied ourselves that till constantly underlies the other deposits, when all occur together in one section, we can have no doubt that the former must be the older accumulation, and that the latter, even when they rest directly upon rock (the stony clay being altogether absent from the district) must have been formed at a later date. A reference to the accompanying diagram (Fig. 1), which represents an ideal cutting or *section*, will help to render these remarks a little clearer. The figure is intended to give a general view of the relation of the underlying till to a very prevalent overlying series of sand and gravel. In this section, *t S* are the superficial deposits resting upon *r r*, the solid rocks. It will be observed that the stony clay or till, *t*, is distinctly covered by the sand and gravel *S*. At $S^\times$ the sand and gravel repose directly upon the rocks *r*, the till being absent at that point ; while at $t^\times$ till alone occurs. When the superficial formations are viewed upon the large scale they are invariably found to follow the order indicated.

Fig. 1.—Diagrammatic section, showing relative position of till *t t*× and over-lying sand and gravel series *S S*×.   *W* = river valley.

It has just been mentioned that besides sand and gravel various other kinds of materials sometimes overlie the till. To determine the relative position of these accumulations the same kind of reasoning applies. There are other methods, however, by which this is ascertained, but a consideration of these must be deferred to a subsequent page. At present our attention is confined to the boulder-clay or till. This deposit and the overlying beds have received one general name—the Drift or Glacial formation ; and it is usual to speak of Lower and Upper Drift, according as we refer to the stony clays or the deposits above them. In this chapter I shall consider the character and phenomena of the most characteristic member of the Lower Drift, namely, the *Till;* for which purpose it will be necessary to enter into some little detail. But these details are absolutely necessary if the reader would understand clearly the nature of the problem which a survey of the drift-phenomena suggests. It would, however, lead me far beyond due limits were I to attempt to give anything like an exhaustive account of the till. All I shall try to do will be to gather together into a short space what appear to be the more salient points in the evidence, from an attentive consideration of which the reader will be able to judge for himself how far the inferences set forth in the sequel are justified.

The deposit known as *till* or *boulder-clay*, is usually a firm, tough, tenacious, stony clay, which gives every evidence of having been subjected to great pressure. So tough indeed does it often become that engineers would much rather excavate the most obdurate rocks. Hard rocks are more or less easily assailable with gunpowder, and the numerous joints and fissures by which they are traversed enable the navvies to wedge them out often in considerable lumps. But till has neither crack nor joint—it will not blast, and to pick it to pieces is a very slow and laborious process. Often, however, the clay becomes coarser and sandier, and when this is the case water soaks through it. It then loses consistency, and is sometimes ready to "run" or collapse as soon as an excavation is made. Again, in certain districts it might be described as a coarse agglomerate of subangular and angular stones set in a scanty matrix of coarse earthy grit and sand, as in the lower tracts of many of the islands of the Hebrides. A still more abnormal kind of till is found occasionally in sandstone districts. It consists of an exceedingly rude débris of the underlying sandstone, intermingled with which occur a few stones derived from a distance. The sandstone blocks are of all sizes and shapes, from two or three inches up to fragments five feet and more in diameter. In some places they are heaped confusedly together, with little or no matrix in the interstices between the blocks. In other places, however, we find the stones set in a more or less meagre matrix of clay and sand. This rude

kind of till sometimes attains a thickness of more than twenty
feet, as in the moors near Kirk of Shotts, Lanarkshire.   It
passes gradually into till of the normal type.

Sometimes the stones in the till are so numerous that
hardly any matrix of clay is visible.   This, however, does not
often happen.   On the other hand, they occasionally appear
more sparsely scattered through the clay, which may then be

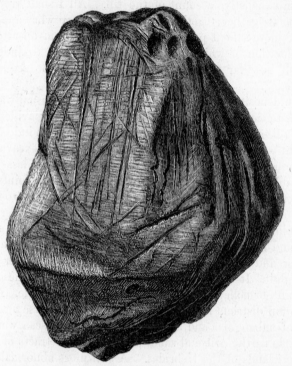

Fig. 2.—Scratched stone (black shale), from the till.   (B. N. Peach.)

dug for brick-making; but this occurs still less frequently.*
As a rule, it is hard to say whether the stones or the clay
form the larger percentage of the deposit in a mass of typical
till. Generally speaking, however, the stones are most numerous
in the till of hilly districts; while at the lower levels of the

* My friend Mr. R. L. Jack informs me that at Port Dundas bricks are made
out of a typical stony till, the stones being crunched up by a machine.

country the clayey character of the mass is upon the whole more pronounced. But to this there are many exceptions.

Fig. 3.—Scratched stone (limestone), from the till. (B. N. Peach.)

The stones vary in size from mere grit and pebbles up to blocks several feet or even yards in diameter. These last, however, do not occur so commonly as smaller stones—indeed

Figs. 4 and 5.—Scratched stones from the till.   4 Clay-ironstone, 5 Limestone.
(B. N. Peach.)

boulders above four feet in diameter are comparatively seldom
met with in the till, and appear to be of commonest occur-

rence in the sandier and less compacted varieties of that accumulation. I think, also, that the bigger boulders are most
commonly found in the lower part of a deposit of till; a
position, however, to which they are by no means confined.
Stones and boulders alike are scattered higgledy-piggledy,
pell-mell through the clay, so as to give to the whole deposit
a highly confused and tumultuous appearance.

There is something very peculiar about the shape of the
stones. They are neither round and oval like the pebbles in
river-gravel or the shingle of the sea-shore, nor are they
sharply angular like newly-fallen débris at the base of a cliff,
although they more closely resemble the latter than the
former. They are indeed angular in shape, but the sharp
corners and edges have almost invariably been smoothed away.

Some characteristic forms are shown in the accompanying
illustrations (Figs. 2, 3, 4, 5) which have been drawn from
actual specimens. Their shape, as will be seen, is by no
means their most striking peculiarity. Each is smoothed,
polished, and covered with striæ or scratches, some of which
are delicate as the lines traced by an etching needle, others
deep and harsh as the scores made by the plough upon a
rock. And what is also worthy of note, most of the scratches,
coarse and fine together, seem to run parallel to the longer
diameter of the stones, which, however, are scratched in many
other directions as well. These appearances are displayed in
Figs. 3, 4, and 5. The distinctness of the markings depends
very much upon the nature of the stones. Hard, fine-grained
rocks, like limestone and clay-ironstone, have often received
a high polish, and retain the finest striæ. Figs. 3, 4, and 5
represent fragments of these. Soft and coarse-grained rocks,
like grit and sandstone, are not usually so well polished and
scratched; and the same may be said of other easily-decom-
posed masses, such as granite, and various metamorphic and
igneous rocks. Fig. 2 shows a fragment of dark carbonaceous
shale; it will be noticed that this specimen is not so distinctly oblong as the others, and that the direction of the
striæ does not coincide in so marked a manner with the
longer axis of the stone—some of the more strongly pronounced scratches, however, do. It is worth mentioning, also,
that there appears to be some curious relation between the

coarseness of the striæ and the size of the stones.   Thus we
usually find that the bigger the stone is the more strongly
marked are the striæ.   The scratches upon a small fragment
are generally very fine, coarse ruts or grooves being absent,
while large stones and boulders, besides being well smoothed
and closely set with fine striæ, usually exhibit also deep scorings
and rough, jagged-edged scratches.   It often happens, moreover,
that the big blocks are not polished equally all over; sometimes, indeed, they show only one well-polished side, the other
faces of the block being rough, and not marked with striæ of
any kind.   No other appearances connected with the till are
more striking than these scratchings and smoothings.   They
become to the geologist what hieroglyphics are to the Egypt-
ologist—the silent but impressive records of an age long passed
away, enabling him to realise the former existence in these
islands of a state of things very different indeed to that which
now obtains.   We must travel to other and distant lands
before we can hope to appreciate the full significance of the
" scratches," or realise all that they suggest.

The stones which, as we have seen, occur so abundantly in
the till consist of fragments of the various kinds of rock to
be met with in Scotland.   It must not be supposed, however,
that any single section of till will yield specimens of all these
varieties.   On the contrary, if we desired to collect from the
clay a complete set of the Scottish rocks, we should have to
traverse an area as wide as that occupied by those rocks
themselves.   The till, in short, is quite local in character, for
in districts where sandstone occurs most abundantly, the
stones in the clay likewise consist almost exclusively of sandstone.   And, similarly, in regions where hard volcanic rocks
prevail, the overlying till is invariably crowded with fragments of the same.   Not only the stones, however, but also
the colour and texture of the clay itself are influenced by the
character of the rocks in whose neighbourhood the till occurs.
Thus, in a district where the rocks consist chiefly of dark
shales, clays, and thin sandstones, with occasional seams of
coal, the overlying till is usually hard and tough, and its
prevailing colour a dark dingy grey or dirty blue; while in
a region of red sandstone it is tinted red or brown, and commonly shows a more open or sandier texture.

It is in the lower-lying districts of the country where till appears in greatest force. Wide areas of the central counties are covered with it continuously to a depth varying from two or three feet up to one hundred feet and more. But as we follow it towards the mountain regions it becomes thinner and more interrupted—the naked rock ever and anon peering through, until at last we find only a few shreds and patches lying here and there in sheltered hollows of the hills. Throughout the Northern Highlands it occurs but rarely, and only in little isolated patches. It is not until we get away from the steep rocky declivities and narrow glens and gorges, and enter upon the broader valleys that open out from the base of the highland mountains to the low-lying districts beyond, that we meet with any considerable deposits of stony clay. The higher districts of the Southern Uplands are almost equally free from any covering of till. Occasionally, however, this deposit puts in a bold appearance in certain hilly regions, as, for instance, in many of the valleys of Peeblesshire, Galloway, and the Border counties, where its aspect is often highly suggestive of its origin. In the localities referred to it frequently forms a more or less broad terrace, sloping gradually with the inclination of the valley in which it occurs. Through this terrace a stream usually cuts a course for itself, and by winding from bank to bank gradually undermines the till, and in some cases has nearly succeeded in clearing it away

Fig. 6.—Diagrammatic section across two upland valleys: t = till; W^1 W^2 = stream courses; r solid rock.

altogether. A transverse section across two such valleys is given in the diagram annexed (Fig. 6). The cuttings made by the streams are seen at W^1 W^2; t represents the till, and r the underlying rocks. Fig. 7 gives a pictorial representation of the same appearances.

In the lowland districts the till never shows this terrace-like appearance, but rolls itself out in a series of broad undulations. It is especially worthy of note, too, that the long parallel ridges, or "sowbacks" and "drums," as they are termed, which are the characteristic forms assumed by the till in broad valleys like those of the Tweed and the

Fig. 7.—Greskin Burn, Dumfriesshire: stream cutting through terrace of till. (H. M. Skae.)

Nith, invariably coincide in direction with the valleys or straths in which they lie.   A section, therefore, drawn across a till-covered area in the Lowlands would give the general aspect represented in the diagram (Fig. 8), where the ridges of stony clay are seen at *t d.*

Fig. 8.—Diagrammatic section across a lowland valley: *td* = " sowbacks " or "drums" *W* = river course ; *r* solid rock.

Throughout the midland districts a number of prominent crags and bosses of rock project beyond the general surface of the ground in such a way as to form conspicuous features in the landscape.   Behind these crags the till often accumulates to a considerable depth.   Edinburgh Castle Rock affords a good example of this appearance, and Arthur's Seat is another instance on a larger scale.   From each of these hills a ridge or tail proceeds with a long gentle slope, and similar appearances characterize the numerous isolated boss-like hills which are scattered up and down the Lowlands. The leading phenomena associated with this " crag and tail " arrangement are shown in the woodcut (Fig. 9). The " crag,"

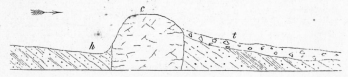

Fig. 9.—" Crag and tail."

c, itself is usually composed of some hard volcanic material, like basalt or dolerite,* which intersects softer and more yielding rocks, such as sandstone and shale. At the base of the " crag" there is not infrequently a hollow (seen at *h*) scooped out of the solid rocks. Here also the till is either very thin or does not occur at all. On the lee-side of the " crag," however, it often attains a great thickness ; but a glance at the diagram will show that even were the till completely stripped from the lee-side of the " crag " a notable " tail " would still remain, for the rock on the lee-side is consider-ably higher than the rock at *h*. The phenomena of " crag and tail" therefore are not entirely dependent upon the presence of the stony clay. They may, and in point of fact do, exist where no till is visible. All that we can affirm in regard to the part played by the latter in the formation of " crag and tail " is simply this—that in districts where till abounds it is usually heaped up on one particular side of projecting crags or bosses. In Edinburghshire, for example, a greater depth occurs on the east than on the west side of prominent isolated hills. In other districts again it may be on the north, west, or south side where the till has chiefly accumulated.

When the till is removed from the underlying rocks the upper surface of these very frequently shows a smoothed (see

* The geological reader will understand that the " crag " is not necessarily formed of intruded igneous rock. The outcrop of any hard bed, that dips with accompanying softer beds at a low angle, has a tendency to produce " crag and tail " when the dip happens to coincide with the direction in which the till has travelled.

Fig. 10) and often highly polished appearance, and the whole
pavement is marked with those peculiar scratches or striæ
that form so characteristic a feature of the stones included
in the till. But the extent to which this polishing is carried
depends very much upon the nature of the rocks. We have

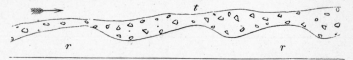

Fig. 10.—Smoothed rock surface below till.

seen that the most perfectly smoothed and striated stones of
the till consist of such close-grained rocks as limestone and
clay-ironstone—the striæ upon fragments of sandstone being
often faint and ill-defined. The same rule holds good in
regard to the rocky pavement upon which the till reposes.
Limestone invariably yields a beautifully smoothed and
polished surface, and some other rocks, such as serpentine,
receive nearly as fine a dressing as a lapidary's wheel could
give them. But soft sandstones and highly-jointed rocks
are much less finely marked, and often show a broken and
shattered surface below till; sometimes, indeed, thick sandstones appear "broken up" to a depth of many feet below
boulder-clay, the coarse angular débris of the sandstone
shading gradually into till of the normal type. [See *ante*,
p. 7]. (Figs. 11, 12).

The direction of the scratches, ruts, and grooves upon the

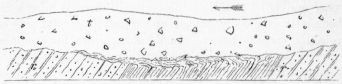

Fig. 11.—Broken rocks below till : near Peebles, river Tweed.

Fig 12.—Broken sandstone below till : near Union Bridge, river Tweed.

PLATE I.

LOCH DOON (lower reach); illustrating rounded outline of hills and hill-slopes. (By B. N. Peach.)

To face p. 17.

rock-head, usually coincides with the trend of the valley in which the till occurs. If, for instance, we took the compass-bearing of a considerable valley running from east to west, we should almost certainly find that the striæ pointed in the same direction. But this rule does not hold true for many of the smaller valleys of the Lowlands. In the Northern Highlands, however, and in the Southern Uplands, the striæ constantly follow the same direction as the valleys, and thus radiate from the high grounds to almost every point in the compass. In the intervening Lowlands, their prevailing course is from east and north-east to west and south-west, and from west to east, according as they occur in the western or midland and eastern districts. But a fuller account of these wonderful markings will be better appreciated when we come to discuss the origin of the till or boulder-clay.

There are few who have studied the aspect of Scottish hills and mountains who can have failed to notice that these frequently present a rounded and flowing outline. [See Plate I.] Save in some of the wilder regions of the Highlands and Western Islands, there is a general absence of abrupt sharp peaks and ridges. Even the projecting masses of rock which roughen the flanks of the highland mountains often present a rounded hummocky aspect when viewed from some distance : and a little observation will suffice to show that this peculiar rounded appearance is most pronounced when the slopes of the rugged glens are scanned in a direction coinciding with the inclination of the valleys. Let us take as examples of what is meant, the well-known Glen Rosa in the island of Arran, or Glen Messan in Argyllshire. As the observer advances up these glens he sees nothing of the rounded outline referred to. The slopes of the mountains bristle with irregular crags and projecting rock-masses, amongst which we look in vain for any such appearance as I have tried to describe. And so the broken and confusedly-tumbled rocks continue until we reach the corries at the heads of the glens. But no sooner do we turn to retrace our steps than the whole aspect of the rocky slopes appears to change, and even the most rugged projecting bosses show as if they had been rounded off by some force pressing over them in a direction down the glens. And so it is with all the other

deep valleys and sea-lochs of the Highlands—the smoothed
and rounded rocks look up the glens, the broken and jagged
masses face down.

In describing the till I remarked that the irregular
manner in which the stones were scattered through that
deposit imparted to it a confused and tumultuous appearance. The clay does not arrange itself in layers or beds,
but is distinctly unstratified. We cannot dig it with greater
ease in any one direction. It shows no lines of division,
but is a homogeneous mass, from top to bottom. Sometimes,
however, especially in the lee of a projecting rock, as in the
case of "crag and tail," it shows a rude kind of arrangement, the stones tending to lie in sloping layers one over
the other, as in Fig. 13. Here and there, too, in other

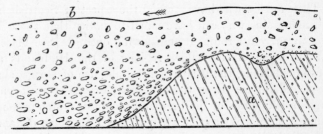

Fig. 13.—Section at east end of Neidpath Tunnel, Peebles. *a*, Silurian rocks;
   b, till, showing arrangement of stones on the lee-side of rock ; *c*, gravel in hollow under till. The arrow indicates direction in which the till has travelled.

places a layer of stones or boulders stretches horizontally
across the clay, and not infrequently nests of sand, gravel,
and brick-clay, and irregular lenticular beds of similar
deposits make their appearance and occasionally attain a
considerable thickness. Such included beds are often curiously curled up and contorted, so as to present the appearance of having been rolled over upon themselves along with
the stony clay in which they are enclosed. At its base the
till often contains numerous very large blocks and boulders,
which are sometimes more or less striated, and at other times
are rough and even sharply angular.

A good example of some of the phenomena in question
is seen in the accompanying sketch-section (Fig. 14). At *l*
a line of stones may be observed running along the face

of the till ; *d* represents earthy sand with stones ; *c*, well-
rounded gravel and shingle.   Several little nests of sand are
scattered here and there through the body of the clay, which,
despite the presence of these and the gravel and layer of
boulders, is a perfectly unstratified and amorphous mass
of clay, and angular stones, scratched and polished.

But although this is the invariable character of the till
or boulder-clay itself, it nevertheless occasionally contains
more or less regular beds of gravel, sand, silt, mud, brick-
clay, and peat, and sometimes similar accumulations underlie
the till and separate that deposit from the subjacent solid
rocks.   These stratified deposits will be described at length
in later chapters, and I need not therefore say more about
them at present.   It is worth noting, however, that the till
or boulder-clay that rests above these intercalated beds
usually differs from the stony clay which immediately under-

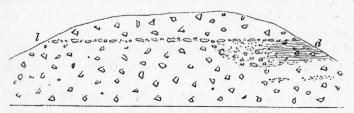

Fig. 14.—Line of stones in till : Glen Water, Ayrshire.

lies them in being less hard and tough.   It is often sandier
and more frequently contains very large blocks and boulders,
while at the same time its included stones and boulders are
not so universally well smoothed and striated—or, to express
it otherwise, angular unpolished stones and boulders are
more common in the upper than in the lower mass of
till.   Again I may note that the intercalated beds often
thin out so as to allow the upper and lower deposits of
boulder-clay to come together.   But to these and other
appearances connected with the intercalated and subjacent
beds we shall return by-and-by.   For the sake of clearness
I shall also defer to another page any account of the fossils
which have been obtained in the till and its associated
beds.

Not wishing to oppress the reader with too many minutiæ

on the very threshold of his investigations, I have omitted from the preceding brief account of the boulder-clay or till many interesting details, which, however, will come before our attention after we have gained some insight into the mystery of the till itself. But before proceeding to consider some of the theories which have been advanced to explain the origin of this deposit, it may be well to recapitulate the principal facts brought forward in the preceding pages. These may be briefly stated as follows :—

1. The loose accumulations of gravel, sand, clay, and other materials that cover so large a portion of the country, belong, for the most part, to what is termed the *Drift* or *Glacial* formation.

2. This formation is divisible into at least two series, namely, *Upper Drift* and *Lower Drift*—the latter being the older series of the two.

3. The most characteristic member of the lower drift is a more or less tough unstratified stony clay, called *till* or *boulder-clay*.

4. The stones in this till are scattered confusedly through the clay, and are not arranged with any reference to their relative specific gravity.

5. They are almost invariably of angular and blunted subangular shapes, and usually exhibit smoothed, polished, and striated surfaces.

6. They are generally local in character, that is to say, the till of a sandstone district is charged chiefly with fragments of sandstone ; and with boulders of volcanic rocks in a region composed for the most part of rocks of igneous origin.

7. A similar connection obtains between the colour and texture of the clay and the prevalent character of the rocks :—in a red sandstone district the till is red and sandy ; in a coal and black shale district it is of a dark dingy grey or blue, and usually excessively tough.

8. Till lies thickest in the Lowlands, and thins away as it approaches the hills.

9. In upland valleys it has a tendency to assume a terrace-like aspect, while in lowland tracts it shows a broad undulating surface, and is frequently arranged in long round-

backed ridges, which are parallel to one another and the direction of the principal valley of the district.

10. Till is often heaped up on one particular side of prominent hills and rocks, especially in the Lowlands.

11. The pavement of rock below till is frequently smoothed, polished, and striated, more especially if the rock be hard and fine grained ; softer rocks, like sandstone and shale, and highly-jointed rocks like greywacké, and many igneous masses, often show a broken surface below till.

12. The direction of the rock-striations coincides generally with the trend of the principal valleys.

13. The hills and mountains commonly exhibit a more or less rounded and flowing outline—the rounded appearance of the crags upon a mountain-slope being most conspicuous to an observer looking down the glens. Viewed in the opposite direction, the rounded and smooth outline disappears.

14. Till, while itself quite unstratified, yet shows an occasional line of stones or boulders, and irregular nests, patches, and lenticular beds of brick-clay, sand, and gravel.

II.

GLACIER MOTION.

—Debacles and waves of transla-
theory.—Accumulation of snow
ion, avalanches, and glaciers.—
nd Tyndall.—Canon Moseley's

perhaps, some little time
l "theories of the earth"
ushered into the world,
popular long after their
ese curious productions
hey abounded with strik-
may still be read with a
after geology had made
re was recognised as the
of the facts that began
minds were occasionally
s in a chain of evidence
n no sufficient "natural
on, of course, was bound
from time to time have
phenomena of the drift,
th of these remarks. It
er, to suppose that an
often wholly pernicious ;
service by warning the
inuous observation, and
scovery which otherwise
might have remained for a longer time unsuspected and
unknown.

To describe the different theories which have appeared
and disappeared, ever since the superficial deposits began to

attract the attention of geologists, would be a thankless and perhaps a useless task. One of these theories conceived that somehow and somewhere in the far north a series of gigantic waves was mysteriously propagated. These waves were supposed to have precipitated themselves upon the land, and then swept madly on over mountain and valley alike, carrying along with them a mighty burden of rocks and stones and rubbish. Such deluges were styled "waves of translation," and the till was believed to represent the materials which they hurried along with them in their wild course across the country. The stones and boulders as they rattled down one mountain's side and up another, were smoothed and scratched, and the solid rocks over which they careered received a similar kind of treatment. After the water disappeared the stones were found confusedly huddled together in a paste of clay, but occasional big blocks, often far-travelled, might be seen perched in lonely positions on hill-tops, or scattered over hill-slopes like flocks of sheep ; while mounds of sand and gravel rolled themselves out here and there in the Lowlands. Such in a few words was the theory of great debacles or waves of translation. It was unfortunate for this theory that it violated at the very outset the first principles of the science, by assuming the former existence of a cause which there was little in nature to warrant. Large waves it was known had certainly been raised by sudden movements of the earth's crust, and had several times caused great damage to seaport towns ; but spasmodic rushes of the sea across a whole country had fortunately never been experienced within the memory of man. The theory, indeed, had only been advanced in a kind of desperation, for geologists were quite at their wits' end to discover any natural cause that would account for the peculiar phenomena of the drift—they could see neither rocks being rounded and scratched nor till being formed anywhere—the causes to which these were due had apparently ceased to operate—and so the perplexed philosophers were in a manner compelled to fall back upon waves of translation. They did not, however, attempt to uphold this theory very strenuously. It was felt that, even granting the probability of great waves of translation having swept across the land, still a number of facts remained which could neither be accounted for nor yet explained away. There was the scratching and polishing of the stones for instance. It seemed impossible that these could have been so dressed by running water, no matter how rapidly it flowed. The stones in the bed of a mountain-torrent show nothing like the scratches so characteristic of those in the till. They are water-worn, truly, but the mysterious markings that streak the till-stones from end to end are nowhere visible. There was also great difficulty in conceiving how large fragments of rock could be carried from the mountains of the Highlands to the south of Scotland by rushes of water. The water might roll them down from one hill into a valley, but it could hardly push them up another hill, and so repeat the process often in a distance of many miles. Then, again, how did the stones come to be inter-mingled with fine clay? Surely the current or wave that was sufficiently powerful to force along blocks of stone several feet in diameter, must have swept the finer matter—sand and clay—to infinitely greater distances. Thus there were a great many loose screws in the theory, and every new fact discovered threatened to make it collapse altogether. Day by day the great waves of translation became more and more apocryphal, until at last they ceased even to be hinted at, and sunk quietly to rest for ever.

Next succeeded the glacier theory of Agassiz, of which more anon, and this again was followed by the iceberg hypo-thesis. The latter accounts in a natural way for the transport of large blocks and boulders from one part of the country to another. It supposes the land to have been submerged to a certain depth during the accumulation of the drift, at which time icebergs setting sail from the tops of the mountains, which then existed as frozen islets, carried with them loads of earth, sand, and rock, which they scattered over the bed of the sea as they floated on their way to the south. This theory is still upheld by some geologists as a satisfactory explanation of the origin of the till, but, as I shall endeavour by-and-by to show, it does not discriminate between deposits which have been accumulated at different times and under different conditions. For the present, however, we must leave it ; but the phenomena of icebergs and what these floating masses are capable of doing, will come before our attention in another place.

The older observers had clearly shown that the agents of geological change as represented in this country failed to supply an adequate solution to the enigma of the mysterious till, with its scratched stones. But the phenomena of glacier regions threw a new light on the subject. Geologists, follow-, ing the lead of Agassiz, gradually became convinced that in some way or other ice had to do with the origin of the till ; and this conviction deepened as the effects of glacial action became better known. I do not suppose that there is any one nowadays who has given this matter the slightest con-sideration without coming to a firm belief in the ice-origin of boulder-clay. But as regards the precise way in which that stony clay owes its origin to ice, there is still some dispute ; and what I propose now to do is to go through the evidence bit by bit for the purpose of ascertaining whether it is not possible to come to a definite conclusion. It is quite clear that no theory can be considered satisfactory which does not explain and account for the various appearances detailed in the preceding chapter. No half-explanation will suffice ; the key which we obtain must open a way into every obscure hole and corner; each and every fact must have full recogni-tion in the theory which may be ultimately adopted. Our first duty, then, must be to find out whether the process of dressing rock-surfaces and smoothing and polishing rock-fragments is now in operation, and whether at present any deposits like boulder-clay are being formed and accumulated. I have just said that geologists agree in ascribing the origin of these and other phenomena of the drift to glacial action. What then, let us inquire, is the nature of that action, and how do the appearances presented by ice-covered regions serve to explain the origin of the boulder-clay or till ?

Every one is aware that the watery vapour which the heat of the sun sucks up from lake and stream and sea, by-and-by condenses and returns to earth. At certain elevations it almost invariably comes down in the form of *snow ;* at lower levels it falls as *rain.* It is customary to speak of an imaginary line, called the *snow-line,* above which more snow falls than is melted or evaporated. This line rises to a great

elevation in tropical countries; but as we follow it to north
and south it begins gradually to descend, until in the icy
regions about the poles it drops to the level of the sea.*
The line, however, is very far from forming an equal curve
from the equator to the poles.   Many circumstances conspire
to render it most irregular and often rapidly undulating.   If
the winds that blow across a mountainous country convey
much moisture, the snow will descend to a lower level than
it would were these winds less charged with moisture.
Hence it frequently happens that the snow-line actually rises
as it recedes from the equator.   The Cordillera of Mendoza
(22° S. lat.), for example, is snow-clad at a height of 13,200
ft., while the Sierra Famatina, which is four degrees further
to the north, shows no snow at a height of 14,764 ft.   This
difference is no doubt due to extensive radiation and the
relative dryness of the atmosphere.   It is for the same causes
that the limit of permanent snow reaches a lower level on
the southern than it does on the northern slopes of the
Himalaya.   The winds that sweep up from India are laden
with moisture, while those that blow from the north have
been sucked dry by the heated plains of Central Asia.   All
the moisture precipitated above the ideal line takes the form
of snow; but there are limits to its vertical increase—it
does not grow in thickness to an indefinite extent.   The
hill-tops are being constantly relieved of a portion of their
wintry mantle by evaporation, and occasionally great shreds
of this mantle suddenly drop away, and disappear down the
steeper hill-slopes, carrying ruin and desolation with them
when they chance to reach cultivated ground.   But neither
evaporation nor the constant discharge of avalanches suffices
to drain the mountains of their vast reservoirs of snow.
This is effected by a regular system of ice-rivers or _glaciers_.
Enthusiastic physicists have described these wonders of nature
in endless volumes, memoirs, papers, and pamphlets, and
each observer has vied with his predecessor in attempting
some novel or fuller explanation of their phenomena.   One
might think it a cold subject enough to discuss, but the

---

* This is not exactly true for arctic regions.   Even in the highest north
latitudes hitherto reached, it would seem that the short summer is sufficiently
warm to melt the snow away from the land immediately bordering on the sea.

records of science tell another tale. Many a warm word, many a hot fight, have these ice-rivers occasioned ; and the battle still goes on, though less briskly now than it did some years ago. Even the briefest account of the various theories which have been advanced from time to time in explanation of the phenomena of glaciers would occupy more space than I can afford. I must therefore content myself by merely recapitulating what appear to be the general results of the controversy.

Pressure, as every schoolboy knows, will convert a handful of new-fallen snow into a hard lump ; and if the pressure be sufficiently severe, the hardened snow will become ice. Over seemingly frail bridges of snow the adventurous mountaineer will traverse yawning clefts and chasms—for the snow, trodden firmly down, becomes stiff and rigid. It is this property of snow which makes a glacier or ice-river possible. When snow has accumulated to a great depth, its own weight squeezes down its lower strata ; and should the pressure of the overlying mass be sufficiently great, the under portions of the snow will eventually be compacted together into true ice. The passage of snow into ice is simultaneously carried on, but to a very limited extent, by alternate thawings and freezings. When the sun shines upon the snow, or a warm wind passes over its surface, the upper layer partially melts, and the disengaged water trickles down drop by drop into the layers below, where it solidifies. Every spring and summer this process is repeated with the last winter's snow, and thus, partly by thawing and freezing, but chiefly by pressure, the whole mass tends to harden into ice.

Thus solidified and apparently rigid, one would at first suppose that the hardened snow or ice would be as immovable as the rock of the mountain upon which it reclined. We know that a bed of tough clay will rest upon a very considerable slope without sliding downward, and even the loose stones and débris which cover so many hill-sides in a highland country find repose upon an incline of 30°. At Fourneaux the débris shot out from the mouth of the great Cenis tunnel forms a still steeper slope. Mr. Whymper tells us that "its faces have as nearly as possible an angle of 45°." *

* *Scrambles amongst the Alps*, p. 62.

But ice, which is a much more rigid body than even the hardest clay, will move upon a slope that is inappreciable by the eye. And thus it happens that wherever snow attains a sufficient thickness to compress itself into ice, this ice, as the overlying mass continues to receive the tribute of each winter, begins to steal down every slope, however gentle the incline may be. Thus it is that in alpine countries the valleys become more or less filled with streams and rivers of ice, which are constantly fed from the snow-fields above. The snow, packed and pressed into ice, gradually moves off the mountains, and the frozen streams thus formed collect at the head of every valley, down which they pour in those great solid masses which are known as glaciers.

Why, then, does this hard body behave so differently from other solid substances? What property does ice possess which enables it to creep upon slopes adown which only fluids and semi-fluids can move?

James David Forbes, whose works on glacial phenomena rank among the classics of physical science, came to the conclusion that the motion of a glacier was due to the viscous or plastic nature of the ice, which moved upon a slope much in the same way as a substance of the consistency of treacle or tar, its own weight being sufficient to urge it forward. When the ice was exposed in the glacier to a peculiarly violent strain, its limited plasticity necessitated the formation of an infinity of minute rents, and the internally bruised surfaces were forced to slide over one another, still producing a quasi-fluid character in the motion of the whole. The same eminent physicist further held that reconsolidation of the bruised glacial substance into a coherent whole might be effected by pressure alone acting upon granular snow, or upon ice softened by imminent thaw into a condition more plastic than ice of low temperature.*

At a later date Professor Tyndall proposed a different explanation of the phenomena. Faraday had previously pointed out that when two pieces of ice with moistened surfaces are brought into contact they immediately freeze together; and the same phenomenon took place, according to Dr. Tyndall, when a piece of ice (at 32°) was subjected to pressure

* *Occasional Papers on the Theory of Glaciers*, p. xvi.

and compelled to change its shape. Under such conditions the ice is broken by the pressure into fragments ; but these fragments being in close contact, immediately re-unite to form a solid mass. If this be true of small pieces of ice, it must be equally true of large masses ; and Dr. Tyndall therefore concluded that the motion of a glacier was due to "fracture and regelation." Under the pressure of the superincumbent snow and ice, fissures were everywhere forming and closing again ; and this rupturing and healing process extended to the smallest particles of the frozen mass. Its own weight crushed, squeezed, and pushed forward the ice, which seemed to flow with a viscous motion, owing simply to the fracture and regelation of all its particles.*

Quite recently, however, certain interesting experiments made by the late Canon Moseley suggest some difficulties which are hard to overcome. He proved conclusively that the mere weight of a mass of ice is not sufficient to cause that ice to move upon a moderate slope. Forbes' theory of viscosity, and Tyndall's theory of fracture and regelation, alike imply that ice descends a slope by virtue of its weight alone. But if ice always remains throughout its entire mass a solid body, it is evident, as Canon Moseley has shown, that the resistance offered by the ice cannot possibly be overcome by the mere weight of the mass. Besides the weight there must be some other force pushing the ice forward. A substance of the consistence of clay, which is a much less rigid body than ice, will nevertheless remain perfectly inert upon a slope adown which ice would move with the greatest ease. The clay cannot descend by gravitation, and if ice were the solid mass which it is commonly supposed to be, it would be just as impossible for it as for a mass of clay to descend a slight incline by gravitation. Yet we know that ice, hard and brittle though it be, does nevertheless move upon such a slope. This movement, however, is not effected by the slid-

---

* A different explanation of the phenomenon of regelation under pressure has been given by Professor James Thomson, and his brother, Sir William Thomson. These physicists ascribe the consolidation of the ice crushed in a mould under Bramah's press to simultaneous liquefaction, which commences at every point of the interior of the ice to which the pressure extends, and to subsequent solidification when the pressure is removed. *Proceedings of the Royal Society of London*, 1857, 1858. See also Professor Tait's remarks in *Life and Letters of Principal Forbes.*

ing of the ice over its bed ; a glacier does not slip down its valley as a disengaged slate or slab of stone would slide off the roof of a house. "All the parts of a glacier," as Canon Moseley has remarked, "do not descend with a common motion ; it moves faster at its surface than deeper down, and at the centre of its surface than at its edges. It does not only come down bodily, but with different motions of its different parts ; so that, if a tranverse section were made through it, the ice would be found to be moving differently at every point of that section. . . . . There is a constant displacement of the particles of the ice over one another and alongside one another, to which is opposed that force of resistance which is known in mechanics as *shearing-force.*" Now the question comes to be, what power is it that compels the ice-particles so to move ? The motion of fluids and semi-fluids upon a slope is undoubtedly due to gravitation ; can the movement of a glacier be owing to the same cause ? If so, then how and in what manner can the glacier assume the properties of a fluid ?

Dr. J. Croll has suggested an explanation of the difficulty, which is so ingenious, and appears to me so suggestive, that I cannot deny myself the pleasure of attempting to describe it, which I shall proceed to do in the following chapter.

CHAPTER IV.

MOLECULAR THEORY OF GLACIER MOTION.——ASPECT OF AN
ALPINE GLACIER.

Heat capable of being transmitted through ice.—Temperature of glaciers.—
Motion of ice molecules in a glacier.—Fluid molecules crystallize in interstices of ice.—Expansive force of crystallizing molecules a cause of motion.—
Ice capable of ascending a slope.—Regelation.—Alpine glaciers.—River-like
character of glaciers.—Crevasses.—Size of glaciers.—Character of the rock-
surface and stones below a glacier.—Glacial rivers.—Moraines.—Waste of
mountains.

WATER in the act of freezing gives out heat, and while
passing into the solid state expands ; so that ice occupies, weight for weight, a greater space than water. On the
other hand, when ice melts it absorbs heat, and upon becoming water takes up less room than it did in the crystallized or
solid state. Bearing this in mind, let us suppose that the
sun shines upon a glacier, and imparts to its surface a certain
amount of heat. The application of this heat will not and
cannot possibly raise the temperature of the ice (taking that
temperature at 32°), but its immediate consequence will be
to melt or turn a certain portion of the ice into water.
When this is done, a fresh surface of ice will of course be
exposed to the same action, and were the process to be continued long enough it is obvious that the glacier would by-
and-by disappear altogether. But as soon as the sun ceases
to shine upon a glacier, the water which has been set free
will freeze again. Meanwhile, however, it will have shifted
its position. The force of gravity compelled it while in the
liquid state to flow from a higher to a lower level ; and now,
when it becomes ice once more, it necessarily rests at some
distance below its former position. But what is true of
the surface of a glacier must also to some extent be true of
every portion of the frozen mass.

We know that heat can be transmitted through a slab of
ice at 32°, and yet the ice as a mass will still continue solid.
This curious result is thus explained.   When heat is applied
to the surface of the slab it cannot by any possibility raise
the temperature of the ice.   The molecules at the surface
merely pass from the solid or crystalline state into the fluid
condition.   The heat is therefore converted into a certain
amount of energy which enables the molecules to overcome
their tendency to assume the crystalline form.   The moment
the molecules are allowed to crystallize they give back in the
form of heat the energy which had forced them asunder ; or,
to put it more simply, heat is given out in the act of freezing.   The same process is repeated with the next adjoining
molecules.   No sooner have their neighbours resumed the
crystalline condition, than the heat given out instantaneously
attacks the others, and forces them to melt.   " That peculiar form of motion or energy called heat disappears in
forcing the particles of the crystalline molecule separate, and
for the time being exists in the form of a tendency in the
separated particles to come together again.   But it must be
observed that although the crystalline molecule when it is
acting as a conductor takes on energy under this form from
the heated body, yet it only exists in the molecule under
such a form during the moment of transmission—that is to
say, the molecule is melted, but only for the moment.
When B accepts of the energy from A, the molecule A
instantly assumes the crystalline form.   B is now melted, and
when C accepts of the energy from B, then B also in turn
assumes the solid state.   This process goes on from molecule to molecule, till the energy is transmitted through to the
opposite side, and the ice is left in its original solid state."*
     Such are the phenomena that take place during the trans-
mission of heat through ice.   Let us now see what light
they throw on the origin of the motion of glaciers.
     The numerous experiments made by Agassiz lead to the
conclusion that the ice of glaciers has a comparatively high
temperature.   He found, for example, that in a hole sunk to
a depth of 200 ft. in solid ice, the thermometer gave an

---

* " On the Physical Cause of the Motion of Glaciers," *Philosophical Magazine*, March, 1869, and Sept., 1870 ; *Climate and Time*, chaps. xxx, xxxi.

average temperature of 31° 24′ Fahr. In winter-time, however, the thermometer marked 28° 24′ Fahr. This, however,
appears to have been a somewhat exceptional temperature.
At all events the experiments clearly proved that in winter
the ice at the heart of a glacier is not nearly so cold as the
external atmosphere, while in summer the mass of the glacier
possesses as near as may be a temperature of 32° Fahr.

The heat that acts upon a glacier comes from various
sources. There is first the heat received directly from the
sun ; then, in spring and summer warm winds will sometimes
blow across it, and mild rains will fall upon its surface. Again,
there is the heat of the rocky cradle in which it lies, and,
not least, that which is derived from the friction of the ice
and stones upon its bed as the glacier slowly creeps away.
In summer-time the numerous small cracks and fissures that
penetrate the ice in all directions are filled with water which
has trickled down from the surface. In this manner heat is
more or less rapidly conveyed from one portion of the glacier
to another. And just as we found that heat when applied to
a slab of ice at 32° will be transmitted through that slab
without the ice as a mass changing its condition ; so must
heat in the same way pass from the various sources mentioned
right through the solid ice of the glacier. But in doing so
it will compel the icy mass to change its position. When a
molecule of glacier ice, A, has momentarily melted owing to
the reception of energy in the form of heat, it will by virtue
of its fluidity tend to move downwards, but the instant that
it resumes the solid state the heat evolved will immediately
attack the molecule behind it, B. This molecule will then
melt and contract in bulk, and will descend by its own gravity
until it stops against A. Here then it will freeze again. But
as A now occupies a lower level than it did before the heat
dissolved it, so B in like manner solidifies a little below its
former position. The heat emitted by B at the moment of
its passing into ice is next transmitted to C, whereupon the
same changes ensue as before, and so on throughout the entire
mass. Thus, while acting as conductors of heat, each individual molecule of ice is compelled by the force of gravity to
move from a higher to a lower level. The result of this
general molecular motion is that the whole body of a glacier

moves gradually downwards, impelled by gravitation, in the same way as fluids and semifluids are urged forwards upon a slope. As a hard and brittle body, ice could not possibly flow—its own weight would be quite unable to compel the particles of ice to lose their cohesion. It is the transmission of heat through a glacier which by momentarily converting each atom of its substance into water renders motion possible. Could heat be entirely withdrawn the motion of a glacier would be at once arrested, and the ice would remain as inert and immovable a body as any other substance equally hard and unyielding.

Now if it were true that the bed of a glacier showed no irregularities of surface,—if the ice had merely to move along a smooth inclined plane, then the foregoing account of the molecular changes which are induced by the action of heat might satisfy us that we had at last obtained a reasonable explanation of the cause of glacier motion. We should perhaps conclude that since ice flows with a differential motion in the same way as running water (each molecule of the frozen mass in the moment of melting being allowed to descend by gravitation), then there can be no slope that induces water to flow which will not also suffice for the downward movement of a glacier. When we become aware, however, that the bed of a glacier is not a smooth inclined plane, but on the contrary is frequently rough and irregular, and when we learn, moreover, that glaciers have actually moved up-hill, in many cases at a considerable angle, we must see at once that the molecular theory, so far as we have yet described it, is incomplete. We may comprehend why ice flows *down* a slope, but how can the molecular theory of glacier motion account for the fact that ice has actually moved *uphill ?* Gravitation explains the general movement of a glacier, which is, of course, from a higher to a lower level, but it does not help us to understand how the ice is forced *up* and over the inequalities of its rocky bed. We may indeed conceive how the *vis a tergo* of a descending glacier might be sufficient to impel the ice for some distance up a gentle slope. An insignificant knoll lying in the path of a glacier might thus be over-ridden by ice forced over it by the pressure of the mass advancing from behind in obedience to the motion of its melting and resolidifying particles. But if the ice poured into a deep hollow surrounded on all sides by steep rocky slopes, should not we expect to find, after the deep basin had been filled to overflowing, that only the upper portion of the ice in the basin would be in motion—that at the bottom lying sluggish and inert ? Is it not most natural to suppose that this would be the case? We can conceive the ice flowing into the hollow, but how is it to get out again ? Will it be forced out by the pressure of the ice advancing from behind ? Surely not, if the sides of the basin are steep. Such pressure will simply cause the ice lying above the level of the basin to move forward over the ice that fills it. All this seems to be quite clear, nevertheless, in despite of these preconceived notions of ours as to how it would act under the circumstances, we know that ice has gone into deep basins and come out again ; we know that it has ascended considerable slopes—that hills, several hundred feet in height, have been surmounted by it. But if this be so, then we must feel convinced that something more than gravitation alone is required to explain glacier motion.

The solution of the difficulty appears to be found in the behaviour of the ice molecules while they are in the act of passing from the fluid into the solid state.* Ice, as we know, is not absolutely solid throughout. It is built up of innumerable crystalline particles, all confusedly interlaced, and crossing and recrossing each other at every conceivable angle. But althougth the particles are thus in mutual contact, they are, nevertheless, not packed so closely together as to exclude the presence of interstices. Being united to one another at special points, determined by their polarity, they on this account require more space than their bulk is sufficient to fill, and this is probably why ice, as Professor Tyndall remarks, is, volume for volume, less dense than water. Bearing in mind, therefore, that ice is permeated more or less freely in every direction with innumerable interstitial pores, let us see how the ice particles behave during the moments of melting and freezing. It is obvious that when a crystalline molecule melts it will not merely descend by gravitation, but capillary

* In this paragraph I give the theory nearly in Dr. Croll's own words, only condensing and omitting a little to save space. See *Climate and Time*, p. 523.

attraction will cause it to flow into the interstices between the adjoining molecules. The moment that it parts with the heat received it will of course freeze again ; but in thus becoming solid it will not fit the cavity which it occupied when in the fluid state, for it has now assumed the crystalline form, and as there is a definite proportion between the length, breadth, and thickness of the crystal, it must always happen that the interstice in which a molecule solidifies will be too narrow to contain it. The result will be that the fluid molecule in passing into the crystalline form will press the two adjoining molecules aside in order to make sufficient room for itself between them, and this it will do no matter what amount of space it may possess in all other directions. The crystal will not form to suit the cavity, the cavity must be made to contain the crystal. And what holds true of one molecule, holds true of every molecule which melts and resolidifies. This process is therefore going on incessantly in every part of the glacier, and in proportion to the amount of heat which the glacier is receiving. The internal molecular pressure, resulting from the solidifying of the fluid molecules in the interstices of the ice, acts on the mass of the ice as an expansive force, tending to cause the glacier to widen out laterally in all directions. But in the case of a glacier lying in a valley motion can only take place in one direction, for the sides of the valley prevent the glacier widening, and as gravitation opposes the motion of the ice up the valley and favours its motion in the opposite direction, it is obvious that molecular displacement will take place in the path of least resistance—that is, down the valley. The ultimate result then is the production of motion in the same direction as that of gravity.

We now see how ice cannot remain stagnant, as it were, at the bottom of a great basin, so as to allow the frozen mass that lies above the level of that basin to flow over its surface. The under and upper portions of the ice form one solid mass, and therefore the latter " cannot move over the former without shearing ; and although the resistance to motion offered by the sloping sides of the basin may be much greater than the resistance to shear, still the ice will be slowly dragged out of the basin." For, as we have seen, heat is continually passing through the glacier, and the molecular action induced causes the under portions of the frozen mass to expand. The warmth received from the sun and the external air melts the ice molecules at the surface, and hence water is continually oozing into the interstices below and solidifying there. The heat thus set free instantly passes over to the molecules underneath, which thereupon melt, descend, and resolidify. So the process continues from the surface of the glacier to its bottom, where the interstices of the ice are being constantly filled by fluid molecules from above which necessarily freeze again and compel the ice to expand to make room for them. It is evident, however, that the ice in a basin at the bottom of a valley cannot expand laterally without passing up the sloping sides of the hollow in which it lies, and in doing so the direction in which it expands or moves must, of course, be the path of least resistance. Now this can only be the direction of the general flow. Hence the ice in a deep basin over which a glacier is passing will gradually creep up the slope at the lower end of the basin, no matter how steep that slope may be, and thereafter continue on its way down the valley.

Heat is thus the great lever which forces the hard masses of compacted snow and ice from higher to lower levels, and relieves the mountains of their loads of frozen water. If it were not for that peculiar property of ice which enables it to behave in many respects like a viscous or semifluid body, all the waters of the earth, the myriad rivers, and lakes, and seas, would gradually be lifted up by the heat of the sun, and carried on the wings of the wind to the mountains, there to accumulate in vast and constantly growing masses until ocean and all its feeders had been exhausted. But the heat of the sun which, falling upon clay, sand, or solid rock, merely raises the temperature without changing the condition of these masses, pulses through the great piles of ice that cumber the higher elevations of alpine countries. The temperature of the ice itself cannot rise, but every atom of its bulk is set in motion, and slowly and gradually the solid heaps creep down hill-slope and valley, their progress being accelerated or retarded according to the degree of heat acting upon and passing through them. It is thus that during day the downward motion of the ice is less sluggish than at night ; and for the same reason a glacier in summer-time moves more quickly on its way than in winter, when its motion is exceedingly slow, sometimes not reaching to half the summer rate.

But it may be asked how it happens that a body built up of atoms which are constantly passing from the solid to the liquid state, and *vice versâ*, nevertheless retains an unvarying hard and brittle condition. This is due to the property of regelation. When two fragments of ice at 32° are brought into contact, they instantly unite, as we have already seen, so as to form one solid piece. What is thus true of ice in the mass is equally true of its most minute atoms. Whenever these impinge upon one another they immediately freeze firmly together. No sooner does a molecule, which has momentarily melted, resume the solid state than it immediately unites to the other solid particles by which it is surrounded ; hence the continuity of the whole is preserved, and throughout its entire bulk the ice remains a solid body. Such is the ingenious theory advanced by Dr. Croll.

We have now learned what are the means which Nature adopts to prevent the increase of snow to an indefinite extent upon the mountains. The under portions of the frozen heaps are gradually squeezed by the superincumbent masses into ice, and this ice thereupon begins to creep outwards and downwards. At the head of an alpine valley streams of ice collect from the contiguous slopes, and, becoming welded together into one mass, creep down the bottom of the valley, forming a glacier or ice river. It depends upon the size of a glacier, whether its journey is to be a long or short one. Often the ice reaches many thousand feet below the limits of permanent snow, amongst which it takes its birth. But sooner or later its progress is at last arrested by the increasing temperature, which melts the ice away as fast as it comes down.

In its course from the regions of perennial snows down to where it is cut off by the increasing warmth the glacier has many analogies with a stream or river of water. The velocity of a river varies according to the inclination of the valley down which it flows, and this it would seem is equally true of glaciers. When the course of a river is rocky and falls rapidly, its waters are broken, and hurry on tumultuously.

In like manner, a glacier that makes its way along a rough and
rocky valley shows a broken and tumbled surface. There
are waterfalls and ice-cataracts. Again it is known that rivers
flow more swiftly at the surface and the middle than they do
at the bottom and sides, where the water is retarded by friction : the same is the case with glaciers. The thread of a
river's current moves from right to left of a medial line
according as the river winds from one side of the valley to
the other ; the icy current of a glacier follows the same direction. Nay, we may carry the parallel yet further, for the
twigs and branches and trunks of trees which drop into a
river and float upon its bosom are represented in alpine
valleys by the blocks and stones and débris which fall upon
a glacier from crag and cliff, and are borne upon its surface
down the valley. From its river-like character and the
wonderful manner in which it accommodates itself to the form
of a valley, narrowing when that contracts to a gorge, and
expanding when the valley again widens out, it is no wonder
that many eminent physicists have maintained that ice is a
viscous body, and not the hard and brittle substance that it
seems. When, owing to the nature of its bed, the glacier
becomes subjected to strain or tension, however, it is always
more or less seamed with gaping cracks or clefts which
descend to a great depth in the ice. These *crevasses,* as
they are called, have undoubtedly been produced by the
snapping of the ice, owing to its inability to resist strain or
tension by stretching out. The beginning of a crevasse is
often notified by a loud report—the rupturing of the ice.
At first the crack may be only wide enough to admit the
edge of a knife, but it gradually opens, until frequently it
yawns into a wide impassable chasm. The origin of these
crevasses is due to the unequal or differential motion of the
ice—the glacier moving faster at the surface and the centre
than it does at the bottom and the sides, and thus bringing
tension into play. Many fissures and crevasses also are
caused by the inequalities of the bed over which the glacier
flows, for the bottom of a valley does not always, or even
often, slope at the same angle throughout : some portions
incline more rapidly than others. Now the ice when it
reaches in its downward progress the edge of one of these

steeper inclines will naturally tend to move more quickly, and to drag forward the ice behind it. At this point then a state of tension is brought about, to which the ice can only yield by snapping asunder. When, afterwards, the ice arrives at a gentler and more equal slope, its motion is at once checked, the gaping crevasses begin to close up, and by-and-by disappear altogether, until finally, under the influence of regelation, the ice becomes solid as before. Thus in its course from the snow-fields to its termination the ice is being continually broken by mechanical strain, and just as constantly these breakages are being repaired by the regelation or freezing together again of the broken faces.

Glaciers, like rivers, are of all sizes. Many have a depth of several hundred feet, and some in polar regions are not less than 3,000 feet, or even more in thickness.* It may easily be conceived that the pressure of such enormous masses of ice must have a prodigious effect. When a glacier advances beyond its usual limits everything goes down before it : loose soils and débris are pushed forward, and the strongest and thickest trees are overborne just as if they were so many straws. But striking as these examples of the irresistible force of a glacier may be, the destructive and overwhelming power of ice in motion becomes still more noteworthy when the rocks over which a glacier passes are examined. This may be done in summer-time, when the glaciers shrink from the sides of their valleys. Creeping in below the ice, which it is often possible to do for some little distance, we find the rocks finely smoothed and polished, and showing long striæ and ruts, that run parallel to the course followed by the glacier. If we pick out some of the stones that are sure to be scattered about below the ice we shall find that many are smoothed, polished, and striated in the same manner as the surface of the rock itself. All this is the work of the glacier. The rocky precipices and mountains that hem in a glacier are always splitting up under the influence of frost, and tons of rock and rubbish are continually rolling down and gathering upon the surface of the ice below. Much

* The vast sheet of ice which covers the south polar regions must attain an enormous thickness. Dr. Croll has endeavoured to show that it cannot be less than twelve miles thick in the interior of the Antarctic continent. *Climate and Time*, p. 375.

of this débris falls into crevasses, and must no doubt frequently reach the bottom of the ice. The stones then get
jammed into the frozen mass, and are pressed against the
underlying rock-head with all the weight of the superincumbent glacier. Graving tools must also be supplied to the
glacier by the wrenching of fragments from its own rocky bed.
These and the stones received from the crevasses, thus firmly
held in the grasp of the ice, become potent agents in grinding
and scratching the pavement over which they are forced,
while the smaller stones and sand and mud that result from
the grinding process, complete the smoothing and polishing
of the glacier's bed. Could the glacier be removed, we should
find the whole bottom of the valley smoothed and polished,
and streaked with long parallel ruts. Every high projecting
boss would be rounded and dressed on the side that looked
up the valley ; while the rock on the lee-side, sheltered from
the attack of ice-plough, and chisel, and graver, would retain
all its roughnesses. Smaller and less abrupt knobs of rock
would be rounded and polished all over, and every dimple and
hollow would be similarly smoothed and dressed.

The finer-grained materials employed by the ice in polishing its bed, the impalpable mud and silt, are carried out from
beneath by the stream that issues at the foot of the glacier.
In this manner almost all glacial rivers have imparted to
them a turbid appearance, the colour of the water depending
upon that of the sediment which it holds in suspension. The
water may thus be bluish or milky, red, yellow, or dark grey.
The stones employed by the glacier in grinding and graving
its rocky bed are themselves ground and engraved, and numbers of such smoothed, polished, and striated fragments are
pushed out at the foot of the glacier. But they here become
intermingled with the vast heaps of débris which have been
discharged from the mountains and brought down upon the
surface of the slowly moving ice.

These heaps are called *moraines*. They are composed for
the most part of rough, unpolished, angular fragments of all
sizes, from mere sand and grit up to blocks many tons in
weight. As might be expected, they show no trace of any
arrangement into beds or layers—large and small stones,
huge blocks and angular gravel, grit and boulders, are all

confusedly mixed together. The moraines are not scattered irregularly over the whole surface of the ice, save when the glacier is very narrow, but gather chiefly upon the sides, at the base of the mountain-slopes. The glacier in this manner becomes fringed from its origin to its termination with long mounds or banks of débris, which are constantly dropping over the end of the ice, and adding to the immense piles of rubbish collected there. These latter are the *terminal moraines,* those fringing the sides of the glacier being its *lateral moraines.* Some terminal moraines attain a great size, forming mounds of débris several hundred feet in height.

One may see from the size of the moraines how great must be the waste of the mountains. In all mountainous regions,* indeed, the action of frost upon the rocks becomes abundantly evident. Even in our own country the tops and slopes of our higher hills are often buried to a great depth with the débris which alternate freezings and thawings have wrenched from the solid rocks. In high latitudes the exposed rocks are almost everywhere broken up in this way. Von Baer found the hills on the west coast of Novaia Zemblia literally covered with their own wreck—no rock, however hard or fine-grained, being able to withstand the summer moisture and intense winter frost of that desolate country. Mr. Kennan also, in his lively-written "Tent Life in Siberia," tells us how, upon crossing the mountains of Kamschatka, he found the table-land and hill-tops crowded with great square and angular blocks and slabs of rock, which looked for all the world as if they had rained from the skies! They were undoubtedly the ruins of the solid rock which they covered and concealed, and had been detached by frost acting along the natural joints and fissures. In alpine countries this wrecking of the mountains goes on chiefly by day, and in summer-time. During night, and at early morn, dead

---

* In the upper valleys of the Himalaya the waste is something wonderful. See some graphic accounts of this in Mr. Wilson's *Abode of Snow.* Not less striking are the prodigious masses of superficial débris which cover the slopes of the Rocky Mountains in certain latitudes. Dr. Hayden describes certain of the valleys (Colorado) visited by him as being "covered thickly with earth, filled with more or less worn rocks of every size, from that of a pea to several feet in diameter. The snow melting upon the crests of the mountains saturates these superficial earths with water, and they slowly move down the gulch much like a glacier. This is another process of grinding the underlying rocks, smoothing and grooving them." *Geological and Geographical Survey of Colorado,* 1873, p. 46.

silence reigns among the snowy peaks : no streams are heard, no water trickles over the surface of the ice ; but when the power of the sun begins to be felt, then the noise of water running, leaping, and falling grows upon the ear ; soon the

Fig. 15.—Alpine Glacier. (H. M. Skae.)

glaciers are washed by numberless little streams ; great avalanches, wreathed in snow-smoke, rush downwards with a roar like thunder ; masses of rock wedged out by the frost of the previous night are now loosened by the sun, and dash headlong down the precipices, while long trains of débris hurry after them, and are scattered far and wide in wild confusion along the flanks of the glaciers.

CHAPTER V.

GREENLAND : ITS GLACIAL ASPECT.

Extent of Greenland.—Character of coast and interior.—The great *mer de glace*.—
Size of glaciers.—Phenomena of arctic glaciers, and origin of icebergs.—
Submarine moraines.—Scarcity of surface-moraines in Greenland.—Glacial
rivers.—Circulation of water underneath the ice.—The habitable strip of
coast-land.—Formation of ice upon the sea.—The ice-foot.—Waste of cliffs.—
Transportation of rock-débris by ice-rafts and icebergs.—Action of stranded
icebergs upon the sea-bottom.

WE have now acquired some knowledge of facts that bear
upon the origin of the Scottish till, but we shall
gather yet further aid in our attempts to decipher the history
of that deposit by taking a peep at some arctic country. For
this purpose we cannot do better than select ice-covered
Greenland. That desolate region of the far north, despite the
bleak and barren aspect of its coasts, and the horrors of the
ice-choked seas that must be traversed to reach its more
northern shores, has nevertheless been frequently visited by
our navigators, who have pushed their investigations many
hundred miles north of the Danish settlements. The
accounts which they give are chiefly taken up with descriptions of the wild ice-bound coast few attempts having been
made to penetrate into the interior. But that cannot be
said to be altogether a terra incognita, for, although it has
never been, and probably never will be, traversed, yet enough
is known to leave us in little doubt as to the general character of these unvisited desolations.

The western shores of Greenland have been traced northwards from Cape Farewell in the latitude of the Shetland
Islands, to beyond the 80th parallel. The eastern and
north-eastern coasts have not been so continuously followed,
but our knowledge of these has been considerably increased
during recent years, thanks to the exertions of German and
Swedish geographers. The superficial area of Greenland

cannot be less than 750,000 square miles, so that the country is almost continental in its dimensions. Of this great region, only a little strip extending to 74° north lat. along the western shore is sparsely colonised—all the rest is a bleak wilderness of snow and ice and rock.

The coasts are deeply indented with numerous bays and fiords or friths, which, when traced inland, are almost invariably found to terminate against glaciers. Thick ice frequently appears, too, crowning the exposed sea-cliffs, from the edges of which it droops in thick tongue-like and stalactitic projections, until its own weight forces it to break away and topple down the precipices into the sea. The whole interior of the country, indeed, would appear to be buried underneath a great depth of snow and ice, which levels up the valleys and sweeps over the hills. The few daring men who have tried to penetrate a little way inland from the coast, describe the scene as desolate in the extreme—far as eye can reach nothing save one dead dreary expanse of white. No living creature frequents this wilderness—neither bird, nor beast, nor insect—not even a solitary moss or lichen can be seen. Over everything broods a silence deep as death, broken only when the roaring storm arises to sweep before it the pitiless blinding snow.

But even in the silent and pathless desolations of central Greenland the forces of nature are continuously at work. The vast masses of snow and ice that seem to wrap the hills and valleys as with an everlasting garment, are nevertheless constantly wearing away, and being just as continuously repaired. The peculiar properties of ice that prevent it accumulating upon the land to an indefinite degree, are just as characteristic of the snow-fields of Greenland as of those of alpine countries. Fast as the snows deepen and harden into ice upon the bleak wilds of Greenland, that ice creeps away to the coast, and thus from the frozen reservoirs of the interior, innumerable glaciers pour themselves down every fiord and opening to the sea. Only a narrow strip of land along the coast-line is left uncovered by the permanent snow-field or *mer de glace*—all else is snow and ice.

Some of the glaciers attain a vast size. The great Humboldt glacier is said by its discoverer, Dr. Kane, to have a breadth of 60 miles at its termination. Its seaward face rises abruptly from the level of the water to a height of 300 feet, but to what depth it descends is not known. Other glaciers of large size occur frequently along the whole extent of the north-western shores of Greenland. Among these is that of Eisblink, south of Goodhaab, which projects seaward so as to form a promontory some thirteen miles in length. This immense glacier flows from an unknown distance in the interior, and buries its face to a great depth in the sea. A submarine bank of débris forms a kind of semicircle some little way in front of it, and may owe its origin, in part, to the stream that issues from underneath the glacier; but, as we shall see presently, a bank would necessarily gather in the same place, even although no water whatever circulated below the ice.

I have already remarked that the Greenland glaciers discharge into the sea by fiords and indentations of the coast. If the ice-filled fiords could be cleared out, we should find that these arms of the sea would occupy deep hollows, continuous with long valleys stretching into the heart of the country. The west coasts of Scotland and Norway afford excellent examples of the kind of scenery that Greenland would present were its fiords and valleys to be freed of ice. In Scotland the fiord-valleys are watered by streams shed from the hills of the interior, but in not a few of the Norwegian valleys, the streams that enter the fiords, when followed up, are found to issue from glaciers. In North Greenland, however, the ice generally fills up the whole valley, and pushes forward into the sea. Only in a few cases do the glaciers terminate inland and thus give rise to rivers. Yet even when they enter the sea, fresh water continues to escape from underneath the ice, discolouring the sea with the sediment which it sweeps out along with it, and even to some extent diminishing its saltness.

Many arctic glaciers are so thick and massive that they glide boldly on over the bed of the sea, and thus displace the water often for many miles. Instead of the deep fiords being filled with sea-water, as is the case in Scotland and Norway, they are occupied entirely by ice. When the glacier in its downward progress first entered the sea at the head of

PLATE II.

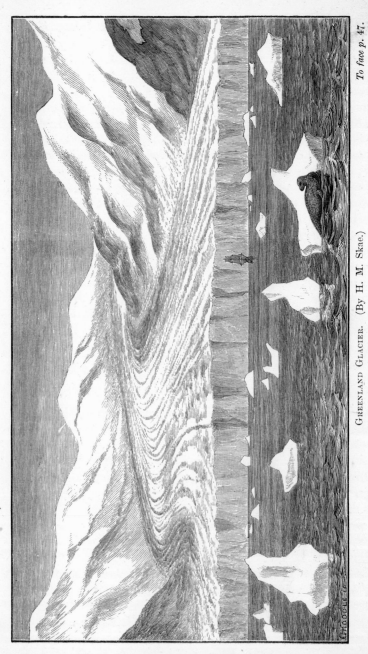

GREENLAND GLACIER. (By H. M. Skae.)

To face p. 47.

a fiord, it must have towered for many hundred feet above
the level of the water. But as it continued on its course,
and crept onward over the deepening bed of the fiord, it
gradually buried its lofty face in the waves, until, when it
reached the lower end of the fiord and entered the open sea,
its front rose only a little height above the reach of the tides.
Thus, the sloping platform of ice that faces the sea, however
lofty it may be, must bear only a small proportion to the
much greater thickness of ice concealed below. [See Plate II.]

It is well known that ice is not by any means so heavy as
water, but readily floats upon its surface. Consequently,
whenever a glacier enters the sea, the dense salt water tends
to buoy it up. But the great tenacity of the frozen mass
enables it to resist the pressure for a time. By-and-by,
however, as the glacier reaches deeper water, its cohesion is
overcome, and large segments are forced from its terminal
front and floated up from the bed of the sea to sail away as
icebergs. As there is considerable misapprehension about
the formation of icebergs, it is necessary to look a little more
closely at the facts, because, as we shall afterwards see, they
have a strong bearing on the origin of the Scottish till.
Some have supposed that the whole mass of the glacier, after
it has entered the sea for some little distance, becomes
buoyed up, retaining at the same time its continuity with
the landward portion of the ice or *mer de glace.* But from
what has already been explained regarding the total inability
of ice to yield to mechanical strain in any other way save by
breaking, it becomes obvious that the seaward portion of an
arctic glacier cannot by any possibility be floated up without
sundering its connection with the frozen mass behind. So
long as the bulk of the glacier much exceeds the depth of
the sea, the ice will of course rest upon the bed of the fiord
or bay without being subjected to any strain or tension.
But when the glacier creeps outwards to greater depths, then
the superior specific gravity of the sea-water will tend to
press the ice upward. That ice, however, is a hard, continuous mass, with sufficient cohesion to oppose for a time
this pressure, and hence the glacier crawls on to a depth far
below the point at which, had it been free, it would have
risen to the surface and floated. If at this great depth the

whole mass of the glacier could be buoyed up without breaking off, it would certainly go to prove that the ice of arctic regions, unlike ice anywhere else, had the property of yielding to mechanical strain without rupturing. But the great tension to which it is subjected takes effect in the usual way, and the ice yields, not by bending and stretching but by breaking. The diagram (Fig. 16) will give a clearer notion of the relation which an arctic glacier bears to its rocky bed and the sea which it displaces. Let *s l* represent the level of the sea. The glacier *g* enters the sea and creeps on until it reaches a point *t*, at which the pressure of the water overcomes the cohesion of the ice, and forces off a large segment from the front of the glacier. This segment then floats away as an iceberg *i*, with probably some stones frozen into its bottom. The débris underlying the

Fig. 16.—Greenland glacier shedding an iceberg.

ice will now be partially exposed at *b*—the place formerly occupied by the iceberg. After a time the glacier will again advance to *t*, pushing before it some portion of the débris seen at *b*. By the successive shedding of icebergs and the continuous advance of the glacier, a mound of rubbish will tend to collect at *m*—the materials of which will probably be partially arranged by tides and any streams of fresh water that may happen to issue from the bottom of the glacier. Of course the seaward front of a glacier does not necessarily present a regularly perpendicular face down to the bottom upon which it rests, such as is shown in the diagram above. In most cases, probably, the ice is deeply excavated below the water-line so as to cause the portion visible at the surface to overhang, and thus ever and anon large masses, losing their support, slip downwards and float away as icebergs. Hence, it is evident, that owing to the continual melting of

the submarine part of the glacier only a very insignificant proportion of the stones and rubbish dragged on underneath can
possibly be carried away by icebergs.   A few stones may
occasionally remain frozen into the bottom of the detached
icebergs, but it is evident that the greater portion of the
subglacial deposit must remain upon the bottom of the sea.
The existence of such frontal or terminal submarine moraines
is not merely hypothetical.   They are well known to occur—
the Tallert Bank in front of the glacier of Eisblink being a
very good example.*

Thus, from its origin in the interior of Greenland, to its
termination in the sea, the glacier clings pertinaciously to its
bed.   It nowhere floats so as to allow the sea to get in
below, but when the pressure of the water becomes too much
for it, immense fragments break away, and rise to the surface, causing the sea sometimes to " boil like a pot."

But before attempting to describe the phenomena connected with floating ice, I have still to glance at some of the
appearances exhibited by the ice upon the land.

In general appearance the glaciers of Greenland do not
differ, save in size, from those of other countries.†   When
the bed of an arctic glacier is rough and irregular, the ice
becomes intensely broken and crevassed, just as we saw was
the case with the smaller ice-rivers of the Alps.   The arctic
glaciers are also in summer-time washed by innumerable
streamlets and rivers due to the melting of the ice.   Professor Nordenskjöld, who made an excursion on the inland
ice for a distance of thirty miles from the head of Auleitsivik
Fiord (68° north lat.), tells us how his retreat was for a time
cut off by a copious deep and broad river which could not be
crossed without a bridge.   But when he followed it in the direction of the current he found ere long that it rushed with a
loud roar down a perpendicular cleft in the ice to the depths
below.   Again, he and his companion " saw at some distance

---

* Opposite the whole front of the great glacier of Edge Island (Spitzbergen),
there is a similar extensive submarine bank which stretches seawards for fifteen
or twenty miles.   *Yachting in the Arctic Seas* (Lamont), p. 242.

† From recent observations in North Greenland, by Mr. Amund Helland, it
would appear that the rate of motion is greater in certain arctic glaciers than in
those of the Alps, from which Mr. Helland infers that the ancient glaciers of the
Ice Age probably flowed as fast at least as those of Greenland.   *Om de isfyldte
Fjorde og de glaciale Dannelser i Nordgrönland ;* (1876.)

from them, a well-defined pillar of mist, which, when they approached it, appeared to rise from a bottomless abyss, into which a mighty glacier river fell. The vast roaring water-mass had bored for itself a vertical hole, probably all the way down to the rock, situated certainly more than 2,000 feet beneath, on which the glacier rested."* This of course is just the same phenomenon as the well-known *moulin* of Alpine glaciers.

It is only very rarely that any scattered stones and débris appear upon the surface of the arctic glaciers. This is owing to the fact that the whole interior of the country is so effectually concealed beneath its coat of snow and ice that no bare rocky slopes from which fragments might be detached are left exposed to the action of the frost. All the inland valleys appear to be filled up and levelled to the tops of the hills, only the extreme tips of which appear here and there above the bleak wastes of the *mer de glace*. Hence there is well-nigh a total absence of those long trains of débris† that thunder down the steeps of the Alpine mountains, and gather in heaps along the sides of the glaciers. It is not until the glaciers of Greenland descend to the sea-coast, where the cliffs and mountains that overlook them are more exposed to the action of the weather, that they begin to receive a goodly tribute of blocks and boulders. But the fiord-valleys in which the glaciers lie, are in general so broad, that vast expanses of ice show no speck of stone or dust—it is only here and there along their flanks that some bare cliff is able to shower down upon them a heap of frost-riven débris. The greatest apparent waste of rocks takes place upon the exposed sea-coasts, where the frost has full freedom to split up the crags and hurl them downwards. But when we think of the immense extent of the glacier system of Greenland, and how in the interior every hill is covered and every valley filled to overflowing with a moving sea of snow and ice, we can hardly overestimate the tremendous tear and wear to which the buried country must be subjected. We

* *Geological Magazine*, vol. ix., p. 360.
† Dr. Rink obtained from the top of a mountain at Upernavik, a good view into the interior of Greenland, and saw lines of stones dotting the surface of the ice as far as the eye could reach ; from which he inferred that still farther to the east there must be bare cliffs or precipices rising above the *mer de glace*.

have seen what effect the small glaciers of the Alps have in smoothing and scoring the rocks of Switzerland, and underneath the ice of Greenland similar grinding, and scratching, and polishing must be taking place. Rough crags and sharp projecting bosses of rock will have all their asperities removed; the tops and sides of mountains will be smoothed and dressed, nor can we doubt that valleys will be gradually deepened, and heaps of striated and polished stones will accumulate and be dragged on underneath those mighty ice-rivers which are ever slowly making their way from the interior to the sea.

But all the glaciers of Greenland do not reach the sea. Some even terminate at a distance of many miles from the coast. From the foot of such glaciers streams of water issue and flow all the year round. In some cases these streams unite so as to form considerable rivers, one of which, after a course of forty miles, enters the sea with a mouth nearly three-fourths of a mile in breadth. Dr. Kane, who discovered and named this river the Mary Minturn River, seems to have been much impressed with the appearance of such a body of fresh water flowing freely at a time when the outside sea was thickly covered with ice. It is highly probable, however, that water circulates to some extent below every glacier, independently of that which rushes down in summer time through clefts and holes from the surface. The intense cold of an arctic winter penetrates to only a comparatively little distance from the surface of the ground. If it were otherwise—if the winter temperature of North Greenland could penetrate to any depth, it is clear that not a drop of water in any of its valleys would be permitted to remain in the liquid state, and the short summer would be unable to set free more than that which laves the surface of the inland ice. It is well known, however, that upon digging down through the snow to the underlying soil, the temperature of the latter is found to be considerably higher than that of the external atmosphere. Snow and ice are bad conductors of heat, and thus the warmth imparted to the ground in summer is never entirely dissipated, but imprisoned, as it were, by the investing sheet of snow. In like manner, the rocks that are permanently concealed under the *mer de glace* and the great glaciers, must retain pretty nearly the same temperature all the year round. It is quite impossible that the intense cold of winter can pierce entirely through the thick ice ; or, on the other hand, that the higher temperature of the rocks can make its escape upwards. Hence any natural springs that may rise below the glaciers will continue to flow on beneath the ice, while the temperature of the rocks themselves, and the heat derived from the intense friction of the glacier grinding upon its bed must tend to melt the under portions of the gelid mass, and thus materially add to the volume of water in circulation betwixt the ice and its pavement.

Between the edge of the *mer de glace*, or snow-field, of Greenland and the sea, there intervenes a narrow strip of country, from which, in summer-time, the snow almost entirely disappears. In the sheltered nooks of this narrow tract of land, the short summer suffices to waken from their long winter sleep numerous feeble flowerets that gleam and twinkle timidly among thick tufted grasses. Here the purple lichnis and white-starred chickweed, with many other sweet little plants, blossom and bloom under the fleeting sunshine. Dwarf heaths, willows, and alders are also plentiful, and the barren rocks put on a gay livery of orange-coloured lichens. The musk-ox, the reindeer, the arctic fox and hare frequent these solitudes, and numerous flocks of sea-birds enliven the coasts ; only to disappear, however, as soon as the fading day warns them of the approach of the long night of winter. Of course the Esquimaux are entirely confined to this narrow belt of ground adjoining the sea ; of the interior of the country they know nothing.

A glance at a map of the western hemisphere will show that Greenland is separated from Labrador, and the bleak islands that flank the northern coasts of America, by a broad belt of water, the wider portions of which are known as Davis Strait and Baffin's Bay. Towards the far north, this water-belt suddenly contracts to a comparatively narrow strait at Smith's Sound, but afterwards expands again into Kennedy's Channel, beyond which nothing until recently was definitely known. Throughout the greater part of the year, this wide belt of sea is always more or less clogged with ice. In winter-time it is nearly all frozen over, but in summer the ice breaks up into a tumbled archipelago of floating islands, through which an adventurous voyager may make his way with difficulty and danger, up to where the belt begins to contract at Smith's Sound. There can be little doubt that the comparatively sheltered character of much of this region aids the formation of the ice upon the sea; for when the expeditions of Dr. Kane and Dr. Hayes traced the coast-lines to the far north, they found, where these suddenly retired, that the ice-choked water of Kennedy's Channel expanded into a wide open sea that rolled its great billows against long lines of black cliffs, and seemed to stretch away as far as eye could reach towards the pole.*

Again, upon the eastern shores of Greenland, which are exposed to the full swell of the ocean, ice never accumulates to such an extent as it does in Baffin's Bay. The high cliffs, therefore, that overlook the water-belt of Davis Strait and Baffin's Bay, must protect the sea to some extent from those fierce storms which in open ocean throw the water into violent commotion and prevent ice forming. Dr. Hayes, with a small party, climbed from the shore near Port Foulke and ventured upwards of sixty miles upon the snow-covered table-land, but was overtaken by a storm of such violence, that it was with great difficulty he succeeded in making good his return. The travellers found, as they descended towards the coast, that they gradually escaped the fury of the wind; and when at last they reached the sea-level, all there was peaceful and quiet: although they could see, by the great clouds of snow-dust which continued to stream out from the crest of the towering cliffs, that the storm still raged with undiminished fury on the bleak table-land above them.

The ice formed upon the surface of the sea, by direct

---

* Captain Hall, in the *Polaris*, subsequently (1871) discovered that the "open polar sea" of Kane and Hayes was merely a continuation of the great inlet or strait of which Smith's Sound and Kennedy's Channel form portions. When Hall sailed farther north he found that the channel again contracted (lat. 81° 16′ N.), but there was still a water horizon to the north-east. It is remarkable that the climate of Hall's winter-quarters in 81° 38′ N., was considerably milder than it is several degrees farther south. Long before these lines appear it is to be hoped that the expedition, which so recently left our shores, will have solved the mysteries that lie beyond Polaris Bay and Robeson Strait.

freezing, rarely attains a greater thickness than eighteen or twenty feet; and where the water is liable to more or less agitation, it is usually much less. There is a limit to the influence of frost upon the sea, just as there is upon the solid ground. The cake of ice protects the underlying water even as snow shelters the earth. As the ice rapidly thickens, the warm temperature of the sea finds increasing difficulty in soaking upwards through its crystalline roof, until at last it becomes practically imprisoned. Thus, with the warmth of the sea shut in, and the cold of the external air shut out, the ice-cake comes to assume its maximum thickness soon

Fig. 17.—Greenland Ice-foot. [H. M. Skae.]

after the winter sets in; the intense cold of the later winter months adding little, if anything, to its depth.

The sea-ice, where it abuts upon the land, reaches a much greater thickness than that which is formed off shore. Along the coast from near the Arctic Circle up to Kennedy's Channel, a narrow shelf or platform, varying from sixty to one hundred and fifty feet or so in breadth, adheres to the rocks, accommodating itself to every sweep and indentation of the coast-line. In the higher latitudes this shelf never entirely disappears, but farther south it breaks up and vanishes towards the end of summer. It owes its origin to the action of the tides. The first frost of the late summer covers the sea with a coat of ice, which, carried upwards along the face of the cliffs by the tide, eventually becomes glued to the rocks. In this position it remains, and gradually grows in thickness with every successive tide until it may reach a height of thirty feet, and sometimes even more, presenting to the sea a bold wall of ice, against which the floes grind and crush, and are pounded into fragments. Its growth only stops with the advent of summer, when it begins to yield to the kindly influence of the sun, and to the action of the numerous streams that issue from the melting glaciers, and lick out for themselves deep hollows in the shelf as they rush outwards to the sea.

During summer, vast piles of rock and rubbish crowd the surface of the ice-foot. These are of course derived from the cliffs, to the base of which the ice-foot clings. To such an extent does this rock-rubbish accumulate, that the whole surface of the shelf is sometimes buried beneath it and entirely hidden from view. In the far north, where the ice-foot is perennial, it becomes thickly charged with successive deep layers and irregular masses of rock and débris—the spoil of the summer thaws; and when, as frequently happens, portions of this ice-belt get forced away from the land by the violent impact of massive floes, the current carries southward the loaded ice, which ere long will drop its burden of rock and rubbish as it journeys on, and warmer temperatures begin to tell upon it. Along that part of the coast of Greenland where the ice-foot is shed at the end of every summer, the quantities of rock débris thus borne seaward must be something prodigious.

But the rafts detached from the ice-foot must occasionally float from the coast other records of the land besides fragments of its bleak cliffs. Dr. Kane describes the skeleton of a musk-ox which he saw firmly embedded in the ice of the ice-foot, along with the usual stones and débris. We cannot suppose that this is an isolated and solitary case. On the contrary, when we consider the position of the ice-foot, stretching as it does along the whole coast-line and constantly receiving the waste of the land, it does not appear at all improbable that the remains of the arctic mammalia may not infrequently get frozen into the ice-foot, and eventually be carried out to sea. It is quite true that these animals do not abound throughout the maritime regions of Greenland, yet here and there in favoured spots they collect in considerable herds.

The ice-foot is not the only carrier of stones from Greenland. Glaciers, as we have seen, enter the sea at many places along the arctic coasts—often filling up those long deep sea-valleys or fiords which, in lower latitudes, form commodious natural harbours, and frequently penetrate for many miles into the interior of a country. Of such a character are the friths and fiords of Scotland and Norway. A glance at a good chart of Greenland will show that similar inlets of the sea occur very numerously along the west coast of that country as far north as Upernavik. But as we follow the coast-line to still higher latitudes, the sea no longer invades the land in the same way as to the south of Upernavik. The deep fiord-valleys still continue, but they are choked up with glaciers, which have pushed out the sea and occupied its place. As these glaciers slowly creep on to profounder depths, a point is reached at which, as already described, the pressure of the dense sea water becomes too strong for the tenacity of the glacier to resist; and thereupon the ice ruptures and great masses surge upwards and float away as icebergs. Some of these bergs attain a prodigious size. Dr. Hayes measured one which had stranded off the harbour of Tessuissak to the north of Melville Bay, and estimated it to contain about 27,000,000,000 of cubical feet. This berg could not have weighed less than 2,000,000,000 tons; it was aground in water nearly half a mile in depth. What, then, must have been the thickness of the glacier from which it had been detached? Captain Ross, in his first voyage, describes another iceberg of gigantic proportions. This mass of congelation had stranded in sixty-one fathoms of water, and its weight was estimated at 1,292,397,063 tons.

It is highly possible, as I have shown at page 48, that icebergs carry away with them stones which were frozen into their bottoms at the time when they formed part of the glaciers. But the proportion of stones thus transported must be very small; only a few boulders at most can adhere in this way to the ice. In places, however, where the glaciers are

overlooked by rocky precipices, as is frequently the case just
before the ice-rivers pour themselves into the sea, the glaciers
become sprinkled along their sides with rocks and débris
detached by frost from the cliffs above.   But owing to the great
breadth of the glaciers, it can be only an infinitesimal portion
of their surface that is so sprinkled.   The great Humboldt
glacier has a breadth of upwards of sixty miles ; and is
continually shedding icebergs along its whole vast extent of
frontage.   But with the exception, perhaps, of those icebergs
that break away from the extreme corners at the north and
south, none of the others carry seawards any stones whatever, save what fragments may have become jammed and
frozen into their bottoms.   By far the larger number of the
arctic icebergs, therefore, contain no extraneous matter, and
melt away in mid ocean without leaving behind them any
record of their voyage.   Now and then, however, icebergs
which have at one time formed portions of the side of a
glacier are heavily laden with débris, and as bergs float much
deeper than detached masses of ice-foot, they come more under
the influence of oceanic currents, and thus, despite winds and
tides, are frequently carried immense distances before they
finally melt away.   Sailors have met with them as far south
as the Azores, so that memorials of the arctic lands must be
widely scattered over the bed of the Atlantic Ocean.   It is
curious to speculate upon the manner in which these
memorials will be distributed across the floor of the sea.
Many deep-sea soundings have made us aware that the ocean
is of very irregular depth ; there are submarine plateaux,
and hills and valleys, just as there are subaerial table-lands,
and mountains, and dales.   And we can easily imagine how,
as the melting icebergs drift southwards and drop their
burdens as they go, fragments of rock, chipped by the frost
or torn by the glacier from the bleak cliffs and mountains of
Greenland, will come to rest sometimes upon submarine hill-
tops, sometimes in submarine valleys.

Occasionally icebergs run aground, and in this position are
rocked to and fro, and sometimes wheeled about, by the force
of the currents.   This oscillatory movement is usually accompanied by loud noises, and the sea becomes turbid often
for more than a mile with the mud which the rocking berg

stirs up from the bottom. It frequently happens, too, that when a strong swell is running in upon a stranded berg, the ponderous mass, after for some time swinging fearfully from side to side, will heel right over, and split up into smaller fragments, which thereupon float away.

Icebergs do not grate continuously along the bottom of the sea ; when they once run aground their progress is stopped, until by gradual melting or by splitting up into smaller pieces, they are again floated off and swept on by the currents. Now and then, however, a berg propelled by the tide may work its way for a short distance over a shoal or up a gently sloping beach ; but it is evident that it will do so in a most irregular manner, and will very soon cease to advance. When a berg has stranded, all that currents can do is to drive it forward into any soft mud and sand that may happen to be lying upon the sea-bottom ; but the motion of the ice will soon be arrested by the accumulation of débris pushed on in front. A mass of ice 3,000 feet thick would certainly make havoc of any loose incoherent beds of silt and sand into which it might plough ; or, should it run aground upon a reef, it would doubtless pound and crush the hard rocks that formed the pivot upon which it oscillated. But although the rocky coasts of North America have often been examined with a view to discover striated surfaces that could be shown to be the work of icebergs, yet nothing has been observed to lead us to believe that striations and markings, like those produced by glaciers, are ever the result of iceberg action.

In this rapid sketch of certain phenomena of the arctic regions attention has been confined to such facts as have a geological bearing. Nor have all these been exhausted ; there still remain some interesting questions to be discussed in connection with the marine life of the arctic regions. But this part of my subject must be deferred to a subsequent page, when I come to consider the history of the later drift deposits.

CHAPTER VI.

ORIGIN OF THE TILL AND ROCK-STRIATIONS AND GROOVINGS OF SCOTLAND.

Stones of the till are glaciated.—Till not like terminal moraine-matter.—Mud of glacial rivers.—Till not an iceberg deposit.—Rock-striæ produced by glaciers.—Scotland once covered with ice.—Direction of the ice-flow in the Highlands; in the Southern Uplands; in the Lowlands of the great Central Valley.—Absence of superficial moraines.—Stones in the till derived from the subjacent rocks, not from precipices overhanging the ice.—Stones and mud below ice forming a *moraine profonde*, or ground-moraine.—Unequal distribution of this deposit explained.

IN Chapter II. some account was given of the till, the lowest-lying, and therefore the oldest, of the superficial deposits of Scotland. It will be remembered that this deposit was described as a more or less tough tenacious clay, crammed with a pell-mell assemblage of stones—these stones being of all shapes and sizes, and almost invariably showing smoothed, polished, or scratched faces. Now, from what we know of glaciers and glacial action, we can have no difficulty in coming to the conclusion that in some way or other ice has been concerned in the production of till. We look in vain for striated stones in the gravel which the surf drives backwards and forwards on a beach, and we may search the detritus that brooks and rivers push along their beds, but we shall not find any stones at all resembling those of the till. Running water is powerless to produce anything of the kind; it will round and smooth rock-fragments, no matter how hard they be, but it cannot cover them with striations. The boulders and stones of the till undoubtedly owe their shaping and scratching to the action of ice. Just such stones, as we have seen, are exposed beneath the overhanging sides of a glacier when the sun has caused the ice to shrink back and disclose a portion of its rocky bed, and numbers might be picked out of its terminal moraines—

those heaps of rubbish which a glacier brings down or pushes before it. But we cannot fail to remark that although scratched and polished stones occur not infrequently in the frontal moraines of Alpine glaciers, yet at the same time these moraines do not at all resemble till or boulder-clay. The moraine consists for the most part of a confused heap of rough angular stones and blocks, and loose sand and débris; scratched stones are decidedly in a minority, and indeed a close search will often fail to show them. Clearly, then, till is not of the nature of a terminal moraine. Each boulder-clay stone gives evidence of having been subjected to a grinding process. Every fragment has either been jammed into the bottom of a glacier, and, held firmly in that position, has been grated along the rocky surface underneath, or over a pavement of the tough stony clay itself; or, enclosed in the slowly moving subglacial débris of gravel, sand, and mud, it has in like manner been brought again and again into forcible contact with the rocky floor, as the material gathering below was pressed and squeezed and rolled forward by the ice. In such a position the stones would naturally arrange themselves in the line of least resistance; hence it is that the most distinct ruts and striæ coincide with the longer diameter of the stones. But when the stones and boulders which are dragged on underneath a glacier approach a round or oval shape they can have no tendency to lie in any particular way, and so will come to be scratched equally well in all directions. For obvious reasons, soft rocks, like sandstone, will not attain so good a polish as hard limestone or close-grained shale; nor shall we expect to find the stones rounded like gravel or shingle, for they cannot move so freely under ice as pebbles do under water. Frequently, however, they will be rolled over and compelled to shift their position; but this process will only result in smoothing off their sharper edges and in marking them with irregular striæ.

We can see also why larger stones should commonly be marked with coarser striæ than are imprinted on the smaller ones; for their own weight in the first place will insure for them a greater intensity of grinding; and in the next place it is evident that the débris in which such big blocks are embedded under the ice will not yield so readily above them, and consequently they will be subjected to greater pressure upon the rocky bed over which the débris is being rolled. Small stones when they are pressed against the glacier bed will, on the other hand, sink more easily upwards into the débris above them, and thus escape the deep scoring that befalls the larger fragments. If each fragment received its striæ only while held firmly frozen into the bottom of the ice, then there is no reason why the smaller stones should not be covered with as many harsh scorings as the bigger boulders : but the fact that a relation does exist between the coarseness of the striæ and the size of the stone upon which these striæ are engraved, points to the movement under the ice of a considerable mass of subglacial débris.

All the appearances above referred to are actually found, as we have seen, to characterize the stones in the till; and such being the case, we can hardly resist the conclusion that the whole deposit—clay and stones alike—has in some way or other been formed below ice. We look in vain, however, amongst the glaciers of the Alps for such a deposit. The scratched stones we may occasionally find, but where is the clay ? We take our stand at the foot of a glacier and watch the river as it leaps forth from its cave of blue ice. Not a few visitors, I suppose, have been surprised at the turbid appearance of the ice-born river. Why should the melting glacier give rise to such a milky-white, or, as is sometimes the case, yellow-brown stream ? If we lift some of the water in a glass and examine it, we shall find that its colour is due to the presence of a very fine impalpable mud. In the more sheltered reaches of a glacial river this mud will occasionally accumulate to some depth. It is an unctuous, sticky deposit, and only requires pressure to knead it into a tenacious clay. There can be no doubt whatever that it owes its origin to the grinding power of the glacier. The stones and sand which the ice forces along are crushed and pulverised against each other and upon the rock below, and the finer material resulting from this action is what renders the glacial rivers turbid and milky. If there were no water to wash out the mud formed in this way below the glacier, it is evident that not only scratched stones but clay also would gather underneath the ice, and be pushed out at its termination ; and this clay, owing to excessive pressure and to the finely divided nature of its ingredients, would be hard and tough.   The till of the Scottish Lowlands, when it has been exposed to the influence of the weather, sooner or later crumbles down, and, when water washes over it, then that which was once a hard tough clay becomes a soft, sticky, unctuous mud, that clings persistently to everything it touches.   No one who compares this mud with that derived from the glacial waters of the Alps will fail to notice their similarity.   Thus, whether we consider the character of the stones in the till, or the nature of the clay, we are almost equally convinced that both have had a glacial origin.

It is clear, however, that the conditions for the gathering of a stony clay-like till do not obtain (as far as we know) among the Alpine glaciers.   The upper reaches of the Swiss valleys are, as a rule, too steep, and there is too much water circulating below the ice to allow any considerable thickness of such a deposit as till to accumulate.   Neither can till owe its origin to icebergs.   If it had been distributed over the sea-bottom it would assuredly have shown some kind of arrangement.   When an iceberg drops its rubbish, it stands to reason that the heavier blocks will reach the bottom first, then the smaller stones, and lastly the finer ingredients. There is no such assortment visible, however, in the normal till ; but large and small stones are scattered pretty equally through the clay, which, moreover, is quite unstratified.* Again, putting aside the unstratified character of the till, we cannot fail to remark that the great mass of stones and débris which icebergs carry seawards, consists almost exclusively of rough, unpolished angular fragments which have tumbled upon the surface of the ice from cliffs and precipices.   The only polished and striated stones that an iceberg can possibly steal away with are the few which may have got jammed into its base before it was shed from its parent glacier, or an occasional boulder that may have worked its way up, as it were, from the bottom in the manner to be described in the sequel (see Chapter XVIII.).   Such being the character of the

---

* To certain appearances of stratification presented by some stony clays, I shall refer in the sequel (see chap. xvii.).

débris borne seawards upon glaciers, it is evident that the till, with its pell-mell accumulation of finely polished and striated stones, cannot be of the nature of iceberg droppings. These are strong reasons for rejecting the iceberg theory of the origin of till or boulder-clay, yet they are not by any means the most cogent, as will be seen by-and-by.

Since till, then, cannot be formed in and deposited by water in the same way as gravel and sand—since no such deposit accumulates as a terminal moraine in Alpine valleys, nor can possibly be the result of iceberg droppings—what other explanation of its origin can be given? To answer this question, we must for a little recall certain other phenomena associated with the till. When that deposit is removed from the underlying rocks, these almost invariably show either a well-smoothed, polished, and striated surface, or else a highly confused, broken, and smashed appearance. But scratched and polished rock-surfaces are by no means confined to till-covered districts. They are met with everywhere and at all levels throughout the country, from the sea-coast up to near the tops of some of our higher mountains. The lower hill-ranges, such as the Sidlaws, the Ochils, the Pentlands, the Kilbarchan and Paisley Hills, and others, exhibit polished and smoothed rock-faces on their very crests. Similar markings streak and score the rocks up to a great height in the deep valleys of the Highlands and Southern Uplands, and throughout the Inner and Outer Hebrides and Orkney and Shetland the same phenomena constantly occur. The direction of the parallel ruts and striations coincides, as a rule, with the line of the principal valleys. In the Northern Highlands, for example, they keep parallel to the trend of the great glens; and in the Southern Uplands likewise they follow all the windings of the chief dales and "hopes." In the Lowlands, however, their direction does not appear to be influenced so much by the configuration of the ground; for they often cross low valleys at right angles or nearly so, and sweep up and over intervening hills, even when these happen to have an elevation of upwards of 1,800 feet above the sea.

The scratches upon the rocks have exactly the same appearance as those that crowd the surface of the boulder-clay stones; but whereas the striations on the latter may cross and recross, those upon a surface of rock usually run in one and the same direction. Sometimes, however, we meet with exceptions to this rule, when two or even three sets of striæ may be observed upon the same surface of rock. But such cross-hatchings do not occur very often, and seem to be confined to the lowland districts ; at all events, I have never seen them in any of the valleys of the Highlands or Southern Uplands. No one who shall compare the dressed rocks with the scratched stones can have any doubt that both owe their origin to the same cause. If glacier ice scratched the stones, then the rocks must have been smoothed and dressed by the same agency. The work cannot possibly have been done by icebergs, for floating ice has no power to grate along the sea-bottom, so as to polish and dress submarine hills and valleys. The agent that performed the work has actually clung to the ground, and accommodated itself to every inequality of surface—here rounding and smoothing knobs and bosses of rock, there sliding into and polishing dimples and depressions. In short, the appearances tally precisely with what has been observed in the valleys of the Alps and elsewhere. When we have the opportunity of examining the deserted bed of a glacier, we find it smoothed and dressed in every part. Wherever the ice has been able to get at the rock it has ground, scratched, and polished it. Nor can any reasonable person resist the conclusion that the dressed rocks of Scotland have been worked upon by ice in the same way. We must believe that all the hills and valleys were once swathed in snow and ice ; that the whole of Scotland was at some distant date buried underneath one immense *mer de glace*, through which peered only the higher mountain-tops. This is no vague hypothesis or speculation founded on uncertain data, no mere conjecture which the light of future discoveries may explode. The evidence is so clear and so overwhelmingly convincing that we cannot resist the inevitable conclusion. Suppose some visitor who had only newly arrived in our country were to stumble in the course of his wanderings upon a deserted line of railway, where the old, battered rails gave evidence of having been well used, he surely would require no reflection to conclude that cars and waggons must frequently have passed along the line. What would be thought of our visitor's sanity if he were to reason in this way :—"Although this looks very like a railway, with its embankments and rails and sleepers, yet I cannot think it is so, for no trains run upon it, and I have been here several months, but in all that time have never seen it used?" Now old embankments and worn-out rails are no more convincing proofs of the former passage of wheeled carriages than the smoothed, scratched, and rounded rocks are of the grinding action of old glaciers ; and the incredulity that would reject the evidence of the latter might well be expected to treat the former in a similar way.

Since, then, we must believe that the dressed and rounded rocks could only have been so dressed and rounded by land-ice, it follows that wherever such rock-surfaces occur, there at one time a glacier must have been. Now the scratches may be traced from the islands and the coast-line up to an elevation of at least 3,500 feet ; so that ice must have covered the country to that height at least. In the Highlands the tide of ice streamed out from the central elevations down all the main straths and glens ; and by measuring the height attained by the smoothed and rounded rocks, we are enabled to esti-mate roughly the probable thickness of the old ice-sheet. But it can be only a rough estimate, for so long a time has elapsed since the ice disappeared, and rain and frost together have so split up and worn down the rocks of these highland moun-tains, that much of the smoothing and polishing has vanished. But although the finer marks of the ice-chisel have thus fre-quently been obliterated, yet the broader effects remain con-spicuous enough. From an examination of these, we gather that the ice could not have been less, and was probably more, than 3,000 feet thick in its deeper parts. What wonder, then, that a mass of this bulk, gliding from the mountains down to the sea during a long course of ages, should have left such an impress of its grinding-power upon the rocks that the lapse of thousands of years has not succeeded in removing it. For even when the fine smoothing and polish-ing have disappeared, the hills yet show in their rounded and flowing outlines that peculiar configuration which is so cha-racteristic of ground over which a glacier has passed.

It is well known that the glaciers of Switzerland are mere pigmies compared to what they have been formerly. The slopes of the Alpine valleys are all smoothed, scratched, and scored up to a considerable height above the present surface of the glaciers; and these smoothed rocks are often separated from the rough, broken, and craggy rocks above by a well-marked line, indicating the height reached by the glaciers in days gone by. But in Scotland such a distinct line of division rarely marks out the upper limits of the glaciation. Frost and rain have made havoc of the ice-work at the higher elevations of the country, and roughened the exposed rocks into crags and peaks.

In the Southern Uplands the ice moved, as in the High-lands, from the central high grounds down all the main val-leys; its track being well marked out by an abundant series of finely preserved striæ.* From the mountains of Galloway and the uplands of the south-east vast glaciers descended in every direction. The valleys of the Annan, the Nith, and the Dee were filled to overflowing with great confluent glaciers that poured their united volume into the Solway Frith and the Irish Sea. In like manner a vast stream of ice that flowed north-east and then south-east buried the wide vale of the Tweed between the Cheviots and the Lammer-muirs.

When the ice-markings are followed into the Lowlands of the central valley, we find that in the vale of the Forth their general tendency is towards the east; while in the lower reaches of the Clyde valley their trend is east, south-east, south, and south-west. The meaning of this apparent confu-sion is perceived when we trace out the track of the glaciers that issued from the Highlands, and follow the spoor of those that crept down from the Southern Uplands. It then becomes apparent that a great current of ice from the high grounds of Lanarkshire set down the valley of the Clyde, and was met near Lesmahagow by a vast glacier coming in the opposite direction. Hence the two opposing streams were deflected to east and south-west; on the one hand sweeping across the Lothians into the Frith of Forth and the German Ocean, on the other overflowing the uplands of Renfrew-shire, and passing south-west into Ayrshire, so as to unite

---

* See the general map showing the direction of glaciation, and Note E, Appendix.

with the glacier masses descending from the Galloway mountains.

Underneath these great streams of ice the whole surface of the country would be subjected to excessive erosion. Hill-slopes would be ground and polished, valleys deepened and smoothed; here the rocks would be finely dressed and striated, there crushed and broken. And what would be the character of the débris that resulted from all this grinding and graving work? In the glaciers of the Alps we have every reason to believe that a considerable proportion of stones used as chisels and stylets by the ice are introduced from above: they tumble from the crags upon the surface of the ice, and drop into those deep crevasses which must sometimes cut a glacier to its bottom. But when ice buried Scotland to a depth of several thousand feet, only a few hill tops would rise above the general level of the *mer de glace*. Consequently little débris would be showered upon the ice; and, even supposing considerable heaps of blocks and rocky rubbish did accumulate here and there at the base of some isolated hill, it is nevertheless very unlikely that any portion would ever work its way to the bottom of the thick ice-sheet. The gravers employed by the ice in dressing the Scottish hills and valleys could not have been derived from above; they must have been obtained from the rocks lying below.

It is quite certain, however, that the ice when it first overflowed the land would find a plentiful supply of loose stones lying upon the ground ready for use. For long ages before the country became locked in ice the climate must have been getting colder and colder. The result of this intense frost would be to split up the rocks everywhere; nor would this be a difficult matter. We must remember that the present deep subsoils that bury the solid rocks to such a depth had no existence before the advent of the ice-sheet. The rocks then would not be covered with a deeper soil than is the case in countries where no drift deposits exist. I have already referred to the heaps of broken rock that cumber the exposed ground in northern and mountainous regions, where whole hills are well-nigh buried in their own ruins. In all arctic and alpine countries, and, indeed, wherever a rock is exposed to the action of frost, it is sure to split up sooner or later. The

moraines of the Alps, the enormous "screes" of the Himalaya and the Rocky Mountains, and the prodigious piles of
débris that collect upon the ice-foot of the Arctic regions, are
sufficient evidence of what frost can do.

It is certain, therefore, that when the ice began to creep
over Scotland, it would have to make its way through piles
of broken fragments and over shattered rock-surfaces. Ice-
chisels would thus be prepared for it beforehand, which
would aid in the work of dislodging others from the rocks.
As the crushing and grinding continued, few stones would
escape being smoothed and striated, while the fine mud
resulting from all this work would get mixed up with the
stones, and form a stony clay. It is true that water would
circulate below the ice to some extent, as we know it does
underneath the glaciers of Greenland, and no doubt much
glacial mud would be carried away by this means ; nevertheless, all that could possibly escape would bear but a very
small proportion to what remained behind. Thus both mud
and stones would tend to collect under the ice ; and as that
great mass moved onwards, pressing with prodigious weight,
the mud and stones would be squeezed and dragged forward
so as to become a confused and pell-mell mixture of clay and
stones, with here and there traces of water-action in the form
of irregular patches and interrupted bands of stones, gravel,
earthy sand and clay—in short, till, or boulder-clay. Such,
then, would appear to be the origin of that remarkable
deposit ; it is the ground-moraine, or *moraine profonde*, of
the old ice-sheet.

We must not suppose, however, that till gathered equally
underneath every portion of the confluent glaciers. On the
contrary, wherever the inclination of the ground was such as
to cause the ice to quicken its flow—in many mountain-valleys
and on steep hill-slopes, for example—clay and stones would
not readily collect; but in places where the motion was slow, as
in broad lowland districts, there the till would have a tendency
to accumulate. In short, the distribution of the till would be
regulated by the varying pressure and erosive action of the ice
above. Some have objected that the moment a layer of till was
formed between the ice and the subjacent rock, all wear and
tear of the latter would cease, and therefore that the forma-

tion of till itself would suddenly come to an end. It would just be as reasonable, however, to infer that all wearing away of a river channel must stop the moment that the channel becomes filled with gravel and sand. But who does not know that the materials in the bed of a stream are continually travelling onward, no matter how slowly? It is quite true that so long as a bank of sand and gravel shall lie in one place, the rock on which it rests will escape the rasp of the river. But the river that piles up such banks will by-and-by sweep them away again, and employ the sand and gravel as agents for wearing down, scouring, and filing the rocks which they formerly protected. And so, no doubt, it must have been with the ice-sheet and its débris. Over many portions of its bed there would be a continual travelling onwards of clay, sand, and stones; while in other areas masses of débris which had collected here and there would be ever and anon ploughed up again, and pushed and dragged forward from one position to another. In this way the underlying rocks would be alternately protected and exposed. The clay itself affords distinct evidence of having been thus rolled forward underneath the ice; for the stones, although confusedly scattered through the deposit, yet often show a curious involved or " curled " arrangement, as if the clay had been rolled upon itself while in a plastic state. This appearance is of course most distinctly visible when patches of water-worn gravel and sand are present (see *ante*, p. 18); but there are few good exposures of till where the stony clay itself, if carefully examined, will not yield some trace of the same peculiar arrangement. Indeed, it is likely that the stones and boulders received most of their fine polishing while embedded in the clay, as that deposit was being squeezed slowly forward and rolled over again and again upon itself—a process which would also result in polishing and smoothing the rocky surface over which the till was dragged. The fact that the larger boulders have not infrequently a tendency to collect at or near the bottom of the till is also explicable, for it is evident that as the ground-moraine was being kneaded and rolled forward, the superior gravity and the wider surface of such blocks would be rather against their rising upwards in the moving mass of clay and smaller stones; in many cases it would be easier simply to push them along.   And hence it is that very large blocks in the till often show striæ on only one side. Other proofs of the subglacial formation and accumulation of till fall to be given further on ; it will be shown that sometimes this deposit has actually been so squeezed and pressed that tongues of it have been forcibly intruded into the beds across which it moved.

CHAPTER VII.

ORIGIN OF THE TILL, AND ROCK-STRIATIONS AND GROOVINGS OF SCOTLAND—*Continued.*

Direction of ice-flow indicated by stones in the till.—Cross-hatching of rock-striæ accounted for.—Intermingling in the till of stones derived from separate districts.—"Debatable land" between rival ice-flows.—Local colouring of till an indication of direction followed by ice-flow.—The Ochils, Pentlands and other hills, completely overflowed by ice.—Deflections of the ice-flow.—Till in upland valleys, why terraced.—Origin of lowland "drums." —Crag and tail, &c.—Islets lying off the coast glaciated from the mainland. —Ice filled up all the shallow seas round Scotland.—General ice-sheet like that of Antarctic continent.

THE course followed by the ice-sheet in its downward progress from the high grounds to the coast is indicated, as described in last chapter, by the directions of scratches and furrows and flutings, and by that peculiar rounded out-

Fig. 18.—Roche Moutonnée.

line which the grinding of the heavy mass has imparted to the mountain-slopes and hill-tops.* But even when these markings do not appear, either on account of the obliterating effect of weathering, or else because they lie concealed below a superficial covering of drift, yet the till itself often furnishes

---

* Rocks which are so rounded are known as *roches moutonnées*—a name probably suggested by a fanciful resemblance to the rounded shape of a sheep's back. That part of a glaciated rock which faces the direction from which the ice came is termed the *stosseite* (literally, *bumping-place*) ; the opposite, or lee-side, is the *leeseite*. When a rock projects prominently above the general level of a glaciated district it is generally glaciated only, or, at least, most conspicuously, on the *stosseite*.

evidence as to the direction of ice-flow. If, for example, we know from what part of the country the scratched stones in the till have been derived, it is obvious that we ascertain at the same time the course followed by the ice that brought them. Hence we are enabled to track out the trail of the *mer de glace* over all the country. And it is worthy of note that the evidence supplied by the stones always corroborates that afforded by the *roches moutonnées* and striated rocks. If these last owe their origin to a current of ice that came from the north, then the stones also will be found to have travelled in the same direction. And, curiously enough, in those districts where the rocks exhibit a "cross-hatching" of striæ, or where the striations on two contiguous rocks do not agree in direction, there also the till shows an intermingling of stones derived from separate districts. Now what does this prove? Clearly this: that the ice-currents were occasionally deflected and forced to go another way. The great stream that crept across the central valley of Scotland was certainly at times turned out of its normal course—now towards the south by the pressure of that powerful current of ice that poured down from the Highlands, and again towards the north when the ice-stream coming from the Southern Uplands overpowered and forced back the other; in short, there was a "debatable ground" between the northern and southern currents, over which sometimes the one and sometimes the other prevailed.* The right of possession to the tract of country that lies between Cambuslang and Lesmahagow seems frequently to have been disputed by the rival ice-streams—the rocks of that area being sometimes striated by ice that moved from the north, and sometimes, again, by the confluent masses that flowed from the Southern Uplands. We find also an intermingling of stones—fragments of mica-schist and gneiss from the highland mountains occurring now and again as far south as Lesmahagow, while stones, apparently derived from the high grounds to the south of that place, appear here and there in the till as far north as Stonehouse. A similar intermingling of stones from the north and south is seen in the till of the valley of the Esk, near the Moorfoot Hills, in

* Reference will be made in a succeeding chapter to certain instances of cross-hatching which are to be explained in a different way. (See chap. xvii.)

Edinburghshire. But beyond this "debatable land" striated rocks and scratched stones alike point to a persistent ice-flow in determinate directions. In the near neighbourhood of the Highlands all the stones, without exception, tell of a move outwards from the mountains, and it is the same with rock-striations. The till in the valleys of the Southern Uplands has in like manner invariably been derived from the contiguous high grounds. Following the till from the base of the Grampians, where it is crammed with fragments of mica-schist, granite, gneiss, quartzite, &c., down into the basin of the Forth, we find the number of these highland stones gradually decreasing, until by-and-by they disappear altogether, or are only met with at rare intervals. And the same is the case with the till that stretches northwards from the Southern Uplands. At first the fragments brought from these uplands are in the majority, but they gradually fall off northwards, until finally we cease to meet with them. It is curious also to notice how the stones lose in size as the parent rock is left further and further behind—the longer the distance travelled, the greater having been the degree of crushing and grinding undergone. The local colouring assumed by the till is another strong proof of transportation by land-ice. As described in a previous chapter, this deposit varies both in colour and texture, according to the nature of the rocks near which it lies. Thus it becomes red, and shows a sandy texture in districts where red sandstone is the prevailing rock; but in a region where coal and black shales abound, there we encounter a hard, tough, tenacious deposit, having a dark greyish-blue colour. The reason of this difference is obvious. The clay is derived from the grinding and crushing of the underlying rocks, and consequently changes its character as the rocks change theirs. But just as the included stones not infrequently have been dragged for a long distance from their parent rocks, so in like manner has the clay formed in one place travelled onward to another. Hence it often happens that the till of a given district—a red sandstone region, for example—will be found to have invaded and covered adjoining ground where the rocks are neither red nor composed of sandstone.

If space permitted, some special proof might be offered in

support of a statement already made, namely : that the ice overflowed the hill-ranges and isolated hills of central Scotland. The Ochils, for example, that separate the basin of the Forth from Strathearn are ground off and smoothed in such a way as to indicate that the mass of ice must first have crossed the valley of the Earn from the Grampian mountains, and thereafter overflowed the Ochils and passed on south-eastwards across the Lomonds and the Cleish hills into the valley of the Forth. The evidence afforded by the till that covers the southern slopes of the Ochils points precisely to the same conclusion, for that deposit is abundantly charged with fragments of gneiss, granite, and other rocks that could only have come from the Highlands. Mr. B. N. Peach found a considerable area of till at a height of 2,200 ft. on the shoulder of Ben Cleugh, and numerous scratched stones occurred on the very top of the hill (2,300 ft.). Similar proof of the passage of land-ice over considerable eminences in the lowland districts might easily be given. For instance, on the very top of Allermuir Hill, one of the highest points in the Pentlands, Dr. Croll got a patch of till containing, amongst other local stones, certain fragments which have been brought from the north or north-west, thus clearly showing that these hills also were overtopped by the *mer de glace*. Again, both rock-scratches and till indicate that the high grounds between Paisley and Kilmarnock have been surmounted by land-ice. According to my brother, Professor Geikie, relics of the till are found near the top of Tinto Hill (in Lanarkshire), which rises to a height of upwards of 2,300 ft. above the sea. I have seen till and striated stones lying in the hollows between the tops of the Cheviot Hills at a height of 1,500 ft.

That the ice should have overflowed the land up to such heights will not surprise one ; for, by a stream of ice some 3,000 ft. or so in thickness, hills like the Ochils, the Pentlands, and Tinto would be as easily surmounted as stones and boulders are overflowed in the bed of a river. And yet, just as these boulders will deflect that portion of the river's current that strikes upon them, so the heights to which I refer appear to have partially turned aside the stream of ice that beat against them. This is shown by the manner in which the flutings and groovings bend round the sides of a hill before they finally cross it and resume their normal direction.

The flutings and groovings in the valleys of the Southern Uplands show distinctly that the ice to which they owe their origin not only filled the valleys, but swept across the intervening hills. The markings referred to run in nearly a horizontal direction along the steep slopes of the hills, so that they appear to rise as the valley descends ; and thus, while we follow the stream, they gradually mount higher and higher until the crest of the hill is reached over which they eventually disappear. The beautiful valley of the Yarrow, below Gordon Arms Inn, affords a fine example of the phenomena in question.

Reference has already been made to the unequal distribution of the till. It lies thickest in the valleys, and thins away towards the hills, being found for the most part in patches when we get above a height of 1,000 ft. In the hilly districts of the south of Scotland it occurs chiefly in the bottoms of the valleys, but it may sometimes be met with nestling in hollows even up to a height of 1,800 or 1,900 ft. The whole appearance of the deposit, however, shows that it never did attain any thickness at these heights, the force of the ice-stream on steep slopes and exposed places having prevented its accumulation, just as a river will not allow sediment to accumulate upon the tops and exposed sides of the large boulders in its bed. But in the lower reaches of the upland valleys, notably in Peeblesshire, the till often attains some depth. It gradually lessens, however, as we trace it towards the heads of the valleys, where it eventually disappears. The general aspect presented by the deposit in these valleys is that of a flat-topped terrace inclining gently from the hill-sides and sloping gradually down in the direction followed by the stream, at about the same angle as the bottom of the valley itself. I believe that this terrace-like appearance of the till was most probably assumed underneath the ice-sheet. In narrow and deep hollows, like the upland valleys, the ice was not liable to such deflections as took place over the " debatable grounds ; " and the till forming below it consequently escaped being squeezed to and fro ; the valleys were filled with streams of ice flowing constantly in one and the same direction, and the probabilities are therefore strong that the débris which accumulated below would be spread out smoothly. In the Lowlands the effect produced by the varying direction and unequal pressure of the ice-sheet is visible in the peculiar outline assumed by the till. Sometimes it forms a confused aggregate of softly-swelling mounds and hummocks ; in other places it gives rise to a series of long smoothly-rounded banks or "drums" and "sowbacks," which run parallel to the direction taken by the ice. This peculiar configuration of the till, although doubtless modified to some extent by rain and streams, yet was no doubt assumed under the ice-sheet—the "sowbacks" being the glacial counterparts of those broad banks of silt and sand that form here and there upon the beds of rivers. Perhaps the most admirable example in Scotland of this peculiar arrangement or configuration of the till occurs in the valley of the Tweed, between the Cheviot Hills and the Lammermuirs. In this wide district all the ridges of till run parallel to each other, and in a direction approximately east and west. This, too, is the prevailing trend of the rock-striations and *roches moutonnées* in the same neighbourhood.

The phenomena of "crag and tail" afford yet another indication of the path followed by the ice. A familiar illustration of the mode in which "crag and tail" have been formed may be obtained by placing a large stone in the current of a stream, and watching the effect produced upon the carriage of sediment by the water. The current sweeps against the stone, and is deflected to right and left—there being of course considerable commotion in front and quiet water behind. The current thus stemmed is forced downwards with a stronger pressure upon the bed of the stream by the water continually advancing from behind, and the result is that a hollow is gradually scooped out in front of the stone, and for some way along its sides. In the rear, where there is comparatively little stir in the water, silt and sand speedily accumulate, until a long sloping "tail" is formed, stretching away from the stone for as great a distance as the quiet water extends. If for a stone we substitute a big crag, standing up in a broad valley, and for the little stream of our illustration a deep current of land-ice, we shall have no difficulty in explaining the origin of "crag and tail." In the valley of the Forth, where isolated hills and bosses of rock are not uncommon, the till is invariably heaped up on the east side of the crags, showing that the set of the ice-stream was from west to east; the direction in which the till has travelled, and the course followed by the rock-striations, both lead us to the same conclusion.

Thus on every hand we are furnished with abundant proof of the former existence of a great *mer de glace* in Scotland. From the tops of some of the higher mountains down to the edge of the sea, no part of the country has escaped abrasion. The hills are worn and rounded off, and the valleys are cumbered with the wreck and ruin of the rocks. Nay, most of the islands which lie off the coasts plainly indicate by striations and other glacial markings that ice has swept over them also. They are smoothed not from the centre to the circumference, as would have been the case had they supported separate glaciers of their own, but the striations go right across them from side to side. It cannot be doubted therefore that the ice, to the grinding action of which these striations are due, actually crossed from the mainland over what now forms the bed of the sea. Perhaps the most striking example of this is furnished by Lewis, the northern portion of the Long Island, which I found to be glaciated across its whole breadth from south-east to north-west. The land-ice that swept over this tract must have come from the mountains of Ross-shire—a distance of not less than thirty miles. Leaving the mainland, it must have filled up the whole of the North Minch (sixty fathoms in depth), and overflowed Lewis to a height of 1,300 ft. at least; for I found that Suainabhal, a conspicuous mountain rising to the south of Loch Roag, near the west coast of the island, was merely a huge *roche moutonnée* strongly glaciated from base to summit by ice which had passed over it from the south-east. The view from the top of this mountain is wonderfully impressive; indeed there is no district in Scotland where the intensity of the old glaciation is better exhibited. The whole country to north and east, far as eye can reach, shows the most evident marks of having been swept and ground by a great glacier. One sees everywhere a moutonnéed surface. Round-backed rocks, hummocks, and hills bare of drift and soil, with countless pools and lakelets nestling in their hollows, impart to the region a character of great desolation, and strongly remind one of similar scenes in the north of Norway.*

In like manner the Island of Bute has been scored and smoothed from end to end by a mass of ice which, streaming out from the highlands of Argyleshire, filled up the Kyles, and then passed southwards over the whole island to occupy the bed of the Frith of Clyde between Bute and Arran. Many of the islets scattered along the western coasts tell the same tale. Again, it may be mentioned as a very striking fact that the lofty cliffs along the south-west coast of Ayrshire are striated along their tops in a direction parallel to the trend of the coast—that is, from north-east to south-west. An examination of the general map will show how these striations have been produced by a mass of ice that filled up the bed of the adjacent sea, and streamed south-west towards the northern coast of Ireland. From these and similar facts geologists have been inclined to infer that at the time the *mer de glace* covered Scotland the whole of our country stood at a higher level relative to the sea than now; in other words, that a large part of what in these days forms the floor of the sea was at that time in the condition of dry land. This being so, the ice from the central parts of the country would creep outwards and overflow what are now islands, in the same way as it surmounted the Ochils, the Pentlands, and other hill-ranges of central Scotland. Now such may quite well have been the case, and there are indeed good grounds for believing, as we shall afterwards see, that, in times anterior to the advent of the Ice Age, Scotland did really stand at a higher level above the sea than

---

* Mr. J. F. Campbell notes the direction of the glacial striæ in Harris and some of the smaller islands of the Outer Hebrides, and is of opinion that these were the work of sea-ice coming in from the Atlantic when the land was more submerged than it is. Dr. Bryce also states that the glaciation of Lewis, Harris, and North Uist has, in his opinion, been effected by ice coming from a land to the westward, since submerged. During two visits to Lewis, when I traversed the island in all directions, I not only found no trace of an ice-flow from the west, but was satisfied from the direction of the striæ, the position of the *roches moutonnées*, and the transport of boulders in the drift (which have certainly travelled from S.E. to N.W.), that the ice flowed across the island from the mainland. (See further, chap. xvi.)

now. There is no proof, however, that the greater elevation of the land in preglacial times (amounting, as far as we can show, to some 300 ft. only, although it may have been as much as 600 ft.), had anything whatever to do in bringing about a glacial period. All we know is that before the Ice Age began the Scottish shores extended considerably farther out to sea ; but the sea may have gained upon the land again, and may even have reached to a greater height than it does now, when the great glaciers commenced to creep out from the mountain-valleys upon the low grounds. The presence of a considerably deeper sea than that which now flows round Britain could not have availed to stay the onward progress of the thick land-ice ; so far as that goes, therefore, it is not necessary to infer, as some have done, that in early glacial times our land stood at a much higher level, and that the sea-bottom between Scotland and the outlying islands then existed as dry land. If the old glaciers entered the sea at a time when the relative level of land and sea was much the same as it is at present they could not have had any diffi-culty in making their way from the mainland to the islands. A mass of ice, upwards of 2,000 ft., and in parts attaining 3,000 ft. in thickness, would fill up every fiord-valley, and dispossess the sea in all the sounds, straits, and channels that separate the islands from themselves and the mainland. A glance at the Admiralty charts will show how this could be. From them it will be learned, that, between the mainland and the islands, the sea seldom attains a greater depth than 70 fathoms or 420 ft., and even this depth is quite excep-tional. The German Ocean between England and the coasts of France and the Netherlands, does not average more than some 150 or 160 ft. in depth : and the soundings show that the water deepens very gradually northwards. To reach the 100-fathom line, we approach quite close to the coast of Norway, and the same line lies considerably north of the Shetland Islands, from which it sweeps west by south, keep-ing outside of the Hebrides and Ireland. In no part of our seas, then, could the water have been of sufficient depth to float those prodigious masses of ice which we can prove were generated in Scotland during the glacial epoch. Before ice will float, it requires water deep enough to accommodate some seven or eight parts of its bulk below the surface of the sea ; and therefore the great *mer de glace*, being unable to float in 600 ft. of water, must have pushed back the shallow seas that flow around our coasts, so as even to coalesce with the ice-sheet that crept out at the same time from Norway.* Indeed, it seems most reasonable to infer that had it not been for the presence of the Scandinavian ice-sheet in the North Sea, the Scotch ice never could have attained the great thickness which we know it did. Had no obstacle to its outflow existed the ice must have crept away to sea long before it reached anything like a thickness of 2,000 or 3,000 ft. For we must remember that Scotland is a very little country after all, with watersheds which are quite incapable of nourishing such prodigious depths of glacier ice. And the very fact that the ice attained such a depth is a proof that the confluent glaciers of Scotland must have been dammed back,—a conclusion which we shall find in the sequel is supported by direct evidence. Bearing in mind the vast thickness reached by the Scotch ice-sheet, it becomes very evident that the ice would flow along the bottom of the sea with as much ease as it poured across the land, and every island would be surmounted and crushed and scored and polished just as readily as the hills of the mainland were. But the ice-sheet would not only enfold the Western Islands and join them to the mainland, it would also extend still farther seawards, and terminate at last in precipitous or vertical cliffs, resembling that great wall of ice which Commodore Wilkes and Sir J. C. Ross encountered in the Antarctic Seas. How far westward the ice would extend into the Atlantic would, of course, depend entirely upon its thickness and the depth of the sea. If it retained at its outskirts only one-third of the great depth under which it buried central Scotland, it must have gone out as far at least as the 100-fathom line—supposing the sea to have been as deep then as it is now. Sir J. C. Ross's striking account of the mighty ice-sheet under which the Antarctic continent lies buried, gives one a very good notion of the kind of appearance which the skirts of our own ice-sheet presented. After reaching the highest southern latitude which has yet been attained, all his

* See further on this point, chap. xvi.

PLATE III.

To face p. 180.

ANTARCTIC ICE-SHEET. (Reduced by H. M. Skae from the drawing by Sir J. C. Ross.)

attempts to penetrate further were frustrated by a precipitous
wall of ice that rose out of the water to a height of 180 ft.
in places, and effectually barred all progress towards the
pole.   For 450 miles he sailed in front of this cliff, and
found it unbroken by a single inlet.   While thus coasting
along, his ships (the *Erebus* and *Terror*) were often in danger
from stupendous icebergs and thick pack-ice, that frequently
extended in masses too close and serried to be bored through.
Only at one point did the ice-wall sink low enough to allow
of its upper surface being seen from the masthead.   Ross
approached this point, which was only some fifty feet above
the level of the sea, and obtained a good view.   He describes
the upper surface of the ice as a smooth plain shining like
frosted silver, and stretching away far as eye could reach
into the illimitable distance.   The ice-cliff described by Ross
is the terminal front of a gigantic *mer de glace*, which,
nurtured on the circumpolar continent, creeps outward over
the floor of the sea until it reaches depths where the pressure
of the water stops its farther advance by continually breaking
off large segments and shreds from its terminal front, and
floating these away as icebergs.   And such must have been
the aspect presented by the margin of the old ice-sheet,
which, in the early stages of the glacial epoch, mantled
Scotland and its numerous islets, filling up the intervening
straits and channels of the sea, and terminating far out in
the Atlantic Ocean in a flat-topped vertical cliff of blue
ice.*

* For further details respecting Scotch ice-sheet, see Appendix, Note E.

CHAPTER VIII.

CAUSE OF COSMICAL CHANGES OF CLIMATE.

Evidences of former great changes of climate during past ages.—Theories accounting for these.—Translation of the solar system through space.—Change in the position of the earth's axis of rotation.—Sliding of the earth's crust round the nucleus.—Changes in the distribution of land and sea.—Elevation and depression of the land.—Sir Charles Lyell's speculations upon the effect of such changes.—Climatic effect of winds and ocean currents.—Effect of accumulation of land within the tropics and of same round the poles.—Peculiar distribution of land and sea inadequate to account for great cosmical changes of climate.

THE stony record everywhere assures us that from the earliest times of which geologists can take cognizance down to the present, our globe has experienced many changes of climate. The plants of which our coal-seams are composed speak to us of lands covered with luxuriant growths of tree-ferns and auracarians, and the fossils in our limestones tell us of warm seas where corals luxuriated in the genial waters. Nor is it only in our own latitudes that scenes like these are conjured up by a study of the rocks. Even in high arctic regions, where the lands are well-nigh entirely concealed beneath the snow, and where the seas are often choked with ice all the year round, we often meet with remarkable proofs of genial and even warm climates having formerly prevailed at several widely-separated periods. Limestones containing fossil corals, and numerous remains of extinct chambered shells, such as are now represented by the nautilus of the Pacific Ocean, occur frequently in the highest latitudes yet reached by man. Dr. Hayes brought from the bleak shores of Grinell Land certain fossils, the nature of which clearly indicates that at some distant date a genial ocean, capable of nourishing corals and chambered shells, must have overspread that region. Similar results have been obtained by many of our most distinguished arctic voyagers, and from their observations it is now well ascertained that over all the regions within the Arctic Circle which have yet been visited, genial climates have prevailed at different times during past geologic ages—climates that not only nourished corals and southern molluscs in the seas, but clothed the lands with a rich and luxuriant greenery.

A close and careful scrutiny of the rock formations of our own country shows us, moreover, that, in the distant past, those warm and genial conditions that extended from our own latitudes up to polar regions, ever and anon disappeared, and were replaced by cold and even arctic climates. Coral seas and swampy jungles pass away, and are succeeded in time by snow-covered mountains, by glaciers creeping down the valleys, and icebergs sailing drearily away from frost-bound coasts. Again a sunny picture rises up before us, to be replaced, as the ages roll on, by yet other scenes of arctic sterility. It was long, however, before geologists began to recognise the evidence for this remarkable succession, or as we may call it, rotation of climates. The old belief used to be, that the climate of the globe, owing in great measure to the escape of the earth's internal heat into space, had gradually and regularly cooled down : so that the older formations were thought to represent ultra-tropical conditions, while the later deposits contained the records of less tropical and temperate climates. The astronomer and cosmogonist assure us that there was a time when this earth existed as a mass of gaseous matter, and that this matter, by parting with some portion of its heat, passed ere long into a fluid condition. After some time a hard crust formed over the surface of the molten liquid, and when long ages had passed away, and the outer shell or skin had sufficiently cooled down to allow of all the varied phenomena of evaporation and rain and rivers, then by-and-by life appeared, and those wonderful organic forces began to act, which, under the guidance of infinite intelligence, have culminated in the beautiful creation of which we form a part. And the geologist, taking up this strange history where the astronomer and cosmogonist left off, fancied that he could trace in the stony record the continuation of the same great world-change. In the earlier pages of the record he found evidence for the former existence

ın the British area of tropical conditions that seemed gradually to fade away as he continued his researches into the
later chapters of geological history.   So that he found, or
fancied he found, a slow transition from an age of tropical
forests and warm oceans to the temperate climate which we
at present enjoy.   But the rapid accumulation of facts proved
fatal to this as to many other theories.   It is no longer questioned that the climates• of the past were due to the very
same causes by which the climates of the present are brought
about.   The earth, no doubt, still radiates heat into space,
but in considering the history of the past, so far back as it is
revealed by geology, this cooling of the earth may safely be
disregarded.   The climates of the world in our times vary
according to the proportion of heat received either directly
or indirectly from the sun, and so it must have been during
all the ages of which any records have come down to us.   At
the very earliest time of which the geologist can speak with
confidence, the climates of the world were probably as well-
marked as they are now.   We must look elsewhere than to
the secular cooling of our globe for the causes which have at
several periods induced a mild and even genial temperature
within the Arctic Circle—periods during which the whole
northern hemisphere enjoyed a kind of perpetual summer.
For we know now that such genial conditions had been preceded and were eventually succeeded by climates of more than
arctic rigour, when our hemisphere, which had luxuriated in
one long-continued summer, became the scene of great snow-
fields and glaciers and floating ice.   This alternation of genial
climates with arctic conditions, obviously cannot be accounted
for by the cooling of the earth, due to the radiation of its
central heat into space.   If we find the remains of full-grown
trees in Greenland, and ammonites and corals even farther
north, we may be quite sure, that, owing to some cause,
apparent or obscure, these regions must at one time have
received from some external source a greater proportion of
heat, either directly or indirectly, than they do now.   And
so, conversely, if in our own land we discover traces of great
snow-fields and massive glaciers, we cannot hesitate to conclude, that in the ages when such frigid conditions prevailed,
this area was deprived of much of the heat which now reaches

it. But if this be so, we may well ask what the nature of that action is which can alternately visit our hemisphere with long-continued ages of fruitful summer, or render it bleak and barren with perpetual snow and ice.

There have been many attempts to account for the phenomena. Some have speculated upon the possibility of the whole solar system travelling onwards through the boundless realms of space, and passing in its course through warmer and colder tracts than that in which it now moves. When the sun with its attendant orbs swept through those hypothetical warm regions, the whole climate of the world it was supposed would be affected, and tree-ferns and cycads would then flourish within the Arctic Circle, while the northern seas would be tenanted by large chambered shells and corals. But when, on the other hand, the colder abysses of space were traversed, a total change of climate would be experienced; the luxuriant vegetation would fade away from the polar regions, and a bleak ice-cap would cover the poles of the globe and spread outwards as the cold increased, until the snow and ice might reach down to latitudes like our own.

Others, again, have imagined a change in the position of the earth's axis of rotation, due to the elevation of extensive mountain tracts somewhere between the poles and the equator. This, they think, would be sufficient to shift the axis so as to confer upon regions which once were circumpolar, the temperature of lower latitudes.* But it has been demonstrated that the protuberance of the earth at the equator, so vastly exceeds that of any possible elevation of mountain masses between the equator and the poles, that any slight change which may have resulted from such geological causes, could have had only an infinitesimal effect upon the general climate of the globe.

---

* This view has recently been advocated by Mr. Evans, in his Anniversary Address as President of the Geological Society. But even if it were possible that the vast movements of elevation and depression, which he suggests as likely to bring about a change in the position of the earth's axis of rotation, actually could have taken place, and within so recent a geological period, yet they would not account for some of the most important phenomena. For, as we shall see presently, the glacial epoch was interrupted by more than one warm interglacial period. It is not therefore only one change in the position of the poles, but several that we should require; and all these stupendous changes, so improbable in themselves, must be supposed to have taken place at quite a recent date, and within a comparatively short space of time.

Mr. Evans has ingeniously sought to account[*] for the remains of large trees that are found in Greenland, and for the traces of glacial cold in this country, by considering whether it might not be possible that the external crust or shell of the globe had actually slid round its fluid or semi-fluid nucleus, so as to bring the same areas of the external surface under very different conditions. Thus it was suggested that lands, which at one time basked under a tropical sun, might, in the slow course of ages, be shifted to some more northern region, while countries which had for long years been sealed up in the ice of the Arctic Circle might eventually slide down to temperate latitudes.

But the theory which has taken firmest hold of the geological mind, is that which the late Sir Charles Lyell upheld so strenuously. This theory maintains that the climates of the past may be accounted for by that continuous change in the distribution of land and sea which has been going on all through the geologic ages. There is no fact more patent than that sea and land have frequently changed places. What are the rocks, of which the continents are mainly composed, but the hardened sediments of mud and sand that gathered upon the floors of ancient oceans? And what are all our so-called "formations" but just so many fossil sea-bottoms, as it were, piled one on top of the other? In the loneliness of the desert, in the streets of populous cities, in deep valleys, and on the crests of lofty mountains—everywhere we meet with traces of the sea. Along some coast-lines abundant evidence shows that the land is sinking down, and the sea slowly but surely gaining ground. In other regions the reverse takes place—the shores extend and the sea retreats. Such changes are due to those mysterious subterranean forces that give birth to earthquakes and volcanoes, and every bed of rock testifies to their unceasing activity. And, therefore, when this theory asks us to believe that the distribution of sea and land must sometimes have been very different to what it is at present, we are asked nothing which the facts do not fully justify us in admitting.

Lyell conceived, that, if land were massed chiefly in the region of the equator and the tropics, the climate of the

[*] *Proceedings of the Royal Society*, 1866.

globe would be such that tree-ferns might grow luxuriantly on any islands that might happen to lie within the Arctic or Antarctic Circle.   For the land, heated to excess under the equatorial sun, would give rise to warm currents of air, which, sweeping north and south, would carry with them the heat of the tropics, and thus temper greatly the climate of higher latitudes.   And some such condition of things, he thought, may have obtained during, for instance, the Carboniferous period,* when tree-ferns and their allies flourished within the Arctic Circle.   On the other hand, were the land to be grouped chiefly round the poles, the reverse of all this, he believed, would come about ; for with no land under the equator to soak up the heat of the sun, and give it to the winds to carry north and south to polar regions, the climates of the northern and southern hemispheres would be so greatly affected, that snow and ice would then gather upon the ground, and creep gradually outwards down to those low latitudes where we now meet with their traces.

In these interesting speculations it will be observed that Lyell considered the atmosphere to be the chief medium by which the heat derived from the sun is carried from one latitude to another: one of the principal reasons given by him for the intenser cold of the Antarctic as compared with the Arctic regions, being the absence of land in the south temperate zone, where its presence would warm the atmosphere and so give rise to genial winds.   It may be questioned, however, whether such would be the result.   It seems more likely that the presence of land in the quarter referred to would only serve to increase the cold by affording another gathering-ground for snow and glaciers.   Even if we supposed the land to remain uncovered with snow, and to succeed in warming the atmosphere, it is difficult to see how this could have any effect in ameliorating the climate of the higher latitudes about the pole.   The heated air would certainly rise and flow towards the pole, while a cold under-current would set from the pole to restore the equilibrium.   Long before the north wind, however, arrived at its destination, it would have radiated all its heat into the colder regions of space, and so would eventually reach the surface of the

* For table of Geological Formations see Appendix, Note A.

earth in its progress towards the pole as a cold, and not a warm wind.

On the same principle it does not appear likely that the massing of the land in the tropics, and under the equator, would have the effect which is supposed. The air, heated to excess over the equatorial and tropical regions, would, of course, rise and flow towards the poles, but its warmth would be filched from it, and dissipated into space before it could again return to the level of the sea. Thus, even supposing most of the land to be distributed between the tropics, it is evident that, as far as aerial currents themselves are concerned, the temperature of the seas about the poles might never rise above the freezing point, while any islands that might chance to lie within the Arctic and Antarctic Circles would be sealed up in persistent snow and ice.

The south-west winds, to which in the present economy of things we are indebted for the temperate character of our climate, do not derive their heat directly from the equator. The equatorial heat which they carry upwards is taken from them in their lofty flight towards the north, and thus they reach the level of the sea as cold, dry winds. But, blowing for many leagues in the Atlantic athwart the heated waters of the Gulf-stream, they gradually become warmed again and laden with moisture, and this warmth and moisture they yield up when they reach our coasts. Were there no broad currents of warm water setting towards the north, from which the cold dry winds on their descent to the sea-level might receive warmth and moisture, there is good reason to believe that the temperature of the northern hemisphere would be greatly depressed, and the cold of the arctic regions might then equal in intensity that of their antipodes. Were it not for the genial influence of the Gulf-stream, Scotland would experience a climate as severe at least as that of Labrador, while the greater part of Norway would be uninhabitable. As it is, however, the temperature of the winter at Hammerfest, in the north of Norway, is only 9° below the freezing point, while in the same latitude in Greenland the winter temperature is 5° below zero ; the difference in summer being 41° in Greenland and 50° at Hammerfest. Again, the temperature in the month of January in Caithness (58° N.

lat.) is about 36°, or 4° above freezing point; but in the same latitude in Labrador the winter temperature falls to 4° below zero ; and the winter temperature of Caithness is not attained on the American continent until we descend to 39° N. lat. on the shores of Chesapeake Bay. Lisbon, which is in the same latitude as the last-named place, has a winter temperature of about 47°, or 15° above freezing point.

These wide differences arise solely from the presence of the Gulf-stream. That great current of warm water, coming from the equatorial regions, washes all the western shores of Europe from the coast of Spain to the north of Norway. It laves the shores of Novaia Zemblia, and can even be traced north of Spitzbergen, where its waters are still appreciably warmer than those of the surrounding seas. The air in contact with this broad ocean-stream is everywhere warmed, and the winds licking up the heated water as they sweep across the Atlantic reach Europe laden with moisture, which is condensed and precipitated as soon as the winds are cooled by coming in contact with high tracts of land or with colder strata of air. For this reason our west coasts, which are the first to receive the winds, enjoy a more genial, but at the same time a more humid climate than the corresponding latitudes on the other side of the island.

The differences of temperature resulting from the presence or absence of oceanic currents become still more striking when we compare the climates of inland tracts like central Siberia with the corresponding latitudes in western Europe. At Jakutsk, Siberia (62° N. lat.), the mean winter temperature is 36°·6 below zero, and the thermometer has registered as low as 40° below zero. But Jakutsk lies only some 6° further north than Edinburgh, and is in nearly the same latitude as Bergen, where the temperature of January is not under 32°, or freezing point ; while the western shores of Novaia Zemblia, lying between latitudes 71° and 76° N., have a winter temperature of about 10° above zero. This last example is exceedingly striking.

But perhaps the best way to get an adequate conception of the influence of a warm ocean current upon climate is to trace out a line of equal temperature. If every portion of the globe received all its heat directly from the sun, and were there no such disturbing influences as marine currents, winds, &c., then a line traced through all those places which enjoyed the same degree of warmth would of course run due west and east, and would correspond in direction with a parallel of latitude ; in short, a place would be warm or cold according as it approached or receded from the equator. But owing to a variety of causes (chief among which is the influence exerted by marine currents and winds), this is not exactly the case. The lines are always undulating, and often rapidly so. Let us follow, for example, the isochimenal line* of $+ 14°$ from Asia into Europe, and we shall find it crossing several parallels of latitude instead of conforming in direction to these. Taking it up a little to the east of the Caspian Sea, in lat. 45° N., we follow it as it undulates northward to lat. 55° N., not far from Smolensk. It then strikes due north until it reaches 60° N. lat., a little east of Petersburg, after which it trends north-west and west, crossing the Gulf of Bothnia in 64° N. lat. Its direction is now south-west, to 61° N. lat. in the south of Norway, and after this it suddenly curves round and doubles upon itself, running away to the north-east and keeping parallel to the Norwegian shores, but at some distance from the sea, for it intersects only a few of the longer fiords with which the coast-line of Norway is indented. After this it turns more to the east, still keeping parallel to the shore, crosses and recrosses 70° N. lat., turns to south-east, and finally terminates on the borders of Finland in lat. 68°. All places to the north and north-east of this line have of course a colder winter temperature than places south and south-west.† In short, as we proceed inland from the western shores of Europe, we find the cold of winter becomes more and more intense the farther we penetrate into the interior, until central Siberia is reached, where we meet with a winter

---

* Lines of equal winter temperature are termed *isochimenal* lines (ἴσος, equal; χειμών, winter) ; of summer, *isotheral* (ἴσος, equal, θέρος, summer) ; while those indicating equal annual temperature are known as *isothermal* lines (ἴσος, equal, θερμός, heat). See Plates XVIII. and XIX.

† The wonderful manner in which this line is deflected to the north is due primarily to the influence of the Gulf-stream. Nor can we estimate too highly that influence, which succeeds so far in overruling the effect of mere latitude, as to be able to confer the same temperature on places situated so far apart as the borders of the Caspian Sea, Petersburg, and the north of Norway.

truly arctic, outside of the Arctic Circle. Before the south-west winds, which temper our winter, can reach this distant region, they are robbed of all their warmth, and only tend to increase the cold.

Thus much, then, is certain, it is the currents of the sea that are the chief carriers of heat from the tropics towards the pole ; and such being the case, it seems quite reasonable to conclude that were the area over which the sea is heated and warm currents formed to be materially limited, as must certainly have been the case had the great continental masses ever been congregated within the tropics, then the chief secondary source of heat supplied to the temperate and frigid zones would be diminished, and the climates of those areas would become colder than they are at present.

While it is extremely unlikely, therefore, that a great accumulation of land within the tropics would have any ameliorating influence whatever on the climate of the poles, it may be admitted that were the continents to be grouped immediately round the poles, an excessively cold climate might possibly result. This low temperature, however, would not be due to the chilling influence of cold winds blowing from the south. Were an excessively cold climate to be the consequence of such a distribution of land as that last referred to, the low temperature would doubtless be caused by the exclusion of oceanic currents. It is quite possible that, among the many vast geologic changes which have taken place, the land may at some time in the past have been so closely gathered round the poles as to exclude the sea to comparatively low latitudes. If such had ever been the case, a vast breadth of land would then circle round the north pole, along the borders of which wet winds coming from the sea would deposit their moisture. But long before these winds could reach any great distance towards the interior of the supposed arctic continent, they would neces-sarily part with all their moisture, and arrive at the circum-polar regions as dry winds. In these regions, therefore, there could not be any accumulation of snow and ice. It is clear, then, that if we exclude the sea from our hypothetical arctic continent, we shall certainly lower the temperature of the polar climate ; but we shall not on that account produce a glacial period, for the exclusion of the sea means absence of damp winds, and consequently no deposition of snow and no accumulation of ice.

But although it is possible, yet at the same time it is very improbable, that the land ever was so closely aggregated around the poles as to exclude the sea to comparatively low latitudes. All analogy would lead us to infer that even during the greatest extension of land in arctic and antarctic regions the ocean must have indented this land with broad straits, with fiords, inlets, bays, and seas. Supposing then that, with Sir Charles Lyell, we imagine all the continents, shaped as they are now, to be grouped around the poles, and a vast sea to extend over equatorial and tropical regions ; what, let us ask, would be the result ? Why surely this, that a much wider extent of sea being exposed to the blaze of the tropical sun, the temperature of the ocean in equatorial regions would rise above what it is at present. This warm water, sweeping in broad currents, would enter the polar fiords and seas, and, everywhere heating the air, would cause warm moist winds to blow athwart the land to a much greater extent than they do at present ; and these winds, thus distributing warmth and moisture, might render even the high latitudes of North Greenland habitable by civilised man.

But on any supposition, it is impossible to conceive of such a distribution of land and sea as would cause an influx of warm water into the frigid zone of sufficient extent to raise the whole temperature of the arctic regions, so as to permit the growth of tree-ferns in the higher latitudes, and to nourish in the depths of the polar seas reef-building polyps and chambered shells of species resembling in general appearance those that are met with only in the genial waters of the sunny south. Were a greater body of warm water than the present Gulf-stream, owing to some revolution of the earth's surface—some readjustment of the relative position of sea and land—to flow into the arctic regions, it would doubtless bring about some ameliorating effect upon the climate ; but, as I have said, we can hardly imagine that a mere redistribution of the land would induce currents of warm water to flow from the tropics towards the pole in such immense volumes as to preclude the possibility of ice forming within the Arctic Circle. And we know that there have been times in the past when snow and ice either did not occur within the Arctic Circle, or at all events could have been present only in very small quantities. Not much certainly could have floated in the polar sea that nourished the delicate corals and molluscs whose fossil remains have been disinterred from the rocks of the bleak shores of the Arctic Ocean. In our day, at all events, reef-building corals do not live in seas the temperature of which is under 66°. Nor is it in any degree likely that while the vegetation of the Coal-measures was flourishing in what is now the frigid zone, large glaciers could have descended from the higher grounds of those regions in broad, deep streams, so as to reach the sea as they do in our day. If glaciers did exist at all, they must have been few and local, and confined to the recesses of lofty mountainous tracts, did any such elevated areas happen to exist within the arctic regions at that time.

It would really seem, then, after allowing all possible influence to such geological changes as may have resulted in redistribution of land and sea, that these changes yet fail to solve the problem before us. No doubt climates may be and have been varied repeatedly by local disturbances of level, by submergence here and elevation there. But, however extensive such changes may have been, yet their influence could not so far affect the general climate of the globe as to confer at one and the same time upon the whole northern hemisphere, down to low latitudes of the temperate zone, a severe arctic climate, and at another period a climate warm and genial, with no extremes of heat and cold, but a kind of perpetual summer.*

---

* The reader will find this interesting question discussed by Dr. Croll in *Philosophical Magazine* for Feb. 1870, Oct. 1870, and Oct. 1871. See also *Climate and Time*, chaps. ii. and iii.

CHAPTER IX.

CAUSE OF COSMICAL CHANGES OF CLIMATE—*Continued*.

Failure of geologists to furnish an adequate theory.—Astronomical phenomena
may perhaps afford a solution.—Movement of the earth on its own axis
and round the sun.—Eccentricity of the orbit.—Precession of the equinoxes.
—Nutation.—Obliquity of the ecliptic.

SEEING that the phenomena of elevation and depression fail
to account for such great cosmical changes of climate, is it
not possible that a solution of the problem may be found in the
relations of our planet to the sun ?   Geologists of the modern
school have always been jealous, and justly so, of attempts to
explain or account for the facts of their science by reference
to causes other than those they see at work in the world
around them.   And perhaps the frequent failure of physicists and astronomers to frame a satisfactory theory for those
great changes of climate to which the rocks bear emphatic
testimony may sometimes have been viewed by geologists
with a kind of secret satisfaction.   Of late years, however,
the opinion has been gaining ground among our hammer-
bearers that in this matter of cosmical climate they must,
after all, be content to follow the guidance of the astronomer
and the physicist, seeing that their own principles refuse, in
this particular at least, to yield as much assistance as would
be desirable.   Nor, after he has sufficiently questioned all the
natural causes with which his own peculiar studies have made
him familiar, ought the geologist to feel surprised that these
sometimes fail to explain the phenomena that come under his
cognizance.   There is no hard-and-fast line separating the
domain of one science from that of another, and as the circle
of knowledge widens boundary divisions become more and
more difficult to determine.   Perhaps of no physical science
is this more true than that of geology.   At one time the
investigator into the past history of our globe had the field

almost entirely to himself, and the limits of his study were as sharply defined as if they had been staked off and measured. Now, however, it would be hard to say on which of the territories of his scientific neighbours he must trespass most. He cannot proceed far in any direction without coming in contact with some worker from adjacent fields. His studies are constantly overlapping those of the sister sciences, just as these in turn overlap his. It will, therefore, only be a further proof of the unity of Nature if those intricate problems which have hitherto baffled the geologist should eventually be solved by the researches of astronomers and the conclusions of physicists.

I have already referred briefly to certain astronomical and physical theories which have from time to time been advanced in explanation of the grand climatic changes we have been considering. Of these, as I have indicated, some are too problematical to be relied upon as guides in our investigations into the origin of cosmical climates; while the most probable of them all, that, namely, which was supported by Sir Charles Lyell and is advocated by many geologists of the modern school, appears to be inadequate to explain the more important phenomena.

Now, if all these theories be rejected, what have we to supplant them ? Well, there are certain considerations arising from the fact that, when long ages are taken into account, our earth upon its circuit round the sun and in its own diurnal revolution does not always hold exactly the same position with reference to the sun. But before entering upon these considerations it may be well to remind the reader of certain astronomical data, without a thorough comprehension of which it will be impossible to convey a clear conception of the theory which I shall attempt to describe.

There are, as every one knows, two principal movements proper to the earth. The first of these is its translation through space, during which it circles round the sun from west to east, and gives us the succession of the seasons in a period of one year. The second movement is that of rotation on its own axis, a movement which, as no one needs to be told, results in the phenomena of day and night.

The orbit or path described by the earth round the sun is

not exactly circular, but rather an ellipse, and this elliptical path is known to astronomers as the *ecliptic*. Neither is the sun placed quite in the centre of the ecliptic or orbit, but somewhat to one end of it, or, in other words, it occupies one focus of the ellipse, so that the earth, during its annual revolution, is nearer or farther from our great luminary according as it approaches or recedes from that focus of the ellipse in which the light-giver hangs. The point in the ecliptic at which the earth approaches nearest to the sun is called *perihelion*, and the point where it reaches its greatest distance from that luminary becomes in astronomical language its *aphelion*. But it must not be supposed that the earth as it journeys year by year round the sun, pursues always exactly the same elliptical path. The attractions of the other planets are producing day by day a slow change on the *shape* of its orbit : in this way its track approaches at one time nearly to a circle, and at another time has a more oval and flattened outline. But these deviations are confined within certain limits, between which they are constantly oscillating backwards and forwards. The eccentricity during a long lapse of years goes on decreasing till it sinks to a minimum value, and the orbit then approaches most nearly to a circle, without, however, ever becoming actually circular. After passing this point the eccentricity begins to increase, and the orbit becomes more and more flattened, till a maximum eccentricity is reached. Then the cycle of changes comes slowly round again in reversed order ; the orbit gradually draws nearer and nearer to a circle till a minimum is arrived at, when it again begins to grow elliptical, and continues to alter in this direction till the next maximum is reached. At present, the path is slowly approaching the more circular route, and in about 24,000 years from this date the ellipticity will reach one of the minimum points. After that the earth will again begin to follow a more and more elliptical course round the sun, until, when thousands of years have elapsed, its orbit shall have attained its maximum eccentricity ; and then the ellipticity will again slowly diminish as before. It is important to notice that the intervals between consecutive turning-points are very unequal in length, and the actual maximum and minimum values of the eccentricity are themselves variable.

In this way it comes about that some periods of high eccentricity have lasted much longer than others, and that the orbit has been more elliptical at some epochs of high eccentricity than at others.

When the maximum of ellipticity is attained, the earth in aphelion will, of course, be farther from the sun than it is now, at that point in the ecliptic ; while on the other hand, the earth in perihelion will be nearer. At present, the earth in aphelion is distant about ninety millions of miles from the sun, but when the eccentricity of the orbit is at its superior limit, in other words, when the planets by the force of their attraction have succeeded in pulling the earth as far from the sun as they can, the earth in aphelion will then be rather more than ninety-eight and a half millions of miles from the sun, or more than eight and a half millions farther than it is at present. Of course the reader will understand that while the earth's orbit varies in its degree of ellipticity, the time taken by the earth to complete a revolution round the sun never does. All that the planets do is to modify the shape of the path traversed by the earth.

Besides its movement of translation through the heavens round the sun, the earth, as we know, revolves or rotates on an axis of its own. Now this axis is inclined to the plane of the ecliptic at a certain angle which we will for the present consider to remain constant, so that the axis is always parallel to itself. This is as much as to say that an imaginary line continued through the poles to the skies will be found to touch nearly the same vanishing-point in the heavens all the year round, so that no matter what the season may be— winter, spring, summer, or autumn, nor whether the earth is in aphelion or perihelion, a pole will always point in one and the same direction—the point in the heavens to which our north pole is directed being situate near to the Pole star.

If we draw through the centre of the sun a plane parallel to the earth's equator, this will cut the earth's orbit at two points, which are termed the *vernal* and *autumnal equinoxes*. The two points half-way between the equinoxes are called the *summer* and *winter solstices*. On the days when the earth passes through the equinoxes the day and night are of equal length all the world over. As the earth leaves the vernal equinox the days in the northern hemisphere begin to get longer than the nights, and continue to increase in length up to the summer solstice ; they then decrease till the autumnal equinox is reached, when day and night are again equal. In other words, the time taken by the earth to pass from the vernal to the autumnal equinox is our summer half of the year. In exactly the same way, the time occupied by the earth in travelling from the autumnal to the vernal equinox is our winter half of the year, when the days are shorter than the nights. A very little consideration will show that in the southern hemisphere just the opposite condition of things exists : while it is our summer they are passing through their winter half of the year, and summer comes to them at the same time as winter is passing over our heads. Further, it happens that our mid-winter now occurs very nearly when the earth is in perihelion, or at that point of its annual circuit which is nearest to the sun, and from this important consequences flow. If we look at the two portions into which a line joining the equinoctial points divides the earth's orbit, we shall see that one is longer than the other. It is the shorter bit of the two which corresponds to the winter of the northern hemisphere, and moreover this is just the part of its path over which the earth, on account of its greater proximity to the sun, moves fastest. Both these causes work together to make our winter at present shorter than our summer. In fact, if we compute from the 20th March, or vernal equinox, to the 22nd September, or autumnal equinox, we shall find that the earth takes 186 days to swing round that portion of its circuit within which the northern hemisphere has its spring and summer—the other half of its orbit, which brings the southern hemisphere its summer and us our winter, being traversed in 179 days : so that the summer period of our antipodes is seven or eight days shorter than our own.

Such is the arrangement of the seasons in the two hemispheres at present—our summer occurs when the earth is in aphelion, and is longer than our winter, while that of the southern hemisphere arrives in perihelion, and the winter is now there longer than the summer. But this arrangement has not always obtained. There was a time when our hemisphere had its winter in aphelion, and a period will again arrive when the present condition of things will be reversed, and the seasons in the two hemispheres will completely change. That is to say our December solstice, instead of being our winter will become our summer, while our future winter solstice will happen in what are now our summer months. This great change is effected by a movement which is known as the *precession of the equinoxes.*

It is not strictly true that the axis of the earth always remains, as we have been hitherto supposing, parallel to itself: for short periods this is nearly true, but nevertheless there is a slight change going on, which in the course of ages comes to be considerable. The attraction of the sun and moon on the protuberant parts of the earth around the equator are for ever, by their unequal pull, causing the axis slightly to shift its position, and the sum total of these displacements results in the motions known as *precession* and *nutation.* It is the first of them only with which we are specially concerned : it may be thus illustrated. Take two straight sticks, unite one end of one to one end of the other by a loose joint, and connect the other ends by a bit of string ; now while one stick is held steadily at rest, move the other stick round it, *so that the string is always kept tight ;* the motion of the second stick will then resemble, in everything except speed, the movement of the earth's axis known as *precession.* The extremity of the movable stick evidently describes a circle in space, and if we in imagination conceive the axis of the earth to be prolonged so as to touch the heavens, we should find that in the great cycle of its revolution the end of the imaginary line we had protracted would trace out a circle among the stars. Now, bear in mind that the equinoxes are the points where a plane through the sun's centre, perpendicular to the earth's axis, cuts the earth's orbit. Since the axis is always in motion, this must also be the case with this plane, and therefore with the equinoxes. As the axis swings round it necessarily carries the last with it, and they travel along the ecliptic in a direction opposite that of the earth's annual revolution ; and calculations show that the average distance traversed by them in a year is just what would be passed over by the earth in twenty minutes and twenty seconds, so that equal day and night come to us every year some twenty minutes earlier than they did the year before. Thus the places on the earth's orbit of those points on which the seasons depend are constantly shifting round. The summer solstice, for instance, will not always, as now, nearly coincide with the aphelion, it will slowly draw up to the perihelion, and we shall then have a disposition of the seasons corresponding to that which now obtains in the southern hemisphere : afterwards, a continuation of the motion will as slowly bring round again our present arrangement.

This great oscillatory movement would run through a complete cycle in about 26,000 years, were it not for another complex movement, due to the action of the planets, which succeeds in shortening the great cycle by some 5,000 years ; so that in half that time, or 10,500 years, our seasons will have completely changed, and the northern will then assume the arrangement of the seasons which at present characterizes the southern hemisphere. In 10,500 years more the equinox will regain its initial position, and the distribution of the seasons that now obtains will return.

This movement of the axis is effected by the attractions of the sun and moon, which act unequally on the globe, owing to the fact that our earth is not an exact sphere, but somewhat flattened at the poles and swollen at the equator. If the world were a perfect sphere no such inequality of action could take place, but the axis would always remain exactly parallel to itself.

The portion of the motion of the earth's axis called *nutation* consists in small deviations, first to one side and then to the other, from the position it would have at any time if precession alone were taken into account. It is as if the string in our illustration were slightly elastic, and kept alternately lengthening and shortening itself a little. Under these circumstances the path of the end of the movable stick will be like the edge of a circular disc with a very slightly crimped or wavy outline ; and this is the character of the path actually described by the pole of the earth's axis in space. The effect of nutation is alternately to increase and diminish the inclination of the equator to the ecliptic, but its amount is so very small that for all the purposes we are now concerned with it may be neglected. Nevertheless astronomers have long been aware that this inclination does vary to a greater degree by reason of a movement due to the joint action of all the planets. This movement is at present gradually bringing the earth's equator to coincide more nearly with the plane of the ecliptic. The effect of this change in the angle at which the axis is inclined to that plane is of course to lessen the duration of the long day and night at both poles. And if it were possible for the obliquity to entirely disappear, and the plane of the ecliptic to coincide exactly with that of the equator, there would then be no difference in the day and night in any part of the world during the year. But the limits within which the position of the axis, with reference to a fixed point in the heavens, can thus change are very moderate. After a vast succession of ages, the obliquity which just now is diminishing will again increase until it reaches its maximum of $24° 50' 34''$. This is a very small change in the angle of inclination after all, but Sir John Herschel thought that, if millions in place of thousands of years were taken into account, the maximum change in the obliquity might increase to $3°$ or even $4°$ on each side of the mean. With such a change as this the polar day and night would of course lengthen out, for the farther the axis bends over towards the sun the larger must be the area round the poles illuminated in the long summer day, and conversely the broader must be the extent over which in winter-time the polar night will prevail.

CHAPTER X.

CAUSE OF COSMICAL CHANGES OF CLIMATE—*Continued.*

Effect of variation of the eccentricity of the earth's orbit.—Sir J. Herschel's
opinion.—Arago's.—Purely astronomical causes insufficient to afford a solution of the problem.—Dr. Croll's theory.—Changes of climate result
indirectly from astronomical causes.—Physical effects of a high eccentricity
of the orbit.—Extremes of climate at opposite poles.—Modifications of the
course followed by ocean-currents.—Perpetual summer and perennial winter.
—Physical effects of obliquity of the ecliptic.—Succession of climatic changes
during a period of high eccentricity.

THE possible bearing that astronomical phenomena might
have upon the climate of our globe has not infrequently
engaged the attention of astronomers. Sir John Herschel
was inclined to admit that variations in the eccentricity
"may be productive of considerable diversity of climate,"
and might so operate during great periods of time " as to
produce alternately in the same latitude of either hemisphere
a perpetual spring, or the extreme vicissitudes of a burning
summer and a rigorous winter." And he was also of opinion
that, owing to the precession of the equinoxes and the shifting of the earth's axis by another movement, these strongly-
contrasted conditions would gradually be transferred from one
hemisphere to another. Hence he thought it not improbable
that some of the indications noted by geologists, of widely-
different climates having prevailed at former epochs in the
northern hemisphere, might in part at least be accounted
for.[*]

Other eminent astronomical writers, among whom was
Arago,[†] came to quite a different conclusion, and were of

[*] *Trans. Geol. Soc.*, vol. iii., p. 293, second series. Herschel appears subse-
quently to have modified these views: see "Treatise of Astronomy," *Cabinet
Cyclopædia*, § 315, and *Outlines of Astronomy*, § 368.
[†] "On the Thermometrical State of the Terrestrial Globe," *Edinburgh New
Philosophical Journal*, vol. xvi. See also a paper by L. W. Meech "On the
Relative Intensity of the Heat and Light of the Sun," *Smithsonian Contributions
to Knowledge*, vol. ix.

opinion that no appreciable change of climate could possibly result from any variation in the ellipticity of the earth's orbit. The earth, they argued, receives the same total amount of heat in the aphelion as in the perihelion section of its orbit. And this, as we know, is due to the fact that our globe moves with greater velocity in perihelion than it does in aphelion. Thus it happens that, although the southern hemisphere in perihelion is turned towards the sun, and must receive *per diem* a larger share of heat than the northern hemisphere derives in the same space of time in aphelion, yet the perihelion section of the orbit is quickly travelled; so that greater nearness to the sun only serves to make up for the short time the earth keeps in that position, just as in aphelion the greater distance of the earth from the sun is exactly counterbalanced by the longer time our globe remains exposed to the solar rays. Nor does it matter, said some of the astronomers, to what extent the ellipticity of the orbit may vary—for it may reach the very highest degree of eccentricity, and yet the equal distribution of the sun's heat in perihelion and aphelion must continue invariable. Any difference in the amount of heat that might follow upon an increase of eccentricity, would, it was thought, rather take effect in bringing about a generally warmer climate for the whole world, than in producing a glacial period in one hemisphere and perpetual spring or summer in the other. And this conclusion was based on the fact that the total heat derived by the earth from the sun is inversely proportional to the minor axis of the earth's orbit.

Such were some of the arguments brought forward to show that cosmical changes of climate could not be due to variations in the eccentricity of the earth's orbit. Each of these arguments is strictly consonant with well-ascertained fact, and cannot possibly be gainsaid; and therefore it may at once be admitted that purely astronomical causes alone will not account for that wonderful alternation of extreme climates to which the geological record bears witness. But in a remarkable paper published in 1864,* Dr. Croll clearly

---

* "On the Physical Cause of the Change of Climate during Geological Epochs," *Philosophical Magazine,* August, 1864; see also *Climate and Time,* chap. iv.

showed that, "although a glacial climate could not result directly from an increase in the eccentricity of the earth's orbit, it might nevertheless do so indirectly." At the present time the ellipticity of the orbit is such that the earth, when nearest to the sun or in the perihelion part of its course, receives in a given time one-fifteenth more heat than it does in aphelion. Now, this being the case, it is quite evident that, did the earth travel round the sun at the same rate in all parts of its orbit, or, in other words, were the seasons of equal duration, the southern hemisphere, which has its summer in aphelion would not only, as it does now, receive more heat *per diem* than the northern, but its annual proportion would also be greatly in excess. But, as the reader has already been reminded, this is prevented by the unequal pace at which our globe hurries on its way—the result being that both sections of the world receive the same yearly amount of heat. Dr. Croll points out that the present difference between the two hemispheres, as regards the proportion of heat derived from the sun in a given time, would be vastly increased when the eccentricity reached its highest value. If at a period of maximum eccentricity the winter of our hemisphere should happen in aphelion, he thinks that we should then be receiving nearly one-fifth less heat during that season than we do now, and in summer-time, of course, nearly one-fifth more. But if, on the other hand, our winter should, as at present, fall in perihelion, the effect of a great ellipticity he believes would be such as to annihilate the difference between summer and winter in the latitude of this country. And he grounds these conclusions upon purely physical considerations.

During a period of great eccentricity of the earth's orbit, the earth in aphelion would be rather more than eight and a half millions of miles farther from the sun than it is now, and the present long frigid winter of the southern hemisphere would then become still longer, and the cold much more intense. If it happened to be the northern hemisphere whose winter occurred in aphelion, of course similar climatic results would ensue, and the mean temperature of our winter would fall below the freezing point. Consequently, all the moisture precipitated in our latitude during that season would fall in the form of snow, and the British seas would be frozen over. Nor would the greater proximity of our hemisphere to the sun in perihelion avail to free these islands from their frost. It is true that the direct heat received in perihelion during the summer of a period of great eccentricity would exceed that which we now derive during that season by nearly one-fifth; but this intense heat, paradoxical as it may seem, would not give rise to a warm summer. The summers of North Greenland, we know, are colder than our winters, notwithstanding that the rays of the sun in that region are so strong as to melt the pitch on the sides of ships. Every one, indeed, has heard of the heat of the arctic sun, which shines day and night during the whole summer-tide. But in despite of the sun's power, the mean temperature of summer in North Greenland does not exceed one or two degrees above freezing point, and this is entirely owing to the presence of snow and ice. Were it not for these, the sun would heat the ground, and the ground would impart its warmth to the atmosphere, and the summer temperature would then rise to something like our own. It is only in this way, or from passing over warm water, that the air can be heated, for the direct rays of the sun pass through it without sensibly affecting it. Now in the polar regions the sun's heat is used up chiefly in melting the snow and ice, and not in warming the ground; so that comparatively little of the summer heat finds its way into the atmosphere by radiation. Such being the case, it is not difficult to follow Dr. Croll when he argues that the sun, during a period of great eccentricity, would not be able to give a warm temperature to that hemisphere whose summer happened in perihelion. An increased amount of evaporation would certainly take place, but the moisture-laden air would be chilled by coming in contact with the vast sheets of snow that had gathered during the long intolerable winter, and hence the vapour would condense into thick fogs, and cloud the sky. In this way the sun's rays would to a large extent be cut off, and unable to reach the earth, and consequently the winter snows would not be all melted away. Nor, supposing there were drenching rains during the summer, would these suffice to dissolve more than one-eighth part of the snow and ice—

for, as Dr. Croll remarks, "it takes nearly eight tons of water at 58° Fahr. to melt one ton of snow."

The accounts given by voyagers who have sailed in the south polar seas are often highly interesting, as showing the great difference in climate between lands situated at the same distance from the poles in the two hemispheres. They all agree as to the intenser cold of the antarctic as compared with the arctic summer, and to the greater frequency of cold raw fogs in the southern polar regions. Captain Forster, of the *Chanticleer*, who spent several months making observations at Deception Island, mentions specially the thick fogs and strong gales which he encountered. The fogs indeed were so frequent and thick, that for ten days neither sun nor stars were seen, and the air was so intensely raw and cold that Lieutenant Kendal did not remember to have suffered more at any time in the arctic regions. And yet this was in January, the very midsummer of the south, and in a latitude corresponding to that occupied by the Faroe Islands, where the climate is much the same as in our own Shetland. Now, when we remember that this cold raw summer of the south happens while the earth is actually nearer to the sun than it is at the time the milder northern polar regions have their summer, we cannot but admit that mere proximity to the sun will not necessarily produce a warm season.

At the time of greatest eccentricity, when the earth would be nearer to the sun in perihelion than it is now, there can be no doubt that the heat received would be correspondingly increased. But during the long winter of aphelion—longer by thirty-six days than the summer of perihelion—such an accumulation of snow and ice would have taken place, that even the diminished distance between the earth and sun in summer-time would be powerless to effect its removal; and so it would go on increasing year by year, until all northern countries (winter happening in aphelion) down to the latitudes of these islands were swathed in a dreary covering of snow and ice. There would then be a glacial period over our hemisphere, while at the antipodes a very different condition of things would obtain. Supposing, as before, that the precession of the equinoxes had caused the summer of the southern hemisphere to happen at the time the earth was in

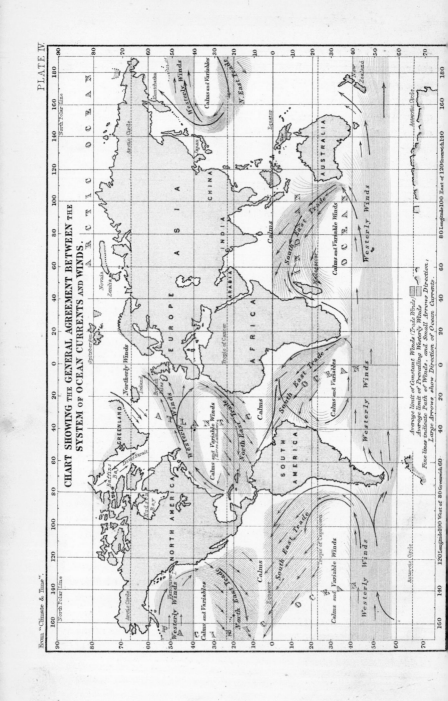

PLATE IV.

From "Climate & Time".

CHART SHOWING THE GENERAL AGREEMENT BETWEEN THE
SYSTEM of OCEAN CURRENTS and WINDS.

Average limit of Constant Winds (Trade Winds);
Average limit of Prevailing Westerly Winds
Fine lines indicate Path of Winds, and Small Arrows Direction;
Large Arrows show Direction of Ocean Currents.

aphelion, we should then have a climate for our antipodes exactly the opposite of that which, as Dr. Croll has shown, a maximum eccentricity would confer upon the northern hemisphere. The heat received would be less in a given time, but then summer would be thirty-six days longer, while winter would be much milder, and correspondingly short, owing to the sun being nearer than in summer by more than eight millions of miles. The result of all this would be to equalise the seasons. There would be a long cool summer and a short genial winter, during which probably little, if any, snow would gather; and thus there would be an approach to what Herschel has called " a perpetual spring."

There is another set of circumstances, however, which, according to Dr. Croll, would help powerfully to increase the difference between the two hemispheres. He maintains that ocean-currents are due to the action of the constant and prevailing winds which press upon the surface of the sea and thus impel the upper strata of water forward, the under strata being necessarily dragged along in the same direction. Ocean-currents will therefore, as a rule, coincide in direction with the trend of the prevailing winds, and Dr. Croll has shown upon a chart, which is here reproduced (Plate IV.), how the system of ocean-currents agrees generally with that of the winds. But it does not necessarily follow that a current in any given part of the ocean will agree in direction with the wind prevailing in that particular quarter. Each current is only a member of one general system of circulation, and its course is determined not by one prevailing wind alone but by the combined action of all the constant and prevailing winds of the globe, while its direction is further modified by the conformation of land and sea. Hence we need not feel surprised when sometimes we meet with a current running in direct opposition to the influence of the earth's rotation and the trade-winds : such, for example, as the great Antarctic Current which flows north into the Pacific, and then actually bends round to the right and strikes eastward against the coast of South America. The phenomena of undercurrents are also susceptible of a simple explanation by the wind theory. Many of these undercurrents merely compensate for water that is being constantly drained off in some other regions. Thus the cold Polar undercurrent that dips underneath the Gulf-stream near Bear Island evidently compensates for the water impelled northward by the southerly winds, just as the warm undercurrent which flows north underneath the Polar current to the west of Spitzbergen makes up for the water driven southwards by the northerly winds. When two opposing currents meet they will either keep to the surface and flow alongside, or should the course of one be strongly opposed by a constantly adverse wind, then it will naturally take the path of least resistance, and this obviously will lie at some distance from the surface. Continuously pressed forward from behind it must dip below the surface and thereafter will keep on its course as an undercurrent. Thus cold currents sometimes plunge underneath warm ones, while in other instances the reverse takes place and warm currents dip down below cold ones. For example, in the case of the Polar Stream just referred to, it is evident that this great current, when it meets the Gulf-stream at Bear Island, has not only to fight against that warm current but is likewise opposed by the winds from the influence of which it can only escape by diving under the surface. And it is precisely the same set of circumstances that compels the Gulf-stream to the west of Spitzbergen to become in its turn an undercurrent.

If, therefore, it be true that ocean-currents owe their existence to the combined action of all the constant and prevailing winds viewed as one grand system of circulation, then it is evident that anything arising to modify the action of the great constant winds (trade-winds) will likewise greatly influence the system of ocean-currents. Let us now see how this must come about.

The trade-winds exist, as every one knows, by reason of the unequal temperature of the atmosphere at the equator and the poles. The air is heated under the equator, and rises to flow towards the poles, while cold currents set from the poles towards the equator to restore the equilibrium. At present all the constant oceanic currents appear to flow out of the Antarctic Ocean. In this way the wide Equatorial Current is only a continuation of the great Antarctic Drift-current, which, flowing north-east, enters the Indian Ocean, sending one branch by the west coast of Australia northwards through the Indian Archipelago, and another stream westwards, so as to strike the east coast of Africa. Leaving the Mozambique Channel, this great current now doubles the Cape, and then continues on its course north-westwards along the African coast, until eventually, sweeping across the whole breadth of the Atlantic, it divides, one stream flowing south along the coast of Brazil, and the other striking for the Gulf of Mexico, from which, when it issues, it takes the name of the Gulf-stream.

During such a glacial condition of things as would follow upon a great increase in the eccentricity of the earth's orbit, the air in the northern hemisphere (supposing the winter of that hemisphere to occur in aphelion) would be chilled down to a very much lower temperature than in the corresponding latitudes of the opposite hemisphere. And as such would necessarily be the case, it follows that the aerial currents flowing from the poles to restore the equilibrium which the upward set of the heated air under the equator had disturbed would be of unequal strength. The winds from the severe wintry north would sweep with much more vigour towards the equator than the opposite winds from the south pole. And hence Dr. Croll contends that with weaker winds blowing from the south the great Antarctic Drift-currents would be reduced in volume, while the subsidiary currents to which they give rise, namely the broad Equatorial and the Gulf-stream, would likewise lose in volume and force. And to such an extent would this be the case, that, supposing the outline of the continents to remain unchanged, not only would the Brazilian branch of the Equatorial Current grow at the expense of the Gulf-stream, but the Gulf-stream, he thinks, would eventually be stopped, and the whole vast body of warm water that now flows north be entirely deflected into the southern oceans. For the same reason also the currents of the Pacific, which carry so much warmth from the tropics to the north, would also be turned back.* If such were the case, we

* The southern hemisphere has a cooler mean annual temperature than the northern, notwithstanding that both hemispheres receive from the sun exactly the same quantity of heat. This anomaly is usually explained by assuming that the southern hemisphere loses by radiation more heat than the northern, the winter of the former being colder and longer than that of the latter; but Dr. Croll points out, with much apparent reason, that the cooler temperature of our antipodes cannot be so accounted for, but is due rather to the constant transference of heat to the north by means of ocean-currents, nearly all the great currents originating south of the equator.—*Philosophical Magazine,* Sept. 1869; *Climate and Time,* chap. v.

can easily conceive that the reduction of temperature caused by the withdrawal from the north of all these great ocean-rivers of heated water would be something enormous. But so much loss to the northern hemisphere would be just so much gain to the southern, which would have its temperature raised to such a degree that, in place of a "perpetual spring" there might well be "perpetual summer" within the Antarctic Circle.*

Besides an increased degree of ellipticity of the earth's orbit, there is also another astronomical cause which may have no mean influence upon cosmical climate. This is a change in the obliquity of the ecliptic. We have seen that the axis of rotation, owing to the action of the planets, is compelled slowly to change the degree of its inclination to the plane of the ecliptic. At present this inclination is gradually growing less, and the effect of this is to shorten the long day and equally long night at both poles. Nor is it difficult to understand how, if this inclination disappeared altogether, and the axis of rotation then became perpendicular to the ecliptic, we should have a perpetual equinox; for the plane of our earth's equator would then exactly coincide with that of the ecliptic, and the sun's light being equally diffused over one entire half of the globe, at the same instant of time, day and night would necessarily be of equal duration in all parts of the world all the year round. But, as we know, the inclination of the earth's axis can vary only within comparatively narrow limits. Narrow though these limits be, however, it is, to say the least, highly probable that a change from a minimum to a maximum degree of obliquity could not take place without considerably influencing the climate of the poles. Dr. Croll has calculated that at the period of maximum obliquity, that is, when the poles in summer-time bend over towards the sun, so as to bring a wider area of the polar regions within the solar influence, there would be "one-eighteenth more heat falling at the poles

* Dr. Croll has endeavoured to calculate what would be the effect upon the climate of the globe if ocean and aërial currents were stopped. At present the mean temperature of the equator is 80° and that of the poles is 0°. But if all currents in air and ocean ceased, then the temperature of the equator would rise 55° above what it is at present, while the poles would become 83° colder—the difference between the two amounting to 218°. See *Climate and Time*, chap. ii.

than at present "—an amount of heat which, were there neither snow nor ice at the poles, would raise the temperature within the Arctic and Antarctic Circles by something like fourteen or fifteen degrees.

The precise time occupied in passing from a minimum to a maximum obliquity has not as yet been determined exactly ; but during that prolonged period of great eccentricity which caused our glacial epoch, a maximum obliquity would no doubt be attained more than once. At this period there was, as we have seen, a vast accumulation of snow and ice in our hemisphere, consequent upon our winter occurring when the earth was farthest removed from the sun. Under such conditions an increase of obliquity could not, so long as the snow and ice remained, raise the temperature ; for the extra heat derived from the sun in the lengthened summer day would in a large measure be consumed in melting the snow and ice. But as there would be one-eighteenth more snow and ice melted than at present, the polar ice-cap would be reduced, and consequently the rigours of glaciation in our hemisphere would be diminished. To some extent, therefore, a change of obliquity would tend to neutralise the effects of a high degree of eccentricity.

At the opposite pole, upon which a large eccentricity had conferred a perennially warm and equable climate, the effects of increased obliquity would be to remove any ice that still remained, and in this manner to increase the general warmth of the atmosphere. When, upon the other hand, the obliquity had reached its minimum, the immediate result of that would be to increase the snow and ice in the northern hemisphere, and to give a somewhat cooler temperature to the southern.*

Thus, while we are considering the effect upon cosmical climate of a great increase of ellipticity of the earth's orbit, we must be careful to remember that an increase of obliquity of the ecliptic will ever have a tendency to modify this. Nor, indeed, is it at all improbable that, when the eccentri-

---

* Mr. T. Belt has recently endeavoured to show that the glacial epoch resulted from great changes in the obliquity of the ecliptic. See *Quarterly Journal of Science*, Oct. 1874. His views have been controverted by Dr. Croll, who shows that Mr. Belt has misapprehended the effects of obliquity on the distribution of the sun's heat over the globe. *Climate and Time*, p. 415.

city is very high without being actually at its maximum, the increase of heat due to an increased obliquity may be quite sufficient, so long as it lasts, to prevent any excessive degree of glaciation in that hemisphere whose winter happens in aphelion.

We have already seen that a high degree of eccentricity would give rise to a whole series of physical changes—every one of which would tend to widen the difference of temperature between the opposite hemispheres. Now, if the obliquity of the ecliptic reached a minimum during our glacial epoch, as indeed it must have done more than once, the effect of great eccentricity and diminished obliquity combined would be to intensify the glaciation of our hemisphere. The result of this would be to aid still more in the transference of all warm ocean-currents from northern into southern seas. I have already referred to the enormous influence exerted upon climate by the presence of these great bodies of warm water : so enormous indeed is this influence that it appears in the highest degree probable that the mere removal, by whatever cause, of such currents from our hemisphere would be sufficient to induce the growth of glaciers in this country, while in the Antarctic Circle, to which the warm currents had been transferred, ice and snow would in large measure disappear.

I would remind the reader, however, that while many eminent physicists maintain that the constant currents of ocean are caused by the continuous impact of the winds, which, by pushing forward in one direction the superficial strata of water, force these to drag forward in turn the strata that immediately underlie them, several writers have advocated other theories of their origin. It would lead me into too long a digression, however, were I to attempt the discussion of these various theories, even if this were the place for doing so. The evidence, and as it would seem, the weight of opinion also, appear to favour that theory which would assign a chief part in the origin of the great constant ocean-currents to the action of the winds. It does, to say the least of it, seem highly suggestive that the course of the main currents from the south should be just the same as that followed by the trade-winds ; and that the south-east trades, being so much more powerful than the north-east trades, the currents from the south should likewise be stronger than those from the north.*

Having shown the probable effect upon the climate of the globe that would ensue from a great increase in the present ellipticity of the earth's orbit, and how this effect would be modified by changes in the obliquity of the ecliptic, it is hardly necessary to point out at length how this astronomical *vera causa* appears to harmonize with the remarkable facts brought to light by geologists. It has already been stated that astronomers have ascertained the time required for the earth's orbit to pass from a minimum to a maximum eccentricity, and this, it appears, is very irregular. It is only, however, when the eccentricity arrives at something considerable that the climatic effects we have been considering will become apparent. During the millions of years that have elapsed since the oldest rocks that we know of were deposited, the earth's orbit has frequently attained a high degree of ellipticity. But by laborious calculations it has been found that the duration of such an eccentricity as would suffice to produce extreme conditions at the poles is very unequal. In the past three millions of years alone, Dr. Croll shows that there have been three such periods, separated by exceedingly irregular intervals, the periods lasting respectively for 170,000, 260,000, and 160,000 years. So that even in the shortest of these periods there would be time for the precession of the equinoxes to complete several revolutions. That is to say that our hemisphere, during this long cycle of great eccentricity, might experience several glacial periods and several periods of such genial climates as we have referred to

* Dr. Carpenter has of late years very vigorously advocated a view of oceanic circulation which is opposed to that generally held by the advocates of the " wind theory." He believes that the difference of temperature between polar and equatorial regions is sufficient of itself to induce a slow general interchange of water between polar and intertropical areas. The great mass of warm water which recent dredging operations have proved to occupy the bed of the North Atlantic could not, he thinks, have been brought thither by the Gulf-stream—the influence of which, according to him, could only affect the most superficial stratum. The only hypothesis, therefore, which seems to him to account for the presence of the body of warm water which lies between 100 and 600 fathoms deep in the North Atlantic, is that of a great general movement of equatorial water towards the polar area, and a like great set of polar water towards the equatorial area. These views (which are set forth in the *Proceedings of the Royal Society*, and the *Proceedings of the Royal Geographical Society*) have been strenuously controverted by Dr. Croll, who has examined Dr. Carpenter's arguments with much minuteness. See *Climate and Time*.

above, and each of these periods would last for thousands of years. For, as we have seen, the equinoctial point takes something like 21,000 years to effect a complete revolution upon the ecliptic, in half of which time the seasons in the two hemispheres would of course be reversed—and the pole which had enjoyed continuous summer would then be doomed to undergo perpetual winter—these conditions being modified from time to time by changes in the obliquity of the ecliptic.*

That our hemisphere has frequently undergone such extraordinary vicissitudes of climate the records of geology sufficiently attest, and some of the proofs referred to are roughly stated in the opening pages of this chapter. It is not necessary, however, to enter into details with respect to all the great changes of climate, whether glacial or the reverse, of which the solid rocks have preserved some relics.† We are at present concerned only with those excessive glacial conditions that were the result, as we have seen reason to believe, of the last great increase in the ellipticity of our earth's orbit, which began some 240,000 years ago and terminated about 80,000 years ago—embracing a period of 160,000 years. The cold was most intense about 200,000 or 210,000 years ago, that is about 30,000 or 40,000 years after the glacial period had commenced. Now, during the continuation of this vast age of high eccentricity, our hemisphere must have experienced several great vicissitudes of climate. Glacial periods, lasting for thousands of years, must have alternated with equally prolonged periods of genial conditions; for the latter, no less than the former, are a necessary consequence of extreme ellipticity, combined with the precession of the equinoxes. And during all these changes the general outline of the continents has remained much as it was before the

---

* Mr. R. W. M'Farland has recently performed the severe labour of testing the accuracy of Dr. Croll's figures by recomputing them, with the result of finding them "correct in most cases, and not in error to the amount of ·001 except in one instance." Dr. Croll's tables were computed from Le Verrier's formulæ, and give a higher superior limit for the eccentricity than the tables given by Mr. Stockwell, which were computed from formulæ of his own. The accuracy of Mr. Stockwell's figures has also been tested by Mr. M'Farland, and it is exceedingly satisfactory to find that, according to him, there is "substantial agreement" between the results obtained by Dr. Croll and Mr. Stockwell. See *American Journal of Science and Arts,* June, 1876.

† See Appendix, Note A.

advent of the glacial epoch. Whatever influence upon climate, therefore, the relative distribution of land and sea may be allowed to have, it is quite certain no one can show that our glacial climate was induced by any peculiar arrangement of land and sea. It has been considered that during the age of ice the land in the high latitudes of the northern hemisphere stood at a relatively higher level than at present. But there is no proof that the land attained either a much greater altitude or covered a much wider area than it does now; on the contrary, all the evidence goes to show that large tracts of the northern hemisphere which are at present in the condition of dry land were, at various times during our glacial epoch, submerged.

If, then, it be astronomically and physically true that extreme eccentricity of the earth's orbit, combined with the precession of the equinoxes, would confer upon our hemisphere long periods of continuous summer, separated by equally long periods of continuous arctic winter, we may next inquire whether there are any geological facts connected with the glacial deposits themselves, which, apart from any other considerations, would lead us to infer that our cold epoch was in reality not one continuous age of ice, but a period interrupted by long ages of milder conditions, during which the ice disappeared from the low-lying parts of the country, and may even have vanished for a time altogether.

CHAPTER XI.

BEDS SUBJACENT TO AND INTERCALATED WITH SCOTTISH TILL.

Lower and upper till or boulder-clay.—Upper deposit most abundantly met with.—Beds in and below till.—Seldom seen except in deep sections.—Examples of superficial deposits passed through in borings, &c.—Sections exposed in natural and artificial cuttings.—Examples.—Beds contorted and denuded in and below till.—Examples.—Fossiliferous fresh-water beds in the till.—Examples.—Fossils in the till.—Striated pavements of boulders in till.

THE reader who has accompanied me so far may remember that, while describing the till, I mentioned that sometimes it was underlaid by deposits of gravel, sand, silt, mud, brick-clay, and peat, and that occasionally similar deposits rested upon it and were themselves covered by an upper accumulation of till or boulder-clay. And I stated that, as a general rule (although not always) the upper deposits of till differed from the lower in being somewhat sandier and not quite so firm and tough, while at the same time they contained a greater proportion of angular unpolished stones and very large blocks and boulders. Otherwise, however, the upper till is often quite as tough and as tumultuous and unstratified a deposit as the lower, and thus, in many cases, it is very difficult to distinguish the one from the other; indeed, in isolated sections where only a single bed of till is exposed it is frequently quite impossible to say which it is. My own impression is that much of the boulder-clay visible at the surface of the ground throughout the length and breadth of the country is not the oldest accumulation of that kind, as will appear obvious enough after we have completed our examination of those subjacent and intercalated beds of gravel, sand, &c., which I am now about to describe. In the interior of the country we can only be sure that we are looking at a lower or upper till when the two deposits appear in one and the same section, which is not a very uncommon occurrence. As a rule, when such is the case, we find them separated by intervening layers of sedimentary materials which may vary in thickness from a mere line up to many feet or yards. Occasionally, however, the upper boulder-clay rests directly upon the lower, but there is always a more or less well-marked line of division between the two—the surface of the bottom bed being frequently irregular and hummocky. In maritime regions it often happens that the upper till contains, scattered throughout its mass, more or less numerous sea-shells, chiefly of arctic and northern species, which, as a rule, are broken, crushed, and even striated, although perfect single valves and univalves are sometimes met with; but although this maritime till is thus fossiliferous it is usually just as tumultuous and unstratified a deposit as any lower or upper till of the interior. No such shelly tills are found in the inland districts, nor have I ever seen or heard of sea-shells, broken, or otherwise, occurring in the heart of the lower till. We shall see by-and-by, however, that arctic marine shells do occasionally occur in beds of clay and sand that either underlie or rest upon, and are covered by masses of till in which no marine organisms can be detected.

For the present, however, I shall reserve all consideration of the shelly tills and other boulder-clays, which either overlie or contain marine fossiliferous deposits, and shall confine attention in this and the three following chapters to those beds of gravel, sand, clay, silt, and peat, which are of *fresh-water* origin, and which are associated either as subjacent or inter-calated deposits with accumulations of till in which *no marine organisms* appear.

The subjacent and intercalated beds which we now proceed to examine must not be confounded with those lenticular patches, layers, and inconstant bands, beds, and heaps of shingle, gravel, earthy sand, and brick-clay, which are here and there enclosed in till, and form part and parcel of that deposit, as described at page 18. On the contrary it is clear that the deposits which underlie the till evidently came into existence before it, and were subjected to considerable erosion by the glacier-mass beneath which the till was formed. Nor is it a whit less clear that the intercalated beds are in like manner older than the boulder-clay above them, and younger than the boulder-clay or till below them—the upper surface of which, one may see, has often been washed and worn into hollows before the overlying beds were laid down.

These beds seem to occur somewhat partially, the till in many districts not showing any such intercalations, but this seemingly partial distribution is more apparent than real. In the upper reaches of the valleys, where the top-covering of till is not often thick, the streams are able to cut down through this to the solid rocks, and thus expose any inter-calated beds of gravel and sand or clay which the till may chance to contain. But where the valleys widen out into the broad undulating tracks of lower ground, there are few natural sections to disclose completely the character of the drift. Many of the streams do not go down through the whole thickness of the till to the underlying rocks, so that we cannot always be sure from the sections seen that the boulder-clay may not contain or overlie beds of sand, silt, and gravel. In such low-lying districts, too, railway-cuttings do not often go deep into the subsoils, so that we get com-paratively little aid from them either. So long as we have only a partial exposure of the drifts, and not a complete sec-tion from the surface down through all the subsoils to the pavement of rock on which these rest, we are not entitled to assume that the whole drift-covering consists of till, merely because that deposit may chance to be the only kind of drift visible at the surface. The results obtained from a number of careful borings should render us cautious in this matter; for in several districts where the superficial covering might have been considered to consist wholly of boulder-clay, that deposit appearing everywhere over the entire surface of the ground, the boring-rods have, nevertheless, after piercing the till, gone down through considerable depths of sand, gravel, and other materials. At the risk of tediousness I shall here jot down a few records of such borings, that the reader may compare them with the sketch-sections.

The two examples that follow show the occurrence of beds of sand and gravel underlying one single mass of till. The first is from the valley of the Lugar, near Old Cumnock, Ayrshire :—

	Ft.	In.
Strong blue till with stones [till]	76	0
Brown sand, very fine	3	6
Gravel and stones with large "whin" boulders . .	7	0
Rock.		

The next is the record of a boring made at Woodhall, near Ormiston, Midlothian :—

	Ft.	In.
Surface soil	2	0
Clay and stones [till]	4	0
Sand and channel [gravel]	6	0
Sandy shales, &c.		

The succeeding show a greater variety in the subsoils. The localities from which they are taken are given within brackets :—

[ELPHINSTONE, MIDLOTHIAN.]

	Ft.	In.
Surface soil	1	0
Clay	5	0
Clay and stones [till]	4	0
Channel [gravel]	4	6
Sand and channel [gravel]	5	6
White sandstone.		

[WOODHALL, MIDLOTHIAN.]

	Ft.	In.
Surface soil	1	0
Clay and stones [till]	17	0
Sand and channel [gravel]	13	10
Sandstone	2	11
Channel [gravel]	2	7
Clay and stones [till]	1	4
Sandy shales, &c.		

[FROM PIT AT ORBISTON, LANARKSHIRE, MOSSEND IRON COMPANY.]

	Ft.	In.
Surface soil	1	0
Red till and stones [till]	36	6
Sand and gravel	4	0
Dark muddy sand	21	8
Brown sandstone in beds	28	0
Whinstone block	0	10
Sand and gravel	4	9½
Whinstone block	0	3
Sand and gravel	1	5
Light sandstone.		

[BORING, DYKEHEAD, LARKHALL, LANARKSHIRE.]

	Ft.	In.
Sandy clay and stones [till]	24	0
Sand and gravel	5	6
Sandy mud	38	6
Tough clay and stones [till]	33	0
Mud	7	0

	Ft.	In.
Sand	11	0
Sandstone block	4	0
Sand and gravel	12	0
Sandy clay	3	0
Soft mud	30	0
Soft mud and beds of sand	5	0

[BORING, IN SAME DISTRICT AS LAST.]

	Ft.	In.
Surface and soft sandy clay	5	0
Soft clay	13	0
Sand	3	0
Mud	24	6
Gravel and sand	25	6
Stiff clay and stones [till]	14	6
Sand	4	6
Sand and gravel	16	6
Sandy clay and stones [till]	2	0
Mud	8	0
Muddy sand	17	0
Hard gravel	3	6
Stiff sandy clay and stones [till]	10	0
Mud	22	6
Mud with broken "metals"	7	6
Carboniferous strata.		

I shall have occasion presently to refer to these "borings," and to adduce others; meanwhile enough have been given to show that shallow stream-sections, and other natural and artificial exposures, do not always tell us the whole truth. Any one going over the ground from which some of these borings are taken could not possibly have guessed that underneath the till, or other deposits he saw at the surface, lay deep beds of sand, gravel, mud, and intercalated masses of till.

But although stream-sections never yield such deep exposures of drift as some of the above, yet the cuttings laid open by the rivers are often highly instructive. And so often do the river-cuts disclose the presence of sand, mud, and gravel intercalated amongst or underlying till, that we must look upon the occurrence of these beds rather as the rule than the exception. It must not, however, be imagined that the beds referred to always, or even often, attain the great thickness indicated in some of the borings given above. They are generally much thinner, and frequently absent altogether, when nothing save sheer till covers the underlying rocks. This is most commonly the case in the hilly districts, the subjacent and intercalated beds becoming more frequent, extending more continuously, and acquiring a greater thickness as they approach the lower levels of the country. Yet, even in these last-named districts, they seldom continue far without interruption, but ever and anon disappear, leaving the stony clay to form the whole of the subsoil down to the rock-head.

I shall now bring forward a few sections to illustrate the general aspect of the till and its associated deposits as pre-

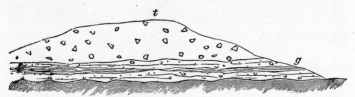

Fig. 19.—Till, *t*, resting on stratified deposits, *g*, Douglas Burn, Yarrow.

sented to us in natural and artificial cuttings. The first I select, not only as an example of the occurrence of beds underneath the till, but also because it serves to show the general position occupied by the till in the valleys of the Southern Uplands.

Fig. 19 represents the section as seen in the left bank fronting the stream ; Fig. 20 represents the same deposit as it would appear in a transverse section ; thickness of deposits 10 to 15 ft.

Fig. 20.—Section across Douglas Burn, Peeblesshire.

A fine example of similar phenomena was pointed out to me by my colleague, Mr. B. N. Peach, in the north bank of the river Tweed, near Melrose. The annexed Fig. 21 will convey a general idea of the appearance of the beds. The rocks *r* were smoothed as if water-worn below the coarse shingle and gravel *g*, and from the arrangement of the gravel there could be no doubt of its fluviatile origin.

It frequently happens, however, as I have remarked above, that the stream-sections do not go down quite to the rock.

In such cases, although we may sometimes surmise what the underlying drifts are, yet we never can be at all certain about the matter—so inconstant are they, so liable to change. In

Fig. 21.—Till, *t*, on river-gravel and sand, *g*, Tweed, Melrose (thickness, 30 to 40 ft.)

the sections that follow it will be observed that the subjacent rock is not seen, and therefore we cannot say whether the aqueous deposits that underlie the till form the bottom beds of the drift or not.

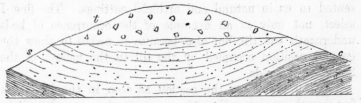

Fig. 22.—Till, *t*, on stratified deposits, *s c*, Glen Water, Ayrshire (thickness, about 30 ft.)

In this section (Fig. 22), a bed of strong tough till rests upon a fine yellowish white sand *s*, containing thin lines or laminæ of brownish clay. Underneath the sand comes fine clay *c*, arranged in leaves, with partings of sand. It is

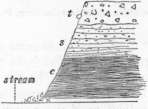

Fig. 23.—Till, *t*, resting on sand, *s*, and clay, *c*, Garpal Water, Ayrshire.

worth noting also that a few well-scratched stones are scattered sparsely through the beds last mentioned.

In the sections now given it will be observed that the till

rests upon a plain or level surface of sand, gravel, or clay, as the case may be. The junction-line, however, is not always or even often so regular. In Fig. 24 the till is represented as cutting down into beds of sand and gravel in a most irregular way—the lines of bedding in these deposits ending abruptly against the till. A still better example of

Fig. 24.—Till, *t*, cutting into stratified deposits, *g*, river Clyde, near Covington.

the same appearance was exposed during the progress of the excavations for the Peebles Railway at Neidpath Tunnel. Here a mass of tough till, with the usual scratched stones *t*, overlies a series of horizontal beds of clay, sand, and gravel, which terminate quite suddenly against the till. The clays were of that kind which is termed "gutta-percha,"

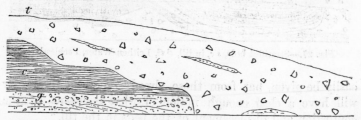

Fig. 25.—Till, *t*, cutting down into stratified deposits, *c g*, Neidpath, Peebles: thickness of drift, 40 to 50 ft.

exceedingly fine, and arranged in extremely regular layers or laminæ, underneath which were earthy gravel and sand.

Only one bed of till is shown in the above sketch-sections, but underneath the aqueous beds represented in Fig. 25 I have reason to believe that another deposit of till occurs. In the next illustration (Fig. 26) two beds of till are apparent. The intercalated beds here consist of sand and clay. They are capped by till, t^2, somewhat sandy, but quite unstratified and full of striated stones; a more tenacious mass of till, t^1, underlies the intercalated beds, which are standing nearly on end, and form a most irregular junction with the till upon and against which they rest.

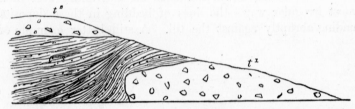

Fig. 26.—Stratified beds, *c s*, intercalated with till, t^1 t^2, Glen Water, Ayrshire (25 to 30 ft.)

Another example (Fig. 27) of somewhat similar phenomena I take from the eastern side of the country. In both these sections the crumpling up of the beds below the upper deposit of till is very marked. Other examples might

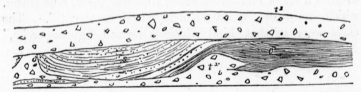

Fig. 27.—Stratified beds, *s c*, in till, t^1 t^2, Leithen Water, Peeblesshire.

easily be given, but from those already produced the reader will have a clear enough notion of what is meant by the contortion and displacement of the beds in the till.*

The sections to which I shall now refer are most interesting, inasmuch as they have yielded organic remains. Some years ago my brother described a section of till seen in the Slitrig Water, near Hawick. Professor Young and myself saw the section at the same time, which is given by my brother as follows :—

> Vegetable soil.
> Boulder clay, 30 to 40 ft.

---

* For a further account of beds subjacent to or intercalated among till, the reader who is interested in the matter may refer to my brother's paper on the "Glacial Drift of Scotland" (*Trans. Geol. Soc. Glas.*, vol. i. part. ii.), in which he will find references to other papers descriptive of the same phenomena.

Stratified beds. { Yellowish gravelly sand.
Peaty silt and clay.
Fine ferruginous sand.
Coarse shingle, 2 to 3 ft.
Coarse stiff boulder-clay, 15 to 20 ft.

It may aid the reader's conception of this succession if I give here a diagrammatic section across the deposits, which

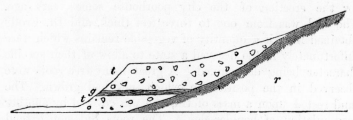

Fig. 28.—Fossiliferous beds in till, Slitrig Water, near Hawick. *t*, till; *g*, stratified deposits; *r*, rock.

will show at the same time the position of the intercalated beds, and the mode in which the till occurs in the valley. "The cliff at this locality" (I quote from my brother's paper) "is at least forty or fifty feet high, and consists of a stiff bluish clay stuck full of boulders. The bed of stones or shingle is well seen, even at a little distance, running as a horizontal band along the face of the cliff at a height of some fifteen or twenty feet above the level of the stream. On closer examination this zone proved to consist not merely of water-rolled shingle : over the lower stratum of rounded stones lay a few inches of well-stratified sand, silt, and clay, some of the layers being black and peaty, with enclosed vegetable fibres in a crumbling state." "So far as it was possible to ascertain the nature of the vegetable remains in the peaty layer, they appeared to be the rootlets of a kind of heath."

On the banks of the Carmichael Water, Lanarkshire, according to the same observer,* beds of sand, clay, silt, and gravel, with a thin peaty layer, and fragments of mouldering wood, rest in a hollow of the till, and are covered up by another mass of exactly the same kind of deposit.

Again, he describes certain contorted beds of tough gutta-

* *Trans. Geol. Soc. Glas.*, vol. i. part ii. I have seen the sections described.

percha clay and finely stratified sands as occurring in the till at Chapelhall, near Airdrie. These deposits varied in thickness up to twenty or thirty feet, and in them layers of peat and decaying twigs and branches have been detected. They were clearly overlaid and underlaid by tough stony till.

At Craiglockhart Hill, about a mile south of Edinburgh, an intercalated bed of sand was exposed during the operations for the erection of the city poorhouse some years ago. The bed was from one to three feet thick, and Dr. Croll[*] obtained from it a quantity of vegetable remains which were unfortunately in too decayed a state to allow of their specific character being determined. A great many tree roots were observed in the position in which they had grown. The sand rested upon a mass of till, and was covered by another accumulation of boulder-clay. The roots did not extend upwards into the overlying till, the stones and boulders of which rested directly upon the upper ends of the roots, which were abruptly truncated.

Mr. John Henderson has described the occurrence of a bed of peat, with associated deposits of sand and gravel, that lay between two masses of till at Redhall Quarry, near Edinburgh.[†]

A bed of clay resting upon, and covered by till, was observed by Mr. R. Craig in a limestone quarry at Overtown, near Beith, Ayrshire. The clay was full of roots and stems of the common hazel, which had evidently grown *in situ* long before the upper till was laid down. Hazel nuts were plentiful in the clay, which occupied a basin-shaped hollow in the surface of the lower till, about 130 yards long, by 30 yards broad.[‡]

At Hillhead, some distance from Overtown, the same observer noticed a similar intercalated deposit of clay full of remains of hazel. The overlying till contained lumps of the freshwater clay with its characteristic fragments of hazel. From the same bed of boulder-clay, Mr. D. Robertson obtained a freshwater ostracode.[§]

---

[*] *Climate and Time,* p. 245.   [†] *Trans. Geol. Soc. Edin.,* vol. ii. p. 391.
[‡] *Trans. Geol. Soc. Glas.,* vol. iv. p. 145.
[§] *Op. et loc. cit.* At Orbiston (Lanarkshire) I have noticed a similar freshwater clay with hazel-nuts. It rested in hollows of the till, and although at the time of my visit I did not see the clay overlapped by till, yet I felt sure from its position that it could not be of postglacial age.

Mr. Craig likewise notes the occurrence of two beds of till at Roughwood Quarry, Beith. The upper bed rests directly upon the lower, save at one place where "a thin bed of water-rolled shale lay in the line of division, and in the bottom of the upper bed a species of moss was found."

The aqueous beds intercalated with the till not infrequently appear to lie in basins or saucer-shaped hollows or depressions. A good example of this was recently exposed near Neilston, in the cutting of the railway from Crofthead to Kilmarnock.* This railway traverses the valley of the Cowdon Burn, and during the progress of the excavations, which were very extensive, some exceedingly interesting phenomena came to light. The section (Fig. 29) shows the face of the cutting as seen in 1868 ; since that date, however, the navvies have not improved it for geological purposes. In the woodcut *t* represents the till, of which there are two beds, one at the top and the other at the bottom of the section. Both beds are good typical examples of till, being quite unstratified, and crammed with angular, scratched, and polished stones. The intercalated beds *c* consist of silt, clay, mud, sand, and fine gravel, all well-bedded, and here and there thin lines and layers of peaty matter occur. The underlying rocks *r* are beautifully smoothed and striated. A section (Fig. 30) drawn at right angles to the preceding one, that is across the line of railway, will show the general relation of these drifts to the valley in which they lie. The intercalated beds are remarkable for having yielded an imperfect skull of the great extinct ox (*Bos primigenius*), and remains of the Irish elk or deer, and the horse, together with layers of peaty matter. From these, Mr. J. Mahony obtained many relics of what must have been a varied fauna and flora. Besides a number of species of Desmids and Diatoms, the pond-weed and eleven species of mosses occurred and were abundantly developed. Many plant-seeds and fragments of wood, chiefly birch and hazel, were also detected. Among animal remains were found traces of infusorial life, spiculæ, and a fragment of a fresh-water sponge,

---

* See papers by the author *Geol. Mag.*, vol. v. p. 393, and vol. vi. p. 73. Mr. Mahony subsequently examined the peaty layers, and has described the organic remains he met with in an interesting paper in the same Magazine. See vol. vi. p. 390.

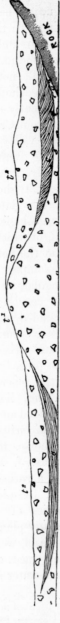

Fig. 29.—Fossiliferous deposits, c, in till, t, Cowdon Burn Railway Cutting, Neilston, Renfrewshire.

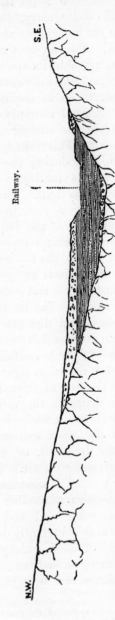

Fig. 30.—Section across the valley of Cowdon Burn, showing fossiliferous deposits resting upon till, and covered by another overlying mass of till.

jaws of a leech, plentiful remains of entomostracans, belonging, probably, to a species of Daphnia, relics of probably
three species of beetles, and the eggs of an insect—one of
the Ephemeridæ. In the clay under the peat containing
these fossils, Mr. D. Robertson obtained several species of
ostracodes. The stratified deposits in which all these organic
remains occur are precisely similar to many of those which I
have already briefly referred to.

In a gravel and sand-pit near Carham, on the Tweed, I
obtained numerous small bones, which Professor Huxley subsequently determined to be those of frogs and water-rats.
They lay in a bed of yellow sand and fine gravel, in which a
few stones occurred sporadically here and there. Underneath
was an irregular mass of rather sandy and loose boulder-clay,
full of the usual blunted and glaciated stones. Above the
sand-bed came a thickness of twenty or twenty-five feet of a
rude pell-mell assemblage of glaciated and rounded stones,
with here and there some unpolished angular fragments and
large blocks of a siliceous limestone which occurs in place
a little farther up the valley. Occasional lenticular patches
of fine sand and gravel occurred in the mass, which was faintly
stratified in part, the lines of deposition pointing in a direction down the valley. This latter deposit has no connection
with the gravels of the present river, the modern river valley
having been excavated through the drifts, of which the one
I refer to forms a part. It seems to have been laid down
during the retreat of the final ice-sheet as a coarse morainic
flood-gravel ; and, consequently, the frogs and water-rats of
the underlying sand-bed must belong to the glacial period.

In the mass of the till itself, fossils sometimes, but very
rarely, occur. Tusks of the mammoth, reindeer antlers, and
fragments of oak and other trees have, from time to time,
been discovered in this position. They almost invariably
afford marks of having been subjected to the same action as
the stones and boulders by which they are surrounded ; that
is to say, they are rubbed, ground, striated and smoothed.
Sea-shells, broken, crushed, and striated, also occur under
similar circumstances in certain deposits of till which fall to
be described further on.

Before leaving the non-marine intercalated beds of the till,

K

it is necessary to call attention to another remarkable appearance sometimes presented by the till. The appearance to which I refer is what has been termed "a striated pavement," that is, a horizontal surface or level of till "where all the prominent boulders and stones have not only their original and independent striæ, but where they have subsequently suffered a new striation which is parallel and persistent across them all."* Such pavements, as one would naturally expect, are more frequently exposed along a seacoast or in a horizontal section than they are in the interior of the country. Nevertheless, some well-authenticated instances of the latter have been observed, where the "pavements" were only exposed upon the removal of overlying till.

* A. Geikie's "Glacial Drift of Scotland," *Trans. Geol. Soc. Glas.*, vol. i. part 2. In this memoir several pavements are described, and references given to similar descriptions by other observers.

CHAPTER XII.

BEDS SUBJACENT TO AND INTERCALATED WITH THE SCOTTISH TILL—*Continued.*

Beds below and in the till indicate pauses in the formation of that deposit.—How the aqueous beds have been preserved.—Their crumpled and denuded appearance.—Their distribution.—Character of the valleys in which they occur.—The present stream-courses, partly of preglacial, interglacial, and postglacial age.—Old course of the River Avon, Lanarkshire.—Preglacial courses of the Calder Water and Tillon Burn.—Buried river-channel between Kilsyth and Grangemouth.

WE may now proceed to the explanation of the facts adduced in the last chapter. The reader has already seen that the till itself is a truly glacial deposit, due to the grinding action over the surface of the country of immense masses of glacier-ice. But no one will doubt that its intercalated and subjacent beds of silt, sand, and gravel have had a very different origin. They occur in such layers as could only have been spread out by the action of running water. Evidently, then, these strata are a very different kind of deposit from the till that encloses them, and it is equally self-evident that at the period of their formation the production of till must for a time have ceased, at least in those particular places where the stratified beds occur. And seeing that these intercalated beds are not confined to any one district, but are found in every part of the country where they have been searched for, it is reasonable to conclude that there were times when the great ice-fields that covered the country receded so far at least as to uncover the lowland tracts and valleys, and permit the accumulation in those regions of clay, sand, and gravel. Nor does it seem less reasonable also to conclude that after such a recession the ice again advanced and covered up the aqueous strata with thick deposits of stony clay. But here a difficulty will occur to the reader which it may be well to notice. How, it may be asked, could soft beds of sand, silt, and gravel escape being ploughed out by the ice-streams which are said to have deposited the overlying stony clay?

It has already been pointed out that the existence of the till itself is a difficulty of the same kind; and I have endeavoured to show that this deposit bore the same relation to the ice-sheet that river-detritus does to a river. There can be no doubt that in many places over which the ice-sheet passed till could not possibly accumulate, just as in the bed of a stream there are bare rocky slopes exposed to the full sweep of the water where detritus is not permitted to gather. It is no less certain that after till had been piled up in some places it was again and again ploughed out, and redistributed below the ice-sheet. Now we find that the intercalated beds of sand and gravel give unequivocal proof of having been subjected to great pressure. They are twisted, bent, crumpled, and confused, often in the wildest manner.* Layers of clay, sand, and gravel, which were probably deposited in a nearly horizontal plane, are puckered into folds and sharply curved into vertical positions. I have seen whole beds of sand and clay which had all the appearance of having been pushed forward bodily for some distance, the bedding assuming the most fantastic appearance† (see Figs. 22, 24, 25, 26, 27).

But the intercalated beds have not been crumpled only; they are everywhere cut though by the overlying till, and large portions have been carried away. Indeed, when we compare the bulk of these beds to that of the till, we must at once allow that they form but a small fraction of the drift deposits. Owing to the erosive power of the old glaciers, comparatively little of the intercalated sand, &c., has been spared; but enough is left to assure us of the former impor-

---

* In certain regions, however, particularly as we approach the limits reached by the old ice-sheets, the stratified beds lying in and below the till or boulder-clay are often comparatively undisturbed over considerable areas. This is specially the case in England and North America, as will be pointed out in the sequel. The remarks in the present chapter have special reference to the preservation of intercalated deposits in a highly glaciated region.

† For a graphic account of contorted intercalated beds, the reader may refer to my brother's description of the Chapelhall deposits (mentioned *ante*, p. 125). He tells us that so great had been the pressure of the ice that the till appeared as if it had been injected between and among the layers of clay and sand. *Trans. Geol. Soc. Glas*, vol. i. part 2.

tance of the intercalated beds. The geological value of a deposit has not usually been measured by its bulk.

In exposed positions, such as hill-tops and hill-slopes, the till never contains intercalated beds ; nor do these occur save as interrupted and fragmentary patches, in places that appear to have been open to the full sweep of the ice-currents. It is usually in positions sheltered in great measure from the pressure and grinding of the glaciers that the stratified beds of the till have been best preserved. But what, it may be asked, is meant by a position sheltered from the grind of the ice ? Do not these sand and gravel beds occur exclusively in the valleys, and is it not just in such positions where the grinding action of the old glaciers was most powerful ? If the ice-sheet covered the whole country, in what possible position could the sand and gravel beds be comparatively secure ? Let me try to make this plain. In Scotland, as in other countries, the large rivers flow in broad open valleys, and are fed by lateral tributaries which issue from narrower and more confined valleys and ravines. The river Clyde, for example, which flows towards the north-west in a valley that gradually expands to a broad open strath, as it approaches its estuary, is joined from north and south by numerous streams, many of which run in deep narrow ravines, until they are just on the point of mingling their waters with the river. This appearance is very well seen in the neighbour hood of Hamilton. The Avon there winds through a deep cool ravine for several miles before it enters the Clyde, and the same is the case with the little tributaries of the Avon itself. The Calder from the north-east also makes its way towards the Clyde in a romantic glen, whose precipitous walls, like those of the Avon, are hung with greenery. Now during the glacial period, the ice-sheet, which followed the lines of the principal valleys, must frequently have crossed the lateral and subsidiary valleys nearly at right angles. In the main valleys the glacier would exert its full influence, but, as my brother has pointed out, it would not be able to do so in the narrow lateral valleys and ravines ; the ice and till would merely topple into the glens referred to, and gradually choke them up, and the main mass of the glacier would then pass on over the whole. Here the analogy of running water again will help us. In a stream-course we see how the detritus accumulates in deep holes and pools, at the bottom of which the water is often well-nigh still, while a current is sweeping across at the surface.

In such narrow glens, then, any silt, sand, or gravel that had gathered during the temporary absence of the ice-sheet would not be so likely to be ploughed out when the ice returned, as the similar materials which had accumulated in those broader and more open valleys where the ice would have full freedom to move and exert its erosive power.

But it may be objected that it is precisely in the narrower ravines where at the present day we meet with no drift whatever, where in fact the streams flow between bare walls of rock; while, on the contrary, the broader and more open valleys show considerable depths of sand, silt, gravel, and stony clay. To this objection it may be answered that the narrow ravines in which so many of our streams flow have been formed almost without exception since the close of the glacial epoch. The ravines are in most cases new cuts excavated by the streams after the confluent glaciers had finally vanished.

How this has happened will readily appear when we remember that the work performed by the old glaciers was twofold. In many cases the massive ice-streams deepened the valleys that already existed—in certain regions digging out great hollows, to the nature and origin of which reference will be made in a subsequent chapter. But after having deepened valleys and widened glens, they very frequently buried these again more or less completely under vast piles of clay, sand, and boulders. Some valleys indeed they completely obliterated, so that when the ice finally melted away, and left the land once more exposed to the light of day, the streams and rivers could no longer flow in their old courses, but were compelled to form for themselves new channels.

It is quite true that, speaking generally, the present drainage-system is very much the same as that which obtained before the advent of the glacial epoch; nevertheless the course followed by each river and stream seldom agrees precisely with that along which the waters made their way in preglacial times. Sometimes the streams flow throughout nearly their entire length in new channels which have been cut in rock since glacial times, the older courses being still choked up and concealed under the clay and stones that were shot into them by the old glaciers. More frequently, however, the present river-courses are partly new, partly old. When, after the ice had disappeared, the water again began to make its way down the slopes of the land to the sea, it is self-evident that the direction of the streams would be determined by the configuration of the ground. But this, as we have seen, would not exactly agree with that of preglacial times. Many of the valleys had been levelled up, and in not a few cases long hills and mounds of drift appeared where deep dells had formerly existed. The chief features of the country, however, remained; the broad valleys and straths, although clothed with drift deposits, yet again received the tribute of the lateral streams, and formed the highways of the principal rivers. But the lateral feeders of these rivers, following the new slopes of the ground, have not always been directed into their old channels. Sometimes, indeed, they wander for miles away from these, and join the main stream either far above or far below where they formerly debouched. Even when, after cutting down through the drift deposits, they have happened to regain their old channels, they usually leave these again and again as they journey on, plunging ever and anon into deep rocky gorges, which, as I have said, have been chiselled out by them since the close of the glacial epoch.

To the wanderer along the course of some of the lowland streams nothing can be more striking than the sudden and complete change of scenery that ensues upon the passage of a stream from its new into its old channel. In the former the water frets and fumes between lofty walls of rock, which, seen from below, appear to rise almost vertically from the river's bed. In such a deep narrow gorge the stream may continue to flow for miles, when of a sudden the precipitous cliffs abruptly terminate, and the water then escapes into a broad vale with long sloping banks of stony clay, sand, and gravel. After winding about in this open glade for, it may be, several miles, the stream not infrequently leaves again as suddenly as it entered, and dashes once more into another dell, whose steep walls of rock shoot up and overhang the water as before. The broader and more open portions of the valley, where the sloping banks are formed of drift débris, is of course that part of the old preglacial channel which the present stream has re-excavated ; while, as already indicated, the narrow and rocky gorges are entirely new cuts made by the stream during the ages that have elapsed since the glacial epoch.

In many cases the present streams seldom continue in their old channels for any distance. We often find them cutting across these nearly at right angles, and in this way fine sections of the old buried river-channels with their contents frequently appear in the rocky glens of the Lowlands, to

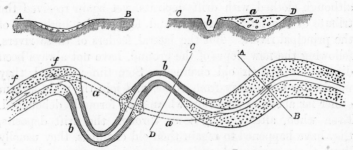

Fig. 31.—Diagram to show preglacial and postglacial river-course. *a a*, buried course ; *b b*, postglacial channel ; *f f*, and dotted parts show re-excavated channel. Sections above indicate character of valley along the lines *A B* and *C D*.

some of which I shall refer presently. A glance at the woodcut (Fig. 31), which is a diagrammatic ground-plan intended to illustrate the phenomena just described, will show how it comes to pass that a postglacial channel may often cut a preglacial course, and yet the present stream coincide in direction with that of preglacial times. The buried course is represented at *a a*, and the new channel at *b b*; the thin line on either side indicating the tops of the cliffs *b b*, and sloping banks *f f*. From *f* to *f* it will be observed that the present channel coincides exactly with the old course, while at × × the latter is cut across nearly at right angles by the former.

In most cases the preglacial channels prove to be wider and sometimes deeper than the new cuts; consequently when a stream, after flowing for some distance in a postglacial course, suddenly enters a preglacial channel, the softer character of the materials it has to excavate enables it to clear out a wider hollow than it has carved in the solid rock of its postglacial course. A section across the valley at *A B*, compared with one drawn from *C* to *D*, shows the relative appearance of the old and new cuts. It will be noticed that not only are the old channels wider and sometimes deeper than the new—facts which indicate, of course, a greater age—but also that their sides are less precipitous. This latter appearance points to the long-continued action of frost, which, by splitting up and detaching the rocks upon a cliff, has a tendency to reduce all such steep river-walls to sloping banks; but the gently-inclined slopes of many preglacial river-courses doubtless owe much of their character to the grinding action of the glaciers during the Ice Age. Not a few old river-courses, however, can be shown to be as steep and precipitous as any which have been formed since glacial times.

I do not believe it was necessary, however, for the preservation of interglacial deposits that they should always have occupied a hollow or depression sheltered from the full sweep of the ice-flow. The great thickness attained by the till in broad open lowland districts shows that over such areas there was a tendency for the till to accumulate, probably owing to a diminished rate of ice-flow. We see analogous phenomena in the case of a river, which, as the fall of the ground lessens, spreads itself out, becomes sluggish, and begins to deposit sediment in its course. Now, wherever the flow of the ice-sheet slackened there would necessarily be less erosive action, and therefore a greater chance of preglacial and interglacial land-surfaces being preserved. For the same reason we ought to find, as we approach the limits reached by the old confluent glaciers, that preglacial and interglacial deposits have suffered less erosion. When we come to consider the English and American drift accumulations we shall meet with some striking illustrations of the phenomena in question.[*]

To the appearance presented by the deposits that fill up the

---

[*] See further on this subject, remarks on the preservation of the interglacial "Forest-bed" of the North-Western States of America, chap. xxxv.

buried river-channels, I must now direct attention. At page
119 I have given the details of a boring made near Larkhall,
for the purpose of testing the position of the underlying coal-
seams.   This boring and another near the same place pierce
a great thickness of detrital materials which I have ascertained
occupy a former course of the Avon—the present river flowing for a considerable distance in an entirely new channel
excavated since the glacial epoch.   The following figure gives
a diagrammatic view of the choked-up channel as it has been
ascertained by borings.   A section of the old channel, where
it is cut by the Avon, is seen on the banks of the river near
Fairholm House, Larkhall; but owing to the incoherent
nature of the silt and sand, these beds have slid forwards with
the overlying clays and thrown everything into confusion. It
will be remembered that the borings prove the existence of

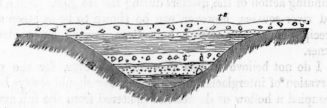

Fig. 32.—Diagrammatic section across preglacial course of the River Avon,
Larkhall, Lanarkshire. t, lower till; t^2, upper till.

two masses of till, with intervening and underlying beds of
silt, mud, sand, and gravel.   The lower of these two deposits
of till indicates the prolonged action of glacier-ice ; yet the
beds below retain a considerable thickness, notwithstanding
their incoherent character.   At this particular place, however, the ice-sheet crossed the gorge in which they lie at an
angle, and hence they must needs have escaped the powerful
erosion to which they would have been subjected had the
path of the ice coincided with the trend of the ravine.   The
presence of 40 ft. of silt, sand, and gravel above the till
indicates a period of lessened cold, when the ice-sheet disappeared from this region and permitted the formation of
such deposits.   But after a time it would appear that the
ice-sheet again overspread the country, doubtless sweeping
out the silt, sand, and gravel from exposed positions, but

sparing them in the narrow glens and gullies that intersected its path.

In the Scottish coal-fields such old stream-courses* as I now describe are of common occurrence, and are locally known to the miners as "clay dykes" and "sand dykes," according to the prevailing character of the material that fills them. The coal is often worked quite close to the side of the buried ravine ; after which, if the nature of the dyke will allow it, a mine is driven through the clay and sand, until the opposite face of the old glen is reached and the coal-seam found again. Sometimes, however, the dyke is charged with soft mud and running sand, and then it becomes impossible to mine, and a new pit must be sunk on the further side of the channel to get out the coal. Many accidents have happened from the breaking in of sand and mud into the pit-workings, when coal has been taken out too close to the dyke.

A very good example of such a dyke, or buried stream-course, was exposed in the cutting made for the railway between Edinburgh and Holytown, quite close to the little village of Cleland, Lanarkshire. The cutting intersected the channel at right angles to its course, and thus a beautiful section of the old ravine, and the materials that choke it up, was obtained.† But the face of the cutting is now so "dressed," that the precise succession of the drift-beds cannot be readily deciphered. There cannot be a doubt, however, that a thick mass of till occupies the highest position, with beds of gravel and sand coming in below. The same old ravine is intersected by the Calder Water a little to the west of Wishaw House, where, however, the trees and brushwood somewhat obscure it.

It is remarkable that in the same neighbourhood there is another buried stream-course, which runs for a short distance parallel to the last-mentioned one, and is in like manner cut

* For notices of some of these see Mr. Milne Home's *Memoir on the Mid-Lothian Coal-Field ;* A. Geikie " On the Glacial Drift of Scotland," *Trans. Geol. Soc. Glas. ;* vol. i. pt. 2; *Quart. Jour. Geol. Soc.,* vol. v. p. 20; *Mem. Geol. Surv.* (34 *Scotland*), p. 50; also 23 *Scotland*, p. 42; *Geological Magazine*, vol. ii. p. 38. There are many "dry valleys" in Scotland which evidently date back to pre-glacial times: they usually contain drift of some kind, but sometimes they do not. See a notice of some of these in *Mem. Geol. Surv.* (33 *Scotland*), p. 63.

† See a paper by Mr. R. Dick, *Trans. Geol. Soc. Edin.,* vol. i. p. 345; Mr. Dick seems to have thought that this buried channel and the one referred to in the next paragraph were one and the same.

across by the present course of the Calder. It is well exposed on the banks of this stream a little below Coltness bridge, upon the side of the road leading from Wishaw. Both buried channels are filled with similar materials, chiefly sand with a little gravel — the whole being covered with till. The coal-workings, which are very extensive in the district, enabled me, while carrying on the Geological Survey, to trace out all the windings of these remarkable sand-troughs; and by connecting the information thus obtained with what I was able to gather from natural sections, it became evident that considerable changes had taken place in the drainage-system of the neighbourhood since glacial times. The Tillon Burn, which is now a tributary of the Calder, was formerly an independent stream; while the Calder Water has forsaken its old channel, and at present flows for some distance in an entirely new course, after which it breaks into and continues along the preglacial or interglacial course of the Tillon Burn.*

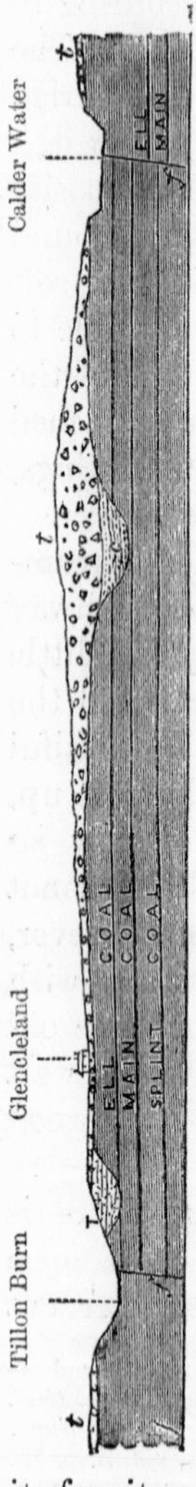

I shall only refer to another example of preglacial and interglacial water-courses.† This buried course has been traced from Kilsyth to Grangemouth, on the Forth, where it enters that estuary at the great depth of 260 ft. below the present sea-level. No trace or indication of the buried river-channel shows at the surface of the ground, and its existence would probably never have been discovered had it not been for the numerous borings and pits which have pierced it, for it cuts right through the coal-strata of that district.

Fig. 33.—Section across Carboniferous strata, showing preglacial stream-courses (scale 6 inches to 1 mile; horizontal and vertical scale the same); *t* till; *e* preglacial course of Calder Water; T preglacial course of Tillon Burn; *f* dislocations, or faults, in coal-bearing strata.

* See Geol. Survey Map of Scotland, Sheet 23.

† This "channel" is described by Dr. Croll in *Trans. Geol. Soc. Edin.*, vol. i. p. 330. See *postea*, p. 151, *footnote*.

The nature of the deposits that fill up the old river-ravine is shown in the following section : *

BORING NEAR TOWNCROFT FARM, GRANGEMOUTH.

		Ft.
Upper Drift.	Surface sand	6
	Blue mud	3
	Shell bed	1
	Gravel	2
	Blue mud	8
	Gravel	3
	Blue muddy sand	15
	Red clay	49
Lower Drift.	Blue till and stones	20
	Sand	20
	Hard blue till and stones	24
	Sand	2
	Hard blue till and stones	40
	Sand	7
	Hard blue till	24
		234

We shall return to a consideration of these old preglacial river-courses when we come to treat of the superficial deposits of England ; for there are certain inferences to be drawn from them which the reader will better appreciate after he has had an opportunity of examining the evidence furnished by the English drifts. At present our chief study is to ascertain if we can the origin of the deposits which choke up the old channels, but we shall have something more to say about the channels themselves when we are discussing the question of the preglacial condition of Britain.

* See J. Bennie's " Surface Geology of the District Around Glasgow," *Trans. Geol. Soc. Glas.*, vol. iii. part i.

CHAPTER XIII.

BEDS SUBJACENT TO AND INTERCALATED WITH THE SCOTTISH TILL—*Continued*.

Stratified deposits passed through in borings.—Probably in most cases of fresh-water origin.—Old lake at Neidpath, Peebles.—Lakes of interglacial periods.—Borings near New Kilpatrick.—Preglacial valley of the river Kelvin.—Origin of the deposits occupying that buried river-course.—Valley between Johnstone and Dalry.—Flat lands between Kilpatrick Hills and Paisley.—Condition of the country in preglacial times.—Leven Valley glacier.—Ancient glacial lake.—Succession of events during recurrent cold and warm periods.

IT will be observed that while the hollows* in which these deposits occur have been described as old river-courses, yet nothing has been said as to the origin of the deposits themselves. Of the nature of the overlying till which is seen at the surface in some of the examples cited, there can be no doubt; but it may be objected that since we do not always see the intercalated and subjacent stony clays, we cannot be sure as to their character. Might not they be something else than glacial deposits? To this it may be answered that we know of no stony clay in Scotland which is not of glacial origin. If the succession of strata disclosed by artificial borings were altogether peculiar and abnormal, we might have good reason for disregarding them; at all events, we could hardly be justified in drawing conclusions from them. But such successions are neither peculiar nor abnormal; on the contrary, similar sections occur at the surface which

---

* Similar preglacial river-courses are known to occur in other countries. An excellent example has been traced out in the underground workings of the Durham coal-fields, by Messrs. Nicholas Wood and E. F. Boyd (*British Association Reports* for 1863, p. 89; *Geologist*, 1863, p. 384). The buried river-courses of North America are also familiar instances. Professor Hitchcock has described these as "antediluvian river-beds;" that is to say, beds of rivers that existed before the glacial period in North America. Logs and fragments of wood are often got at great depths in the buried gorges ("Illustrations of Surface Geology," &c., *Smithsonian Contributions*). Professor Newberry and others have more recently given interesting accounts of the like phenomena. See *Geol. Surv. of Ohio*, vol. ii. chap. xxx.

answer precisely in character to the accumulations passed through by the boring-rods. In the open-air sections the intercalated stony clays are true till, and the stony clays in the deep bore-holes must be till, or at all events, deposits having a glacial origin.

With regard to the aqueous strata which are associated with the stony clays, the almost total absence of fossils makes it in many cases difficult to decide whether they are of fresh-water or marine origin. In some cases, at low levels, it is not unlikely that they are partly one, partly the other. It must be admitted, however, that the absence of organic remains tells more against a marine than a fresh-water origin for the mud, sand, and silt that fill up the buried channels and hollows. It is unfortunate that a greater number of these should not have been exposed to the light of day ; nevertheless, enough perhaps are actually exhibited to enable us to form a correct idea of those whose existence is only revealed to us by borings and pit-workings. The opinion to which I incline is that the aqueous beds now filling up the old hollows and depressions of the land are in large measure of fresh-water origin (not by any means exclusively so) ; but if this be so, it seems certain that they cannot all have been laid down in the old ravines and valleys under conditions like those now obtaining in similar water-courses and depressions. No geologist would be inclined to admit that the great depths of fine sand, silt, and mud, which occupy the buried hollows, could possibly have been deposited by such streams as now flow in like places.

In many cases the deep aqueous drifts, as exposed in open section, have more of a lacustrine character than anything else. This was well seen in the section at Neidpath Tunnel, briefly described on page 123. The stratified beds in that locality appear to have been once very extensive—traces of the same deposits having been found in and below the till for some distance up the valley of the Tweed. At Neidpath there was a depth of from 40 to 50 ft. exposed, and the bottom was not seen. The beds partook of fluviatile and lacustrine characters (chiefly the latter), and appear to have been deposited in a lake-like expansion of the Tweed, at a time when that river flowed, not by its present course, but round by the back of Cademuir Hill. The accompanying sketch-map (Plate V.) will serve to render this intelligible.

It will be seen that from Cademuir Farm to Bonnington there extends a broad flat hollow, the bottom of which at its highest level is only some 100 ft. or so above the bed of the Tweed at Neidpath. Were the narrow glen at this latter place to be filled up, the Tweed would be dammed back, a lake would be formed, and thereafter both the Tweed and its affluent, the Manor Water, would flow round by the Cademuir hollow. That such actually was the course of one or both these streams at a comparatively recent geological date is proved by the fact that the Cademuir hollow is paved with river gravel, which could have come from no other source.

An examination of the present and the former course of the Tweed and the surrounding drift phenomena led me to conclude that the "gutta-percha clays" of the Neidpath section were deposited at a time anterior to the cutting-out of the Neidpath glen by the river; that, in short, the Tweed during preglacial and interglacial periods flowed by the Cademuir hollow; and that Neidpath glen has been to some extent at least hollowed out since the final disappearance of the ice-sheets. The alterations of surface brought about by the massive glacier that cut through the gutta-percha clays and deposited the tumultuous mass of till above them, and the modifications of level induced by denudation in later glacial times, eventually compelled the Tweed to leave its old course and take the more direct route by Neidpath.

The occurrence of preglacial and interglacial lacustrine beds in the river-valleys is only what one might have reasonably anticipated. Whenever the ice-sheets retired an irregular surface of glacial drift would be exposed, in the hollows and depressions of which lakes and pools would gather. Nay, in some cases the mouths of small lateral valleys would be closed up with drift, and thus, streams being dammed back, sheets of water would be formed in which fine sediments would accumulate. In like manner the retiring glaciers themselves would not infrequently become barriers to the drainage of small lateral valleys, and in this way produce

PLATE V

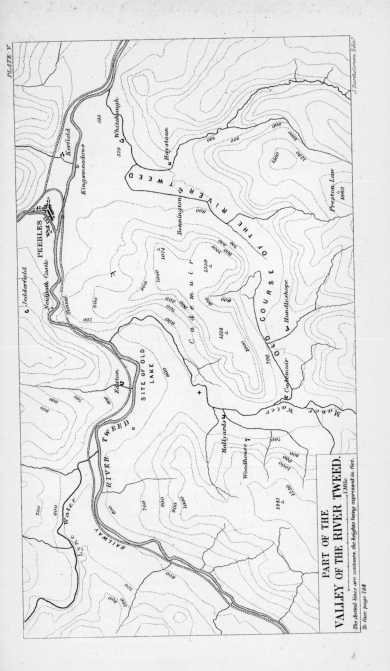

PART OF THE
VALLEY OF THE RIVER TWEED.
1 Mile

The dotted lines are contours, the heights being expressed in Feet.

To face page 144

J. Bartholomew, Edin.

true glacial lakes. Hence we need not be surprised at the frequent appearance of old lacustrine beds in the valleys. It would be much more surprising if they did not occur.

It is well known that in the valley of the Kelvin, near New Kilpatrick, a number of borings prove the existence in that district of a very great depth of superficial deposits. Two examples* of these borings may be given; they are as follows :—

	Ft.	Ins.
Sandy clay	5	0
Brown clay and stones	17	0
Mud	15	0
Sandy mud	31	0
Sand and gravel	28	0
Sandy clay and gravel	17	0
Sand	5	0
Mud	6	0
Sand	14	0
Gravel	30	0
Brown sandy clay and stones	30	0
Hard red gravel	4	6
Light mud and sand	1	8
Light clay and stones	6	6
Light clay and whin block	26	0
Fine sandy mud	36	0
Brown clay, gravel and stones	14	4
Dark clay and stones	68	0
	357	0

ANOTHER BORING IN THE SAME NEIGHBOURHOOD GAVE—

	Ft.	Ins.
Soil	1	6
Muddy sand and stones	4	0
Soft mud	4	6
Sand and gravel	45	0
Sandy mud and stones	20	6
Sandy gravel and mud	52	4
Brown clay and stones	25	0
Sand and gravel	6	0
Brown sandy clay and stones	12	0
Sand	2	0
Brown sandy clay and stones	4	0
Mud and sand	15	9
Sand and blue clay and stones	7	9
	200	4

Dr. Croll has suggested that these deep drifts may occupy a preglacial bed of the Kelvin. If so, then this ancient buried channel must enter the Clyde at a depth of more

* For these and other borings, see Mr. Bennie's paper, *Trans. Geol. Soc. Glas.*, vol. iii. p. 133.

than 200 ft. below the present sea-level. There is nothing abnormal in this. It has already been mentioned that an old buried river-channel enters the Forth near Grangemouth at a depth of at least 260 ft. below the sea ; from which we must infer that at some period anterior to the filling-up of that channel the land stood at least 260 ft. higher than the present datum-line. In a subsequent page I shall have occasion to point out that the great sea-lochs of the western coasts are merely submerged land-valleys. Indeed, if we could but remove the superficial deposits from the surface of the Lowlands there can be no doubt that the sea would also reach a great way into the heart of these districts, penetrating sometimes for many miles by such valleys as that of the Clyde, the Ayr, the Stinchar, the Tweed, and other rivers.

Of all these valleys that of the Clyde has yielded the greatest depth of superficial accumulations—these deposits reaching, in at least one place, the excessive thickness of 357 feet. No one can glance over the borer's sections given above without feeling assured that, whether or not the gravels, sands, and muds occupy a buried river-valley, they at least could not have accumulated underneath a river—they are either estuarine, lacustrine, or marine, or finally they may partake of a mixed character, and be partly of fresh-water and partly of marine origin. Their general resemblance to similar deposits exposed in other districts would incline me to consider them as for the most part of lacustrine origin, and an examination of the physical features of the district certainly tends to support this suggestion. As the question is an interesting one, it may be well to consider it in detail.*

Those who have travelled from Glasgow by Paisley and Johnstone into Ayrshire will remember that the railway in its course towards the latter place skirts the base of some rising ground which towards the south slopes up to form what we may call for want of a general name, the Paisley

---

* Mr. D. Bell has advanced an explanation of these intercalated beds somewhat similar to that given in the text. He speculates on the damming-up of the Clyde at Bowling, the consequent formation of a lake, and the egress of the waters by Lochwinnoch and Dalry (*Trans. Geol. Soc. Glas.*, vol. iv. p. 66). Mr. Bell's views and mine were arrived at independently ; but since his have the priority of publication, he is justly entitled to claim the "copyright" of the glacial lake described in the text.

Hills. From the base of these hills a wide stretch of flat or gently-undulating country extends northwards to the foot of the Kilpatrick Hills, and westwards until it abuts upon the lower slopes of the Kilbarchan Hills. On north, south, and west, then, this plain is encircled by a screen of hilly ground. The screen, however, is breached in two places : at Bowling by the Clyde, and at Johnstone by the Black Cart Water. From Johnstone the railway runs up the valley of this water, passing Castle Semple Loch, Barr Loch (now drained) and Kilbirnie Loch, beyond which it follows the same hollow through the hills to the low grounds south of Dalry. The surface of Kilbirnie Loch is very nearly on the same level as that of Castle Semple Loch, but there is a sluggish flow of water from the former to the latter. The head of Kilbirnie Loch, then, we may take as the watershed between the Black Cart Water and the streams that drain along the same hollow towards the south-west. But any one who examines the ground will have no difficulty in concluding that this long hollow has not been excavated by the streams that now flow in different directions along its bottom. They are quite inadequate. The whole appearance of the valley suggests strongly the idea of an old water-course that once drained along its whole extent from the north-east. That is to say that at some former period a river flowed from the valley of the Clyde across what is now the watershed of the Black Cart Water, and so on south-west into Ayrshire. This no doubt does at first sight seem an impossibility, but that it actually must have happened I shall now try to show.

Let me ask my reader to carry his mind back to the pre-glacial period—to that far distant past before ice and snow filled the valleys, and ere yet any accumulation of glacial deposits covered the surface of the country. In those days the Clyde and its affluents certainly flowed at a considerably lower level than they do now. Could we clear away all the superficial deposits that rest in the basin of the Clyde between Glasgow and the sea, we should find, not as at present the broad undulating plain that stretches from the base of the Kilpatrick Hills to the heights behind Paisley, but a deep valley dotted with rocky knolls and ridges. We should find also that at least one deep lateral valley, carrying the drainage of the Campsie and Kilpatrick Hills, entered that of the Clyde from the north-east. The bed of the preglacial Clyde at or near Bowling must lie buried at a depth of more than two hundred feet below the level of the sea. Even at Glasgow the old channel of the river is not less than eighty feet under the same datum-line.* Now when the river was flowing at these levels it need hardly be said that the land must have stood relatively higher than it does now ; at all events it is certain that our shores extended much farther out to sea.

Let us, then, conceive that while the Clyde valley is in the state I have described, glacial conditions of climate super-vene, that snow and ice begin to thicken in the mountain-valleys, and great glaciers to creep out and deploy upon the low grounds. One immense stream of ice fills up Loch Lomond (or the place where Loch Lomond was afterwards to be), and flowing onwards through the vale of the Leven, advances across the bed of the Clyde until it abuts upon the opposite slopes of the Kilbarchan Hills. This invasion results of course in damming back the Clyde, and a lake accumulates over the low grounds which are encircled by the Kilpatrick, Kilbarchan, and Paisley Hills. But as the Clyde continues to flow and the surface of the lake to rise, the water must eventually find a channel of escape. Now supposing the valley of the Black Cart Water to have existed at this time, it is evident that as the lake rose it would penetrate this valley until it reached the watershed, over which a river would pour south-westward into Ayrshire. It is highly probable, however, that the great hollow now occu-pied by Kilbirnie and Castle Semple Lochs and the Black Cart was not so strongly pronounced in preglacial times. Be this, however, as it may, it is evident that the old Clyde, swollen in summer-time by melting ice and snow, must have

---

* In a series of borings made for the Clyde Trustees at Mavisbank Quay the rock was attained at 70·48 ft., 77·60 ft., and 80·23 ft. below high water mark in three bores respectively. At Stobcross, on the opposite bank of the river, the borings, at a distance of two or three hundred feet from the water, reached the rock at a nearly similar depth from the same datum line. But when the borings were continued at the distance of a few hundred feet farther from the river, the rock-head appeared at a less depth from the surface. The superficial deposits were thus shown to thin off towards the north, but they did so in a very irregular manner. For these details I am indebted to the kindness of Mr. Deas, Mem. Inst. C.E., Engineer to the Clyde Trust.

swept through the notch or breach * in the hills with great force, and this condition of things continuing for a long period, as it must have done, the hollow along which the water flowed would be widened and deepened. But before the river had commenced to widen and deepen this secondary course, the lake from which it flowed would cover a large tract of country and stretch along the base of the Kilpatrick Hills as far at least as Kilsyth. In this manner the old lateral valley mentioned above as being probably the pre-glacial channel of the Kelvin would be completely sub-merged, and so also would be the bed of the Clyde up to and beyond Glasgow.

The area covered by the lake would then necessarily become an area of deposition. Gravel, sand, mud, and silt would accumulate upon the bottom, the finer sediments settling down in the deeper parts, and thus all the drowned river ravines would have a tendency to silt up. The process would be a gradual one, and sometimes it might even be interrupted by some local recession of the Leven glacier, which would lower the surface of the great glacial lake and allow the streams to re-excavate a portion of their beds. But these and other obvious considerations I need not stop to point out.

Let us now further conceive that the arctic cold continues to increase, that the snow and ice grow in depth and breadth until even the Kilpatrick and Campsie Hills are overflowed by massive confluent glaciers descending from the Highlands, and the whole of the great central valley of Scotland—the broad lowland country—is brimful of ice, forming one wide and far-stretching *mer de glace*. The effect produced in the old lake-bed of the Clyde basin by such an advance of the glaciers would no doubt be most destructive. Over broad areas the soft and incoherent masses of sand, mud, gravel, &c., which had gathered upon the bottom of the old lake would be ploughed up and intermingled with the other débris continually gathering and being pushed onward underneath the ice-sheet. But it might well be that in deeper hollows

---

* The reader will, perhaps, understand my meaning better, if I merely state here that the work I conceive to have been done by the Clyde was simply the denudation, or wearing away, of the *col* between two valleys, and the subsequent deepening and widening of those valleys.

and in such ravines as intersected the path of the ice, some portions of the lake deposits might escape and receive a covering or cap of ground-moraine or till.

But a glance at the "borings" given above (pp. 141, 145) will show that the buried hollows and ravines may contain more than one stony clay, separated by considerable depths of aqueous deposits. These stony clays probably indicate just so many incursions of the ice-sheet; the intermediate beds of silt, sand, and gravel,* may point on the other hand to periods when the ice vanished from the low grounds and crept back to the mountain-valleys. Every time the Leven glacier advanced and choked up the Clyde valley, a lake would form over the region under review, and fresh-water beds would be deposited; every time the ice-sheet covered the whole country fresh masses of stony clay would accumulate in protected hollows and ravines; every time the ice-sheet retired the lake would reappear, until the Leven glacier finally drew back from the valley of the Clyde. It is therefore unnecessary to call in the aid of the sea to explain for us the occurrence of those beds of gravel, sand, and mud which are intercalated with the stony clays in the buried valleys and depressions of the Clyde basin.

I have spoken of the outlet of the ancient glacial lake of the Clyde having been by the valleys of the Black Cart and the Rye. It is quite possible, however, and even highly probable, that the discharge at some periods may have been to the north-east by Kilsyth into the basin of the Forth. In attempting to restore the physiography of the land during successive stages of the glacial epoch, we have to bear in mind that after every descent of the glaciers very considerable changes would be effected here and there upon the configuration of the ground. In one place the level would be lowered by the abstraction of rock—in another it would be raised by the accumulation of superficial deposits. And it might quite well be that, owing to some such changes, the Clyde lake might during certain interglacial periods drain into the Forth—for even now the difference of height be-

---

* The thinner intercalated beds of sand, &c., may of course form part and parcel of the till itself: it is only the very thick intercalated deposits which, in a case of this kind, where the beds are not actually seen, we should feel inclined to consider as of interglacial age.

tween the watershed at Kilsyth, and that of the Black Cart is only some fifty feet or so.*

The actual certainty that such great disturbances of the drainage-system must have taken place during the glacial epoch has not received so much attention from glacialists as it deserves. Yet no one who gives the subject any considera- tion can fail to see how disturbances of the kind must have occurred in many other valleys besides that which I have selected for illustration. Long before the land-ice increased to such an extent as to overflow the Kilpatrick Hills, the Campsies, and the Ochils, many of the streams that drained into the Forth must have been dammed back by the great glacier which occupied the principal valley, and which in all likelihood extended many miles below Stirling, before the hills referred to were overtopped and buried. In attempting to read the records of the glacial epoch such considerations as these ought not to escape us; had they always been fully realised perhaps we should have been less liable to set down

---

* Dr. Croll (*Climate and Time*, p. 485) does not agree with me that the inter- glacial beds in the buried channel of the Kelvin are fresh-water, because they closely resemble the similar intercalated deposits met with in the preglacial valley that extends from Kilsyth to Grangemouth (see above, p. 141), which he believes are marine. I might answer that mere similarity of the deposits does not prove simi- larity of origin. The intercalated beds in the buried course of the Kelvin might be fresh-water, even although it could be demonstrated that those in the old ravine between Kilsyth and Grangemouth are marine. I still hold, therefore, that the physical evidence, so far as it goes, decidedly favours the views expressed above. In the former edition of this work I gave no opinion as to the origin of the aqueous deposits in the buried channel at Grangemouth. It is evident, however, that some are of Lower and some of Upper Drift age. All the deposits from the surface down to the bottom of the "Red clay" are marine, and of later date than the till, and their average thickness is not less, as Dr. Croll states, than 85 ft., and in some cases 100 ft. With these, therefore, we have nothing at present to do—they are quite beside the question. The fact of their being marine throws no light whatever upon the origin of the aqueous beds intercalated with the underlying till. I see no reason, however, for believing the latter to be marine; they are more likely to be fresh-water, and were probably formed in the same way as the interglacial beds of the old Kelvin valley. Dr. Croll's chief objection to the fresh-water origin of the beds in question is the great depth from the surface at which they occur; he thinks that if we hold this belief we are forced to assume, "not that the water formed by the melted ice was dammed back, but that the sea itself was dammed back, and that by a wall extending to not less than 200 to 300 ft., so as to allow of a lake being formed in which the deposits might accumulate; *assuming, of course, that the absolute level of the land was the same then as it is now.*" But this is what we are hardly entitled to assume; for not only have we no proof that the relative level of sea and land was the same then as it is now, but all the evidence goes to show that during the Ice Age there were frequent oscillations of level, and if the land stood in certain glacial and inter- glacial times only 200 or 300 ft. above its present level, as there are many reasons for believing it did, then Dr. Croll's objection has no force.

every thick bed of interglacial silt, sand, or gravel, to the action of the sea.*

It is quite certain, however, that marine deposits do sometimes occur intercalated among true morainic accumulations, and to these we shall refer presently. Meanwhile I must direct attention to some examples of interglacial fresh-water deposits which have already been briefly described.

* I am reminded here of those deposits of sand and gravel covered with morainic débris, that occur abundantly in the low grounds of Switzerland, and which geologists have shown to be of fresh-water origin, but which, had they occurred in similar positions in our country, some of us might have had small hesitation in assigning to the action of the sea, so difficult is it for a speculative islander to escape the influence of his geographical position.

CHAPTER XIV.

BEDS SUBJACENT TO AND INTERCALATED WITH THE SCOTTISH TILL—*Continued*.

Interglacial deposits of the Leithen Valley, Peeblesshire.—Other examples of similar deposits.—Crofthead interglacial beds.—Climatic conditions of Scotland during interglacial ages.—Fragmentary nature of the evidence not conclusive as to the climate never having been positively mild.—Till at surface chiefly " upper."—" Striated pavements."—Fossils in till.—Duration of glacial and interglacial periods.

AT page 124 Fig. 27 shows certain stratified deposits of gravel, sand, and clay, which betray all the usual characteristics of river detritus. They rest, as will be observed, upon a very uneven surface of till, and show a considerable degree of confusion. The Leithen (Peeblesshire), on the banks of which they occur, flows in one of those deep, narrow, but softly-outlined valleys that form so familiar a feature in the Southern Uplands. The stream has its source at a height of 1,750 ft. above the sea, and after a course of nine miles joins the Tweed, at Innerleithen, some 500 ft. above the same level. Its drainage-area does not exceed 22 square miles ; its watershed, however, attains a height of upwards of 2,000 ft., and the highest point in this hilly tract of south-eastern Scotland is only some 750 ft. higher. The significance of these details will appear presently.

Both lower and upper masses of till shown in the section, are crammed with well-striated stones and boulders, and are in all respects typical deposits—the upper bed, however, being somewhat less tough and compact than the lower. From what has been said in regard to the origin of till, it is quite clear that at the time the lower mass was being accumulated, the whole drainage-area of the Leithen must have been filled with ice to overflowing. And not only so, but the same must have been the case with all the valleys in the

Southern Uplands. This follows, as a matter of course, as any one may convince himself, by studying the Ordnance Survey maps of the region under review. It is quite inconceivable that the Leithen valley, which is by no means one of the highest in that district, should alone have been filled with glacier-ice, but the presence of a deep ice-mass here necessarily implies the like presence of large glaciers in all the main dales and hopes of these uplands.

The presence of the intercalated fluviatile gravel and sand indicates plainly that an interruption to this arctic condition of things took place. Before these river deposits could be laid down, the ice must have vanished from the Leithen valley, and if such was the case with this mountain-valley, we are driven to conclude that the great ice-sheet could not then have covered any portion of the Scottish Lowlands. Glaciers may have lingered still in the higher valleys of the country, but it is obviously impossible that a great ice-sheet could exist while upland streams like the Leithen had freedom to flow.

The aspect of the upper deposit of till in the section testifies to the disappearance of the mild conditions under which the river accumulations were formed, and to the return of an intensely arctic climate. The stones and boulders in this till are all well blunted, scratched, and smoothed, thus indicating the former presence of a depth of ice sufficient to overflow the heights overlooking the valley, and so to prevent the introduction of sharply angular and unpolished blocks amongst the glacial débris gathering underneath.* The contortion and confusion of the river deposits were no doubt caused by the pressure of this second ice-flow.

A similar train of reasoning applies to the sections shown in Figs. 26 and 28, and, therefore they need not be more particularly referred to. Referring back to Fig. 29, page 128, another interesting section will be seen. Here beds of clay, sand, silt, &c., are represented as completely enclosed in till. These strata showed lines and layers of peaty matter, and yielded, during the railway operations, an imperfect skull of the great urus, remains of the Irish deer and the horse, and other fossils. The beds are clearly of lacustrine formation,

* See *ante*, p. 67.

and their position proves that after a mass of till had been deposited by some great ice-sheet, a milder climate ensued, when streams once more flowed down the valleys, and lakes occupied the hollows and depressions of the land, which was clothed with vegetation and tenanted by oxen, deer, and horses. Finally, the presence of the overlying mass of till indicates that this mild period passed away, and was succeeded by severe arctic conditions, when thick ice again streamed over central Scotland.

Precisely the same inference as to change of climate is to be drawn from the other instances of interglacial beds with organic remains, mentioned at pp. 124—129, ; the stratified deposits in all these instances point to oscillations of temperature—to periods when the great ice-sheet disappeared from the low grounds, and shrunk into a series of local glaciers among the mountain regions.

But, as I have endeavoured to show, the same conclusion must be arrived at, even supposing the interglacial deposits had never yielded any organic remains whatever. These, however, are extremely valuable, inasmuch as they enable us more fully to realise the nature of those physical conditions that characterised the interglacial periods. Combining the evidence we learn that not only did the great ice-sheet sometimes retire from the low grounds, and give place to lakes and streams and rivers, but also that, during such periods of milder conditions, a vegetation like that of cold temperate regions clothed the more open moors and valleys with grasses and heaths, the sheltered hollows with hazel, and the hillsides with birch and pine. Reindeer wandered across the country, while herds of the great urus, the horse, the Irish deer, and the woolly-coated mammoth frequented the grassy vales. If one might draw conclusions from the aspect of the few fossil remains disinterred from the deposits in the till, he might compare Scotland during the interglacial periods to that tract of country which extends along the extreme southern limits of the Barren Grounds of North America— a region where a few firs and other hardy trees cover the drier slopes, and where carices and grasses grow luxuriantly enough in the sheltered valleys—those favourite breeding-places of the reindeer, which roam over the dreary deserts to the north. Whether during any of the interglacial periods the climate was ever mild enough to melt away all the ice and snow from the highland valleys, the record does not say. What positive evidence we have points rather to the existence of local glaciers in the higher valleys—to moderate summers and severe winters—during such interglacial periods as we have any certain records of.

And yet we might be committing a grave error were we to assume that Scotland, during interglacial times, never enjoyed milder conditions than now obtain in the forest regions and barrens of North America. We must ever bear in mind that the interglacial deposits are the veriest fragments. They have been preserved, for the most part, only in sheltered hollows from the ravages of the great ice-plough; and the interrupted and patchy portions that remain are mere wrecks of what must once have been, in the broader valleys, widespread and continuous deposits. Every renewed descent of the glaciers upon the low grounds would tend to effect the removal of these accumulations; and it may well be that of several interglacial periods, not a single representative deposit now remains. Even during the interglacial periods themselves, the streams and rivers would help to clear away and redistribute those beds of sand, gravel, and silt which the glaciers had spared—just as in our own day the streams are gradually excavating and washing away the materials that fill up old preglacial and interglacial ravines and watercourses. Moreover, we must not forget that if really warm climates ever did supervene during interglacial times, every such warm period must have been followed successively by temperate, cold-temperate, and arctic conditions; and these last would consequently be the most fully represented of the series.

The reader will now appreciate what was meant when I stated, at the beginning of Chapter XI., that much, if not most, of the till now lying at the surface of the ground is not the oldest accumulation of the kind. For it is clear that a great proportion of the till that was formed during the first and earliest cold periods would be ploughed out by subsequent ice-sheets, while much of it would be so modified and rearranged as to become practically a newer till. Here and there, however, the older till has been preserved, and generally shows, underneath interglcial deposits and superincumbent till, a worn hummocky surface. Sometimes, indeed, we may observe how the hard tough old till has resisted the erosive action of the latest ice-sheet, just as well as if it had been a solid rock. The later ice has ground over its surface, scratching each projecting stone and boulder, and producing what we now know as a "striated pavement." And I am not sure but that the appearance of these "pavements," to any one who carefully weighs the evidence, is just as eloquent of great climatic changes as the actual occurrence of interglacial beds.

It is also highly probable that the isolated elephant tusks, reindeer horns, bones, and fragments of oak and other trees which occur here and there like boulders in the heart of a mass of till, really belong to interglacial rather than preglacial times. For it is evident that the till containing these remains, which occurs at the actual surface of the ground, is more likely to have been laid down during one of the latest ice-periods, if not during the very last great extension of the glaciers, than to have been the product of the first ice-sheet. And consequently it seems most reasonable to infer, that the scattered organic remains referred to are relics of that interglacial era which preceded the advent of the last period of confluent glaciers.

So far as the Scottish glacial drifts are concerned, it is clear there is no evidence to show that the interglacial periods might not have been warm enough at times to cause all the ice and snow to disappear from the country. Whether we shall ever obtain any decisive evidence on this head will probably depend upon the assiduity with which the interglacial deposits are examined. The till was for many years looked upon as a deposit destitute of all traces of life, and only a few hammerers continued, Micawber-like, to hope for something turning up. I believe that mammalian remains have been oftener obtained from the beds in the till during shaft-sinking and other mining operations than geologists are aware of. While carrying on the Geological Survey of the Scottish coal-fields, I have frequently heard of "bones" and "horns" having been met with by the workmen in sinking through the deep drifts. These relics, unfortunately, have almost invariably been lost or mislaid, but there can be little doubt, from the descriptions that were given to me by intelligent overseers, that the relics were true fossils, and still less doubt that these fossils were obtained, not in recent alluvial but in glacial deposits.

We may, perhaps, never learn how many great changes of climate took place during the accumulation of the till and its associated deposits. This arises from the fact, already adverted to, that during every period of intensest cold, when the country was covered with a more or less thick sheet of snow and ice, the loose materials, which in the preceding age had gathered in river-valleys and in lakes, would almost inevitably be subjected to excessive denudation. That the records of mild interglacial periods should be at the best but fragmentary, is no more than one might have expected. The wonder is not that they should be so interrupted, but that any portion whatever has been spared. Owing to this interrupted mode of occurrence it is obviously impossible to correlate them, bed with bed. The interglacial deposits in one place may or may not be contemporaneous with the similar accumulations in some other locality. There were more changes than one during the formation of the lower drifts; and hence, in the case of isolated interglacial beds, we can seldom tell whether they ought to be referred to an earlier or a later stage of that period.

The disappearance of a *mer de glace*, which in the Lowlands of Scotland attained a thickness of nearer 3,000 ft. than 2,000 ft., could only be effected by a very considerable change of climate. Nor, when one fully considers all sides of the question, does it appear unreasonable to infer that the comparatively mild and genial periods, of which the interglacial beds are memorials, may have endured as long as those arctic or glacial conditions which preceded and followed them. We have a difficulty in conceiving of the length of time implied in the gradual increase of that cold which, as the years went by, eventually buried the whole country underneath one vast *mer de glace*. Nor can we form any proper conception of how long a time was needed to bring about that other change of climate, under the influence of which, slowly and imperceptibly, this immense sheet of frost melted away from the Lowlands and retired to the mountain recesses. We must allow that long ages elapsed before the warmth became such as to induce plants and animals to clothe and people the land. How vast a time, also, must have passed away ere the warmth reached its climax, and the temperature again began to cool down! How slowly, step by step, the ice must have crept out from the mountain fastnesses, chilling the air, and forcing fauna and flora to retire before it; and what a long succession of years must have come and gone before the ice-sheet once more wrapped up the hills, oblite- rated the valleys, and, streaming out from the shore, usurped the bed of the shallow seas that flowed around our island! Finally, when we consider that such a succession of changes happened not once only, but again and again, we cannot fail to have some faint appreciation of the lapse of time required for the accumulation of the till and the interglacial deposits.

The interglacial beds which have so far engaged our atten- tion are all of fresh-water origin. They occur at all levels in the valleys down to the neighbourhood of the sea. Indeed, if the intercalated beds that help to fill the buried channels and depressions in the lower reaches of the Clyde basin be, as I have tried to show they most likely are, of fresh-water formation, then fluviatile and lacustrine beds of interglacial age occur even below the present sea-level.

In concluding what we had to say about the changes of climate that were likely to result from astronomical causes, we found that a full consideration of the question led us to infer that glacial periods lasting for thousands of years, must alternate with equally prolonged periods of genial conditions, every time that the orbit of the earth reaches a high degree of eccentricity. Now, if I have succeeded in making the geological evidence at all clear, it must be apparent that the tale told by the glacial deposits strikingly confirms the truth of the astronomical and physical theory which we considered in Chapter X. In the next chapter I shall proceed to describe other examples of interglacial deposits which are somewhat more complicated than those already adduced, inasmuch as they afford distinct evidence of oscillations of the sea-level.

CHAPTER XV.

BEDS SUBJACENT TO AND INTERCALATED WITH SCOTTISH TILL—*Continued.*

Marine deposits associated with till at Woodhill Quarry, Kilmaurs, Ayrshire ; at Tangy Glen, Campbeltown ; at Chapelhall, near Airdrie ; at Oakshaw Hill, Paisley.—Shelly till of Croftamie, near Drymen ; of Caithness ; of Aberdeenshire ; of Berwick ; of Ballantrae, Ayrshire ; of Wigtownshire ; of Lewis.

IT will be observed that hitherto we have done no more than make a brief reference to the occurrence of undoubted marine beds in and underneath the till. For the sake of clearness I have delayed considering these intercalated and subjacent marine deposits until now.

The first example I select is remarkable, because it shows how these marine beds are occasionally associated with deposits which are clearly of freshwater origin.

Below a mass of till at Woodhill Quarry, near Kilmaurs, Ayrshire, which precisely resembles the tumultuous stony clays that underlie and overlie the fresh-water beds described in the preceding pages, remains of mammoths and reindeer and certain sea shells have several times been detected during the quarrying operations. The first notice of these discoveries dates so far back as 1817, when Mr. Bald described* two elephant tusks as having been got at a depth of seventeen and a half feet from the surface. The tusks lay in a horizontal position, with some small bones near them, and the light-brown clay in contact with the bones was discoloured and emitted a very unsavoury odour when turned over. Mr. Bald mentions that several marine shells were found amongst the dark-coloured earth ; but as the species were not determined, some doubt was subsequently expressed as to whether they were sea shells or not.† Since the date of

---

* *Memoirs of Wernerian Society,* vol. iv. p. 64.
† *Trans. Geol. Soc. Glas.,* vol. i. p. 69.

Mr. Bald's discovery, several other tusks (nine or ten), a portion of a molar tooth of an elephant, the horns of a reindeer, and remains of insects and freshwater plants have been met with at the same locality.* There can be no doubt, according to Dr. Bryce,† that all these remains came from one and the same stratum—a bed of peaty clay a few inches thick, which occurs between two thin beds of sand and gravel that lie underneath a thick mass of tumultuous unstratified till. Messrs. J. Young and Craig have also shown‡ that the shells are restricted to the sand-bed that overlies the freshwater clay with its mammalian remains, and they have put beyond all doubt the marine character of the shells referred to by Mr. Bald. During the operation of sinking a coal pit about half a mile from the old Woodhill Quarry arctic marine shells were obtained from a thin bed of sand that underlay some fifty feet of till and other superficial deposits. The section is given by Messrs. Young and Craig as follows :—

> Surface drift and boulder-clay, 50 feet.
> Sand-bed containing arctic marine shells, 1 foot 3 inches.
> Sandy peaty clay, about 1 foot.
> Coarse gravelly sand, 1 foot 6 inches.
>   Carboniferous strata.

There can be little doubt that the peaty clay and overlying shelly sand of this section are the same as those which were exposed below the till in the Woodhill Quarry; and from their infraposition, Messrs. Bryce, Young, and Craig have inferred their preglacial origin. But the results obtained during the examination of the ground by the Geological Survey show that the strata containing mammalian and molluscous remains really occupy an intercalated or *interglacial* position, and that the cause of their sometimes being found to rest on the solid rock and not upon a lower mass of till is due to the irregularity of the surface on which the whole of the drift beds have been deposited ; for where the level of the rock slopes down far enough it passes below the horizon of the stratified beds, and a lower and underlying till then

---

* Mr. J. Young, Curator of the Hunterian Museum, Glasgow, obtained seeds of the pond-weed (*Potamogeton*) and the aquatic Ranunculus by washing the mud which adhered to the reindeer's horn and filled the cracks of the elephant's tusks which had lain in the museum for half a century. *Antiquity of Man*, p. 292.

† *Quart. Jour. Geol. Soc.*, vol. xxi. p. 213.

‡ *Trans. Geol. Soc. Glas.*, vol. iii. p. 310.

makes its appearance.* The only deposit in Scotland which seems entitled to the appellation of *preglacial* is that described by Mr. Jamieson† as occurring in the parishes of Slains and Crudens, on the eastern coast of Aberdeenshire. It consists of thick masses of sand and gravel, which are charged here and there with rolled and broken shells belonging to species which are not known either in Scotch glacial beds or in our present seas, but which occur in the Crag beds of England. Mr. S. V. Wood, who examined the shells obtained by Mr. Jamieson, was of opinion‡ that they are "derivatives" in the gravel, but "they clearly showed," according to him, "that some bed of Crag, or more probably of very early glacial age,

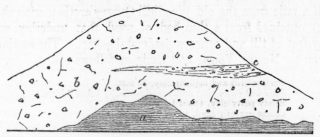

Fig. 34.—Section of till in Tangy Glen, near Cambeltown. [Robertson and Crosskey.] *a*, bedded shelly clay; *b*, till; *c*, gravel, sand, &c., in till.

had existed in the north-east of Scotland." The gravels are covered in many places with red boulder-clay.

Messrs. Robertson and Crosskey describe§ a section of boulder-clay with underlying stratified clay as occurring in Tangy Glen, near Campbeltown, at a height of 130 feet above the sea. The till here exposed is "of the usual character, stiff, compact, and full of stones, many of them distinctly striated." It is quite unstratified, but exhibits one of those lenticular beds of sand, &c., which I have already mentioned as being a

* *Mem. Geol. Surv. of Scotland;* Explanation of Sheet 22, p. 29. Mr. Craig appears, subsequently, to have changed his opinion as to the preglacial character of the fossiliferous beds underlying the till of Woodhill Quarry; and now, having found that the peaty layer of that neighbourhood is really underlaid as well as overlaid by till, he adopts the view of its interglacial character. See *Trans. Geol. Soc. Glas.*, vol. iv. p. 150.
† *Quart. Jour. Geol. Soc.*, vol. xxi. p. 162.
‡ *Geol. Mag.*, vol. viii. p. 406.
§ *Trans. Geol. Soc. Glas.*, vol. iv. p. 134· "Monograph of the Post-Tertiary Entomostraca of Scotland," *Palæontographical Society*, vol. xxviii.

common enough feature of the Scotch till. Underneath the boulder-clay occurs a bed of laminated clay, showing a hummocky and denuded surface, as represented in the accompanying woodcut, which I have borrowed from Messrs. Robertson's and Crosskey's paper. The underlying rock is not seen, but it is probable that the laminated clay rests directly upon it. A few fossil shells are found in this clay, among which there are some of an extremely arctic character. A number of species of ostracodes also occur, which, according to Messrs. Robertson and Crosskey, "have much in common with those found in the clays on the east coast of Scotland, which are held to represent more arctic types than those generally found in the west."

Mr. Smith, of Jordanhill, to whom geologists are indebted for the first discovery of arctic shells in the drift deposits of the west of Scotland, has mentioned[*] the occurrence of shells in a clay at Chapelhall, near Airdrie, at a height of 510 ft. above the sea. The shells were embedded in a layer of fine brick-clay, some two feet thick at most, which had undoubtedly formed part of an old sea-bottom. The clay is intercalated between an upper and a lower till. The upper till, which attains a thickness of fourteen feet, is not so hard and tough as the underlying till, nor are its included stones and boulders so well striated.[†] Neither the upper nor the under till contains any shells. Mr. Crosskey gives the height of this deposit above the sea as 526 feet. The same observer says the shells of the intercalated clay consisted of two species only—*Tellina calcarea* and *Cyprina Islandica.*

Dr. Fraser has described[‡] the occurrence at Oakshaw Hill, Paisley, beneath a mass of unfossiliferous till, of a bed of shelly clay "with a bed of *Mytilus edulis* on its surface." This shelly clay is the same as that which throughout the whole of that district rests upon a worn and hummocky surface of till.

It will be observed that in the sections hitherto adduced the till is described as quite unfossiliferous, and not only so,

---

[*] *Researches in Newer Pliocene Geology*, pp. 17, 141.

[†] *Quart. Jour. Geol. Soc.*, vol. xxi. p. 219; "Monogr. of Post-Ter. Entomos.," *Palæont. Soc.*, vol. xxviii. p. 9.

[‡] *Trans. Geol. Soc. Glas.*, vol. iv. p. 180.

but from its unstratified and tumultuous character there is no doubt that it cannot be distinguished from much of the till that occurs in the interior of the country. We come now to consider certain sections in which the till differs from that which we have hitherto been examining : and this difference we shall find consists chiefly in the presence of broken, crushed, and striated shells, which are scattered confusedly through the mass much in the same way as the stones and boulders with which they are associated.

During the construction of the Forth and Clyde Railway an interesting section of drift was exposed at Croftamie (Drymen Station). The upper part of this section consisted of a stiff till, twelve feet thick, beneath which came seven feet of a laminated blue clay which rested on broken sandstone. In this underlying clay were found a few marine shells, and near its base, portions of a horn, which Professor Owen believed to be the antler of a young or female reindeer of the existing species.* My colleague, Mr. Jack, who geologically surveyed the district where this section occurs, has given a very interesting account of the drift deposits.† The section that yielded the reindeer's horn is now tumbled and not well seen, but the till there exhibited is, he believes, the same as a remarkable deposit of shelly till which he traced over a considerable area in the lower valley of the river Endrick, which flows into Loch Lomond at its eastern angle. This till does not rise to a greater height than 320 ft. above the sea. He describes it as "a true typical till, in every respect analogous to the old boulder-clay or till of the Lowlands of Scotland." The clay is stiff, unstratified, full of glaciated stones, and brown in colour like the subjacent Old Red Sandstone. But its most noteworthy peculiarity is the presence of worn and broken fragments of marine shells, which are scattered irregularly through the clay just in the same way as the stones and boulders. He believes this shelly till to be of more recent date than the unfossiliferous till which was formed during the greatest extension of the ice-sheet. The shells in the Endrick till,

---

* *Proc. Roy. Phys. Soc., Edin.,* vol. i. pp. 163, 247 ; *Trans. Geol. Soc. Glas.,* vol. i. p. 70.
  † *Trans. Geol. Soc. Glas.,* vol. v. p. 5.

according to him, have been derived from a pre-existing interglacial deposit, of which the laminated shelly clay that contained the reindeer's horn is a fragment.

One of the best known examples of a shelly till is that which covers a large part of Caithness. This deposit has been described by a number of geologists, but the best account of it is given by Mr. Jamieson.[*] It occurs scattered over all the low grounds of Caithness, appearing deepest in valleys and other depressions, and attaining its greatest thickness in the neighbourhood of the sea, along the shores of which it forms cliffs in many places. It is generally of a dull, dark leaden-grey or slate colour, and as a rule shows no trace of stratification. Its included stones and boulders are of the usual subangular blunted form, and many of them are well striated. In some places stones larger than one's head are rare, while in other places large blocks, more or less ice-worn, may be observed. The matrix is often a more or less tough gritty clay, but not infrequently it becomes sandier ; and although it now and again preserves the former character over considerable areas and through a thickness of 100 ft. at least, it yet occasionally exhibits a number of irregular sandy patches, which, however, do not impart a stratified appearance to the mass. Now the stones are disseminated pretty equally through the deposit,—again they are more or less aggregated, just as is the case in typical unfossiliferous till. The stones consist principally of fragments of the so-called "Caithness flags"— rocks which belong to the Old Red Sandstone formation and of which a considerable part of Caithness is composed. But fragments of granite and mica-schist are common enough throughout the whole deposit, and sandstone, conglomerate, and other rocks also occur. But the most remarkable stones are certain fragments of oolitic rocks and chalk, neither of which are found *in place* in Caithness. Oolitic strata, however, are developed in a narrow strip along the coast of Sutherland, but chalk is not met with anywhere in Scotland. Throughout this coarse tumultuous deposit occur numerous broken shells, not a few of which show fine striations. It is not common to meet with a perfect shell,

[*] *Quart. Jour. Geol. Soc.*, vol. xxii. p. 261.

but one was found with both valves complete and in a fine
state of preservation, and more or less perfect single valves
are not very rare. In general, however, the shells are mere
fragments, and are disseminated through the clay in the
same irregular manner as the stones and boulders. It is
noteworthy that they show a curious mixture of arctic and
boreal and southern forms.

Now at various places in Caithness this shelly till is found
resting upon a dark pebbly silt, containing broken shells,
which Mr. Jamieson thought " looked more like an ordinary
marine deposit" than the stony deposit which has just been
described. But he could not say that a clear sharp line
of separation could always be drawn between the stony till
above and the pebbly silt below. Sometimes the line was
pretty well marked, but at other times the two deposits
seemed to graduate into each other.

The same observer has described* the occurrence at Invernettie, near Peterhead, of a similar mass of shelly boulder-
clay overlying beds of sand and fine clay ; and again at
King-Edward (Aberdeenshire) he obtained the following
interesting section † — the deposits being named in descending order :—

Feet.
1. Stratified sand and gravel (no fossils) . . . . 10 to 25
2. Unstratified boulder-clay, with shell fragments in lower
   part . . . . 20 to 30
3. Fine sand ; in some places rich in shells . . . 1 to 2
4. Fine silt, with whole shells, excavated to a depth of
   10 feet: bottom not reached.

Shelly boulder-clays are commonly found in the maritime
districts, but it is not necessary to describe every section met
with. I shall content myself therefore with mentioning
some localities where they have been seen, and thereafter we
shall pass on to consider the occurrence of shelly clays
which are not only covered by, but rest upon, shelly till or
boulder-clay.

In the sea-cliffs at Berwick some good sections may be
observed, of which the annexed section may be taken as an
example. At the bottom may be noted a reddish clay stuck
full of scratched stones (*t*), and which, as far as I have seen,

contains no shells. Owing, apparently, to the copious perco
lation of spring-water (at *w*) between it and the overlying
looser deposits, it is rendered soft and incoherent. The
immediately superjacent bed consists of coarse bouldery
shingle, in a sandy clay matrix (*g*). The stones look water-
worn, but are more or less angular and blunted, and some
are striated. The base of this shingle-bed is not well seen,
and consequently the junction-line between it and the till is
not distinctly visible. This arises from the action of the
springs, which are continually producing little slips of the
bank. Overlying the coarse shingle occurs a dark reddish

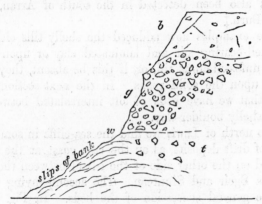

Fig. 35.—Section seen in sea-cliff at Berwick.

brown clay (*b*) with a few scattered stones, which are in
other places more closely aggregated. They are generally
ice-worn, but some show no traces of glaciation. In this bed
broken and worn shells occur, but they are not common. In
other parts of the cliff irregular beds of sand are intercalated
with *g* and *b*, and sometimes the whole of the drift deposits
overlying the solid rocks consist of a red boulder-clay, often
very coarse, overlaid with beds of sand and clay.

Shelly boulder-clay may be seen in the old sea-cliff
between Bennane Head and Ballantrae, Ayrshire ;* and some
good sections are exposed upon the coast of Wigtownshire,†
as at Clanyard Bay, and at the south end of Port Logan

* *Mem. Geol. Surv. Scot.*, Expl. of Sheet 7, p. 14.
† *Op. cit.*, Expl. of Sheet 1, p. 8 ; "Monograph of Post-Tertiary Entomostraca
of Scotland," *Palæontographical Society*, vol. xxviii. p. 69.

Bay, both on the west coast of the Mull of Galloway, and again at Monreith tileworks,* about two and a half miles south of Port William on the shores of Luce Bay. In the same county, at the Cleshmahew tileworks, one mile south of Stranraer, shelly till is covered by brown laminated shell-bearing clay, which in turn is overlain with an upper stony clay containing apparently no fossils. My colleague, Mr. Irvine, who surveyed the western districts of Wigtownshire, states that fragmentary shells occur at various places in the stiff till of the low grounds, as at Lady Bay, Innermessan, and Sandhead on the shores of Loch Ryan.† Shelly boulder-clay has also been detected in the south of Arran, in the Cloined Burn.‡

In the examples now adduced the shelly tills either rest upon shell-bearing silt and laminated clay or upon a pavement of unfossiliferous till, or, if this be absent, they recline directly upon the solid rocks. In the next sections it will be seen that we have beds of silt intercalated between two beds of shelly boulder-clay.

In the north of Lewis we find the sea-cliffs in some places formed of drift deposits, as on the east coast at the Port of Ness, and on the other side of the island between the points of Cobha Sgeir and Sinntean. The accompanying sections show the general succession of the beds. In Fig. 36 two beds of boulder-clay, with intermediate deposits of sand, gravel, and clay or silt, are seen. The lower boulder-clay bed rests upon gneissic rocks, which in some places have a smoothed surface under the clay, although they are more often, perhaps, somewhat rough and broken. I found that throughout Lewis the gneissic rocks seldom preserved their striæ.§ Even where the *roches moutonnées* looked exceedingly fresh it was rare to detect the "ghosts of scratches." I often observed, however, that the quartz veins which projected above the surface of the rounded rock-faces were well striated. This was particularly observable on the sides of

---

* *Mem. Geol. Surv. Scot.*, Expl. of Sheet 2, p. 9.
† *Op. cit.*, Expl. of Sheet 3, p. 23.
‡ *Trans. Roy. Soc. Edin.*, vol. xxiii., p. 523; *Arran, and other Clyde Islands*, by Dr. J. Bryce, 4th ed., p. 184; "Monogr. Post-Tert. Entom., Scot.," *Palæont. Soc.*, vol. xxviii. p. 7, *et sqq.*
§ See a paper by the author, *Quart. Jour. Geol. Soc.*, vol. xxix. p. 532.

Suainabhal and other *moutonnée* hills in the south ; and in one place, where the till had only been recently stripped from the ground, I noticed that the gneiss was beautifully polished and striated over an area of several square yards, although the rock-faces immediately adjoining, which had long been exposed to the action of the weather, had lost all their striæ and presented only a smoothed outline.   From these facts it becomes apparent that the Lewisian gneiss is not well adapted to preserve the finer etchings of the ice-chisel.   Rain and frost soon corrode its surface, and the rock then crumbles away, so as to leave its quartz veins standing out in relief ; and these, as I have said, often show striæ.*
But to return to our drift section.

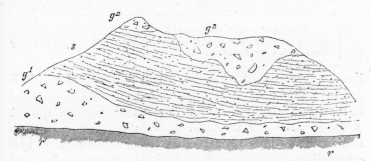

Fig. 36.—Boulder-clay and associated deposits, Traigh Chrois, Island of Lewis. *r*, Gneiss. *g*¹ *g*², Lower and upper boulder-clay. *s*, Sand, gravel, and clay.

The lower bed of boulder-clay is a dark greyish brown sandy or earthy clay, quite unstratified, with numerous blunted stones and boulders.   These consist almost exclusively of gneiss of a kind which does not preserve striæ, consequently only a few of the finer-grained, harder, and more compact stones show any striations.   At Port of Ness this boulder-clay is of a dark brown colour, and often very sandy, and contains patches of sand.   Here some of the

* There are some remarkable changes in the "strike" of the gneissic rocks of Lewis: thus in the neighbourhood of Stornoway the strike is north-east and south-west, and the dip is to south-east.   West of Stornoway, in the central district of the island, the strike is only a little north of east and south of west, —the dip being a little east of south.   In the Great Bernera, all along the shores of Loch Roag, and throughout the Uig district, the strike is distinctly north-west and south-east, with a prevalent dip to the north-east.

stones are well striated; and many boulders of red sandstone
and conglomerate, which probably came from the Cambrian,
were seen in the clay. But the most remarkable feature
of this stony clay is the presence of broken arctic and boreal
shells, which occur in an irregular manner through the mass.
The upper surface of the boulder-clay is denuded—a character better shown in Fig. 37, which is taken from the same

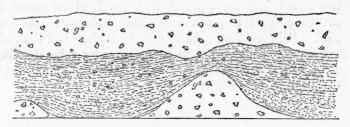

Fig. 37.—Boulder-clay and associated deposits, Traigh Chrois, Island of
Lewis. g^1 g^2, Under and overlying boulder-clay. s, Fine sand and clay
partings, with a few scattered stones.

locality. The stratified beds contain shells, most of which
are in a fragmentary state, but some perfect specimens may
be detected. They belong to arctic and northern species.
A few stones occur here and there in the beds. In some
sections these beds consist of an upper series of sand and
gravel deposits, more or less distinctly separated from an

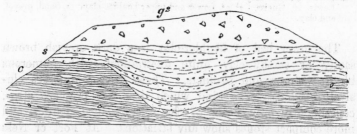

Fig. 38.—Boulder-clay overlying stratified deposits, Traigh Chrois, Island of
Lewis. g^2, Boulder-clay. s, Sand and gravel. c, Clay and silt.

underlying deposit of imperfectly laminated dark blue and
grey clay and silt or mud (as in Fig. 38). Shells occur in
both. At Port of Ness the stratified deposits are represented
by coarse gravel and shingle with large rolled boulders; the
whole very rudely bedded, but containing worn fragments

of shells. At Traigh Shuainaboist the stratified beds show occasional contortion. Above these deposits comes another mass of unstratified boulder-clay, which in some places is of a reddish brown colour, and somewhat more sandy in texture than the lower mass, already described. But it is very irregular. Thus at Traigh Shuainaboist it is a tumultuous, unstratified, dark blue silty clay, very tough in places, and shows irregular veins and bands of sand and gravel. The boulders and stones are unequally aggregated in parts, and are of all sizes up to blocks four or five feet across ; most of them being angular and subangular, and not often showing striæ. Amongst the prevalent gneissic fragments are a few of red grit and sandstone. Here and there, as at Port of Ness, this boulder-clay contains fewer large boulders, and the stones are scattered more equally through the mass. At this latter place it is not so stony as the underlying clay, and seems, moreover, to graduate down here and there into the inter-mediate stratified beds. Broken shells occur in the upper boulder-clay, but they appear to be somewhat rare. It may be worth noting that towards the north end of the sea-cliff at Traigh Shuainaboist a mass of coarse shingle caps the cliff and passes down into sandy boulder beds, some stratified portions of which consist of shelly grit, gravel, and sand.* The line of junction between the upper boulder-clay and the underlying sand and silt beds is as a rule well defined, but occasionally, as I have said, one may note a passage or gra-duation of the former into the latter.

I have been thus minute in my account of these drift sections because, as we shall see by-and-by, they seem to throw considerable light upon the origin of similar shelly boulder-clays that occur upon the mainland. That the reader, therefore, may have the main facts clearly before him, I will tabulate them here. Beginning with the upper bed, we have the following succession in descending order :—

---

* I ought, perhaps, to mention that here and there the drift beds are overlaid with sand and gravel full of rolled shells of species that are even now living in abundance round the coasts of Lewis. These beds, however, are much more recent than the glacial deposits—they belong to the "Raised Beach" series, and, therefore, it would only tend to confusion were I to describe them along with the deposits which we are at present examining.

1. Boulder-clay; unstratified, sometimes reddish brown, and sandy, with stones pretty equally scattered through the matrix; at other times dark greyish blue and more clayey, becoming very tough here and there, with stones and boulders unequally aggregated. Contains irregular beds and patches of gravel, silt, sand, &c. Stones generally subangular and blunted, and occasionally well striated. Broken shells rare. Passes down here and there into beds below, but is usually separated from these by a more or less well-defined line. Passes up in one place into stratified shingle and gravel.

2. Sand, gravel, and coarse shingle, with rolled and angular fragments of shells. Stratified, but sometimes obscurely so. Contains here and there large boulders. Often passes down into and interosculates with beds below: sometimes entirely replaces these; here and there rests with a local unconformity upon them.

3. Dark blue and grey, sometimes brown laminated clay, silt, and mud. Lamination not always distinct. A few stones are scattered through this bed. (Sometimes 2 and 3 are represented by a sandy mud with intercalations of sand, clay, silt, and fine gravel, with stones, generally not larger than one's fist, sparsely scattered throughout.) Contains shells, sometimes whole, but usually in detached valves, many of them being mere fragments.

4. Boulder-clay; unstratified dark greyish brown sandy or earthy clay; contains irregular lenticular beds and patches of sand, gravel, clay, &c.; stones generally blunted, subangular; chiefly of gneiss, but in some places many of red sandstone, conglomerate, and quartz-rock. Some of the stones are well striated. Broken shells occur somewhat plentifully throughout the mass. Line of separation between it and overlying beds generally distinct.

In the sequel I shall point out that at many places along the sea-coast of Scotland beds of clay and sand containing northern and arctic species of shells are found. These occur at various heights, from 300 ft. downwards, but are most common at levels ranging from 40 ft. down to the actual shore, some of the beds passing under the sea. None of them, as we shall see, is covered by boulder-clay, and they are therefore considered by many geologists to be of later date than any of the tills, whether shelly or otherwise, which have formed the subject of this chapter. I have hitherto been of this opinion myself, but some recent explorations in the Outer Hebrides have tended to throw some doubt upon the matter, and I now think it quite possible that some of the shelly beds referred to may really be of interglacial age. But my reasons for this view will be given in Chapter XXII.

CHAPTER XVI.

BEDS SUBJACENT TO AND INTERCALATED WITH THE SCOTTISH TILL—*Continued.*

Climatic changes indicated by marine interglacial beds—Origin of the shelly till. —Mr. R. L. Jack on shelly till of Endrick valley.—Dr. Croll on shelly till of Caithness.—Professor Geikie and Mr. B. N. Peach on glaciation of Caithness.—Deflection of striæ in north-east maritime districts ; in the estuary of the Tay and in Fife ; in the estuary of the Forth and in Haddingtonshire ; in the valley of the Tweed and maritime districts of Northumberland.—Origin of the glacial deposits of Lewis.

WHEN marine organisms occur in a stratum in such a way as to show that they must have lived and died where we now find them, we are compelled to infer that the land must have been submerged to a certain extent at the time these organisms flourished. But if the state of the fossils and the mode of their occurrence be such as to indicate that the creatures could not have existed in the position their shells, &c., now occupy, then the proof they furnish of a former submergence is by no means so satisfactory. The deposits that formed the subject of the preceding chapter present us with a number of examples of both kinds of evidence. Sometimes the proofs of former inroads by the sea upon the land are indisputable, at other times the presence of sea-shells is no proof of submergence at all. An examination of the evidence will make good these points.

It will be remembered that underneath a mass of till at Woodhill Quarry, near Kilmaurs, there occur certain marine and freshwater deposits which rest directly upon the rocks. From this it might at first be inferred that these latter deposits are of preglacial age ; but when we bear in mind that Scotland has been subjected to the grinding action of several successive ice-sheets, we must admit that very strong evidence is required to prove that any portion of the old preglacial surface of that country has been preserved. It is more reasonable to believe that deposits like those under the till at Woodhill Quarry belong to one of the latest, if not to the very last interglacial period—to that warm era, namely, that preceded the final great extension of land-ice. This belief, so reasonable in itself, is justified by the fact that in the immediate neighbourhood of Woodhill the stratified beds that underlie the till are themselves in certain places underlaid by another deposit of boulder-clay. The succession of changes to be inferred from the evidence is therefore as follows ;—First, a period of intense arctic rigour, when the whole country was covered with ice, underneath which was formed the lower-lying mass of till ; second, a period when the ice melted away from the low grounds and retired to the mountains, and when streams flowed in the grassy valleys, and the climate was such as to nourish herds of the woolly-coated mammoth and the reindeer ; third, a period when the sea gained upon the land to a height of 100 ft. at least, and when molluscs of arctic and northern species lived and died and were buried in silt and sand that gathered over the peaty accumulations in which the remains of the old mammals were stored up ; fourth, a period when intense arctic conditions again prevailed, and another vast ice-sheet crept out from the mountains and covered the low grounds with its *moraine profonde*.

The section of drift exposed at Tangy Glen at a height of 130 ft., clearly proves in like manner a former submergence of the land, for the shells in the underlying clay evidently occur *in situ*. The clay, in short, is part of an old sea-bottom. But although the shelly clay rests directly upon the solid rocks, yet it is by no means certain that the deposit is of preglacial age. Indeed the probabilities are against its being so. We must always remember that the glacial deposits now visible at the surface are more likely to belong to the later than the earlier stages of the Ice Age, and the shell-bed at Tangy Glen is therefore most probably of interglacial age. This inference is much strengthened by the fact that similar shell-bearing clays have been found superimposed upon and covered by till, such as that at Oakshaw Hill, Paisley, where the intercalated shell-bed indicates an interglacial depression of not less than 64 ft. A still more striking example of the same kind is the *Tellina-cal-carea* bed of Chapelhall, Airdrie. Evidently the shelly clay interposed between the under and upper till at that place marks an old sea-bottom, when the sea rose not less (indeed, certainly more) than 526 ft. above its present level.

I have spoken of these shell-beds as *interglacial* deposits, although their fossils indicate the presence of a much colder sea than now flows round the British coast, simply because they are links in the evidence which goes to show that the intense cold of the glacial epoch was interrupted by more or less prolonged intervals during which milder conditions of climate prevailed. In our attempts to realise the physical conditions that obtained at various periods during the glacial epoch, it is necessary, as I have tried by some examples to show, that we should keep in view not only the height above the sea, but also the geographical position of the deposits. Chapelhall, where the shelly clay was got, lies nearly in the centre of that broad tract of lowland country, which is drained by the river Clyde and its tributaries. At the time when a free ocean flowed over the site of the district in question, it is evident that a very large part of the Scottish Lowlands would be submerged. The sea would wash the base of the Kilsyth Hills in the north, and towards the south would extend up the Clyde valley as far, at least, as Hazelbank, a few miles below Lanark.

Now such being the case, a very little consideration will suffice to convince us that however cold the climate may then have been, Scotland could not by any possibility have presented such an intensely arctic aspect as when the ice-sheet was at its thickest. The till that underlies the shelly clay speaks to us of a time when the great central valley of Scotland brimmed with glacier-ice. Under no other condition could a *moraine profonde* gather in the position of that till at Chapelhall. But the presence of the clay with shells shows that a great physical change had supervened, and it seems reasonable to conclude that at the time this shelly clay was deposited the greatest intensity of glacial cold had passed away. But if the accumulation of the lower mass of till at Chapelhall implies the former existence of one great confluent ice-sheet in Scotland ; then, in like manner does the overlying mass of till compel us also to conclude that after a comparatively mild period had endured for some time another mighty ice-sheet again overflowed the land.

I come now to discuss the origin of the shelly tills and the beds with which they are associated. The occurrence of broken shells in boulder-clay has always been a puzzle—many geologists being inclined to support the view of the marine origin of such deposits. But there are insuperable objections to this view. For in most cases the shelly tills do not differ in general structure and appearance from unfossiliferous boulder-clay. They contain perhaps a greater percentage of sand and rolled gravel and grit, and are as a rule less tough than the hard azoic till of the interior, and their included stones and boulders are certainly not generally so well ice-worn and striated as those of the old bottom till of inland districts. But leaving their fossil contents for the moment out of account, they can yet be paralleled by many deposits of unfossiliferous till, more especially by those somewhat looser and less tenacious masses that overlie most of the inter-glacial beds described in the preceding chapters. And if these upper or overlying deposits of till be of the nature of true *moraine profonde,* then the shelly tills must be so like-wise. They certainly bear no resemblance to what we con-ceive iceberg droppings to be ; but their stones and boulders have evidently travelled in one and the same direction, and this coincides with the trend of the underlying rock-striæ ; moreover, the colour of the clay is influenced by the nature of the subjacent rocks in the same way as the typical azoic till of the interior. But these and other points will come out as we examine the evidence.

The first example of a shelly till which I have cited is that described as occurring in the lower part of the Endrick valley, which opens upon the south-east corner of Loch Lomond. I have mentioned this example first because, as it seems to me, the evidence bearing upon the origin of the shelly till is very complete ; and I must refer the reader to Mr. Jack's paper for a very full and able discussion of the question. Only the general results he arrived at can be given here. The shelly till of the Endrick valley overlies at one place a bed of clay containing marine shells, near the bottom of which a reindeer's antler was found, and my colleague has given various reasons for believing that this shelly till was laid down during one of the latest cold periods of the glacial epoch. Having visited the district, I quite agree with this view, and consider the section to be closely paralleled by that at Woodhill Quarry. According to Mr. Jack the succession of changes was as follows : *first,* a period of excessive glaciation, when the whole country was smothered in ice,—a condition of things which may have been interrupted by several interglacial warm eras, although no record of these has been detected in the Endrick valley ; *second,* a time when the great ice-sheet melted away and Loch Lomond formed an arm of the sea, which was tenanted by shells that indicate a somewhat colder temperature than that which now prevails round our shores : at that time the sea must have risen at least 108 ft. above its present level, and the reindeer may then have browsed on its shores ; *third,* a period when ice once more filled up the great mountain-valley in which Loch Lomond lies, and "mounted the rising ground between the Lower Endrick and the Leven to a height of at least 320 ft." This latest great advance of the glacier resulted in the wholesale demolition of the marine deposits which had gathered in the Loch Lomond fiord during the preceding interglacial period. The ice ground up the loose clays, sands, and gravels along with the shells and other marine organisms that lay upon the bottom of the sea and incorporated these with its ground-moraine. Thus it is that broken and rolled shell fragments, and occasional water-worn stones are found scattered confusedly through the matrix of the tumultuous unstratified till. The shelly till of the Endrick is capped by certain other deposits, but we shall refer to these when we come to consider the origin and history of the Upper Drift of Scotland.

It is worth noting that the section where the reindeer's horn was found is just about the same height above the sea as the mammaliferous and marine deposits underlying the till at Woodhill Quarry. Of course this fact does not in any way prove that the shell-beds at the two places are contemporaneous. One may be older than the other, but if it be so, there is really nothing to show which was the first formed.

On the other hand, we cannot help surmising that they may be contemporaneous, and that the reindeer's antler may possibly be a relic of pre-existing freshwater deposits that were demolished during the submergence that gave rise to the marine beds at the bottom of which it was discovered.

I have stated at page 80 that the Scotch ice in all probability coalesced on the floor of the North Sea with the ice that streamed out at the same time from the Scandinavian peninsula. Certain proofs of this extraordinary junction of these ice-sheets which could not well be given before may now be brought forward.

Mr. Jamieson, whose account of the Caithness till has already been referred to, came to the conclusion that the glaciation of the rocks and the transport of the till have been produced by ice coming from the north-west. The distribution of the dark grey till clearly indicates, as he points out, that the movement could not have been from the interior of the country—for the drift derived from the degradation of the "Caithness flags" overlaps the red grit and conglomerate which bound the "flags" in the south-west. But the appearances described by him are equally explicable on the supposition that the ice had come from the south-east. He states, indeed, that where he "observed any indication of a *stosseite* it was on the north-west side;" but as he does not describe any particular instances of this appearance, it is probable that they were not very pronounced, and they can hardly be taken therefore as sufficient to prove a movement in the direction inferred by him. But more than this: a movement from north-west does not explain how it comes to pass that boulders of chalk, oolite, and other rocks that do not occur in Caithness, are nevertheless met with in the Caithness till. Mr. Jamieson holds that marine conditions prevailed during the deposition of the drift in question, and he infers that the agent which produced it was sea-borne ice. He admits, however, that but for the presence of the shells the till could not be distinguished from any typical boulder-clay of the interior. To the iceberg hypothesis of its origin many objections might be taken; but into these I need not go, as they have already been disposed of when treating of the origin of till. It is quite clear that the till of Caithness is just ordinary boulder-clay, *plus* sea-shells, which do not occur in regular beds, but are disseminated through the deposit in the same way as the pebbles and boulders.

Dr. Croll was the first to point out that the presence of the shells is no proof of the marine origin of the till. He showed that all the phenomena could be accounted for by a movement of glacier-ice from the south-east, a direction which at first sight seems impossible. He reminds us, however, that the great ice-sheet deriving from Scandinavia could not possibly have broken up into icebergs in the shallow North Sea, but must have become confluent with that of Scotland; and this junction would necessarily result in the deflection of the large glaciers that streamed out from the north-eastern districts of our island. The natural direction of that ice was undoubtedly down the beds of the Moray and Dornoch Friths away to the north-east, but its path was obstructed by the vast ice-masses that already occupied the bed of the North Sea. Instead of flowing, therefore, in that direction it was forced to turn to north-west, and so to creep across the broad flats of Caithness. In doing so it dragged along with it the silt and mud and marine organisms that were previously distributed over the sea-bottom; and mixing up all these with the usual stones and débris that gathered underneath as it ground on its way, formed thus a bottom-moraine through which broken and scratched shells were dispersed in the same way as stones and boulders. This theory also accounts for the occurrence in the till of Caithness of bits of chalk and oolitic rocks, for there is every reason to believe that areas of these strata occupy the bottom of the Moray Frith. Along the coast of Sutherland a strip of oolitic beds is seen, and the probabilities are that these strata are succeeded out to sea by a series of Cretaceous rocks, from which the chalk fragments in the Caithness till may have been derived.

Dr. Croll's conclusions have recently been confirmed by my brother (Professor Geikie) and Mr. B. N. Peach, whose observations put it beyond doubt that the north-east part of Caithness has really been over-ridden by land-ice flowing in a direction from south-east to north-west. Before I quote what Mr. Peach says, I may mention that the dark greyish shelly till which is found scattered over all the low grounds of Caithness, does not extend farther west than a line drawn between Berriedale on the south to Reay on the north coast of the county.   South-west of Berriedale the till contains no shells, is of a reddish colour, and contains no stones which may not have been derived from the interior of the country. Mr. Peach remarks,* " Near the Ord of Caithness and on to Berriedale the striæ pass off the land and out to sea ; but near Dunbeath, six miles north-east of Berriedale, they begin to creep up out of the sea on to the land, and range from about 15° to 10° east of north.   *Where the striæ pass out to sea* the boulder-clay is made up of the materials from inland and contains no shells, but *immediately the striæ begin to creep up on to the land* then shells begin to make their appearance ; and there is a difference, moreover, in the colour of the clay, for in the former case it is red and incoherent, and in the latter hard and dark coloured."

Dr. Croll has further suggested that the headland of Fraserburgh has been overflowed by ice coming from the south-east.   I think, however, it is more likely that in this case the ice came from the north-west.   The fragments of chalk and oolite which occur in the drifts at so many different points along the shores of Elgin, Banff, and the north of Aberdeenshire, have more probably been derived from rocks lying at the bottom of the Moray Frith than from any submarine district south-east of Fraserburgh.   Mr. Jamieson has also pointed out that along the coast from Banff to Peterhead the prevailing colour of the till is quite like that of Caithness. Moreover, the striæ indicate the former presence of ice moving out to sea by way of the Moray Frith, but compelled to hug the coast in obedience to the same opposing power that forced the ice to overflow the flats of Caithness.   In short, the point of deflection of the Scotch ice I would put about midway between the coast of Caithness and the southern shore of the Moray Frith.

South of Fraserburgh we shall find that all along the eastern seaboard of Scotland the rock-striations on the low grounds have a tendency to turn to the south-east, when there is often no very obvious reason for their doing so.   For example,

* *Climate and Time,* p. 453.

instead of trending down the estuary of the Tay they strike
right across the Fife hills ; and when we trace the striæ along
the southern shore of the Firth of Forth they gradually lead us
away to south-east, until at Coldingham we find them running
parallel with the coast line. Again, if we follow the valley
of the Tweed we shall meet with the same appearances. In
this valley the ice flowed at first towards the north-east
(about Melrose), but as it crept farther down the valley it
began, for no apparent cause, to turn away, first to east, then
to south of east, until at last it rounded the northern spurs
of the Cheviots, and thereafter flowed right away to the
south-east, hugging the maritime district of Northumberland.

Now such a remarkable deviation out of what must have
been the natural course of the Scotch ice, can only be accounted for by inferring the presence in the North Sea of the
Scandinavian ice-sheet. With that vast mass blocking up
its outlet to sea, the Scotch ice was forced away to the south-
east and compelled to invade Northumberland, just as, for
similar reasons, it overflowed so large a part of Caithness.
As good evidence that England was thus invaded, I may
point to the shelly till in the sea-cliff at the mouth of the
Tyne, which contains besides broken shells a number of
stones and boulders which have certainly been derived from
the north.*

We see, therefore, how the appearance of sea-shells in a
tumultuous unstratified till is no evidence in favour of that
till having been formed in the sea. The broken shells occur
precisely in the same way as stones and boulders, and hence
they yield the same kind of evidence as these. For just as
these show in what direction the land-ice moved, so, in like
manner, do the broken shells. Boulders of Perthshire granite
in the till of Fife indicate an ice-flow from the Highlands
towards the south-east—broken shells in the till of Caithness
point to an ice-flow from the sea-bottom to the north-west.

It must be observed, however, that not only in Caithness
but also in Aberdeenshire, beds of silt, &c., containing sea-
shells have been noted underneath the till in various places.
It is highly probable, therefore, that considerable portions of
the low grounds of Scotland were actually submerged, or had

* See further on this subject Chapter xxv.

only recently been vacated by the sea, at the time when land-ice began to creep over Caithness, and that a large proportion of the material (both clay and shells) of the Caithness till was derived from the demolition of those soft marine deposits which cloaked the low-lying parts of the country before the ice-sheet attained its great development. There is no evidence, however, to show that the shelly silt and clay, &c., which here and there occur below the shelly tills of Caithness and Aberdeen are of preglacial age. It is much more likely, as Mr. Jamieson has remarked, that they are of more recent date than the earliest stage of the glacial epoch. I would therefore class them all as interglacial, for the same reason that I include the shell-beds of Chapelhall, Tangy, Glen, &c., among interglacial deposits. That this is not an unreasonable view will, I hope, appear when we have considered the conditions under which the drift deposits in the north of Lewis have been accumulated.

Lewis, as I have already mentioned,* has been glaciated across its whole breadth by land-ice, which poured out from the rugged wilds of Ross-shire, filled up the Minch, and thereafter traversed the northern portion of the Outer Hebrides in a direction from south-east to north-west. The course followed by the ice is proved not only by the position of *roches moutonnées* and other glaciated surfaces, but also by the stones in the till. Thus boulders of red sandstone and conglomerate which could not have been derived from any place nearer than the neighbourhood of Stornoway, occur in the till of the west side of the island. None of the till of the interior, as far as I have examined it, contains a vestige of shells, nor does it ever assume the character of a dark clay, like the shelly tills which I have described as occurring in the extreme north of the island. Indeed, throughout the whole of Lewis the general character of the till † is that of a greyish earthy or clayey grit, often hard, as if it had been subjected to great pressure, and always more or less thickly charged with blunted angular and subangular stones, among which only the finer grained ones show striæ. Such is the general aspect of the deposit on east and west coasts alike. The shelly tills that occur near the Butt are the only fossiliferous

* See *ante*, p. 77.   † *Quart. Jour. Geol. Soc.*, vol. xxxix. p. 532.

clays of the kind I observed. But a dark grey clay, with shells, and covered by sand, may be seen in the Eye Peninsula at Garabost, and it is possible that shelly tills may yet be found at some points along the east coast, between Port of Ness and Broad Bay. I can only say that, with the exceptions already mentioned, no shelly till, to the best of my knowledge, occurs, either in the interior or along the west coast.

The shelly tills shown in the sea-cliffs near the Butt appear to stretch across the island from shore to shore, a distance of two miles, or thereabout, forming a narrow belt of low ground, which does not rise more than 90 feet or so above the sea. The deposits extend for somewhat less than a mile along the east coast, but on the west side of the island one can trace them for a distance of three miles. They die off against the underlying rocks to the north, and disappear to the south under peat.

Having given these additional details, only a few words are needed to show what appears to have been the succession of events in Lewis, so far as these are chronicled by the glacial deposits.

First, then, we have, as in previous cases, evidence of a period of most intense glaciation, when the ice, deriving from the mainland, attained so great a thickness that it filled up the Minch and overflowed Lewis to a height of not less than 1,300 ft. It was underneath this great ice-sheet that much of the unfossiliferous till of Lewis was formed.

It is at first sight difficult to conceive how such a vast thickness of ice could have been generated in this region. But we must remember that just as the rainfall is greatest now along the west coast of Scotland, so in glacial times, as Mr. Jamieson has remarked, the snowfall would likewise be most considerable there, owing to the greater proximity of the sea. Moreover, the Outer Hebrides would act much in the same way as the Scandinavian ice, and tend to block up the ice-flow, which was further impeded by the great sheet that overflowed Caithness in a north-west direction. For I believe it will eventually be found that the Caithness ice, as it swept out over the bed of the Atlantic and was joined by the great glaciers that poured northwards from the wild glens of Sutherland, turned more to the west, so as to surmount the little islets of North Rona and North Barra, which lie rather more than forty miles to the north of the Butt of Lewis.*

Second, there ensued a milder condition of things when the great ice-sheet melted away, but to what extent we cannot tell.

Third, after the partial or complete disappearance of the ice-sheet the sea got access to the Minch, and arctic and boreal species of molluscs lived in its depths, indicating a temperature for the sea somewhat colder than it is in the north of Scotland now.

Fourth, there next ensued a return of glacial conditions, which, however, were probably not so intense as before; glacier-ice, however, filled up the Minch, and was even thick enough to overflow the north end of Lewis, on its way to the deep water beyond; at that time the mud and clay and shells lying at the bottom of the Minch were incorporated with the ground-moraine which the ice dragged with it across the island.

Fifth, a milder condition of things now appears once more to have ensued, the sea again invaded the Minch, and even rose to a greater height than it does at present, while arctic and boreal shells, as before, became its tenants. After a considerable deposition of fine clay and silt had taken place, the sea retired for some distance and the land emerged so far as to allow the waves to denude and re-arrange the shelly silt

---

* I have not visited North Rona, but a quaint story, which I heard from an old man in Lewis, leads me to think that *roches moutonnées* and striated rock-faces must be very conspicuous there. Once upon a time there lived a saintly priest at the Ness, in the north of Lewis, who strove very hard to make the naughty folks in that neighbourhood good men and women. But somehow he didn't succeed: and at last, wearying of his task, he went to the rocks at the Butt and prayed heaven to deliver him from Ness, and its naughty people. And so it came to pass that even while he prayed, a crowd of seals bobbed up their heads at his feet, and seemed to invite him to go with them. The good man consented, and they floated him far away to the island of North Rona. Now whether it was that the rocks of that island were unusually steep and slippy, or the holy man was just as heavy in body as in mind, will perhaps never be known; but, anyhow, the seals had hard work in getting their freight landed. They clawed and scratched, and scratched and clawed at the rocks, but slid back into the water again and again, until after a supreme effort the gasping father was rolled safely ashore. "Now," said my friend, "whether that story is true all through or no I will not presume to say; but if you go to North Rona there you will see the rocks on the shore all polished and smoothed, and much marked with long deep scratches."

and clay and to form coarse gravel, sand, and shingle along an exposed coast-line.

Sixth. Again the cold increased and ice filled up the Minch, rising high enough upon Lewis to overflow its northern extremity, and in doing so to plough into the older drifts, cutting them out in some places, crumpling and confusing them in other places, and here and there mingling its bottom-moraine with them in such a way that now it is sometimes hard to separate the one from the other by any well-defined line.

Seventh. The ice-sheet next finally retired from this region, and its *moraine profonde* and the older drift-deposits were subjected to denudation, and here and there sand and gravel, containing broken and rolled shells of recent littoral species were spread over their surface—thus showing that after the final disappearance of the ice (but how long after we cannot say) the island was submerged to a depth of not less than sixty feet, or thereabout. When this submergence took place the temperature of the neighbouring sea was probably much the same as it is now.*

* When I first (1872) visited the north of Lewis I was under the impression that the succession of shelly tills and intercalated deposits occurring there might be explained by supposing them to have been deposited at or near where an ice-sheet terminated in the sea. I thought the beds between the two tills or boulder-clays might indicate merely a short temporary retreat of the ice during some exceptionally mild years, but subsequent and more detailed observations in the island have satisfied me that the appearances presented by the drifts cannot be thus explained. When we come to consider the glacial deposits of England, we shall find that the succession described above is very closely paralleled by the drifts of Lancashire as these are described by Mr. De Rance and others.

CHAPTER XVII.

INTERGLACIAL DEPOSITS AND SHELLY TILL OF SCOTLAND.— SUMMARY OF RESULTS.

Correlation of interglacial freshwater and marine deposits.—Shelly tills belong mostly to later stages of glacial epoch.—Probable condition of Scotland during deposition of the most recent deposits of boulder-clay.

HAVING now passed in review the evidence supplied by the marine deposits that occur either intercalated with or subjacent to the till, we must next endeavour to sum up the main results obtained.

We have seen, then, that the evidence we have just been considering not only does not contradict but really confirms the conclusions to which an examination of the intercalated and subjacent freshwater beds appeared to lead us. The accumulation of till or boulder-clay was not continuous all over Scotland throughout the glacial epoch. There were periods when the ice, which had extended over all the mainland across the adjacent seas to the outlying islands, eventually melted away so far as to allow the sea to stretch into the interior of Scotland. Such a recession of the ice-sheet could only have been due to an amelioration of climate. A mere submergence of the land could not have brought about so great a change. The ice that covered the low grounds of Scotland, during the early cold stages of the glacial epoch, was certainly more than 2,000 feet in thickness, and it must have been even deeper than this between the mainland and the Outer Hebrides. To cause such a mass to float, the sea around Scotland would require to become deeper than now by 1,400 or 1,500 feet at the least ; and this deepening must have happened more than once, if we are to explain the occurrence of intercalated marine beds in the till by means of extensive depressions of the earth's crust. But

there is what seems to be positive proof that the presence of
a shell-bed, lying between two accumulations of till, really
and truly indicates an interglacial period of milder climatic
conditions. The interglacial shell-bed at Woodhill Quarry,
for example, rests, as we have seen, upon freshwater deposits
containing mammalian remains. We have, therefore, in this
case clear proof that a great ice-sheet melted away from the
low-grounds without the intervention of the sea, leaving
behind it a *moraine profonde*, which, by-and-by, supported
terrestrial vegetation, and was occupied by mammoths and
reindeer—proof, in short, that the ice disappeared and
exposed not a sea-bottom but a land-surface. It was only
after this land had been tenanted for some considerable time
by large quadrupeds that submergence ensued, and molluscs
of boreal and arctic species flourished over the graves of
defunct mammoths and reindeer. Thereafter, confluent
glaciers once more crept out from the mountains, and accumulated their bottom-moraine above the silt and sand over
which the sea-shells had lived.

But it may be asked why the intercalated shell-beds, if
they really mark mild interglacial periods, do not contain an
assemblage of fossils betokening milder conditions of temperature than boreal and arctic. I have already remarked,
in the case of the freshwater interglacial deposits, that, if
Scotland, during the milder intervals of the Ice Age, ever did
experience a warm climate, we could yet hardly hope to meet
with any abundant or decided proof of such genial conditions.
For every mild period of that kind must have been gradually
succeeded by arctic conditions; and, consequently, deposits
laid down during the former stage would be afterwards subjected to excessive denudation; first, by rivers and other
subaerial forces, and lastly, by glaciers. We have also to
remember that the land, during the invasion of the sea,
would be still further acted upon, and loose freshwater accumulations would often be obliterated. I suspect that the
solitary reindeer's antler, found underneath the shell-bed at
Croftamie, may be the sole surviving relic of some such
interglacial freshwater deposit which was broken up and
re-arranged by the sea when it first got access to the Endrick
valley. In short, if we only give the question a little con-

sideration, we must perceive that of all interglacial deposits, those betokening cold temperate conditions would stand the best chance of preservation.

The occurrence of interglacial marine beds shows us that the glacial epoch was characterised now and again by considerable submergence of the land—the greatest submergence of which we have proof being upwards of five hundred feet. But the land may have been drowned to a greater extent than that—the traces left by the sea having been destroyed by the later glaciation. How many submergences there were, we cannot at present, and, perhaps, never may be able to say. That many of the interglacial shell-beds referred to in previous pages may be contemporaneous is quite possible, nay, even probable. But there is nothing sufficiently distinctive in the deposits to justify us in attempting to correlate them. Some, indeed, have evidently been accumulated in deeper water than others, and it is quite clear that all the deposits cannot be strictly contemporaneous. It is certain, for example, that the *Tellina-calcarea* bed of Chapelhall (526 ft. above the sea) could not have been accumulated at the same time as the mussel-bed of Oakshaw Hill (53 ft. above the sea). One of these beds (perhaps that of Chapelhall) is clearly older than the other. But then they may both have been deposited at different stages of one and the same interglacial period.

And if the difficulty of correlating the various marine interglacial beds be great or even insuperable, we do not find it any easier to dovetail these with the interglacial deposits of freshwater origin, or even to correlate the latter with each other. The evidence points to there having been several great changes of climate, and that is about all we can say. Nevertheless, we may be allowed to suspect that many of the Scotch interglacial deposits, as well marine as freshwater, belong to one of the latest, perhaps to the very last, mild interval that preceded the final great extension of confluent glaciers.

One may note in many cases that the till which overlies interglacial deposits is not infrequently a somewhat looser clay than the generally excessively tough lower till that clings to the rocks underneath. Often, too, the stones and

boulders of the overlying till are, as a whole, less well
smoothed and striated than those in the boulder-clay below.
Too much stress, however, may easily be laid upon these
circumstances, for the nature of the till depends very largely
upon the character of the débris out of which it has been
formed. But even after making all due allowance for this,
one cannot help being struck with the fact that the upper or
overlying boulder-clays should so often differ from the under
till; for, when two beds of boulder-clay occur in one and
the same section, the lower almost invariably proves the
tougher of the two, and its included stones very frequently
show stronger marks of glaciation, than the somewhat more
angular and less polished stones and boulders of the upper.
Moreover, in not a few instances, one can be pretty sure that
the upper boulder-clay above an interglacial bed does really
belong to the last great extension of the ice-sheet, and therefore he may reasonably infer that in such a case the interglacial deposits most probably belong to the latest mild
interval of the glacial epoch. I have no doubt, for example,
after having carefully surveyed the drift deposits of the
valley of the Irvine and the adjacent regions, that the till at
Woodhill Quarry was laid down as ground-moraine at the
time of the very last incursion of the great ice-sheet, and
that therefore the deposits of that place give us a glimpse of
the conditions that obtained in Scotland during the latest
interglacial era. And these, as it will be remembered, were:
first, a land-surface followed in the next place by submergence. But whether it was during that same period of submergence that the sea rolled over the site of Chapelhall with
a depth of not less than five hundred and twenty-six feet, one
cannot positively assert; although this is much more likely
to be true than that the Chapelhall shell-bed should belong
to any earlier period of submergence.

In the present state of the evidence, it appears most
reasonable to hold that the shelly tills, as far as these have
yet been studied, belong, for the most part, to the latest
stages of the glacial epoch. They seem to show that the
last great ice-sheet that enveloped the mainland had to make
its way over considerable heaps of silt, mud, and sand, which
had accumulated during a considerable submergence of the

land in the quiet recesses of bays and fiords. We have seen how this conclusion is borne out by an examination of the shelly tills of the Endrick Valley, Caithness, Aberdeenshire, and Lewis. The shelly tills of Wigtownshire have had a similar origin, and probably belong to the same date as those just mentioned.

I do not go so far, however, as to infer that all deposits of till in which shells occur have been formed in precisely the same way as those of Caithness and Lewis. In some cases, they appear rather to have been deposited at, or near, where great glaciers terminated in the sea. The till at Berwick may have been formed under such conditions, and the boulder-clay with intercalations of sand and gravel and rolled shells which occurs near Ballantrae probably had a similar origin.

It is well known that in alpine countries the glaciers sometimes advance beyond their usual limits, and the same in all likelihood is the case with the great glaciers of Greenland. It is, therefore, not unreasonable to believe that during our glacial epoch the ice-rivers may have been subject to similar fluctuations, which may well have continued to recur even up to the time when the great ice-sheet had retired from the neighbouring seas. It is easy, therefore, to see how, during such a temporary advance, the submarine heap of clay, stones, sand, and gravel lying in front of a glacier that projected from the land, would be pushed forward and thrown into confusion. The shells would often be crushed and broken, and the deposits themselves would become intermingled with the *moraine profonde*.

The annexed section from the south of Ayrshire (Fig. 39)

Fig. 39.—Upper and lower till or boulder-clay ; River Stinchar.

exhibits not a few of the very features which a little consideration would lead one to expect in a deposit accumulated under these conditions. The section shows at *t* a tough tenaceous brown clay, quite unstratified and stuck full of finely-scratched and smoothed stones ; it has a hummocky, uneven surface, and has evidently suffered much denudation, no trace of it being found upon the solid rocks at *r*. This is undoubtedly a portion of some of the oldest till which accumulated under the ice-sheet when that had reached a great development. The overlying deposit is more or less distinctly bedded in parts, the bedded portions being indicated by the faint lines. At x it consists of thin layers of fine gravel, earthy clay, and sand, with stones scattered throughout, some of which are striated. Towards the top, the gravel is much coarser, not so well-bedded, and contains many angular blocks and stones, some of them smoothed and scratched. At *g*, we see a stony clay, looser and earthier than the subjacent till, and only faintly stratified. The stones, while usually smoothed and scratched, are, upon the whole, not so distinctly marked in this way as the stones in the till below.

Such accumulations as this are not infrequently met with in maritime regions, and although they do not always or even often contain shells, yet these, as in the cases of the Berwick and Ballantrae sections, do sometimes occur. When followed inland they are often replaced by till of the usual character, into which they appear to pass. At other times they graduate into a rude kind of débris, not distinguishable from that boulder-earth and moraine-rubbish, which shall come before our notice presently.

The confused, semi-stratified, and occasionally fossiliferous boulder-clays which I have just described, seem therefore to have been the conjoint production of the ice-sheet and the sea—consisting partly of true *moraine profonde*, and partly of the nature of a submarine terminal moraine. Hence it is that they sometimes show more or less distinct bedding, and at other times contain bands and layers of sand, gravel, and clay, in which sea-shells or fragments of sea-shells are occasionally detected. The absence of these, however, cannot always be considered decisive against the marine-morainic origin of such deposits. We know that even in arctic regions rivers and torrents escape freely all the year round from the

glaciers that terminate on shore, and it can hardly be otherwise with those which shed their icebergs in deep water.
Now the presence of any large body of fresh water constantly
flowing out from beneath the ice could hardly fail to keep
away marine organisms from that portion of the sea-bed
immediately in front of the glacier.   And it seems, therefore,
far from improbable that this may be one reason why the
stratified portions of the rude boulder-clays described above do
not more frequently contain shells and other exuviæ.

From the examples of fossiliferous till now adduced and
commented upon, we may gather that the mere presence of
shells scattered through the matrix of a stony clay is no
proof that the sea has had any direct influence in its production.
The geographical position of the deposit must always be considered.   Thus, in the case of the Caithness till, we may feel
assured that it could not have been laid down at or near the
front of a glacier terminating in the sea, and the same may
be asserted of the shelly tills in the north of Lewis.   But it
is otherwise with such fossiliferous boulder-clays as occur at
or near the coast immediately opposite the mouths of valleys,
which may well have been occupied by glaciers at a time
when the great ice-sheet was melting away, and when the
sea reached to a greater height than it does at present.

We have now seen, as the result of an examination of the
stratified deposits that occur underneath or are intercalated
with the till or boulder-clay, that the accumulation of a
moraine profonde by one great ice-sheet was interrupted
several times ; that the ice-sheet vanished from the low
grounds, and even from many of the upland valleys, and that
rivers and lakes then appeared where before all had been
snow and ice.   We have also learned that during such mild
interglacial periods, oxen, deer, horses, mammoths, reindeer,
and no doubt other animals besides these, occupied the land,
which was clothed to some extent with grasses and such trees
as oak, alder, willow, and hazel.   Moreover, we have ascertained that the land itself experienced at least one considerable submergence, which probably occurred immediately
before the last great extension of the ice-sheet, and during
which the sea that covered the drowned districts of the
country was tenanted by molluscs of northern habitats.   No

definite conclusion, however, as to the climate of interglacial times can be drawn from these organic remains. The deposits which contain them are much too fragmentary to enable us to say, with anything like certainty, that interglacial Scotland never enjoyed a milder climate than is now experienced in cold temperate regions. But, as we shall see in the sequel, a study of the glacial deposits in other countries throws no small light upon this difficult question. Again, we can have no doubt that the generally looser consistency of the upper boulder-clay or till, and the less severely glaciated aspect of its included stones and boulders, point to ice-sheets of less depth and extent than that underneath which the lowest-lying tough tenacious till was formed. During the formation of the latter, the whole of Scotland was buried underneath snow and ice, and such being the case, the surface of the great *mer de glace* could not be covered with stones and débris, as are the puny glaciers of the Alps. The moraines gathering below and in front of the earlier great ice-sheets would, therefore, contain few or no rough unpolished stones. But when, in later cold stages of the glacial epoch, the ice-sheets failed to attain the vast breadth and depth of the earlier *mers de glace*, there would not only be less pressure exerted upon the bottom-moraine, but angular blocks and stones, derived by the action of frost from slowly emerging crags and cliffs, would be introduced from above, and, sinking through fissure and crevasse, would mingle with the loose débris of sand and clay and gravel that travelled on underneath the ice. By-and-by, as mountain-tops and ridges began to stand boldly up above the general level of the melting ice-sheet, and so by degrees to separate it into a series of large local glaciers, it is evident that long trains of blocks and rubbish would begin to sprinkle the surface of the glaciers. This débris, slowly carried downwards, would eventually topple over the terminal front of the ice, and mingle with the glacial mud and stones which were being extruded upon the sea-bottom. Thus there would be mixed together in one and the same deposit heaps of scratched stones, with quantities of rough blocks and débris ; and it is plain, moreover, that the action of the sea upon the morainic rubbish-heaps in front of the glacier would tend occasionally to give a stratified arrangement to the detritus, sometimes even sifting the materials and forming beds of clay, sand, and gravel. In such beds it would only be natural that shells of arctic species should sometimes become entombed.

During such a condition of things the rocky parts of the coast between separate glacier valleys would no doubt be fringed with a belt of ice, just as at present is the case in Greenland, and this ice-foot occasionally breaking off would float away with the rocky rubbish and débris which alternate freezings and thawings had detached from the cliffs and showered upon it. In this manner rock-fragments from a distant part of the country might be dropped upon the bed of the sea, and so get intermingled with morainic matter carried down by glaciers from the interior.

The conditions that brought about the accumulation of the more recent deposits of boulder-clay are thus seen to have differed to some extent from those that prevailed when the older stony clays were formed. During the formation of the latter the ice was much thicker, and extended farther nto the sea. It may even have been that the land itself stood at a greater elevation, as it certainly appears to have done in preglacial times.* But in the later glacial periods the ice-sheets were most probably of less extent than in the earlier stages of the great cycle. When the youngest boulder-clay of certain maritime regions began to be thrown down, all the valleys were filled with ice, but not to overflowing. The watersheds and elevated ridges now broke up the *mer de glace* into a series of separate glaciers, and it is to this period that some of the crossing sets of rock-striæ described at p. 64 must be referred. When the *mer de glace* became less continuous the glaciers would sometimes change their direction, being less impeded in their course by the pressure of neighbouring ice-masses. During the former periods of great confluent ice-sheets the condition of Scotland closely resembled that of the antarctic polar continent, but at the time the latest deposits of boulder-clay were being accumulated it more nearly approached to the present aspect of Greenland. Great glaciers reached the sea, which probably did not then reach a much higher level than now, and presented steep faces of ice

* See Chapter xxx.

to the swell of the Atlantic ; but between the glacier-valleys were long stretches of rocky coast-line, fringed with a shelf of ice like that which flanks the shores of many regions that border on the dreary Arctic Ocean. Coast ice and bergs floated about, and the bottom of the sea was tenanted by arctic molluscs.

CHAPTER XVIII.

UPPER DRIFT DEPOSITS OF SCOTLAND.

Morainic débris and perched blocks of Loch Doon district; of Stinchar valley; of northern slopes of Solway basin; of Rinns of Galloway; of the Clyde and Tweed valleys; of the Northern Highlands.—Erratics; carried chiefly by glaciers; have travelled in directions corresponding with the trend of the rock-striæ.—Condition of Scotland during the carriage of the erratics that occur at high levels.—Occurrence of erratics at higher levels than the rock masses from which they have been derived.

WE come now to consider the nature and origin of the upper drifts—those deposits, namely, which belong upon the whole to a later date than the till or boulder-clay. They consist, as will be seen presently, of very diverse materials, and the mode of their formation has long been the subject of contention. It is a matter of no little moment, as the sequel will show, that we should ascertain what was the precise sequence of events that followed upon the deposition of the upper or newest accumulations of boulder-clay; and this we can only do by carefully considering the evidence in detail.

Turning attention first to the hilly districts—to the great uplands of the south—we find that the till, in a sorely denuded state, is frequently covered by a coarse earthy débris of angular fragments and large blocks and boulders, some of which show traces of glacial striæ, although as a rule these are faint. This débris, which is of very variable thickness, ranging from a few feet up to many yards, ascends to great heights upon the sides of the mountains, and may be traced far down the valleys, even into the low grounds beyond. Thus, for example, the mountains that hem in Loch Doon (Ayrshire) are sprinkled with loose angular and subangular stones, some of them striated, and with immense numbers of large boulders of grey granite which do not belong to the hills upon which they rest, but have travelled outwards from the central mountain region. The angular débris, as we trace it down the valley, appears to become thinner and thinner, until, when we reach the low grounds about Dalmellington, it cannot be distinguished. But the grey granite boulders are more easily detected, and appear here and there on the hill-sides for several miles farther down the valley. They are not, however, confined to the immediate slopes of the valleys of that district, but are scattered promiscuously over all the hill-tops up to a height of 1,700 ft. In the valley of the Stinchar, which drains the same great mountain tract, similar appearances may be noted; angular rubbish, occasionally forming irregular hummocks and low mounds, and large boulders are scattered abundantly over the hill-slopes down as far, at least, as the village of Colmonell, and they even appear near the very top of Beneraird (1,400 ft. above the sea). The same facts have been observed by my colleagues on the Geological Survey in the valleys that drain towards the Solway Frith. The wild mountain tracts of Galloway that overlook the Water of Luce, the Cree, the Ken, the Urr, &c., are abundantly coated with earthy débris and angular rubbish. Everywhere great boulders are distributed over the valley-slopes and hill-tops and even over the low grounds beyond. Thus the low-lying Rinns of Galloway, according to Mr. D. R. Irvine,* show numerous loose boulders of grey granite which have come from the hills of Cairnsmore to the north-east. In all these districts, in short, there is abundant evidence to show that both the angular débris and the boulders or *erratics*, as they are termed, have radiated outwards from the central knot of mountains down all the principal valleys to the low grounds. We meet with the like phenomena in the valleys of the Clyde and the Tweed. Loose earthy and clayey rubbish, containing some scratched stones, and large erratics sprinkle the sides of the hills up to considerable heights, and this for many miles down the course of those valleys. In the Tweed valley, for example, such débris appears in decided masses as far down as Drummelzier, and it occurs loosely scattered over the valley-slopes even as far down as Traquair. The deep glens of the Highlands present us with similar phenomena. The mountain-slopes are everywhere sprinkled

---

* See *Mem. Geol. Surv. Scot.*, Exp. of Sheet 3, par. 39.

with loose earthy rubbish, in which a few faintly glaciated stones sometimes appear, and large erratics occur up to all levels, even as high as 3,000 ft., according to Mr. Jamieson.

The angular rubbish is unquestionably of morainic origin —it answers in every respect to the rude débris which gathers on the surface of an Alpine glacier and is shot over the end of the ice, where it mingles with the detritus pushed out from underneath, to form a terminal moraine. It speaks to us, then, of a time when all the mountain-valleys were yet filled with ice—with massive local glaciers, the direct descendants of the great ice-sheet that produced the till or boulder-clay. While the youngest boulder-clay was being deposited the ice-

Fig. 40.—Perched Block.

sheet continued to retire until at last it no longer reached the sea, but deposited its moraines upon the land. It still covered a large part of the Lowlands, but such hills as the Lammermuirs, the Pentlands, and the Ochils, now rose above the level of the *mer de glace*, while in the Highlands and the Southern Uplands the ice was restricted, for the most part, to the valleys. It was only under conditions such as these that the morainic débris, sprinkled over the hill-tops and occurring far down the valleys, could have been deposited.

Now let us glance for a little at the testimony of the erratic blocks, and see how this agrees with the evidence yielded by the ancient morainic débris.

Erratics are of all shapes and sizes—occasionally reaching

PLATE VII.

COOLIN MOUNTAINS, SKYE.   Erratics resting on glaciated rocks in foreground.   (By H. M. Skae.)   *To face p.* 199.

colossal proportions, and containing many hundred cubic feet. Some are well rounded, others only partially so, and very many are angular and subangular; not a few also show one or more scratched surfaces. In certain districts they are exceedingly abundant. I have already described how they occur in the valleys of the Southern Uplands and are plentifully scattered over the hill-tops up to considerable heights in that region, and how common they also are in the low grounds that sweep out from the base of these hills. Reference has likewise been made to their frequent occurrence in similar positions in the Highlands.

In the intermediate Lowlands they are not wanting, but large numbers have disappeared in the progress of agriculture, so that they are not so plentiful as they used to be. But upon the slopes of those more or less isolated hilly tracts which rise up between the Highlands on the one hand and the Southern Uplands on the other, they are often abundantly met with. Along the northern flanks of the Sidlaws and the Ochils, for example, we find them thickly strewn. They consist in those districts of such rocks as mica-schist, gneiss, granite, &c., all of which have evidently been derived from the highland mountains to the north and north-west. Boulders of similar rocks also make their appearance still farther south. They are met with here and there in the low-lying parts of Fife, and Mr. Maclaren has described the occurrence of a large mass of mica-slate at a height of 1,020 ft. on the Pentland Hills—the nearest rock from which it could have come lying fifty miles to the north, or eighty miles to the west. Boulders of highland rocks have also been noted on the northern slopes of the Lammermuir Hills. They likewise occur in considerable numbers on the crests of the trappean heights that rise between the valleys of the Clyde and Irvine. In the south-west of Scotland, as already indicated, those undulating and hilly districts that roll out from the foot of the Galloway mountains, are studded with innumerable boulders which have radiated outwards from the central heights. Even the islands that lie off the coasts are dotted over with loose boulders or erratics, which can frequently be shown to have travelled great distances. Thus, for example, I found in Lewis large erratics of red sandstone, and certain

porphyries which, from their position, could only have been
derived from the mainland.

Erratics rest on bare rock, till, and angular débris alike, and
they are also found on the slopes of certain hillocks of gravel
and sand in the Lowlands.   The position they occupy in the
mountain-valleys is often precarious—perched at a great
height on some narrow ledge or jutting point of rock, where
it would seem as if a slight push might send them bounding
to the bottom.

As a general rule they prove to have been carried from
higher to lower levels ; the rocks of which they once formed
a part stand at a greater elevation than those upon which
they now repose.   But to this rule there are exceptions ; for
loose boulders are occasionally found at a considerably greater
height than the rock from which they have been broken.*

What, then, do we learn from the erratics ?   How do we
account for the scattering of these far-travelled blocks over,
we may say, the whole face of the country ?   Some of them,
it is evident, must have crossed wide valleys and considerable
hills before they came to a final rest.   The highland boulders
on the Pentlands and the Lammermuirs, for example, after
crossing Strathallan or Strathearn, traversed either the Campsie
or the Ochil Hills, and passed athwart the broad vale of the
Forth before they finished their journey.   By what agent
were they transported ?   The answer is—by a colossal glacier.
So in like manner would I account for the presence of the
numerous grey granite boulders that strew the slopes of the
Galloway mountains, and are found distributed far and wide
over the low grounds at their base ; for the boulders that
cluster so numerously along the northern face of the Sidlaws
and the Ochils ; for the perched blocks that occur up to great
heights in the glens and valleys of the Highlands ; and for
those that dot the surface of Orkney and Shetland and the
islands of the Hebrides.   But, as I shall point out in the
sequel, ice-rafts may also have had something to do with the
distribution of certain erratics.

It is a fact that most, if not all, the erratics have travelled

* Some of the most remarkable examples of this kind are met with in Galloway.   My colleague, Mr. J. Horne, found large erratics of granite up to a height
of 2,764 feet, on the Merrick,—the highest level reached by the granite *in place*
being only 2,270 feet.

in directions that coincide with the trend of the rock-striæ. Thus in Lewis we get boulders of Cambrian sandstone on the beach at Barvas (on the west side of the island), and at the Butt, which have evidently travelled either from Stornoway, or the mainland ; now the low grounds of Lewis are glaciated from south-east to north-west. In Aberdeenshire and Forfar all the erratics have streamed outwards from the mountains. It is the same in Perthshire, Argyle, Ross, and other highland districts. In the southern counties the same rule holds strictly true. The erratics lying loose upon the ground have moved in the identical direction followed by the till of the same regions—a direction which it need hardly be said coincides with that of the underlying rock-striations. Indeed, when the till is carefully searched it not infrequently yields fragments of the same rocks as those of which the erratics lying loose at the surface are composed. Thus, as mentioned in a previous page, fragments of highland rocks are got in the till of the Ochils, the Campsies, and the Paisley Hills. I have seen also bits of mica-schist in the till at Reston in Berwickshire.

Let us for a moment recall the appearance presented by Scotland during the accumulation of the till, and then consider what would be likely to result upon a gradual change of climate. When the cold was at its climax one great sheet of snow and ice enveloped the whole country, above which perhaps only the tips of some of the higher mountains appeared. As this ice-sheet melted away, and the great confluent glaciers withdrew from the bed of the shallow seas, of course the surface of the ice must have been lowered in proportion, for melting would take place atop just as at the extremities. As a consequence of this, more and more of the mountain districts would peer above the waste, and frost would then rupture the rocks—and rubbish, and débris, and great blocks falling upon the ice, would be carried outwards in the direction of its flow. In this way long trains of erratics would be travelling north, south, east, and west, from the Highlands, and in similar directions from the Southern Uplands. As the ice continued to melt, hills like the Pentlands would begin to rise above the level of the ice, and form islands in a great *mer de glace;* and just as the retreating tide will strew the beach with the waifs of ocean, so the ice-current, as it pressed upon and slowly crept away from these desolate islands, would leave upon their frozen shores the wreckage of the distant mountains. The surface of the ice still sinking, erratics would be left stranded on mountain-slopes and hill-sides at ever decreasing levels, until at last, the *mer de glace* having shrunk beyond the reach of the waves, erratics toppled over the terminal fronts of the glaciers upon the Low-lands themselves. And so the process would continue until the glaciers had melted away from the low grounds and shrunk back into the mountain-valleys.

It would thus appear that the erratics belong to different stages of the glacial epoch. Those that lie upon the islands, and, at great heights on such hills as the Pentlands, are, in all probability, as old as some of the upper boulder-clays, while those occurring at lower levels, and nearer to the moun-tains, must date to less remote times.

Among the many puzzling phenomena which glacialists have endeavoured to explain, not the least perplexing is the occurrence of loose erratics and perched blocks at considerably higher levels than the rock masses of which they once formed a part. Such erratics have been noted, not only in this country, but in glaciated regions elsewhere ; perhaps the most remarkable examples being those which Scandinavian and American geologists have made known to us.* Mr. Darwin, many years ago, attempted to explain such anomalies in the glacial phenomena of our own country, by supposing that the erratics had been floated about on massive icebergs during a period of depression. He conceived that, as the land sank down, the bergs stranded or dropped their stony burdens at higher and higher levels of the drowning country. This ingenious explanation compels us, of course, to make one of two assumptions—namely, either that the movement of depression was rapidly effected, or that the icebergs were endowed with extraordinary longevity. Or, again, we might combine the two assumptions, and hold both that the down-ward movement was rapid, and that the icebergs took long years to melt away. I fear, however, that the theory is more ingenious than satisfactory. There are many considerations

* See Chapters xxxii. and xxxv.

that militate against it, amongst which I shall only mention this, that we have no evidence of such a degree of submergence having obtained in this country, Scandinavia, or North America, as would be necessary to account for the elevated position of many of the erratics in question. There are, no doubt, other objections which might be urged to Mr. Darwin's explanation ; but it is hardly necessary, at least for my present purpose, to specify the reasons that have led me to the belief that another explanation of the difficulty must be sought for.

The opinion held by Scandinavian geologists, and by many glacialists in this country, with whom I have conversed upon the subject, is that the erratics under review have been deposited in their present positions by land-ice. No one, however, has yet succeeded in showing how land-ice could have carried these large blocks from lower to higher levels. It is obviously impossible that the boulders could have travelled upon the surface of the ice in the usual way, nor is it credible that they could have been pushed on underneath along with the *moraine profonde* or till—for frequently they show no marks of abrasion or striation, but are in all respects similar to the large angular blocks that fringe the sides of Alpine glaciers.

Recent researches of my own having directed my attention more particularly to this curious problem, I am induced to believe that an explanation of the difficulty may eventually be found in certain phenomena which have been observed in Alpine glaciers. Among the late Principal Forbes' numerous letters on glaciers, addressed to Professor Jameson, there is one bearing date 12th December, 1846, in which some remarkable observations are recorded. I am not aware that the observations to which I am about to refer have ever been considered by geologists, nor do I know that any physicist has attempted another explanation of the phenomena than the one which seems to have satisfied Forbes.* The phenomena in question relate to " the supposed tendency of glaciers to

---

* Dr. Croll's molecular theory of glacier motion accounts well for the transport of boulders from lower to higher levels underneath the ice—it shows how the *moraine profonde* could be forced up a hill-side ; and it is not opposed to the explanation given above of the mode in which rough unpolished erratics have been carried from lower to higher levels.

reject impurities, and the undoubted fact that stones are always found near or upon the surface of the ice." "It is strange," says Forbes, "that it should not have occurred to every one who sought to explain the appearance of stones on the surface by the *ablation* of the ice, that in order to arrive there at all, the blocks must previously have been embedded in the virgin ice, where popular belief, and, generally speaking, more accurate observations also, give them no place." Forbes then proceeds to give several examples of the phenomena, which I cannot do better than quote in his own words. Referring to the extruded stones on the Glacier du Nant Blanc, near Chamouni, he remarks that "the right bank of this glacier is at first bounded by rocky summits, but in the lower part of its course by a mound-like moraine of the usual form. The surface-blocks can only be derived from the precipices near the origin. Yet they do not even appear on the surface opposite the rocks, but only opposite to the moraine; and they increase in number and quantity towards the lower end of the glacier, where they almost blacken the surface of the right side, the left side remaining almost clean. It is difficult to believe that this accumulation is not due to the gradual denudation of the blocks by the melting of the ice in which they have been in some way or other embedded; but it is scarcely less difficult to admit that having fallen from the rocks above the *névé*, they should have remained unperceived in the ice during all the intermediate space.

"To take another example. The Glacier of the Rhone is distinguished by the extraordinary purity of its surface, and the consequent absence of lateral moraines. But this general freedom from stones on the surface is subject to one exception, which is remarkable. *Stones begin to appear at the surface on the terminal slope at a considerable height.* How came they there? Not a stone the size of the fist can be seen on the surface farther up; and in examining a number of the crevasses I could not see any engorged in the ice. The explanation seems to be, that these stones are actually introduced into the ice by friction at the bottom of the glacier, and forced upwards by the action of the *frontal resistance* which produces the *frontal dip* of the veined structure, and they are finally dispersed on the surface by the melting of the ice."*

This explanation is of course bound up with the "viscous theory," and those who hold that the subsequent researches of Dr. Tyndall, and other physicists, have overturned Forbes' theory of the origin of the ribboned structure of glaciers, may be inclined to put these observations aside. But the facts recorded by Forbes have an interest for geologists, apart altogether from their bearing on the cause of glacier motion. Whether, as Forbes supposed, stones are carried upwards through the solid mass of a glacier by the filamentary sliding of the particles of ice—the curves of ejection corresponding exactly with those of forced separation—is a question for physicists to consider. It is enough for the geologist to know that stones apparently do travel upwards through the ice, nor will *ablation* alone suffice to explain the fact. If, for example, a boulder which has fallen into a crevasse and become embedded at a depth of 80 or 100 feet, should re-appear upon the surface of the glacier at a point farther down the valley, it is evident that its reappearance at a relatively higher level in the glacier cannot be due to the melting of the ice alone. At one place it lies at 80 or 100 feet below the surface, but after the glacier has flowed for some distance, it reappears at the surface; that is to say, it seems to have risen 80 or 100 feet through the ice. If 80 or 100 feet of ice have been removed by melting and evaporation, then this loss has been again made good, but not by the accumulation of snow upon the surface of the glacier—the ice has been kept at its general level by the new supplies which are con-tinually pouring into the valley at its origin. In other words, the ice in front rises just as fast as the ice advances from behind; it is thus that the general level of the glacier is maintained. Now the line of ejection along which the boulder has travelled cannot possibly dip at the same angle as the slope of the valley; for if that were the case the boulder would always remain embedded in the ice, at the same distance from the underlying rock, until it was ejected at the terminal front of the glacier. But although the line of ejection must always dip at a less angle than the valley,

* *Edin. Phil. Jour.*, January, 1847.

yet it will in most cases still have a more or less perceptible dip in the same direction as the valley. A great deal will depend upon the boldness of the obstructions that impede the flow of the glacier. If these are numerous and formidable, then the lines of ejection will approximate more and more to the horizontal, and even at last curve upward, so as to dip *up* instead of *down* the valley ; and thus boulders introduced into the ice at a given point will, as they are borne down the valley, not only rise as it were through the glacier, but eventually be extruded at a level which may be many feet, or even many yards, higher than the point in the valley from which they originally started.

It seems to me that such must be the case, no matter what theory of glacier motion we hold. Forbes may be wrong in having maintained that the curves of ejection correspond with those of " forced separation," and his explanation of the veined structure may also be entirely wrong, although this can hardly be said to have been established, for not a few of the objections to his theory proceed upon the assumption that " the fracture and regelation theory " of glacier motion is demonstrably true. Tyndall has shown that the ribboned structure is due to pressure, and this may be freely admitted by those who may still cling to the " viscous theory." It remains to be proved, however, that there is no such filamentary sliding of the ice particles over each other as Forbes contended for. The experiments of the late Canon Moseley seem indeed to cut away the legs of both Forbes' and Tyndall's theories, but the molecular theory advanced by Dr. J. Croll obviates Canon Moseley's difficulties, and may eventually show us that Forbes was not so far wrong when he insisted that there is a motion of the ice particles parallel to the direction of the blue veins in glaciers.

But however this may be, it is enough for us, as geologists, to know that stones introduced into the body of a glacier, whether from above or below, tend to rise upwards in the ice, as the glacier flows on its way. And I now ask whether this fact does not throw some light on the curious problem which forms the subject of our present inquiry ? Let us picture to ourselves a mountainous country, such as Scotland or Scandinavia, covered with a wide ice-sheet, or series of confluent

glaciers, and endeavour in imagination to follow the course
of some hypothetical boulder which has become embedded in
the ice. We shall conceive that this boulder has been introduced by friction into the ice at the bottom of some valley
in the interior of the country. As the ice creeps outwards,
the stone gradually rises, the path which it follows sloping at
a less angle than the bed over which the ice flows. Did no
obstruction intervene, it is evident that the boulder, while it
rose through the body of the ice, would be at the same
time travelling gradually to lower levels than the point from
which it originally set out. And it is quite conceivable that
under such circumstances a stone might rise as it were
through a thickness of several thousand feet of glacier ice,
and yet be eventually extruded at a lower level than the
rock of which it once formed a part. But then we know
that countless obstacles intervened to impede the flow of the
massive ice-sheets of the Glacial Epoch ; and with every such
obstruction the glacier masses must have been forced to
bulge upwards by the intense *vis a tergo ;* and such upward
movement of the ice, being again and again repeated, imprisoned boulders and débris would be compelled just as
often to rise to higher and higher levels. Let us suppose
that our hypothetical boulder is travelling in a nearly level
course towards some ice-smothered hill. As the ice approaches this obstacle, it begins to bulge upwards, and our
boulder is, as it were, forced up an inclined plane. Eventually, however, the ice sweeps round and overflows the
obstacle, and thereafter continues on its course. There being
now less longitudinal pressure, the included boulder will not
rise so rapidly, but will travel either in a horizontal line, or
down a gently-inclined plane. Let us suppose, further, that
such obstructions to the flow of the ice supervene again and
again, until at last the boulder is carried into some embayed
recess of the ice-drowned country, such as one may see
represented in miniature by sheltered hollows in the bed of
a river. Now, in such a recess our boulder may linger for a
considerable time, but as the ice is always melting and
evaporating at the surface, and the loss thus caused is being
continually made good by the advance of ice from behind, it
is evident that unless the stratum of ice containing our

boulder manages to creep out of the embayed recess as an "undertow," it will be forced to rise higher and higher until it becomes coalescent with that portion of the current which overflows all obstacles at a higher level. By this time our boulder, having travelled, let us say, fifty or a hundred miles, may have been carried to a level many hundred feet or yards above that from which it originally started. We have now only further to conceive that, after a greater or lesser number of such vicissitudes, the boulder is at last extruded at the surface, and stranded on the side of some rocky hill that peers like an island above the surface of the far-stretching *mer de glace.*

Now, cases like this must have occurred again and again during the growth, continuance, and decay of the massive ice-sheets that once enveloped Scotland. We know from actual observation that just such obstacles as I have alluded to did really obstruct the flow of the Scotch ice. The confluent glaciers were frequently deflected, now to the right, now to the left, sometimes by opposing high grounds, at other times by masses of ice flowing in a different direction. This we can read in the trend of *roches moutonnées* and striæ, in the dispersal of the stones in the till, and the distribution of loose erratics and perched blocks. Nay, we have even clear evidence to show that sometimes the under strata of the ice flowed in one direction, while the ice sweeping along at the surface followed a different route. Hence we can have no difficulty in admitting that such heaping up and bulging of the ice as is required to account for the transport of boulders from lower to higher levels must frequently have taken place in Scotland during the Glacial Epoch.

The generally non-glaciated aspect of the boulders in question is also perfectly accounted for on the theory I have ventured to advance. Once embedded in the ice, stones and boulders might travel for hundreds of miles without suffering abrasion. The well-known incident of the knapsack[*] which was lost in a crevasse of the Glacier du Talefre on 29th July, 1836, and disgorged by the coalescent Glacier du Lechaud on 24th July, 1846, after having travelled, em-

[*] *Edin. Phil. Jour.*, January, 1847.

bedded in the ice, over a distance of 4,300 feet, shows how little change a hard lump of rock would sustain in travelling through a mass of glacier-ice. Occasionally, however, such an included block might be rubbed against the rocks of a hill-side, and so receive a dressing on one or more faces.

CHAPTER XIX.

UPPER DRIFT DEPOSITS OF SCOTLAND—*Continued.*

Sand and gravel deposits resting on till.—Kames.—Erratics associated with
kames.—High-level terraces of sand and gravel.—Association of kames with
morainic débris.—Valley moraines.—Mode of origin of kames.—Distribution of kames in Scotland.—Their relation to river valleys.—Flood gravels.

IF it be true that erratics and the morainic débris described
in last chapter were scattered over hill-tops and strewn
along mountain-slopes by gigantic glaciers, it is evident that
much morainic matter must also have been left upon the
Lowlands, as the ice gradually drew back to the mountain-
valleys. Have we any trace of such terminal moraines; and,
if not, what has become of them? To answer these questions we must consider now the upper drift deposits of the
lowland districts.

In the districts referred to, the till or boulder-clay is

Fig. 41.—Sand and gravel resting on denuded surface of till, railway cutting,
near Douglas Mouth Bridge, Lanarkshire.

overlaid in many places by great masses of distinctly water-
worn materials. These deposits occur at all levels, from the
coast up to a height of more than 1,500 ft. above the sea.
The most characteristic form assumed by them is that of
rolling mounds, cones, and ridges, all of which consist, for
the most part, of gravel and sand. To such an extent,
indeed, is this the case, that the whole group is often spoken

of as the "sand and gravel series." It does not cover nearly so large a tract of ground as the till. In the higher mountain regions many miles of country may be traversed without discovering a single patch of sand or gravel. As a general rule the deposits belonging to this group are confined to lowland districts, where they appear at first sight to be distributed in a most arbitrary manner. Occasionally we may follow them for miles, when all at once they will die out, and then we may not meet with them again until we have passed into quite a different district. Again, they may be represented by only one or two mounds, often widely separated, with no trace of sand or gravel in the intervals. I have not infrequently come upon a solitary and isolated mound of sand and gravel, in regions where for many miles around the only superficial covering upon the rocks was till. But capricious as the distribution of the series may be, we shall yet find that this drift is arranged and grouped with a certain definite relation to the external form or contour of the country.

The sands and gravels have, as I have just said, a tendency to shape themselves into mounds and winding ridges, which give a hummocky and rapidly undulating outline to the ground. Indeed, so characteristic is this appearance, that by it alone we are often able to mark out the boundaries of the deposit with as much precision as we could were all the vegetation and soil stripped away and the various subsoils laid bare. Occasionally, ridges may be tracked continuously for several miles, running like great artificial ramparts across the country. These vary in breadth and height, some of the more conspicuous ones being upwards of four or five hundred feet broad at the base, and sloping upwards, at an angle of 25° or even 35°, to a height of 60 ft. and more above the general surface of the ground. It is most common, however, to find mounds and ridges confusedly intermingled, crossing and re-crossing each other at all angles, so as to enclose deep hollows and pits between. Seen from some dominant point, such an assemblage of *kames,* as they are called, looks like a tumbled sea—the ground now swelling into long undulations, now rising suddenly into beautiful peaks and cones, and anon curving up in sharp ridges that often wheel suddenly round so as to enclose a lakelet of bright clear water. Fine examples of sand and gravel hills are seen in Lanarkshire, at Carstairs and Carnwath. They are also well developed in Haddingtonshire, near Cockburnspath ; in Berwickshire, at Dunse, and north of Greenlaw ; in Roxburghshire, at Eckford ; and another fine set is seen in the valley of the Tweed, at Wark and Cornhill, Northumberland. At Leslie and Markinch, in Fifeshire, a similar series occurs, and like accumulations appear more or less abundantly throughout the lowland districts.

Not infrequently the slopes of the kames are carpeted with fresh green turf, in strong contrast to the more sombre-hued vegetation of the surrounding clay-covered tracts. The local names in the country sufficiently attest this peculiarity. " Green Hills " are of very common occurrence, and I have usually found the name restricted either to kames or to certain little projecting bosses and cones of friable, decomposing, igneous rocks. When the kames are composed of large stones, the vegetation on their slopes becomes coarse and poor, and the fresh green grass then gives place to clumps of broom or stunted gorse. This is more usually the case with the sharper ridges and peaked cones, these being made up chiefly of coarse gravel and shingle. The gentler undulations consist for the most part of fine sand and gravel, and hence, in a rough way, the slope of a kame and the character of the vegetation that clothes it serve as a kind of index to the nature of the materials lying below.

Almost all the isolated solitary mounds that I know of are made up of fine sand, and some of the best examples of these occur in Fifeshire. A small one, quite close to Dunfermline, is locally famous under the name of Mont Dieu. According to old story this drift mound owes its origin to some unfortunate monks who, by way of penance, carried the sand in baskets from the sea-shore at Inverkeithing. A similar tradition accounts for a conical hill of fine sand at Linton, in the valley of the Kale Water, Roxburghshire ; of this hill it is said that " two sister nuns were compelled to pass the whole sand through a riddle or sieve as a penance for their transgressions or to obtain pardon for a crime of a brother."*

Another mound of the same material (Norrie's Law), a few miles north from Largo, in Fifeshire, is noted as the burial-place of some great worthy of past times. Who he was does not appear, but no doubt he must have been "a superior person," for he was buried in a suit of silver armour, most of which, unfortunately, found its way to the melting-pot soon after its discovery by a farmer. Other isolated cones, in various parts of the country, have often been described by local antiquaries as tumuli, apparently for no other reason than that they resemble these in external appearance. It is not unlikely, however, that such cones

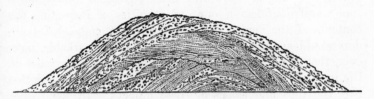

Fig. 42.—Section across kame, Douglas Railway, near Lanark.

may occasionally have been used as burial-places. It is certain, too, that some of the bolder ridges and mounds have been fortified and utilised for purposes of defence, the ditches scooped in their sides being still apparent. Protected by strong palisades of wood, and surrounded as most of them probably were by dense forest, one can easily see how an abrupt kame or steep cone might be made a very formidable fortress in the days of spears and arrows.

The deposits of which the kames are composed are usually stratified, and, in some of the finer-grained accumulations, very beautiful examples of false or diagonal bedding frequently occur. But in many cases the coarser heaps of gravel and shingle do not exhibit any traces of stratification, the stones being piled up in dire confusion. It is remarkable, however, that the gravel-stones, whether small or large, are almost invariably well-rounded and water-worn. To this, however, there are occasional exceptions, for sometimes the

* *History and Antiquities of Roxburghshire.* By A. Jeffrey, vol. i. p. 41.

deposits are not only unstratified but earthy, and the stones are angular and subangular, some even showing faint ice-markings ; and such accumulations are associated with heaps of well water-worn gravel and hummocks of sand in such a way as to show that they all form part and parcel of the same series. At the highest elevation reached by the kames the water-worn aspect of the stones becomes, as a rule, much less conspicuous than it is at moderate elevations, say at 900 ft. above the sea down to lower levels, and now and again it vanishes altogether, and we then have heaps of débris which are hardly distinguishable from morainic rubbish.

Erratics do not often occur embedded in the sand and gravel, but they are met with in this position from time to time ; and doubtless if our opportunities of inspecting the contents of the kames were more frequent, embedded boulders would appear more numerous. It is remarkable, however, that if they appear to be of infrequent occurrence in the interior of the kames, they are found often enough dotted over the tops and slopes of these hillocks. In some cases their appearance at the surface may be due to denudation ; they may once have been embedded in the gravel and sand, and only have become exposed by the gradual washing away of the deposits in which they lay concealed. But this has certainly not always been the case. Many of the mounds and hummocks upon which these erratics rest have evidently suffered little or no denudation since the period of their formation. The shape of such heaps and ridges is undoubtedly original, and we cannot but conclude that the erratics in question were dropped upon the surface just where we see them.

Sometimes the bedding of the kames is much confused, as if, after the layers of sand, clay, and gravel had been laid down in a horizontal or nearly horizontal plane, some force had squeezed and pushed them out of place, twisting, folding, and crumpling them up ; but this, as far as my experience goes, is not a common occurrence.

Associated with the sand and gravel, we here and there come upon deposits of silt and clay which have occasionally been worked for brick-making. These beds are usually finely laminated. But neither in them, nor yet in the sand and gravel, have any organic remains been discovered.

In some hilly districts we find the slopes of the ground fringed, at uniform levels, with shelves and ter-races of sand and gravel. These shelves and terraces generally dip outwards and downwards, with a gentle inclination from the high grounds against which they abut. Occasionally, several such platforms occur in succession, and, when seen in profile, resemble giant staircases. The deposits of which they are composed are usually more or less well bedded, and consist of gravel and sand, with which clay is sometimes intermingled. The deposits, however, are not always well waterworn; sometimes, indeed, they consist of only angular or subangular stones, and a kind of earth or earthy sand and clay. None of them has yielded any organic remains.

A very fine example of the phenomena described occurs at Enoch near the village of Eaglesham, about twelve miles south-west from Glasgow. In the accompanying section (Fig. 43), the general outline of this series of terraces is shown; *t* repre-sents the till, *s* the sand and gravel, and the figures indicate the height in feet above the sea-level.

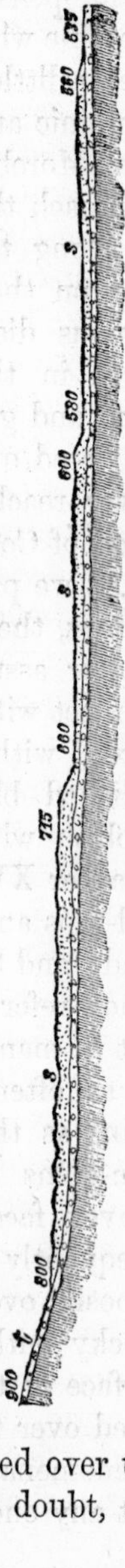

I have said that when we trace the sand and gravel drift up to high levels we find it passing into a rude kind of angular débris like moraine-matter, and that now and again similar morainic detritus occurs closely associated with kames. This is frequently the case along the base of a moun-tainous or hilly region, especially opposite the mouths of valleys. Thus in the hollow traversed by the railway between Perth and Crieff we find numerous sand and gravel hummocks, heaps, ridges, and undulating flats closely associated with banks and mounds of earthy sandy débris full of large erratics, numbers of which are also sprinkled over the surface of the mounds. These, there can be no doubt, are

Fig. 43.—High level terraces of gravel and sand at Eaglesham.

moraines belonging to the same date as the gravel deposits that surround them. Similar appearances may be noted along the foot of the Cheviot Hills, especially where the valley of the Kale opens out upon the low grounds of the Teviot. A large moraine with associated hummocks of gravel and sand can be seen a little to the south of Eckford, and similar heaps of morainic and waterworn detritus occur at the foot of the hills near Morebattle. In many other places where the Lowlands approach the mountains the same phenomena may be studied, as along the base of the Moorfoots and the Lammermuirs, and on the low grounds at the foot of the hilly and mountainous districts in Ayrshire, Galloway, and Dumfriesshire. Even in the Western Highlands a similar commingling of sand and gravel heaps and moraine-matter may be observed, scattered over the undulating moory tracts that lie along the lower reaches of some of the sea lochs, as in the neighbourhood of Connel Ferry and Dunstaffnage.

As we proceed from the low grounds into the mountain-valleys, the gravel deposits become coarser and the morainic matter assumes a more tumultuous aspect. Here we begin to meet with rude accumulations of earthy and rocky débris mixed with coarse gravel and sand, and large angular unpolished blocks—deposits exactly resembling that angular rubbish with large erratics which has been described in Chapter XVIII. as being more or less thickly scattered over hill-tops and mountain-slopes at high elevations in the Highlands and Southern Uplands. Like this latter, the deposits I now refer to are sprinkled loosely over the mountain-slopes, but in many places they assume a more or less distinct shape, so as often to form rather striking objects in a landscape, rising as they sometimes do in the throats of rugged mountain-glens into abrupt concentric ridges and mounds—the convex faces of which invariably look down the valleys. Frequently the whole bottom of a valley is covered with these deposits over wide areas—the ground presenting a very hummocky outline. Erratics of all shapes and sizes strew the surface of the cones and mounds and ridges, and are scattered over the bare rock itself. Excellent examples of these phenomena will be found in every glen in the Highlands, but any one who wishes to have a good idea of their general character can hardly do better than visit Strath Bran and Glen More in Ross-shire, which are now so very easy of access. Even in such mountain-valleys we shall find that the coarse moraines are often associated with heaps of sand and gravel, which not infrequently cannot be distinguished from the similar mounds that occur in the kame-areas of the Lowlands, while terraces of gravel and sand occur ever and anon fringing the valley-slopes often at considerable heights above the present streams.

The higher valleys of the Southern Uplands furnish us with similar phenomena. In the wild district of Galloway we find the mountain-slopes abundantly coated with angular débris and erratics, and numerous true moraines associated with coarse gravels crowd the bottoms of the valleys that open out from the Merrick and other heights of that region. In the Peeblesshire uplands moraines are not so numerous, but well-marked ones occur at Loch Skene and a few other valleys in its neighbourhood. I have noticed true moraines also at the heads of certain valleys in the Cheviot Hills, but they are comparatively insignificant.

If there have been many opinions held concerning the mode of formation of till, there have been just as many theories offered in explanation of the origin of kames. Some writers have insisted that these find their nearest analogues in the terminal moraines of Alpine glaciers, others have maintained their fluviatile origin, while a yet larger number of observers unite in ascribing them to the action of the sea.

In the first edition of this work I showed that they could only have been the result of fluviatile and torrential action; their distribution being enough of itself to prove, as we shall presently see, that this must have been the case. But as I held at that time the still generally received opinion that a period of submergence followed upon the disappearance of the great glaciers, I thought that some of the peculiar appearances presented by the kames might have been due to subsequent marine action. Later researches, however, in some of the Border counties, along the southern slopes of the Perthshire Highlands, and in the Long Island and West Ross-shire, have rudely shaken my belief in the "great submergence," and I now feel strongly inclined to agree with Mr. Jamieson that no considerable submergence has overtaken the Scottish area, since that of which the intercalated shell-bed near Airdrie is a notable relic. The whole question of the origin of the kames, however, is beset with difficulty, and I am still far from thinking that we have found the true explanation of all the peculiar appearances they present. That the deposits are, in the first place, of freshwater origin can be satisfactorily proved ; and that the sea has had no share in subsequently modifying them can be shown to be at least highly probable. Let me now try to point out the line of reasoning which has led to these conclusions.

It appears to hold generally true of all the larger areas of the kame deposits that these occur in valleys at or near where the rivers escape from the confined mountain-glens or upland dales to enter upon the broad low grounds. And not only so, but the extent of the gravel beds seems frequently, if not always, to be in direct proportion to that of the drainage-area in which these occur. When this last is very extensive the kames almost invariably attain an extreme development. On the other hand, when the river system is comparatively insignificant, so likewise are the deposits of sand and gravel that cumber the ground where the main valley begins to open out upon the Lowlands. A few examples will illustrate my meaning.

If the Ordnance Survey map (sheet 23) be examined, it will be observed that the river Clyde, after leaving the hilly country through which it flows in a general northerly direction, suddenly turns to the west, near where it is crossed by the Caledonian Railway, so as to skirt for some miles the base of the uplands from which it has just escaped. Immediately to the north of this westerly part of the river's course (in the neighbourhood of Carstairs and Carnwath) the ground rises in a very gentle incline, and undulates away to north and north-east for several miles, at a general level of little more than one hundred feet above the river. It is precisely here where we encounter a widespread series of kames, cones, mounds, and banks of gravel and sand. Standing among these hillocks and turning towards the south we look right up the valley of the Clyde and into the great Southern Uplands. But the gravel deposits in this case are not restricted

to the low grounds on the northern slopes of the river-valley.
Considerable heaps of gravel and sand may be traced up to
and even beyond Lamington, at heights which could not
possibly be reached by the present river, and these deposits
are clearly a continuation of the similar accumulations near
Carstairs.

Some four or five miles below Carstairs the Clyde receives
on its left bank the tribute of the Douglas Water, a considerable stream, draining a large area. It takes its rise on the
slopes of Cairn Table, at a height above the sea of 1,500 ft.,
and reaches the Clyde after a course of fifteen or sixteen
miles. In the lower reaches of its valley we find numerous
heaps and mounds of gravel and sand, and the same deposits
are cut through by the Clyde opposite the mouth of the
Douglas Water. These deposits, however, are by no means
so extensive as those in the neighbourhood of Carstairs.

Another considerable assemblage of mounds, hillocks, banks,
and undulating flats of sand and gravel occupies a similar
position in the valley of the Kale Water, between the base of
the Cheviot Hills and the river Teviot, near Eckford. This
is a rather striking example of the phenomena under review.
The Teviot here runs north-east, skirting the outlying spurs
of the Cheviots, which are seen rising up boldly in the south.
After receiving Jed and Oxnam Waters, the river suddenly
wheels away from the hilly ground and makes directly north
for the valley of the Tweed, being joined about a mile below
Eckford by the Kale Water. From this point the whole
valley of the Kale, up to where the stream escapes from the
Cheviots, at Morebattle, is more or less covered with gravel
and sand, which rises into banks and mounds, and extends
in broad undulating flats. Similar deposits are seen opposite
the junction of the Kale with the Teviot on the west bank of
the latter river. None of these accumulations could possibly
have been formed by the present streams ; they are not only
too extensive, but they occur also at too great an elevation.

We find similar appearances characteristic of the Lammermuir districts. The Whiteadder Water, for example, after
leaving the Lammermuir Hills, enters upon a low-lying undulating country, which is thickly strewn with sand and gravel
over an area many square miles in extent ; and the great

bulk of these deposits is strictly confined to the drainage-area of the water. Along the northern flanks of the same hills similar phenomena recur, the low grounds being plentifully coated with gravel and sand opposite the mouths of the larger upland valleys.

On the opposite slopes of the Forth Basin excellent examples are not wanting. Considerable accumulations of gravel and sand extend along the low grounds of Kinross-shire, opposite the valleys that open from the Ochils. Again, if we follow the course of the Leven we shall find that, shortly after leaving the Loch, it flows through a great series of mounds, hillocks, and banks of gravel and sand, which are especially well seen at Leslie and Markinch.

Reference may also be made to the great sand and gravel heaps that occupy the low grounds at the base of the Kilsyth Hills, within the drainage-area of the Carron Water.

Mounds, irregular banks, and extensive sheets of the like materials attain a very considerable development along the great trough that lies between the Perthshire Highlands and the Ochil Hills. It will be found throughout this wide tract that the sand and gravel appear most abundantly opposite the mouths of the large mountain-valleys.

In Forfarshire, and indeed along the whole north-east of Scotland, we invariably find that the greatest gatherings of gravel and sand are collected in similar positions, and that they frequently ascend the larger valleys for long distances. Vast deposits, for example, crowd the valleys of the Don, the Dee, and the Ythan, and the same appearances are repeated, as Mr. Jamieson has shown, in the rivers that drain north-east into the Moray Frith, as for example the Deveron, the Spey, and the Findhorn. In the neighbourhood of Inverness like masses of water-worn materials form conspicuous objects in the Vale of the Ness, and at the head of the Beauly Frith the lower reaches of the Farrar exhibit similar accumulations.

In all the cases now cited, and many more might be given, the extent of the gravel and sand deposits, which frequently assume the form of cones, peaks, and ridges, is invariably proportionate to the drainage-area of the valleys in which they occur. The same fact becomes more conspicuous when we limit our attention to any well-defined hilly region of the central Lowlands. Take, for example, that broad, undulating hilly district, which, beginning at the Frith of Clyde, extends south-east along the borders of Renfrewshire, Ayrshire, and Lanarkshire, until it gradually falls away into the valley of the Clyde, near Strathavon. (See Plate VI., p. 146.) This wide district forms the watershed between the Irvine and numerous small tributaries of the Clyde.

Along both banks of this wide, hilly, and moorland district it holds generally true that all the larger accumulations of gravel and sand are disposed at or near where the streams leave the hills and enter upon the low grounds—the extent of these deposits being in proportion to that of the drainage-area and the height of the watershed. Valleys draining a limited district of low elevation have no marked accumulations of gravel and sand at their mouths; on the other hand, valleys draining from lofty sheds invariably contain in their lower reaches extensive deposits of gravel and sand, which are frequently heaped up into mounds, and the larger the valley the bulkier the accumulations of water-worn materials. These phenomena are well illustrated by the valleys of the Dusk, the Lugton, the Crawick, and the Crawfurdland Waters, and by the Avon and its tributaries—the Glengavel, the Calder, the Kype, and the Lochar Waters.

We may now glance very briefly at some of the low-lying districts in the extreme north of Scotland. Some reference has already been made to the glacial phenomena of Lewis. The northern portion of that district may be described as a wide undulating moorland, no portion of which rises higher than a few hundred feet above the sea. It is drained by several inconsiderable streams flowing from the central axis of the island to north-west and south-east. In the extreme south there rises a bold line of mountains, against which the moorlands somewhat suddenly abut. But from this mountain district only one large valley opens upon the low grounds to the north, and this hollow is entirely occupied by Loch Langabhat.

Now, nowhere in Lewis, neither in the undulating moorlands to the north, nor along the slopes of the mountains in the south, do any heaps of gravel and sand occur. Not a single trace of kames is to be met with in any part of that

region.   A similar absence of gravel mounds and heaps, as
Mr. Jamieson has remarked, characterises the great flats of
Caithness.

Enough, perhaps, has now been said to give the reader
some notion of the mode in which the larger accumulations
of gravel and sand are distributed throughout the country.
A word or two may be added in regard to certain appearances
presented by the deposits themselves.

I have said that in the case of the larger valleys and glens
the gravel beds frequently ascend these hollows for some
distance.   When this happens these deposits almost invariably give evidence to show that they have been carried along
by a force acting in a direction down the valley.   This is
most conspicuous in the long flat-topped banks and irregular
terraces with an undulating surface, but it may also be sometimes noticed in the lower or undermost portions of well-
marked ridges, or typical kames.   Abundant evidence on
this head will be found in the valleys of the Tweed and some
of its tributaries ; in the upland districts traversed by the
Clyde ; in Annandale, and many other drainage-areas in the
south of Scotland.   Mr. Jamieson, several years ago, recorded
the fact in reference to the great valleys of the Spey, the
Findhorn, and other rivers in the north.

Another peculiar appearance has next to be noticed.   When
the gravel beds are traced far up the valleys, they are frequently seen to pass into a kind of earthy angular débris,
and the same kind of angular earthy stony rubbish is often
found to form the upper limits of the sand and gravel series
when these deposits are followed up the sides of the valleys.
This angular débris is not to be confounded with that coarse
rubbish which the frosts are yearly sprinkling over steep
mountain-slopes.   It forms in places distinct mounds, which
are usually quite unstratified.   Such angular gravels are well
developed along the foot of the Moorfoot Hills.   They bear a
close resemblance to the morainic rubbish which accumulates
in front of an Alpine glacier, and a close search among them
will sometimes detect a glaciated stone or two.   But for
many reasons, which will presently appear, it is often
extremely difficult to say what relation the kames and
mounds of the low grounds bear to the angular rubbish and

perched blocks of the mountain regions. These kames, as we have seen, form part and parcel of vast gravel and sand deposits which frequently ascend the valleys for great distances, until, as just stated, they pass into a kind of loose morainic débris. Now the sides of such valleys are usually sprinkled with moraine-matter, and dotted over with erratics, from the head of the valley down to the low grounds. When this is the case it is clear that the gravel and sand occupying the bottom of the valley must be of more recent date than the coarse débris that hangs upon the mountain-slopes on either side. The gravel beds of the Tweed at and above Drummelzier, for example, are clearly of more recent formation than the morainic débris over which and against which they lie. But the more typical assemblages of kames usually occur upon the low grounds just beyond the mouths of the valleys in places where there is as a rule no morainic débris to be seen. Cases, however, do occur where well-marked kames run along hill-sides which are sprinkled with moraine-matter and dotted with erratics, in such a way as to show that these last were deposited before the kames.

One other fact remains to be mentioned. In all the valleys that contain gravel and sand in any quantity both the till and the morainic débris have suffered extensive denudation—often all that is left being a few large boulders scattered here and there along the sides of the valleys. Nor can we be in doubt as to the direction from which the denuding agent came ; for while the till and morainic débris have been stripped from the faces of such knolls and projecting rocks as look up the valley, the same deposits are found sheltering in the rear. And again one may note how sand and gravel banks in such valleys often appear in a similar manner, stretching out from behind more or less prominent bosses of rock, and bearing every mark of having been accumulated just as we see them.

Now putting these various considerations together the conclusion seems forced upon us that all those accumulations of water-worn materials whose peculiar distribution has now engaged our attention, owe their origin to currents that once flowed down the valleys. And not only so, but we must also admit that those currents were proportionate in size to the extent of each particular valley-system in which such accumulations are found. In short, we can only, as I think, account for the appearances described by attributing the deposition of the greater areas of gravel and sand to river-action. But if so, then the rivers must have greatly surpassed in volume and breadth their present puny representatives. It is impossible to conceive that the masses of gravel and sand occupying the lower reaches of the upland valleys, and some of the highland glens, could be laid down by rivers like the present, even although these were to continue in constant flood. Some great change has taken place since the old gravel beds were deposited—the amount of water circulating in the valleys has in some way vastly diminished—some of the rivers have even ceased to flow in their old courses and are now working out for themselves new channels—driven from their former beds by the huge heaps of detritus which they themselves, at some early period, carried down from the mountain regions.

The explanation appears to be simply this. The great ice-sheet underneath which the till accumulated continued to retire until, as already described, it was reduced to a system of gigantic local glaciers. In summer-time the streams and rivers would be vastly swollen by the water derived from melting snow and ice, and from drenching rains. Great currents would sweep down the valleys, carrying with them the angular débris derived from terminal moraines and from freshets rushing down the slopes of the hills. As this débris was hurried along, it would gradually be rounded by attrition, and eventually pass into good gravel. At the same time the till and ancient morainic débris over which the river rushed would be denuded and washed away from exposed positions. As the valley widened the river also would expand and begin to deposit material; if, however, the valley continued comparatively narrow until where it suddenly opened into the low grounds, then the river would suffer but little gravel to gather in its course, but would sweep everything onward until it escaped from the hilly regions, when it would at once expand and throw down the major portion of its burden. One may still see upon a small scale how this process was carried on, by examining the behaviour of such little mountain brooks as are liable, upon every thunder shower, to be converted into roaring torrents. When these torrents are swollen with rain, they rush impetuously downward, often completely filling the deep gullies in which they flow. Arrived at the base of the mountains, they immediately spread out and deposit heaps of stones, débris, and coarse sand. In course of time long sloping banks are thus formed, which expand in fan-shape from the foot of the gullies. When but little water is flowing the brooks employ themselves in cutting courses through that thick débris which only sudden floods could have enabled them to carry.

The larger areas of gravel and sand are, therefore, strictly analogous in origin to the heavy masses of gravel and coarse sand that strew the beds of Alpine valleys. Those who are familiar with the appearances presented by such areas as that of the Aar, the Rhone, and other well-known Swiss districts, or by the glacier valleys of Norway, as that of the Justedal, or the smaller but even more interesting ones of Fondalen, will be the first to recognise the close similarity of the Scottish gravel beds to those characteristic of glacier regions.

CHAPTER XX.

UPPER DRIFT DEPOSITS OF SCOTLAND—*Continued.*

Glacial lakes.—Parallel Roads of Glen Roy.—High-level terraces at Eaglesham, Lanarkshire; in Moorfoot Hills; in Nithsdale, &c.—Kames crossing from one drainage-area into another.—Origin of kames in valleys of Southern Uplands.—Kames at base of Lammermuir Hills.—Torrential origin of certain kames.—Recapitulation.

SO far as we have yet gone into the subject we have had no difficulty in assigning by far the larger proportion of the sand and gravel series to the action of swollen rivers and torrents that escaped from melting glaciers. The peculiar distribution of these water-rolled masses in and opposite the mouths of mountain and upland valleys leaves us in no doubt as to their origin. But there are many kames and mounds and elevated shelves, ledges, and terraces of gravel and sand which bear no apparent relation to valleys. Sometimes, as I have said, we find them ranging across wide open moorlands, at other times they occur upon water-sheds, and not infrequently they can be traced up one valley over the dividing *col* into quite a different drainage-area. Again, they occasionally appear fringing the slopes of hills and mountains, in positions and at elevations where it is plain that no mere river issuing from the end of a glacier could possibly have deposited them. It is the knowledge of such remarkable phenomena as these which has chiefly weighed with geologists, myself amongst the number, in attributing the formation of some portion of the drift sand and gravel series to the action of the sea. I now feel persuaded, however, that this view is erroneous, and that all the drift sand and gravel scattered up and down the interior of the country is of freshwater origin. To illustrate the mode in which I believe those abnormally situated heaps and ridges of water-worn materials to have been formed, I shall describe one or two examples.

In a previous chapter I have pointed out that during the retreat of the great glaciers from the Lowlands, it frequently happened that glacial lakes formed in lateral valleys in the mountainous districts, and even at comparatively low levels. At that period the main valleys continued to be occupied with massive ice-streams, while the glaciers had either disappeared from, or become greatly reduced in, the smaller lateral and tributary valleys. In these last, therefore, the streams were dammed back by the ice of the main glaciers, and thus gave rise to glacial lakes. In the district of Lochaber, for example, it is well known that the slopes of certain valleys are fringed with successive horizontal shelves of coarse angular shingle and débris which are believed to indicate the margins of ancient glacial lakes. These are the famous " Parallel Roads."

In Glen Roy there are three distinct shelves, 856 ft., 1,065 ft., and 1,149 ft. respectively above the level of the sea. At one time these shelves were thought to be old sea-beaches, and this continued to be the general belief even after Agassiz had suggested their lacustrine origin. The later observations of Mr. Jamieson, however, would seem to have convinced most geologists at last that the glacial-lake theory is the true explanation of the phenomena. A massive glacier descending from Glen Treig filled up Glen Spean, and thus formed a barrier to the escape of water from Glen Roy. Along the margins of the lake thus formed angular shingle and débris collected—derived in great measure, no doubt, from the degradation of the rocks under the influence of frost. As the icy barrier decreased, either by gradual melting or by sudden rupture, the lake was lowered, and thus another terrace of débris gathered along the slope of the valley at a lower level than the former. The farther shrinking or bursting of the ice in like manner again lowered the lake, and so gave rise to the third and lowest shelf.

It is not necessary that I should enter here into all the arguments which can be brought against the marine theory. Those who desire to inquire more fully into the subject cannot do better than read the very excellent accounts of the Parallel Roads given by Chambers in his " Ancient Sea Margins," and by Mr. Jamieson in the Geological Society's Journal. The bibliography of these remarkable terraces is a somewhat copious one, as will be seen from the note below, which is by no means exhaustive.* One very good proof of their non-marine origin is the fact that the highest terraces, although they go up to the summit-levels between two glens, yet do not reach a greater height nor cross these *cols* into the open valley beyond. This is just as we should expect, on the supposition that the terraces mark the margin of an old lake ; for when the water reached the summit-level between two glens (such, for example, as that between Upper Glen Roy and the valley of the Spey), it would immediately overflow, on the same principle as a cistern with its escape-pipe. But if the terraces were marine we should be at a loss to account for this connection between the highest terraces and the summit-levels. It would be very extraordinary to say the least, if the sea had reached just to the *cols* between the glens and never any higher. Again, one may well ask why Glen Roy and the little glens in its neighbourhood should be favoured above all other highland glens with sea-beaches. There is no reason in the world why such shelves (if they really be ancient sea-beaches) should not occur abundantly in the valleys, not only of the Highlands but of the Southern Uplands also. A visit paid to Lochaber some years ago left me no alternative but to conclude with Agassiz, Jamieson, and others, that a glacier did at one time fill Glen Spean, and that during the existence of this local glacier Glen Roy, owing to its limited drainage-area, could not support a glacier big enough to fill its own valley. Under such conditions this valley must in the very nature of things have filled with water, and so shelves and terraces

* " On the Parallel Roads of Glenroy " (Macculloch), *Trans. Geol. Soc.*, First Series, vol. iv. p. 314 ; " On the Parallel Roads of Lochaber " (Dick Lauder), *Trans. Roy. Soc. Edin.*, vol. ix. ; *Edin. Phil. Jour.*, vol. iv. p. 417 ; " Observations on the Parallel Roads," &c. (Darwin), *Phil. Trans.*, 1839, p. 39 ; " Account of the Parallel Roads of Glenroy in Invernesshire," *Edin. New. Phil. Jour.*, vol. xxvii. p. 315 ; " On the Parallel Roads of Lochaber," &c. (Milne-Home), *Trans. Roy. Soc. Edin.*, vol. xvi. p. 395 ; *Proc. Roy. Soc. Edin.*, vol. ii. pp. 124, 132 ; *Edin. New. Phil. Jour.*, vol. xliii. p. 339 ; " On the Parallel Roads of Lochaber " (J. Thomson, M.A.), *Edin. New Phil. Jour.*, vol. xlv. pp. 49, 404.

would form, having precisely the same character as those that are found fringing its slopes.*

Here, then, we have a good example of high-level terraces, the freshwater origin of which appears sufficiently obvious. To form terraces like the Parallel Roads the damming up of a valley by a sufficiently lofty barrier is all that is required. In the next example, however, we have a series of terraces which are by no means so easily explained. The terraces referred to are shown in Fig. 43, p. 215. Any one may see that these have been deposited in water, which, when the upper terrace was being formed must have washed the slopes of the Dunlop and Strathavon Hills at a height of 800 feet above the present sea-level. By referring to the map, Plate VI., p. 146, the reader will observe that the hills, upon the slopes of which the terraces occur, form the watershed between a number of feeders of the river Clyde that flow towards the north, and certain streams that go south to join the rivers Garnock and Irvine. Towards the east the hills fall away into the vale of the Avon, which unites with the Clyde near Hamilton. The terraces, as I have said, skirt the open hill-side ; they do not lie in any deep valley, neither is there any spacious mountain-glen from which we might suppose some massive glacier to have protruded and dammed up a water-flow in the same way as the glacier of Glen Spean dammed up the water in Glen Roy. Standing on the terraces them-selves we find ourselves overlooking the broad vale of the Clyde, with no higher ground than our own between us and the Campsie Fells. Here, if anywhere then, we seem to have relics of old sea-beaches, and such indeed I at first took them to be. To be sure there is not a single trace of any marine organism to be met with, and the deposits themselves do not strike one as being characteristically littoral ; in some places indeed they consist rather of an earthy angular débris than gravel. Yet, how otherwise can we account for them ? Surely the water that spread them out along the slopes behind Eaglesham must have stretched away north for sixteen miles at least, until it abutted against the Kilpatrick Hills and

* The Rev. T. Brown recently obtained from the deposits forming one of the shelves a number of freshwater diatoms, which were determined by Professor Dickie of Aberdeen. No trace of any marine organism was met with. *Proc. Roy. Soc. Edin.*, vol. viii. p. 340.

the Campsie Fells ?   It is not necessary, however, to suppose
that the water extended so far.

Let me recall to the reader's remembrance some of the
phenomena that would present themselves during the dissolution of the great ice-sheet.   I have pointed out (see p. 201)
how, as the surface of the *mer de glace* became lowered, the
higher hills of the lowland districts would begin to appear.
Among such hilly tracts that broad ridge of high ground that
extends along the county boundaries of Renfrew, Ayr, and
Lanark is one of the most conspicuous, for it reaches
in places to a height of more than 1,230 ft. above the sea.
The time must have come, then, when the *mer de glace*
melted away from the higher parts of the Strathavon and
Dunlop Hills until its surface had sunk to the level of
800 ft.   At this period these hills would form an island in
the sea of ice, from which in summer-time streams would
flow north and south just as they do now.   But as the heavy
snows that had gathered over the hills and moors in winter-
time would melt during the short but warm summer, it is
evident that very large bodies of water would descend to the
margin of the *mer de glace*.   According to the astronomical
and physical theory supported in these pages the heat
received from the sun would be much greater then, for
although the eccentricity of the earth's orbit was diminishing
it was yet considerably larger than it is at present ; and consequently the torrents and floods of water set free by the
sun's heat would far exceed any rushes of water which the mild
summers that we now enjoy could have disengaged under the
like circumstances.   In Norway and the Alps the glaciers
melt away in summer-time to some extent from the slopes
that form their lateral boundaries, and it is often possible
for one to make his way for some distance below the ice,
which seems to shrink as it were from contact with the heated
rocks.   Between the mountain-slope and the frequently overhanging sides of the melting glacier torrents of water often
make their way over a rough bottom of rocky débris, gravel,
and boulders.   Now, as Mr. Jamieson has shown,[*] something
like this, only on a larger scale, must have taken place in
Scotland during the melting of her ice-sheet.   The margin

* *Quart. Jour. Geol. Soc.*, 1874, p. 329.

of the *mer de glace* would retreat, as it were, for some distance from the slopes of the Dunlop and Strathavon Hills, while a raging torrent, derived partly from the thawing snow of the hills and partly from the melting of the ice-sheet itself, would rush along the broad trench formed between the slopes of the hills and the edge of the great glacier. Here and there, where the hill-slopes retired so far as to form a broad bay, the water would spread itself over a wider area, and the débris and gravel and sand which it hurried along would in such places be distributed more or less evenly over the bottom. But in places where the whole space between the margin of the ice-sheet and the hills was coursed over by a tumultuous rush of waters, it is clear that the detritus could not be so evenly spread out, but would be heaped up in irregular mounds and ridges, whose trend would coincide in direction with the flow of the water.

Such are the results one would naturally expect to follow from the melting of the ice-sheet in a hilly region like that under review. And the appearances now visible certainly seem to tally very closely with the conditions inferred. The terraces of gravel described above occupy an embayed recess of the hills, and passing eastwards from them at about the same elevation (nearly 800 ft.) we follow the spoor of the old torrents in a remarkable series of ridges, mounds, hummocks, and flats of gravel, with occasional patches of sand, which lead us along the face of the hills at a gradually decreasing elevation by Clachearn, Cladance, and Chapelton, into the vale of Strathavon. The two lower terraces mark the successive lowering of the old lake or bay by the melting of the ice barrier; it is quite possible, however, that this may have been suddenly effected by the instantaneous giving away of some part of the glacier and the opening of a readier outlet for the water.

Terraces resembling those at Eaglesham have been detected in other hilly districts. I have met with some good examples in the Moorfoot Hills, at a height of 1,050 or 1,100 ft., which I now believe have been formed in the same way as the gravel flats of the Dunlop and Strathavon Hills. Still farther south high-level shelves of gravel and sand have been detected by my colleague, Mr. H. M. Skae, in Nithsdale, at a height of 1,250 ft. above the sea. These, he agrees with me in thinking, have probably been deposited in a temporary lake during the melting of the *mer de glace,* and while a massive stream of ice yet occupied the broad vale of the Nith. Several instances of the occurrence of stratified accumulations of sand, gravel, clay, and silt, at considerable elevations in the Northern Highlands, are given by Mr. Jamieson ;* and at one time he was inclined to consider these as of marine origin. But that notion was subsequently abandoned by him, and he now holds that none of the unfossiliferous stratified drifts of the interior of the country can be accounted for by the action of the sea.

I have mentioned the fact that kames and hummocks of gravel and sand may occasionally be followed up a valley to its *col,* and even across that into the drainage-area beyond. When this is the case it invariably happens that the *col* is one of the lowest in the hilly regions where it occurs. And if we reflect for a little upon what would happen in such a hilly region when the ice-sheet was melting away and becoming divided into a series of large local glaciers, we shall hardly fail to see that in those valleys whose *cols* were lowest, the glaciers would disappear more rapidly than they would in valleys that drained higher elevations and wider gathering grounds. Let us conceive then, that torrents and floods are sweeping along heaps of detritus between some given hill-slope and the margin of the ice-sheet, just as we saw must have been the case near Eaglesham. It is evident that the tumultuous rush of water will overflow the dividing ridge wherever that sinks to the level of the glacier, and will thereafter descend the valley beyond. Should a glacier still occupy this smaller valley, then it is most probable that the water will flow between it and the hill-sides that bound it, so that when it finally melts away ridges and heaps of shingle and gravel will be found fringing the hills at some height above the bottom of the valley. And these we shall be able to trace more or less continuously up to and even across the *col* into the other drainage-area from which the deposits were derived.

I could mention many instances in which these very appearances are visible. Thus, in the Muirkirk district my

* *Quart. Jour. Geol. Soc.,* 1865, p. 177

colleague, Mr. B. N. Peach, traced a number of gravel hillocks along the hill-slopes that overlook the head of the Greenock Water, a tributary of the river Ayr, across a narrow *col* into the valley of the Glengavel Water which joins the river Avon. The torrents that carried these deposits seem to have spread out over what is now the watershed of the river Irvine: and the evidence which I gathered during the geological survey of the district has led me to believe that a considerable glacial lake must have existed at that place for a long time when the ice-sheet was melting away. In this lake considerable accumulations of gravel, sand, and clay took place ; and although these are now much denuded they still form wide flats, while traces of horizontal ledges cut into the rocks, and evidently marking old water-levels, indicate successive margins of the lake as its waters were drained away. No trace of anything organic was found in the deposits.

I pointed out, a number of years ago, that there was something peculiar in the distribution of kames and hummocks in the valleys of a hilly region. In regard to the hilly district of Peeblesshire, I showed that these do not occur in all the valleys alike ; some they quite choke up, while from others they are entirely absent. Nor at first sight is there anything remarkable in the valleys themselves to account for this anomaly. They may be wide or narrow, deep or shallow, winding, or comparatively straight. But when the height of the various watersheds and dividing *cols* is compared with that of certain high-level shelves of gravel and sand, the kames are then found to be restricted to valleys whose *cols* are either at, or below, the level reached by the gravel terraces. From this, I inferred that the kames were of marine origin, and had probably been formed in what, during submergence, had been narrow straits communicating between comparatively open spaces of sea. And I thought further, that the absence of the gravel ridges and mounds from certain valleys with lofty *cols*, might be accounted for by supposing such valleys to have formed quiet fiords in which no marine currents could take effect. But this explanation does not now satisfy me. When sedimentary deposits contain no fossils, they are, as a rule, more likely to be freshwater than marine. Of course, it may not be very easy to prove that they are freshwater, but we have no right to infer their marine origin, until we have first exhausted every possible mode of accounting for their presence as fluviatile or lacustrine accumulations. It is so difficult to realise all the conditions which obtained during the melting of the ice-sheet, that one need not feel surprised if sometimes mounds of water-worn detritus should occur in the most anomalous positions. Yet I think that the peculiar distribution of the kames in the Peeblesshire district, can be reasonably accounted for in the same way as those in the neighbourhood of Glengavel Water. The valleys in which they extend up to the dividing *col*, are just those from which the glaciers would disappear soonest, and which would, therefore, form the readiest channels of escape for the water derived from the thawing ice-sheet. The valleys that drained wider and more elevated regions would, on the other hand, long continue to be filled with glaciers, and when at last these had ceased to be confluent with those of adjoining valleys, the gravel deposits that gathered over the bottoms of the valleys would no longer take the form of confused heaps of ridges, but would spread out in undulating flats in the same manner as the morainic gravels, or so-called " ancient alluvium," of Switzerland.

On the hypothesis that the high-level terraces of gravel are marine, we find it impossible to account for their sporadic character. If these terraces be marine, why are they not much more common ? True raised beaches are always more continuous ; some of them, as we shall see in the sequel, extend for miles along our maritime districts, and have, moreover, yielded abundant fossils in proof of their marine origin. In the interior of the country, however, the shelves and terraces occur only here and there in little patches and show a very insignificant breadth, while they do not contain a vestige of any marine organism. On the supposition of their marine origin, how are we to account for their non-appearance in more or less continuous lines along what must, under the circumstances, have been ancient sea-margins ? Such terraces as do remain are often exceedingly well-marked ; indeed, that is their common character. They have suffered very little modification since the time of their formation ; sometimes they are as perfect as if the forces that spread them out had only recently finished their work. Nor is there anything in the conformation of the ground to show why they should have been specially exempted from denudation, while their supposed continuations were swept away.

At the foot of the Lammermuir Hills, especially in the neighbourhood of West Gordon and Greenlaw, occur numerous kames, heaps, hummocks, knolls, and undulating flats of angular gravel, shingle and rounded gravel, and sand, which conform in their distribution to the configuration of the ground ; that is to say, they lie for the most part in the hollows, and have evidently been laid down by currents of water that flowed from higher to lower levels. Erratics now and again occur embedded in the deposits, while many of the mounds are crowned with similar angular boulders of various rocks, all of which have been carried from higher levels than they now occupy ; most of them, indeed, have come from the west, while others have been derived from the slopes of the Lammermuir Hills which lie immediately to the north. From the "carry" of the erratics, and the distribution of the deposits with which they are associated, it is clear that the main current of water flowed from west to east along that hollow which is now traversed by the Berwickshire Railway from Earlston to Greenlaw and Dunse, and this main stream was joined by others flowing south from the Lammermuirs. I may mention that the kames frequently repose upon a mass of very hard red till full of striated stones, and that the line of separation between the two deposits, when they occur together, is always very sharply defined ; and this, I may add, is invariably the case with the till and the overlying kames in every part of the country which has yet been carefully examined.

A review of these, and other appearances which can hardly be described here,* leads to the belief that when the kames along the foot of the Lammermuir Hills were being heaped up, the ice had already disappeared, or was fast dis-

* An account of the drift phenomena of the interesting region that stretches between the Lammermuir Hills and the Cheviots will be given in forthcoming Memoirs of the Geological Survey, descriptive of sheets 16, 17, 25 and 26 of the one-inch map of Scotland.

appearing, from the major portion of these uplands, and that heavy torrents, which must sometimes have flooded large areas of the low grounds, descended from the melting snow and ice. To the action of these torrents, I ascribe the tumultuous hummocks of gravel and angular débris, while the flats of finer materials show where the torrential waters expanded themselves over the low grounds. The erratics may have come on ice-rafts; for, during winter, the waters would become frozen over, and erratics and boulders lying loosely over the deserted path of the old ice-sheet might now and again get encased in ice, and be carried down the valley on the breaking up of the ice when the flood-season returned. "Ground-ice" might also be a means of floating stones and small boulders. The rafts would often drift into the quieter reaches of the swollen waters, and there running aground on sand-banks would drop their stony burdens. Not a few travelled stones might at the same time be scattered promiscuously over the surface of the inundated districts, coming to rest sometimes upon sand or gravel, sometimes upon till or bare rock.

I might go on illustrating by examples the mode in which the kames of Scotland may have been heaped up during the melting of the ice-sheet, but must confine myself to a few general remarks. From the examples already adduced, it will be observed that we can give a reasonable explanation of some of the most puzzling phenomena presented by the kames, without having recourse to the sea for assistance. We have satisfactorily accounted for those great assemblages of kames, &c., which crowd the lower parts of mountain-valleys, and are heaped up on the low grounds beyond; almost all the more conspicuous areas of drift-gravel and sand occur, as I have described in Chapter XIX., in such positions. We have found, also, that the appearance of terraces of angular shingle, and gravel, and sand at high levels, indicates the former presence of glacial lakes and the action of torrential waters; and torrents likewise explain the anomalous position of certain gravel hummocks which extend across a watershed from one drainage-area to another. Again we have seen that the peculiar distribution of the kames in a hilly district like that of Peeblesshire and other parts of the Southern Uplands, can be accounted for by the unequal rate at which the ice melted away. In the valleys with low *cols* and a limited "catchment," the ice would disappear sooner than in valleys that drained loftier and wider areas, and the former would therefore become the channels by which the disengaged water would find the readiest outlet. Further, it has become apparent that the occurrence of erratics embedded in, or perched upon kames, or scattered over the surface of the low grounds in certain districts, may be due to the disengagement of ice-rafts during flood seasons.

There are still some appearances, however, connected with the distribution of the stratified drift that overlies the till, which are hardly explicable by the modes we have just been considering. Such, for example, are those long linear ridges of gravel that occur in the central parts of broad lowland valleys, like the kames near Falkirk, and those that stretch along the course of the Tweed near Kelso. In the same category are the isolated mounds of sand that appear sporadically in the low grounds, often far removed from any water-course, and whose distribution seems to bear no recognisable relation to the configuration of the ground. To explain the occurrence of these anomalously-situated deposits, I believe we shall be compelled to have recourse to the solution proposed by a Swedish geologist, namely, that they have been formed *underneath* the ice-sheet, and the manner in which they may have been accumulated, I shall proceed to describe in the next chapter.

CHAPTER XXI.

UPPER DRIFT DEPOSITS OF SCOTLAND—*Continued.*

Probable effect of subglacial waters during melting of ice-sheet.—Long gravel ridges are not marine.—Origin of certain gravel ridges and sand mounds under ice-sheet.—Morainic origin of some gravel deposits.—Trend of gravel ridges coincides with direction of glaciation.—Erratics and morainic débris associated with kames.—No evidence of marine action.—Succession of changes.

WHEN the Scotch ice-sheet ceased to be confluent with that of Scandinavia, its waste would be somewhat rapid. It has already been remarked that the great thickness attained by the Scotch ice in the low grounds of the country was, to a large extent, due to the presence of the Scandinavian ice-sheet in the bed of the German Ocean; the watersheds of the country, as we have seen, are too inconsiderable to have supplied a gathering ground for the vast ice-masses that overflowed the Sidlaws, the Ochils, the Pentlands, and the Lammermuirs. And we can hardly doubt that the ice accumulated to such an extent on the low grounds chiefly for the reason that its outward progress was stemmed by the great confluent glaciers of Scandinavia, which thus compelled the Lowlands to become, more than they would otherwise have been, a glacier-ice-producing region. When this obstruction was removed, and even for some time before the two ice-sheets had ceased to coalesce, the hill regions between the Southern Uplands and the Grampians would begin to peer above the level of the decreasing ice-sheet; while, at the same time, many of the narrower mountain ridges and summits both of the Southern Uplands and the Northern Highlands would reappear, and divide the ice-sheet into separate glaciers, which, however, would only be separate so far as their upper extremities were concerned. The ice in the Lowlands, no longer

impelled by the same overwhelming *vis a tergo*, would now
be impeded by obstacles which during its greatest extension
it had previously found little difficulty in surmounting, and
it would no more exert the same influence upon its bed.
Over large and constantly increasing areas till would cease to
be formed, while the loose débris introduced from above
through *moulins* and crevasses and gathering below would
be washed down the valleys of the still partially ice-covered
country by subglacial streams and rivers.

Such streams, as we know, exist under all glaciers, and
we have seen that, even during the climax of glacial cold,
waters underneath the ice gave rise to stratified clay, sand,
and gravel, which ever and anon were liable to be crumpled,
contorted, and rolled over and over upon themselves and the
till, so as to become inextricably mixed up with the latter.
But after the ice-sheet had been greatly reduced, and a hard
tenacious tough till (which, under enormous pressure, was
sometimes actually squeezed tightly into the crevices, cracks,
crannies, and sometimes even between the bedding-planes, of
the rock below) had ceased to be formed, a coarser and earthier
accumulation began to be accumulated here and there in its
stead.   In many places this débris would be re-assorted and
rolled forward by the subglacial waters, and thus heaps of clay,
sand, gravel, and boulders, more or less water-worn, would
gradually be piled up.   As a rule the subglacial channels
would now remain open all the year round, and the deposits
would therefore not be so liable to be disturbed by the action
of the slowly-moving ice, although, sometimes, they might be
subjected to pressure and thrown into more or less confusion.
When the ice finally melted away from the lowland valleys
the subglacial gravels would in many cases lie beyond the
reach of river-action, and, so escaping denudation, would often
preserve their original contour.

Such are some of the results which we may reasonably
infer were brought about during the melting of the ice-sheet,
and many appearances connected with the stratified drift tally
with them so remarkably that it is difficult to escape the
conclusion that we have here hit upon the true explanation
of the phenomena referred to.   Thus, I think, most of the
long gravel ridges in the central lowland districts may be

accounted for. Their trend, it will be found, coincides as a rule with that of the ice-sheet, which of course is just the direction that would be chiefly followed by the subglacial waters. These ridges, every one admits, could not have been formed by any ordinary river-action, and the general belief at present is that they must be marine. It is very difficult, however, as Mr. Jamieson remarks, to see how they could possibly have been heaped up by tides. I have examined many of the Admiralty Charts of the British Seas, but have not found any submarine bank that has more than a mere superficial resemblance to a typical kame. There are, for example, a number of banks represented as occurring off the east coast of Ireland which, as they are drawn upon the charts, look not unlike the ground-plans of kames. Such are Kish Bank, Bray Bank, Codling Banks, and many others that extend parallel to the coast-line between Dublin Bay and Wexford Harbour. But when we come to measure them and ascertain their contour we find that they are very much broader than the broadest of our kames, while their sides are not nearly so steep. Nor have the shingle banks, which are often heaped up along a sea-coast opposite the mouths of rivers, a much closer resemblance to the mysterious kames. Putting aside the significant circumstance that the latter never contain shells while the former often do, we must yet admit that the inclination of the sides of such gravel-banks is never so steep as the slopes of many kames, and this of itself alone is strongly against the presumption that both kinds of banks have been heaped up in the same way. Moreover we cannot shut our eyes to the conclusive fact that most of the long sharp-ridged kames of Scotland occur far out upon the low grounds in positions where, during submergence, they certainly would not lie opposite the mouth of any river-valley either large or small.

All the sharp-ridged kames with steep sides are composed of gravel, which is often exceedingly coarse and shingly and usually quite unstratified—the kames of sand on the other hand are commonly broad-backed mounds and banks, having gently sloping sides; or, more frequently still, they form a series of swelling hummocks and knolls, in which the bedding is generally well-marked. The former may have been formed in the narrower passages under the ice, through which the waters would rush with some force. Such passages would become paved in time with considerable depths of shingle and gravel, while the wider channels would receive accumulations of finer grained materials. I think it is quite possible, too, that where lateral channels opened into the main subglacial hollows there would often be little cross-currents that would give rise to confused stratification and false-bedding. Similar results would take place even without the assistance of lateral feeders to the main streams : for the volume of water circulating under the ice would be liable to considerable variation. It would increase and diminish with the change of the seasons ; and even during one and the same season it is easy to understand how the quantity of water descending by moulins and crevasses, or seeking its way down between the ice-sheet and the mountain-slopes and hill-sides that rose above its surface, would vary day by day with the external temperature. And such constant variations in the volume of the subglacial streams would of itself give rise to many modifications of bedding in the deposits of sand and fine gravel.

But while there does not appear to be much difficulty in accounting for the formation underneath the ice of broad-backed mounds of sand and gravel with more or less gently sloping sides, it is yet very hard to understand how the long sharp-ridged kames of gravel have received their characteristic outline. Dr. R. Chambers long ago suggested their morainic character, and there can be no doubt that in some places the kames do present much the appearance of terminal moraines. In some upland districts, indeed, we find moraines and gravel heaps in such close union that we cannot doubt both were formed at approximately the same time. Mr. Jamieson remarks of certain kames in the north of Scotland that they " often lie across valleys in long sinuous lines, forming curves or segments of a circle, the concavity of which is presented to the head of the valley, and their convexity towards the sea or downward end, as in terminal moraines." "The material they consist of and its mode of arrangement point to streams of water flowing over the surface of the glaciers, and washing the gravelly débris into heaps along their margins. A mass of gravel reposing against the side or end of a glacier would lose its support when the ice melted away, and, falling down in a slope, would assume the form of a steep-sided mound. Glaciers are subject to oscillations, sometimes advancing, sometimes receding, according to the varying nature of the seasons. Suppose the end of a glacier to push forward into a sheet of gravel lying in front, the result would be to force it up into a mound all along the edge of the ice." * Mr. Jamieson further reminds us of another resemblance which certain kames bear to moraines, namely, that one side of the ridges is often steeper than the other,—the same being the case, according to M. Collomb, with many of the old moraines in the Vosges Mountains. That not a few of the ridges, mounds, and hummocks of gravel and sand which occur both in mountain-valleys and opposite their mouths, upon the low grounds beyond, may have had such an origin is exceedingly likely, but the same explanation will hardly account for the sharp-ridged kames of gravel that run in long sinuous lines through the undulating districts of the Lowlands. These kames neither lie opposite the mouths of glacier valleys, nor can we suppose from their position that they could have been deposited along the margin of the decaying ice-sheet. Let me add further that many kames stand completely isolated from all other accumulations of gravel and sand. They rest either upon till or solid rock, and their gravelly contents terminate at once with the slope of the ridge itself. Frequently we shall find in a wide lowland district that the only drift gravel to be met with occurs in the solitary kame that runs like a tortuous embankment across broad stretches of boulder-clay or bare rock. Nor even when such kames appear in the middle of a valley, up which we know the ice-sheet must have retired when the final melting took place, do they lie across that valley. As far as my own experience goes, and it is borne out by that of my colleagues, the direction of the long gravel ridges in the wide valleys of central and southern Scotland, as, for example, in the Lothians and the lower reaches of Nithsdale and Tweeddale, invariably coincides with the trend of the valleys—in short, as I have remarked above,

---

* *Quart. Jour. Geol. Soc.* 1874, p. 329. I would call the special attention of the geological reader to this paper. Mr. Jamieson's argument against the marine origin of the kames is very convincing, and his remarks on the mode of their formation are both ingenious and suggestive.

the ridges run *along* and not *across* the path of the great ice-sheet.

It is quite clear, then, that such kames must have been formed by currents that flowed down the valleys. Ordinary river-action, however, will not account for them, for they often lie in positions which preclude the possibility of such fluviatile origin. We seem shut up, therefore, in the present state of our knowledge, to the belief that they have been formed by subglacial water in narrow channels below the ice.* To these subglacial deposits would be added the stones and débris introduced from above, and the whole would be carried along the channels underneath the ice. Many of these we may conceive might thus be filled to a considerable depth with gravel and shingle in the narrow channels, and with laminated clays, sand, and finer gravel in the wider subglacial tunnels. When at last the ice melted away, we should find ridges and banks which would preserve to a large extent the contour they received under the ice ; the steeper sloped narrow kames of gravel representing those confined channels whose walls slanted abruptly upwards—the broader mounds of sand, &c., corresponding to the more open recesses with gently curved roofs and sides. Such a subglacial origin would likewise account for the not infrequent association of morainic débris, angular boulders, and gravel in one and the same kame. Angular blocks and rubbish would often reach the bottom by moulin and crevasse, while the *moraine profonde*, with its faintly striated boulders and stones, would often escape complete re-assorting and become covered up with gravel, into which it would sometimes appear to pass. But the fact that the kames rest either upon bare rock or a highly denuded surface of tough till, shows that a large proportion of their materials must often have been derived from the demolition of the old boulder-clay.†

* This is the view advanced by Mr. D. Hummel, of the Geological Survey of Sweden, in explanation of the gravel ridges of that country. See *postea*, chap. xxxii.

† Mr. J. G. Goodchild, of the Geological Survey of England, recently advanced (*Quarterly Journal Geological Society*, vol. xxxi., p. 75; *Geological Magazine*, vol. xi., p. 496) an explanation of the origin of till and its associated deposits, which ascribes not only the sand and gravel but the till also to the melting of the ice-sheet. He thinks that the materials of which all the drift deposits are composed were originally embedded in the ice itself, and that when the ice melted some of these were merely dropped, while others were assorted by the

I have mentioned the frequent occurrence of angular erratics
on the tops and slopes of gravel ridges and sand mounds, as
one of many puzzling appearances connected with the kames;
and it has been shown, how in some cases these may have
been dropt by ice-rafts set adrift during the flood seasons
when the ice-sheet was melting out of the broad valleys of
the Lowlands. In many, perhaps in the majority of cases,
however, the erratics referred to seem to have been carried
on the surface of the ice and to have been quietly dropt over
the terminal front of the decaying ice-sheet. The subglacial
banks and ridges, while they were gradually emerging from
underneath the melting ice, would thus ever and anon be
dotted with erratics and sprinkled with angular débris. And
if the ice that covered the Lowlands had been copiously supplied with superficial moraines, no doubt the kames would
sometimes have been completely buried under débris and
erratics. But even when the hill-ranges of central Scotland
were beginning to appear above the level of the decaying
ice-sheet, very little angular débris would be discharged from
these hills, which, as a rule, show few crags and cliffs from
which blocks and stones could be dislodged by frost. Never-

action of subglacial streams. (This view seems to be very much the same as
that maintained by Professor J. D. Dana; see chap. xxxv.) I have no space
here to point out in detail how this explanation fails, as I think, to account for
the phenomena. No doubt gravel and sand were formed underneath the ice by
water-action contemporaneously with the till (and we have seen how the two
kinds of deposit were often confusedly mingled and rolled over and upon each
other), but the great mass of sand and gravel, the hummocks and undulating
expanses of water-worn materials which cover such extensive areas in the low
grounds of Scotland, Switzerland, and other glaciated countries, everywhere rest
upon either bare rock or till, and are clearly of later date than the latter, which
usually affords evidence of having been much denuded before the deposition of
the overlying kames. There are other equally strong objections to Mr. Goodchild's views which might be stated, but without entering into controversy I
shall merely refer the reader to the account which I have given of the Scotch till
and its associated deposits. It is obvious that Mr. Goodchild has left out of
account many important facts, and that the succession of deposits, not only in
Scotland but in England and Ireland also, clearly indicates a series of great
climatic changes. I have shown above that erratics may travel upwards through
the body of the ice; and no doubt the old ice-sheet in the time of its decay would
be sprinkled in many places with superficial morainic matter, much of which,
falling into crevasses, would find its way into the heart of the ice. There is no
reason to believe, however, that during the climax of glacial cold the ice would
contain more included blocks than are seen in the great icebergs of arctic and
antarctic seas, which of course are only fragments broken off the terminal fronts
of vast glaciers,—erratics occurring either embedded in or resting upon such
icebergs having been very rarely noticed. Mr. Goodchild is no doubt right,
however, in holding that no inconsiderable portion of the water-worn and stratified drift that overlies the till has been formed by water flowing under the ice.

theless, torrents from the melting snows might here and there sweep upon the surface of the glaciers considerable quantities of the earthy rubbish and stones with which the retiring ice had sprinkled the hill-slopes ; and gravel and sand also might now and again be conveyed upon the ice by torrents, and would travel down in the direction of its slope, to pour over the terminal front in the way that Mr. Jamieson has suggested.* Some isolated abrupt hills in the lowland districts appear, however, to have discharged many large blocks and erratics upon the surface of the ice-sheet, which were borne onwards and dropt over its margin ; and great numbers of similar erratics were showered upon the ice in the Highlands and Southern Uplands, many of which were carried for great distances before they rolled down the terminal front of the glacier to rest upon mounds of gravel and sand, some of which were being formed here and there as moraines along the sloping face of the ice, while others were slowly emerging from underneath as the melting of the mass continued.

In fine, it seems most reasonable to conclude that neither the water-worn and stratified drift, nor the loose angular débris, nor yet the erratics that lie scattered over the low grounds and hilly regions of the Lowlands of Scotland, give any indications of a former submergence of the land below the sea. The loose angular débris or morainic matter and erratics have been carried down and dropt over the terminal front of the ice-sheet, or have stranded upon mountain-slope and hill-side, or have been left lying in what once formed the bed of the old ice-sheet. The sand and gravel drifts have been produced by the action of water escaping from the melting ice-sheet, which re-arranged the morainic débris, &c., heaping it up in banks or spreading it out in undulating flats. Gravel ridges and sand banks appear also to have been accumulated by streams underneath the ice ; even the most elevated terraces and shelves of sand, gravel, and angular shingle afford no evidence of marine action, but plainly disclose the former presence of old glacial lakes and of torrents of fresh water. But if we were still in doubt as to whether the sea might not have had some share in the formation of the

* *Quart. Jour. Geol. Soc.*, 1874, p. 329.

kames and terraces, the total absence of any trace of marine organisms in these deposits ought perhaps to satisfy us that it had not. I have always felt that this non-appearance in the kames, &c., of sea-shells or other exuviæ was, if not an insuperable, at least a very great difficulty in the way of accepting the marine theory, and I am therefore glad now to find myself in accord with Mr. Jamieson, who holds that no great submergence of the land supervened after the final disappearance of the ice-sheet.

In the previous edition of this work I laid some stress upon the very frequent occurrence of erratics perched upon the tops and slopes of the kames, which I contrasted with their general absence from the interior of these peculiar ridges and hummocks; and I held that the erratics were probably dropt where we now see them by floating ice during a period of submergence. I found great difficulty, however, in distinguishing between those wandered blocks and boulders which had been left behind upon the land by the old glaciers, and such erratics as might have been transported by ice-rafts —for they had one and all been carried outwards from the mountains and distributed along the paths of the ice-sheet. For example, the boulders of grey granite which occur so abundantly in the deep valleys of the Galloway mountains and are scattered over the hills up to a height of 1,700 ft., are also widely sprinkled over the low grounds at the foot of the mountains ; they appear as far north as the valleys of the Girvan and the Doon, and, along with other erratics derived from the same knot of mountains, appear to be distributed over all the low grounds bordering on the Solway Frith. Blocks of the granite of Criffel are also widely scattered along the maritime districts of the north-west of England. But, as we have seen, it was precisely in these directions that the gigantic glaciers moved. If all, or even if any proportion, of the erratics derived from the Southern Uplands had been transported by bergs and rafts during a period of submergence, surely we might have expected to meet with them in the Lowlands to the north. Why, for example, should not they occur in the north of Ayrshire, in Lanarkshire, and even in the Lothians ? The fact is, explain it as we may, that the erratics from the Southern Uplands never appear beyond the districts which are known to have been occupied by the great glaciers of the south.

The same fact holds true in regard to the boulders which have travelled from the Highlands. These are scattered over all the regions which are proved to have been covered with ice that flowed from the Highlands, but they never appear within the districts which, during the last cold period, were occupied by the great glaciers of the Southern Uplands. Yet if rafts and bergs did carry them south, why is it that we do not meet with erratics from the Highlands in the extreme south of Ayrshire, and indeed along the whole front of the Southern Uplands? We get them on the Pentland Hills, and we find them on the Lammermuirs, but both rock-striations and till assure us that the highland ice rubbed the northern slopes of these hills as it swept east and south-east into the bed of the German Ocean. But not a single trace of any highland erratics occurs within those districts of the south-west and south which are plentifully sprinkled with the grey granite boulders from the Galloway mountains.

An impartial consideration of these facts and of the phenomena connected with the retreat of the great glaciers, led me strongly to suspect that we had hitherto greatly exaggerated the carrying powers of floating ice during the supposed period of submergence—in other words, that erratics in themselves were no proof at all of the former presence of an iceberg-laden sea. I now go a step further, and hold that neither the erratics nor any portion of the stratified and re-assorted upper drifts of the interior afford any evidence in favour of marine submergence, but that all the phenomena must be attributed to the combined action of the retreating ice-sheet and local glaciers, and those great floods and inundations that marked the gradual disappearance of arctic conditions.

Having now reviewed the evidence supplied by the erratics, morainic débris, and kames, I shall attempt to point out as shortly as I can the succession of changes of which the phenomena we have been considering are the proofs.

When the great ice-sheet was beginning to deposit the more recent boulder-clay which is now met with in some maritime districts, the higher hills of the central Lowlands stood above the level of the *mer de glace* like islands in a frozen ocean. At the same time the mountain ridges of the Highlands and the bold hills of the Southern Uplands rose up so as to separate the ice-sheet into a series of gigantic local glaciers, which, however, still coalesced to form one mighty stream upon the broad Lowlands. Frost shivered the rocks and loosened out great blocks, which eventually toppled down upon the ice below, and, along with heaps of angular rubbish, were slowly carried away. Sometimes the stones and boulders fell into crevasses or between the ice and the rock of the mountain-slopes, and so got ground and polished on one or more sides : but they always travelled farther and farther off from their parent mountains. The tops of the lowland hills, peering above the ice, caught some of the wanderers as they drifted past, but many were borne out to the terminal front of the ice and dropped into the sea, where they mingled with the scratched stones that were being pushed out from underneath the glaciers.

As the ice continued to melt,[*] erratics and angular débris were stranded at ever-decreasing heights upon the mountain-slopes and hill-sides, and at last the ice melted back from the sea and the glaciers then dropped their rubbish upon the land. Much of the angular rubbish, however, that lay scattered over the surface of the ice-sheet was subjected to the action of countless streams and rivers that laved the surface of the ice in summer-time, just as similar currents of water pour over the surface of arctic glaciers, so that at many points along the margin of the melting ice-sheet the moraines were made up to a large extent of gravel. Great streams of water escaping from above and below swept much of the morainic matter down the valleys, and angular stones and rubbish, as they were pushed along, became rounded by attrition, and arranged by the torrents and rivers in great flats and hummocky heaps of gravel and sand : but in regions which are not traversed by great river-valleys draining from mountainous regions, such as the low grounds of Caithness and Lewis, no gravel deposits of the kind were

---

[*] I would again remind the reader that some of the crossing of striæ upon the rocks was in all probability caused during this recession of the ice-sheet. As the glaciers ceased to be confluent, their courses would in many cases be modified. A good example is given in *Trans. Geol. Soc. Glas.*, vol. iv., p. 223.

formed. At the same time torrents derived from the melting of the thick snows that covered the isolated hill-ranges
of the Lowlands carried down in summer quantities of angular
débris to the margin of the ice-sheet, part of which was
swept upon the ice, while part was rolled along the hollows
that lay between it and the hills upon which it abutted, and
either piled up in hummocks and banks or spread out over
the bottoms of temporary lakes. Underneath the ice the
older glacial deposits and the angular blocks and stones,
and gravel, sand, and rubbish introduced from above through
holes and clefts, were subjected to extensive erosion and reassortment, and banks and ridges of more or less water-worn
materials were heaped up and rolled forward in the beds of
subglacial streams and rivers, in the quieter expanses of
which fine clay, silt, and sand were now and again deposited.
Large and small erratics and, here and there, angular débris
travelled slowly down the broad valleys and toppled over the
margin of the ice-sheet upon the tops and slopes of subglacial banks and ridges, as these slowly emerged from underneath the thawing mass. Over wide areas, however, the
surface of the ice-sheet showed no superficial moraine-matter,
so that along many parts of its front no terminal moraines
collected and no erratics were dropped upon the sand and
gravel mounds. And even where such morainic débris did
gather it was often ploughed down and distributed over the
bottoms of the valleys, or piled up in heaps and hummocks
by the swollen rivers and torrents. Hence it is that in the
wider vales of central Scotland we find little or no trace of
moraines which can be compared with those that occur in
Alpine valleys ; such morainic matter as we do meet with
being always associated with heaps of water-worn detritus.
The winter cold was still extremely severe, consequently the
rivers in winter-time were much reduced in volume, and here
and there thickly covered with ice which enclosed loose
stones and boulders. When the short but warm summer
returned all the rivers rose in flood, torrents streamed off the
melting ice-sheet, and the thawing snows of the hill-ranges
discharged great volumes of water ; the river-ice everywhere
broke up, and rafts transported gravel and erratics and
scattered them over the surface of the drowned districts.

Besides such periodical floods there were probably others more sudden and destructive, caused by glacial lakes bursting their barriers. We have abundant evidence to show that such temporary lakes existed, and their icy ramparts must sometimes have given way and caused great inundations; at all events, we know that similar accidents have happened again and again in glacier regions within historical times. In 1818 the lower glacier of Giétroz dammed up the passage of the Dranse, a tributary of the Rhone. In consequence of this a lake more than half a mile wide, and reaching in places a depth of between two hundred and three hundred feet, was formed, the contents of which were estimated at more than six millions and a half of cubic yards. The inhabitants of the valley below, fearing that the barrier might burst, attempted to lower the water by digging a channel across the ice, and succeeded in draining a portion off. Suddenly, however, the rampart of ice gave way; "the pent-up water, driving before it both ice and rocks, sprang into the valley with such rapidity that in twenty minutes the whole basin was empty. This formidable cataract swept away woods and chalêts, and laying bare the rocks, and carrying away the very meadows, emptied itself into the plain like a mingled avalanche of water, trees, and débris, three hundred feet in height, and preceded by a black and thick vapour, like the smoke of a conflagration." *

As the breadth of ice in the low grounds continued to decrease, its covering of morainic matter became proportionately more continuous. Trains of erratics travelled outwards from isolated rocky hills, such as Ruberslaw in Roxburghshire and other trappean eminences in the vale of the Tweed, and from various projecting crags and knolls along the flanks of the hill-ranges that diversify the Lowlands of central Scotland. Eventually the ice melted away from all the low grounds, leaving behind it wide stretches of gravel and sand in the broader valleys, and sporadic heaps and ridges dotted about the hill-slopes and moorlands, while numerous erratics lay sprinkled over the surface of the country from the tops of the hills down to the bottoms of the valleys. When the edge or margin of the ice had melted back to the

* *The Earth.* By Elisée Reclus, vol. i. p. 216.

close proximity of the Southern Uplands and the Grampians, the erratics and angular débris covering the ice became proportionately still more abundant, and the result was the heaping-up of terminal moraines of a more decided character than the gravelly débris which lies strewn over the bed of the old ice-sheet in the wide lowland valleys. By this time the glaciers were ceasing to coalesce, and becoming more and more restricted to the mountain-valleys of southern and northern regions. The rivers were much larger then than they are now, and overflowed wide tracts in the lowland valleys which are no longer within their reach. The increasing temperature having caused the ice to vanish from all the low grounds, the glaciers next began to cumber the bottoms of the mountain-valleys with their terminal moraines. The retreat of the ice-rivers, however, was probably very unequal. In some valleys that drain inconsiderable areas of no great elevation the disappearance of the glaciers was comparatively rapid, while in other glens that received the drainage of wide and lofty regions the ice maintained its ground for a longer time. Now and again, indeed, when a succession of somewhat colder seasons had greatly replenished its frozen reservoirs, the ice even re-advanced, pushing moraines and gravel-beds before it, and sometimes neither advancing nor retreating, it made longer or shorter pauses, during which large moraines gathered in front which the rivers were unable to sweep away.

At this time many of the smaller lateral valleys from which the glaciers had either partially or entirely disappeared, were dammed up by the main trunk glaciers of the principal glens and dales. Glacial lakes were thus formed, some of which endured so long that they were partially or even completely silted up with more or less deep deposits of mud, sand, and gravel. When the icy barrier was at last removed, the lacustrine deposits were excavated by the brooks; but their remains are still often to be seen fringing the sides of the valleys and forming more or less distinct terraces, frequently at considerable heights above the present streams. Such horizontal ledges are not to be confounded with those old river-terraces which occur so frequently in many of the mountain-valleys of northern and southern Scotland. The latter slope with the inclination of the valleys in which they appear, and evidently mark former levels at which the rivers flowed when the body of water descending to the low grounds was much more considerable than now.

Thus by slow degrees the ice forsook the vales and glens as the amelioration of the climate continued. The snows and frosts of winter became less severe, and the floods of summer less excessive. Everywhere the streams and rivers began to cut their channels into the deep drifts, denuding and re-assorting the materials, and spreading these out in low-level flats and terraces.

CHAPTER XXII.

UPPER DRIFT DEPOSITS OF SCOTLAND—*Continued*.

Shelly clays of maritime districts.—Position of these deposits with respect to older drift accumulations.—General character of brick-clay sections.—Organic remains.—Ice-floated stones and boulders.—Crumpled and contorted beds.—Probable interglacial age of some shelly clays.—Summary of events during deposition of interglacial and late glacial shelly clays.

THE deposits which we are now about to consider are memorable in the annals of geological discovery. Mr. Smith, of Jordanhill, was, as already mentioned, the first to introduce them to notice, and the phenomena as described by him at once convinced the most sceptical that an arctic climate had really at one time characterized our country. The deposits referred to occur more or less abundantly at many points along the sea-board, especially where the shore shelves sufficiently to give rise to a flat beach. They appear, for example, in the low flats that fringe the margins of the Forth and the Clyde, where they are more or less concealed below a thick covering of re-arranged or recent accumulations. The low ground upon which Glasgow is built, and which, as we trace it westward, widens out on either side of the river Clyde, especially south, by Paisley, Johnston, and Houston, so as to form a broad expanse many square miles in extent, is composed, for the most part, of fine sand, silt, and brick-clay, the lower portions of which deposits all belong to the glacial series. Of like nature are the under portions of those wide terraces of sand, silt, and clay, through which the river Forth flows for several miles before joining its estuary. Along the borders of that estuary similar deposits continue, and are occasionally exposed when the upper or more recent accumulations are thin or wanting, as at Kirkcaldy, Elie, and Portobello. The same appearance recurs upon the coasts of the Frith of Clyde, and many of the sea-lochs in that region.

Brick-clays occupying a like position are found in several
localities south from the Clyde, as at Stevenston, Monkton,
Girvan, Ballantrae, and Stranraer.　North of the Clyde they
have been detected here and there in some of the fiords, and
they occur also in the Outer Hebrides.　On the east and
north-east coast they have not been so frequently observed,
but deposits of this age appear at Glencarse, Errol, Barry, and
Montrose, and like accumulations have been noted in the low
grounds of Aberdeenshire that border on the sea.　It is
highly probable, indeed, that if the recent shingle, sand, and
silt were removed from the flat beaches that skirt a large
part of the coast-line, the deposits which we are now about
to consider would be found more frequently.　There can be
little doubt at all events that in some places they cover the
bed of the sea ; for the fossil shells which they contain, and
to which I shall presently refer, have occasionally been
brought up in dredges.

None of these deposits has ever been detected at high
levels or in the interior of the country.　It is true that beds
of brick-clay, loam, and silt are of common occurrence there ;
but these beds, however much they may sometimes resemble
those I now refer to, yet cannot be confounded with them.
The superficial brick-clays in the interior of the country are,
for the most part, unfossiliferous ; but when they do contain
fossils, these invariably prove to be the remains of terrestrial
and freshwater organisms.　Now the brick-clays of maritime
and low-lying districts more frequently contain fossils, and
these are all without exception marine.　The greatest elevation to which fossiliferous marine deposits (not covered by till
or boulder-clay) have been traced is in Aberdeenshire, where
Mr. Jamieson met with them at a height of 300 to 360 ft.
above the sea.

In the Clyde district, where these deposits were first
studied, they have been identified by means of their fossils at
a height of 125 ft. above the sea.[*]　The flat ground that
stretches up the valley of the Clyde from Glasgow to near
Hamilton appears to be composed for the most part of these

---

[*] I may remind the reader that the shells got near Airdrie, at a height of 526 ft.
above the sea, rest upon and are overlaid by till, and therefore do not belong to
the period of submergence during which the later glacial-marine clays, &c.,
were deposited.

accumulations, covered up, however, over wide areas with considerable depths of river-sand and gravel. At Uddingston they yielded sea-shells. But fossils are certainly by no means of common occurrence in the brick-clays at this level. It is not until we descend to the level of 40 or 50 ft. above the sea that organic remains begin to be plentifully present. It is from the brick-clays occupying this and lower levels that Scottish geologists have made their largest and most varied collections, and it was from an examination of these very clay-beds that the earlier observers were enabled to demonstrate that an arctic climate had at a comparatively recent date characterized the country. But before we proceed to inquire into the nature of the evidence they relied upon, it is essential that we first ascertain what relation the clay-beds bear to the other glacial deposits which have already engaged our attention.

When the bottom of the clay-beds is reached, they are found resting sometimes upon solid rock, and sometimes upon an irregular and hummocky surface of till. But in many places we do not see the basement beds. We know only that in deep borings and other mining operations the clay-beds frequently alternate with silt, loam, sand, and sometimes gravel ; but whether the beds of gravel and sand, which are often passed through between the clay-beds and the till, are part .and parcel of the shelly series, we cannot tell. Most of the shelly clays now under review appear to be of more recent date than the kames and river-gravels described in last chapter. We find, especially in the basin of the Forth, that while the kames come down in many places to the margin of the great plains or terraces in which the shelly clays occur, they never in any case overlie the deposits of the estuarine flats ; on the contrary, they appear to extend below, and are overlapped by the latter. A careful examination of the physical features of the Forth and Clyde basins will convince one that this is the true succession of the superficial deposits. Proceeding inland from the margin of the Frith of Forth, we first pace over extensive flats or gently undulating ground which numerous sections have shown to be composed chiefly of estuarine and marine deposits. After leaving these plains, we find that the ground, where it begins to ascend more rapidly, has for a subsoil either till or gravel and sand—the latter in many places assuming the form of cones and irregular tortuous banks. The same is the case with the Clyde. At the lower levels we have the usual wide stretches of fine sand, silt, and brick-clays, which as we trace them inland are seen to abut upon the till. No true kames, however, come down in the Clyde district to the level of the brick-clays. The annexed diagram will serve to illustrate the succession as seen in the basin of the Forth.

At the top of a good section of the series of deposits which occur associated with the brick-clay beds we commonly get sand and fine gravel—sometimes loam and silt, below which come layers of clay of variable thickness. These clays are

Fig. 44.—Diagrammatic view of drift deposits of the basin of the Forth.
b, Recent beach deposits; *c*, brick-clay, &c.; *k*, kame-series; *t*, till or boulder-clay.

usually exceedingly fine-grained, and are often arranged in thin leaves or laminæ. Fine exposures of such deposits were seen at the old College of Glasgow during the recent railway operations. Below the clays, and sometimes intermingled with them, occur occasional beds of mud, sand, silt, and, but only rarely, gravel. Irregularly scattered throughout all these deposits, a few angular, subangular, and smoothed stones and boulders are not infrequently met with—here and there crowding thickly together; and not a few of the stones and boulders referred to exhibit glacial scratches. But these glacial markings are seldom so well marked as in the case of the stones and boulders of the till; many of the fragments indeed bear no trace whatever of glaciation.

The following section,* taken at the Kilchattan brick-works in Bute, shows the general character of the beds at and below the level of 40 or 50 ft. above the sea :—

* See *The Glacial Drift of Scotland*, by A. Geikie, where this section and others are given; also papers by Messrs. Crosskey and Robertson (in *Trans. Geol. Soc. Glas.*, and *Palæontographical Society*, vol. xxviii.), who are the best authorities on the subject of the Clyde brick-clay deposits.

1. Vegetable soil.
2. Sand and gravel, well stratified, false-bedded, passing down into a sandy clay with gravel, 10 or 12 ft.
3. Red clay without stones or shells, becoming dull olive-green in lower part, 1 to 2 ft.
4. Bed of fine dark clay, full of *Tellina proxima,* &c., many of the shells retaining both valves, 2 ft.
5. Finely laminated brown and reddish brick-clay without stones or shells, 15 to 18 ft. *
6. Hard tough red boulder-clay with striated stones; its upper surface hummocky and irregular.

The brick-clays of the maritime districts of central and southern Scotland at higher levels than 40 ft. or so are comparatively poor in fossils. These, however, have occasionally been got at heights of 100 ft. and 125 ft. above the sea.

A large percentage of the fossils derived from the brick-clay beds are northern and arctic forms. And since these clearly occupy their natural position—having lived and died and become entombed just where we now find them—there can be no doubt whatever that the sea in which the brick-clays and associated deposits were accumulated was considerably colder than the water that now laves our shores. In short, it seems clear that the climate during the lifetime of these shells must have approximated in severity to that of Greenland. This is the certain conclusion to which we are brought by a study of the molluscs and other organisms yielded by the clay-beds ; but it is a conclusion which, even in the absence of fossils, we could not fail to have arrived at from an examination of purely physical evidence alone. I have mentioned the fact that occasional stones and boulders are here and there sparsely scattered through the fine clay-beds. A little consideration will suffice to assure us that the gentle currents which disseminated the impalpable mud and silt over the bed of the sea could not possibly have carried along at the same time stones and boulders. These have clearly been dropped into their present position. We can often satisfy ourselves that this is so by closely examining the fine laminæ upon which the stones and boulders lie. Fig. 45 represents a boulder of sandstone about 2 ft. in diameter, which occurs all alone in a fine deposit of laminated clay. It will be observed that the laminæ below the stone

---

* This clay very commonly occurs between the underlying till and overlying shelly clay. It is generally unfossiliferous, but, according to Messrs. Crosskey and Robertson, occasionally yields entomostraca and foraminifera.

S

are bent down as if by pressure from above—showing that
the stone fell with some force upon what was then the bottom of the sea or estuary. The upper part of the boulder
which projected above the level of the bottom was then gradually buried by the increasing sediment, as one may see by

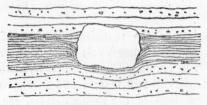

Fig. 45.—Boulder in stratified deposits, near Uddingston, Lanarkshire.

the mode in which the laminæ curve up, and at last sweep
over the wanderer. We can hardly doubt that the carrying
agent in this case was floating ice.

Some [of these boulders have frequently been floated for
considerable distances. Thus in the Portobello brick-clays

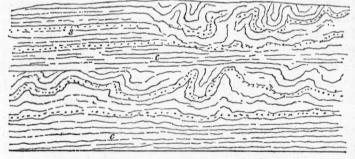

Fig. 46.—Contorted beds; clay c, and sand s; Portobello.

Mr. J. Bennie has obtained fragments and boulders of chalk
which may have crossed the German Ocean from Denmark.*

Again, we have strong evidence to show that during the
accumulation of the brick-clay beds, coast-ice and perhaps
icebergs frequently floated and ran aground in the seas. In

* I have seen chalk fragments also in brick-clay, with arctic and boreal shells,
at Barry, in Forfarshire. Chalk fragments, as we have seen, occur in some of
the older drift deposits in the north of Scotland, and it is just possible that the
bits of chalk in the Portobello and Barry beds may have been floated from the
north by coast-ice.

many places the beds are confusedly twisted, crumpled, and contorted—the laminæ being bent violently over, now in one direction, now in another. Excellent examples of these appearances are exposed from time to time in the clay-pits, as at Tyrie in Fifeshire and at Portobello.

I have in a previous chapter described the crumpling and contortion of the beds in the till. It will be remembered that

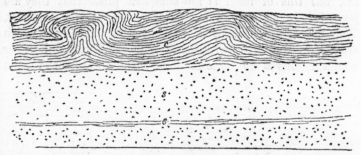

Fig. 47.—Contorted beds; clay *c*, and sand *s*; Leith. [Depth of cutting, 6 ft., J. Croll.]

the character of these contortions and crumplings plainly pointed to the exertion of force in one determinate direction. The beds, in short, were shown to be curved over in the direction followed by the till and the rock-striations, indicating the violent pressure of glacier-ice. But the case is widely different with the contortions visible in the maritime brick-clays. These are exceedingly irregular, and are just of such

Fig. 48.—Contorted beds; clay *c*, and sand *s*; Portobello.

a character as we should expect would result from the grounding of ice-rafts and bergs. The rough sketches give a general idea of the appearances presented. One can hardly doubt that the submarine banks of sand and mud off the American coast must present very similar appearances after they have been bumped and crushed, and pushed forward by the bergs

which are every now and then running aground, and stirring
up the sediment in their frantic gyrations.

From the foregoing facts it has been inferred that the
shelly deposits described in this chapter were accumulated
towards the close of the glacial epoch. It is doubtful, however, whether they can all be relegated to so late a period.
It is quite true that they rest upon and are not covered by
till, but this of itself is not sufficient proof that they are
posterior in date to the final recession of the ice-sheet.
They do not differ in any degree from those shell-beds which
are overlaid by till or enclosed between lower and upper
accumulations of the same material. The *facies* of the fauna

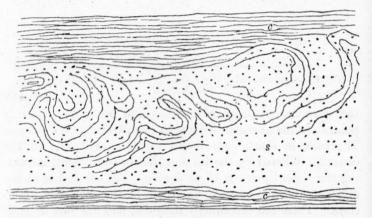

Fig. 49.—Contorted beds: clay *c*, and sand *s*; Portobello. [Depth of cutting,
6 ft., J. Croll.]

is the same in all, and for aught that the fossil evidence
can tell us, all the fossiliferous clays may have been deposited at various levels in one and the same sea during a
period of slow submergence and emergence of the land.
My colleague, Mr. Jack, who surveyed the lower reaches
of the Clyde below Glasgow, formed the opinion that the
arctic shell-beds of that area really occupy an interglacial
position, for when he traced them inland he found them
at various points overlapped and covered by till—the
junction between them and the overlying boulder-clay
being usually much confused. And he came to the conclusion that the till had been greatly denuded in the lower

reaches of the Clyde valley—wide terraces of erosion having been cut into the deep drifts, and the upper stony clay almost entirely demolished within the area of terrace-erosion. But no sooner do we leave the terraces and go inland than we find the upper stony clay or till coming on in force and overlapping upon the stratified clays. The mere absence, therefore, of an overlying till is no proof that the shelly clays of the Clyde basin and the west of Scotland are posterior in date to the last great advance of the ice-sheet. There is yet another fact that would seem to point to the same conclusion. In some cases, as Messrs. Crosskey and Robertson remark, the clays are covered *unconformably* by more recent deposits : there is a "break in the succession" between the arctic beds and those above them ; arctic forms do not one by one disappear, to be gradually replaced by recent British species, but the one fauna is sharply marked off from the other. Between the deposition of the arctic beds and the accumulation of the overlying recent deposits, some considerable period of time must have elapsed, and the probabilities therefore are against such arctic shell-beds being of the late glacial age to which they are usually assigned.

Turning to the east coast of Scotland we find similar proofs of a break in the succession between certain arctic shelly clays and more recent deposits. Mr. Jamieson has indeed stated his conviction that none of these arctic shell-beds is of later date than the last advance of the ice-sheet, but that all must be relegated to the preceding period of submergence. He points to the fact that they occur only in patches which are evidently the mere wrecks of what were once much more extensive and continuous deposits. And Dr. Howden has shown that they are covered at Montrose by the morainic shingle and gravels derived from the melting of the last great ice-sheet.[*]

It is pretty clear, then, that some shelly clays which have hitherto been classed as of late glacial and postglacial date must eventually find their place among interglacial deposits. Others, however, afford what seems to be indisputable evidence of their late glacial and postglacial age. We find, for example, that occasionally the arctic character of the fauna which marks

* *Trans. Geol. Soc. Edin.*, vol. i. p. 138.

the lower portions of a fossiliferous deposit gradually disappears upwards, so as to show a passage from a cold to a temperate condition of climate—in short, the arctic forms are gradually replaced by the fauna that now lives in the adjacent seas. Sometimes, also, we may trace a gradual succession of physical changes in one and the same deposit. Thus in a brick-clay near Girvan, Ayrshire, a passage from marine through estuarine and freshwater beds can be followed.*

But much yet remains to be done before we can separate all the shelly clays, &c., which are of older date than the latest advance of the ice-sheet, from the similar deposits that were laid down after the confluent glaciers retreated for the last time. The clearing-up of this part of the evidence will throw much light upon certain points which still remain obscure. We cannot tell, for example, to what depth the land was covered by the sea after the final recession of the ice-sheet. Mr. Jamieson does not believe that any of the arctic shell-beds of the north-east of Scotland belong to this date, but not a few of the fossiliferous clays of central and southern Scotland can hardly be assigned to an earlier period. They pass up gradually into recent deposits, and evidently point to the slow disappearance of an arctic climate and the gradual supervening of the present temperate conditions. None of these undoubtedly late glacial deposits, however, occurs higher than 100 feet above the sea, and most of them are found at considerably lower levels. Mr. R. L. Jack has indeed described a series of beds of stratified mud, clay, sand, and gravel which occur in the Endrick valley, and have been traced over a considerable area from 35 ft. up to 262 ft. above the level of the sea. This series contains a number of marine shells which indicate a climate little more severe than the present, for nearly all belong to species that are still living in British seas. Mr. Jack considers that these deposits could only have been accumulated after the last great extension of the ice-sheet, and it is difficult indeed to believe that any massive ice-sheet could ever have passed over the deposits without denuding them to a much larger extent than they seem to have been eroded; but the presence of associated

* "Monograph of the Post-Tertiary Entomostraca:" *Palæontographical Society,* 1874.

"beds of stiff clay with stones," which rest upon the sand and gravel, indicates, as Mr. Jack admits, the action of ice,— "perhaps floating-ice." It is not impossible, however, that the "stiff clay with stones" may really be the ground-moraine of the last ice-sheet. The escape of interglacial deposits from utter destruction under the grinding action of the confluent glaciers is often exceedingly puzzling and hard to be accounted for, and it may be truly very difficult to explain the preservation of the shelly beds of the Endrick valley on the supposition that they belong to interglacial times ; but, as we shall find in the sequel, there are many instances in other regions of the preservation of much more considerable masses of incoherent deposits that belong to interglacial times—deposits which are more or less buried underneath great accumulations of boulder-clay and morainic débris.* I hardly think, therefore, that we can take the Endrick-valley beds as certainly indicating a period of submergence posterior to the last great advance of the ice-sheet.†

The general conclusions that may be derived from the foregoing brief sketch of the shelly clays and associated marine deposits which are not overlaid by morainic accumulations, appear to be briefly these : first, that certain of the beds are really of interglacial age, and ought to be classed with those fossiliferous marine deposits that underlie and are intercalated with till or boulder-clay. In this category ought probably to be included most of, if not all, the high-level shelly clays, such as those in the Endrick valley, and many of the similar deposits in the north-eastern districts of Scotland. At the time these deposits were being accumulated the sea covered the land to a depth of several hundred feet above the present coast-line. The water was cold and tenanted by northern and arctic species of molluscs and other organisms. A long arm of water extended up the valley of the Clyde, as far as and even beyond Hamilton ; all the low

* A case in point has already been mentioned, the occurrence, namely, of massive beds of sand and gravel of probably preglacial age, which Mr. Jamieson describes as being covered by red boulder-clay. See *ante*, p. 162.

† For details as to the character of the fauna met with in the shelly clays, the reader is referred to the Appendix, where a copious list of all the species met with in Scotch glacial deposits will be found. This catalogue has been kindly compiled for me by my colleague, Mr. R. Etheridge, jun., who has also added a number of notes on various localities where fossiliferous beds have been observed.

grounds between the Paisley and Kilpatrick Hills were submerged, as also were extensive tracts in the maritime districts
of Ayrshire, and the western counties. An arm of the sea
connected the Clyde basin with the Forth on the one hand,
and a second stretched up the valley of the Black Cart, and
communicated with the open sea in that direction. At the
same time wide areas in the Friths of Forth and Tay were
drowned, and the ocean overflowed all the low grounds along
the east coast, and the maritime provinces of the Moray Frith
and the north were likewise under water. Glaciers nestled in
many of the higher mountain-glens and valleys, and at the
heads of not a few of the deep fiords of the west they actually entered the sea and shed their icebergs. The rivers,
flowing in greater volume than now, carried down immense
quantities of fine glacial silt and mud, which gradually settled
upon the quieter reaches of the sea-bottom. Coast-ice clogged
the shores, and ever and anon breaking away took with it
stones and blocks, which it sprinkled irregularly over the
floor of the sea. In the mountain-valleys the local glaciers
continued the polishing and striation of the rocks, while at
levels which these local glaciers could not reach, the frosts
were busy obliterating the traces of the massive ice-streams of
earlier times. The wreck of the mountains overlooking the
glaciers was slowly borne down the valleys and shot over the
terminal front of the ice—here forming subaerial ridges and
mounds, there accumulating as submarine banks. At the
same time in some favourable localities glacial lakes were produced by the damming-up of lateral valleys.

Of the plants and animals that may have clothed and
peopled the less desolate portions of the land during the
deposition of these interglacial shelly clays we know very
little. Scotland was probably not a more cheerful residence
then than North Greenland and Spitzbergen are now. Such
brick-clays as have yielded plants and animal remains belong
for the most part to late glacial and postglacial times, when
the climate was evidently becoming ameliorated. Yet it is
likely enough that Scotland may have been the favourite
haunt in summer-time of sea-birds, just as arctic coasts are
now. And to the close of the last interglacial period, therefore, may or may not belong the bird bones which have

at rare intervals turned up in the brick-clays. It seems extremely improbable, however, that a country in our latitude, under such physical conditions as we have above attempted to describe, could present a less forbidding aspect than the dreary island of Georgia, in the Antarctic Ocean. And, perhaps, the extreme paucity in the arctic clay-beds of land waifs, either plant or animal, may really point to the barren and sterile condition of the country at this time.*

The cold becoming more intense, the glaciers once more crept out of their mountain-valleys, coalescing upon the low grounds, ploughing out the shelly beds in many places, and in other places burying them more or less deeply under deposits of boulder-clay, which in long subsequent times were removed by the denuding action of rivers and the sea, so as to uncover again the shelly deposits.

By-and-by the confluent glaciers melted away for the last time, retreating into the mountain regions, and leaving the lowland districts abundantly coated with accumulations of gravel, sand, mud, morainic débris, and erratics, as we have seen in Chapters XVIII to XXI. To what extent the sea encroached upon the land during this final recession of the ice-sheet we cannot say, but the submergence may not have exceeded 100 ft. or thereabout. To this point, however, we shall return when we come to discuss the postglacial accumulations. Such fossiliferous marine beds as were deposited during the last retreat of the glaciers (and probably most of those at low levels belong to this date) show us that the cold gradually abated. But the climate was still somewhat excessive, as is proved by the presence of ice-floated stones and crumpled and contorted bedding such as that in the brick-clay of Portobello. Brick-clays of this age have yielded the small arctic seal (*Pagomys fœtidus*)—a species which also occurs in interglacial shelly clays.

* It is remarkable that the shell-bed of Elie gives evidence of somewhat colder conditions than the fossiliferous deposits of the Clyde would seem to imply. From this it has been argued that the Elie shells belong to an older date than the Clyde beds—to a period when the cold was more intense. But for this conclusion there does not seem to be any need. The North Sea, filled with bergs and floating ice, derived from Scandinavia, and even from Scotland itself, would in all probability have a lower temperature than the freer ocean that washed the western sea-board; and, therefore, it is not surprising that this difference of temperature should have taken effect and influenced the distribution of the fauna.

We have now completed our rapid sketch of the Scottish glacial deposits ; the accumulations which fall next to be described contain the record of the geographical and climatic changes that followed upon the close of the glacial epoch. But before we enter upon this latest chapter in the history of Scottish geology we must for a little retrace our steps for the purpose of considering the origin of certain remarkable features in the contour of the land, of which as yet no special mention has been made.

CHAPTER XXIII.

ROCK-BASINS OF SCOTLAND.

Different kinds of lakes.—Lakes occupying depressions in drift.—Lakes dammed
  by moraines and older drift deposits.—Lakes lying in rock-bound basins.—
  Origin of rock-basins discussed.—Ramsay's theory.—Sea-lochs.—Submarine
  rock-basins.—Their glacial origin.—Silted-up rock-basins.

WHEN we glance at a good map of Scotland,* one of the
first appearances to catch the eye is the wonderful
profusion of lakes.   Moreover, it will not fail to strike us that
these lakes are confined, for the most part, to the deep valleys
of the Highlands.   From the lowland tracts they are singularly absent.   South of the Friths of Tay and Clyde comparatively few are seen, and these are nearly all restricted to the
high grounds of Carrick, Galloway, and Peeblesshire.   There
would thus appear to be some connection between lakes and
mountain-valleys.   We cannot but see this when it is pointed
out ; yet it is not more than some sixteen years ago that the
attention of geologists was called to the fact.   It was reserved

---

* A good handy general map of Scotland has yet to be made.   There is no
scarcity of maps which can be relied upon for showing the proper direction of
roads and county-boundaries, position of towns, &c., &c. ; but one which shall
by shading give an approximately correct impression of the outline of the ground
does not exist.   When will map-constructors cease to cover the area of the
Highlands and Southern Uplands with a series of black caterpillars, which only
serve to confuse and mislead ?   A plain unshaded sheet with a few heights
indicated would be infinitely more instructive than a map elaborately covered
with all those incomprehensible crawling masses of printer's ink, which do duty for
mountains.   This conventional manner of mountain-shading, which has been so
long in vogue, is, I firmly believe, in no small measure answerable for the
persistency with which crude notions as to the origin of hills and valleys are
maintained.   Had hill-shading really been made to represent truthfully the
form of the ground, we should have heard a great deal less of mountains being
proximately due to upheaval, and valleys owing their origin to gaping fractures.
[When this note was penned I did not know that my colleague, Mr. Sydney
B. J. Skertchly, had published (Murby, London) a very excellent map of the
British Islands, in which the hill-shading really represents the form of the
ground.   Now that so large a portion of these islands has been actually surveyed,
and beautifully shaded maps issued by the Ordnance Department, is it too much
to expect our map-constructors to follow Mr. Skertchly's example ?]

for Professor Ramsay not only to indicate the very remarkable manner in which lakes are distributed in alpine and northern countries, but also to bring forward an explanation of the phenomena which has already commended itself to many physicists and geologists, and bids fair to become ere long one of the most generally accepted theories in geology.

The Scottish lakes may be grouped under three heads, viz. :—

1. Lakes occupying hollows in the till or other superficial deposits.

2. Morainic and drift-dammed lakes.

3. Lakes resting in basins of solid rock.

The lakes of the first group have no importance, and indeed are little more than shallow pools. They are developed chiefly in the Lowlands, and have at one time been much more numerous than they are now. Many have been silted up with alluvial matter, others have been converted into peat-

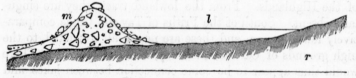

Fig. 50.—Morainic Lake.

bogs, and not a few have been drained. They rest sometimes in the hollows between banks of till, and not infrequently in cup-shaped depressions of sand and gravel. The most considerable assemblage of these lakes of which I know is in the island of Lewis—the low-lying tracts of which are literally peppered with lakelets. Not a few of these, however, belong to the drift-dammed series. But hundreds of them appear to rest in hollows of the till—their longer axis pointing north-west and south-east. They are, for the most part, very shallow, and have been much encroached upon by peat.

The lakes of the second group are also somewhat insignificant. Those which are dammed back by moraines are confined, as one would naturally expect, to mountain-valleys. An excellent example of the kind is that of Loch Skene, in the south of Scotland. In this instance a series of morainic mounds, left behind by one of the last local glaciers, extends from one side of a mountain-valley to the other, and has thus formed a barrier to the escape of the water. In not a few mountain-valleys where such lakes have at one time existed, we may see how the waters have been drained off by the gradual cutting down of the moraines.

Besides the lakes which are confined behind barriers of morainic débris, we occasionally meet with small sheets of water which appear to rest partly in rock and partly in till or other superficial accumulations. Fine examples of this variety of lakelet occur in the low grounds of Lewis. Unlike those lakelets of the first group, which occur in the same region, these drift-dammed lakes do not range from south-east to north-west, but exactly at right angles to that direction—namely, from south-west to north-east. They lie between parallel ridges of rock, and are dammed up at either end by accumulations of till. In Lewis * it is common to find both kinds of lake represented in one and the same sheet of water—one elongated portion of which will trend south-east or north-west, and another arm extend itself in a north-east or south-west direction, as the case may be.

In the Lowlands there are a few lakes, such as Loch Leven (Kinross-shire), the original shape of whose bed it is difficult to determine. Probably most of them, however, are merely due to the unequal distribution of the till and other superficial deposits over the underlying rocks. Others, again, may really belong to the third group, and occupy rock-basins the nature of which is now concealed by the accumulation of alluvial matter along their margins. I am not sure but that Loch Leven is a case in point.

The third group embraces the largest and most important lakes in Scotland, and to it also belong a vast number of mountain-tarns which are neither large nor important. All these lakes and tarns rest in hollows of solid rock. In very many cases we may trace the rock all round their margins ; and even when this is partially obscured by superficial deposits there are yet other circumstances which enable us to show that, although these deposits were to be entirely removed, there would still be a lake completely surrounded by rock.

* The features referred to are beautifully delineated upon the Ordnance Survey map of Lewis. See paper by author, *Quart. Jour. Geol. Soc.*, 1873.

These lake-hollows are what Professor Ramsay has termed *rock-basins;* and his ingenious theory of their origin I must now attempt to describe.

When we reflect for a moment we shall find that it is a very hard thing indeed to account for a rock-basin. The usual agents of erosion, those which we see at work in our own country, fail to afford any solution of the problem. We may, for example, dismiss the sea as utterly inadequate. The action of the sea upon the land is that of a huge horizontal saw ; the cliffs are eaten into, and gradually undermined ; masses of rock, loosened by rains and frosts, tumble down, and are pounded up by the breakers into shingle and sand. Thus in process of time a shelf or terrace of erosion is formed, and were the shore to be sufficiently elevated to-morrow, we should find that such a platform would extend all along our rocky coast-line—narrowing where the rocks were hard and durable, broadening out where the cliffs had yielded more easily to the ceaseless gnawing of the waves. But nowhere should we be able to detect anything approaching to the character of a rock-basin ; for it is self-evident that the sea " cannot make a hollow below its own average level." Its tendency, indeed, is quite in the opposite direction—much of the material derived from the denudation of the land being carried out and deposited in quiet depths.

If the sea does not help us to discover how rock-basins are formed, will rivers do so ? Most assuredly they will not. Rivers will flow down any slope, but they cannot run up an inclined plane. What they do is to cut channels which carry them down persistently from higher to lower levels. The only approach to something like a rock-basin which can be excavated by river-action may be observed at the foot of a water-fall, where a more or less deep hollow always appears. This hollow is of course scooped out by the forcible impact of the falling water, aided by the filing action of the stones and pebbles which are kept in constant motion. But it would be idle to suppose that such has been the origin of the rock-basins. Yet this action of the falling water, as I shall try to show presently, may aid us in appreciating more fully Professor Ramsay's theory.

Since rock-basins owe their origin neither to rivers nor to

the sea, may not they be simply due to disturbances of the strata? We know that the solid aqueous rocks of which our country chiefly consists have been elevated and depressed times without number since the date of their formation. We know further that they have been dislocated and displaced by movements of the earth's crust, and confused by the intrusion among them of melted volcanic materials; and this has happened over and over again. Strata which we have every reason to believe were laid down in horizontal or approximately horizontal planes have been puckered and thrown into inumerable folds, or here pushed up into ridges, and there carried down into troughs. May not the lakes then occupy such troughs, or rest in cracks and chasms or depressions caused by dislocation and displacement of the rocks? To those who have made no special study of physical geology this may appear a ready and simple explanation. In

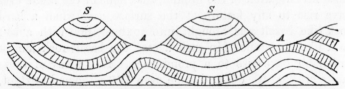

Fig. 51.—Diagrammatic view of synclines and anticlines. *AA*, anticlinal arches; *SS*, synclinal troughs.

sober truth, however, it is no explanation at all; for when we come to examine the rock-basins themselves, we do not find them occupying "hollows formed of strata bent upwards at the edges all round into the form of a great dish, the uppermost bed or beds of which are continuous and unbroken underneath the waters of the lake." No such synclinal troughs occur anywhere in Scotland; indeed, as Professor Ramsay remarks, they are the rarest things in nature. As a general rule, we find that synclinal troughs or geological hollows form hills, while conversely anticlinal ridges or geological hills give rise to valleys. And it not infrequently happens that the hollow in which a lake lies, is geologically speaking, a hill or anticline. But still more frequently rock-basins occur in regions where the strata are "bent and contorted in a hundred curves all along and under the length of the lake," nor does the direction or slope of the basins bear any relation whatever to the prevailing inclination of the strata. We may conclude, then, that the bedding of the underlying rocks affords no clue to the solution of the problem.

Do the lakes lie in gaping fissures, or in chasms produced by dislocations of the solid rocks, or, as they are technically termed, *faults?* As a matter of fact, no single instance has yet been adduced, either at home or abroad, where a *fault* could be said to be the proximate cause of a lake-hollow. My duties in connection with the Geological Survey have afforded me exceptional opportunities for the study of dislocations and displacements. Some time ago I completed the mapping of the major portion of the coal-fields in the west of Scotland—perhaps one of the most abundantly faulted districts in Britain; and I found, as the result of a minute examination of all the carefully-prepared mining-plans and a close investigation of the ground, that none of the faults ever gave rise to any feature at the surface, save when a hard rock like basalt was brought into juxtaposition with a soft rock like sandstone. In such a case the basalt-rock almost invariably gave rise to a prominence. Now many of these faults are 20, 40, 60, and some even 100 fathoms in extent, and they frequently cross and shift each other; yet no yawning crack or irregular depression at the surface gives one any indication of their existence. In walking over a level turnip-field we may traverse a dozen in the space of a few hundred yards. My impression is that none of these dislocations ever showed at the surface. This is hardly the place to describe the observations which have led me to this conclusion; but I may state that, as a general rule, faults increase in extent downwards and diminish upwards, so that the upper seams are not dislocated to the same extent as the lower seams of the same coal-field. Some of the smaller faults, indeed, die out upwards altogether.

Now we know that hundreds of fathoms of solid strata have been planed off the central Lowlands of Scotland since the close of the Carboniferous epoch, and not a few of the dislocations that now come to the light of day may have died upwards long before the original surface of the Coal-measures was reached. But even if these faults did actually traverse

the whole thickness of the strata at the very time the movement of the earth's crust took place, yet they could not have
produced any external feature—they could not have been
actually visible at the surface. Had it been otherwise—had
all the faults which we now see cutting and shifting the strata
in every direction shown boldly at the surface—what a very
remarkable landscape would have been the result!—straight
cliffs intersecting at all angles ; here a great parallelogram of
strata forming a solid embankment, there a profound and
extended chasm fantastically shifted in a hundred places ; in
one place a long descent, terminating abruptly against the
blank wall of a frowning precipice ; in another place an
inclined plane, rising for a considerable distance, and all of a

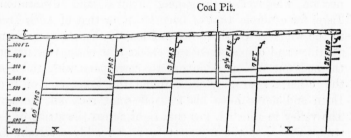

Fig. 52.—Section across Coal-measures at Muirhouse Colliery, near Wishaw
(horizontal and vertical scale the same). The horizontal lines represent coal-
seams ; *f*, faults, the amount of displacement shown in fathoms and feet ; X line,
550 ft. below sea-level ; *t*, till.

sudden stopping on the edge of a wall that dropped perpen-
dicularly for 500 or 1,000 ft. Instead of all this wild
vagary, we have a softly-outlined country, with its regular
valley-system—the direction of the streams never being in
any degree influenced by the rock-dislocations, which, as far
as the trend of the valleys is concerned, might never have
existed.

Judging, therefore, from the contour of the ground in this
district, where the direction and amount of the faultings have
been so well ascertained, it may be concluded that these dislocations have not been the proximate, nor even the remote
cause[*] of the formation of the valleys. Many of the faults

* It may be well to remind the reader that I am speaking of the Carboniferous
areas of the west of Scotland. I am very far from affirming that faults have
never in any case given the initial direction to a line of drainage. I could

may have died out upwards without reaching the original surface, while others that did reach that surface may have displaced the strata so gently, by such gradual creeping, that atmospheric or other superficial denudation may well have kept pace with the movements, and so removed the inequalities as these arose.*

Since, then, rock-basins do not occur in these highly faulted districts, it seems idle to speak of such hollows being due to dislocations, unless we are prepared to bring forward some well-proved cases in point. But while no such case has been adduced, geologists have been referred by Professor Ramsay and others, both at home and abroad, to numerous examples of rock-basins which it can be shown have no connection whatever with gaping fissures and dislocations. Take, for example, that of Loch Doon, or that of Loch Trool in the wilds of Carrick. In neither of these cases do any shiftings and displacements or cracks and chasms occur, but the beds on the one side exactly correspond with those on the other. One may walk round the lower end of Loch Doon and never have his feet off solid rock all the way. The valley in which it lies cuts right across the strike of the strata, which, as the merest tyro may readily ascertain, are quite continuous.

Nay, more than this, rock-basins are of all sizes ; many of them are no larger than an ordinary drawing-room ; myriads are a great deal smaller—mere pools ; and between this and basins that are square miles in extent we have every gradation. One may wade through or swim across the shallower

mention a number of instances where they have certainly done so. A good case in point is that of Glen App, in the south of Ayrshire, which coincides with a large fracture. Again, the great north-east and south-west fault that traverses Scotland from the shores of the Frith of Forth to the Irish Sea, gives rise in many places to a distinct feature, and streams occasionally follow it for some distance. The Great Glen would also appear to lie in a line of dislocation. I have never seen, and would travel a long way to see, a gaping fault.

* Although these remarks have special reference to Scotland, they have really a much wider application, as many geologists will readily admit. It has been shown again and again, that even in highly disturbed mountainous districts the valleys most frequently bear no relation, either proximate or remote, to rock dislocations. Thus Dr. Hayden and his associates, who have been engaged in the geological exploration of the Rocky Mountains, state very strongly that the channels of the large rivers in those regions "have not been determined by special lines of depression or fractures, and that there is no necessary connection between them." *Bulletin of the United States Geological and Geographical Survey of the Territories*, vol. ii. p. 208.

ones, and satisfy himself that the rock is all solid underneath ; and no one indeed has ever ventured to suggest that
these smaller hollows are due to fractures. Yet it is just as
difficult to account for a rock-basin fifty yards in length, as
it is to explain the origin of one a hundred times larger. If
big ones be caused by fractures, and little ones owe their
existence to—something else, where are we to draw the line?
—how many square yards are we to be allowed free of
fracture ?

Some of these objections apply with equal force to another
explanation which has been advanced—to this, namely, that
the lakes lie in special areas of depression ; in other words,
that the land has sunk down underneath each lake. It is
simply incredible that such could have happened. No one
will deny that special areas of depression do exist, but to
have produced the innumerable lakes of all sizes that stud the
surface of alpine countries and many northern regions, the
rocky crust of the earth must needs have been in a condition
nearly as unresisting as putty. If movements of depression
were allowed to explain the existence of a sheet of water like
Lake Superior, they would still leave utterly unaccounted for
the vast number of smaller lakes that crowd the surface of
the northern part of North America, as well as the innumerable lakes of Scotland, Cumberland, Wales, Ireland, Scandinavia, Finland, Switzerland, and Italy.

Sir Charles Lyell held that the lake-basins of the two last-
named countries owed their origin to a depression of the
central region of the Alps, by which the slope of the great
valleys was reversed ; an explanation which, as Professor
Ramsay pointed out, would compel us to assume that the
Alps in preglacial times were some 28,000 or 30,000 feet in
height—thus implying an amount of subsequent depression
which in itself is improbable, and for which certainly no
evidence is forthcoming. He also showed that if the Alpine
lake-basins were really produced by a depression of the central region, lakes " ought also to occur in other valleys that
run north and south of the central chain and open on the
plains, but which are merely river-courses." A still stronger
objection to Lyell's hypothesis lies in the fact that the trend
and outflow of Lakes Geneva and Neuchâtel " are, roughly,

at right angles to those of the other great lakes of Como,
Lugano, Maggiore, Orta, Varese, Garda, Thun, Lucerne, Zug,
Sempach, Zurich, and Constance ; and, to dam up the lakes
of Geneva and Neuchâtel, we should require a central depression running north-west between them at right angles to the
chain of the Alps, and quite across the Miocene rocks.   For
this we need," continues Professor Ramsay, " a special proof,
which has never been attempted ; and I do not see but that
to produce the whole of the lakes by depression, the supposed
great movement must merely resolve itself into a number of
minor ones."

Lyell never, as far as I am aware, applied his hypothesis
to account for the rock-basins of Scotland—probably because
he knew the configuration of that country too well, and was
aware that no single movement of depression along the
watersheds or of upheaval in the lower parts of the valleys
would suffice to explain the phenomena.   Indeed, when we
come to apply his hypothesis to that country, we find that
instead of one great movement of upheaval or subsidence we
require hundreds of local ones—so very local, indeed, that
vertical movements of 1,000 feet must in many cases have
been restricted to an area of only a few square miles.   Not
only so, but the lakes trend to every point in the compass,
necessitating, on Lyell's hypothesis, a manifold series of
movements, so confused, opposite, and contradictory withal,
that really one feels it much easier to believe in a special
depression for each particular rock-basin.   More than this :
not a few valleys contain two or even three lake-basins, separated from each other by only a few miles, and sometimes by
only one mile.   What general but " unequal movement of
upheaval or subsidence " will account for these ?   Is it not
plain that if the basins in question owe their origin to "earth
movements," there must have been one special upheaval or
depression as the case may be for each particular lake.   Let
any one try how otherwise he can account, on Sir C. Lyell's
hypothesis, for such lakes as Loch Voil and Loch Lubnaig,
or the lakes of the Trossachs, or for Loch Lydoch, Loch
Rannoch, and Loch Tummel, or for the lakes in Glen Quoich
and Glen Garry, or those in Strath Affrick, Glen Cannich,
and Strath Monar.   Not only do the mountain-valleys often

contain more than one lake, but we frequently find that lake-basins are composite, consisting in reality of two or more rock-basins, such as Loch Etive and many other sea-lochs, as I shall presently point out. This, indeed, is a very common characteristic of the lake-basins of Scotland : they have a hummocky, uneven bottom—the rock sometimes rising to the surface in little islets, which are often beautifully glaciated all over—at other times sloping up from considerable depths on one or both sides, so as to form a more or less narrow ridge, which would divide the lake in two were the water to be lowered for only a few feet or fathoms as the case might be. Now, if it be impossible to account, on the hypothesis under review, for the presence of several separate lake-basins in one valley, how can that hypothesis explain the appearance of the rocky islands, the subaqueous ridges, and the irregular depths that so often characterise one and the same lake-basin ? *

If, then, all the above " explanations " be rejected, we have only one agent left which can possibly account for the origin of rock-basins, and that is *ice.* Professor Ramsay points out, in the first place, that these remarkable lakes abound in every region which is known to have been subjected during the glacial epoch to the grinding action of glaciers ; while conversely, in tropical areas or such countries as have not supported glaciers, true rock-basins do not occur. Thus, if we exclude the great African lakes, of which we know too little as yet to justify us in coming to any definite conclusion in regard to the mode of their formation, and if we also put aside lagoons and crater-lakes and other lacustrine hollows in volcanic regions some of which owe their origin to local depressions, while others may be due to the damming-up of valleys by lava, &c., we shall find that in our hemisphere rock-basins increase in number as we pass from south to north, and are always specially abundant in mountainous districts. And this peculiar distribution Professor

* Sir C. Lyell's hypothesis is so manifestly inapplicable to the rock-basins of Scotland that in the previous edition of this work I passed it in silence, and this I was the more inclined to do as Sir Charles himself never tried to apply it to the Scotch lakes. I hardly thought it possible that any geologist could indulge the hope that " unequal movements of upheaval and subsidence " would account for the phenomena in question, but I have been mistaken ; hence the above paragraphs.

Ramsay accounts for by the bold suggestion that the basins have been scooped out by the grinding power of glaciers.

He shows that the erosive action of a glacier must necessarily be less at the lower end, where the ice is comparatively thin, than farther up the valley, where the ice attains a much greater thickness. Obviously, then, were a glacier to continue to flow for a sufficient length of time, this unequal pressure upon the underlying rock would produce some effect; there would be a great deal more tear and wear where the ice was thick than where it was thin, and thus a rock-basin would eventually be formed.

Take the case of a glacier creeping down an alpine valley, and spreading itself out upon the low ground at the foot of the mountains. Let us suppose that in the upper part of its course, that is to say, within its mountain-valley, the incline down which it moves is greater than the slope of the low ground upon which it eventually deploys. When the ice reaches this latter point, it is evident that its flow must be retarded, and there will therefore be a tendency in the ice to accumulate or heap up. Now we know that the pressure of a body in motion upon any given surface varies with the degree at which that surface is inclined; as the inclination decreases the pressure increases. It follows from this that when the glacier leaves the steeper part of its course, and begins to creep down the gentler slope beyond, it will press with greater force upon its rocky bed, and this increased pressure will be further intensified by the greater thickness of the accumulated ice. But as our glacier continues to flow on, it gradually loses in bulk, its rate of motion at the same time diminishes,[*] and thus its erosive power becomes weaker and weaker. The result of all this is the formation of a rock-basin, the deeper portion of which lies towards the upper end, just where the grinding force of the glacier is greatest.

Such is the effect we might naturally expect glacial action to produce. When we turn to the rock-basins in our own country, we find that these occupy precisely the very positions which theoretically might have been expected. And not only so, but they almost invariably reach their greatest depths

[*] *La Névé de Justedal et ses Glaciers,* by C. de Seue.

PLATE VIII.

Loch Doon (upper reach) : a Rock Basin, showing roches moutonnées.   (By B. N. Peach.)

To face p. 279.

towards the upper end, shallowing away gradually down the valley. Cases in point are Loch Doon, Loch Trool, and numerous other rock-basins amongst the Carrick and Galloway mountains. One of the best examples of a rock-basin is furnished by Loch Lomond, a map and sections of which, drawn on a true scale, will be found in the Appendix. No fault or dislocation of the solid strata is known to cross the area occupied by the Loch; but my colleague, Mr. R. L. Jack, has detected one that crosses below the foot of the loch, passing through Tullichewan Castle on the west side and Haldane's Mill on the east; and the downthrow side of this fault is to the south—a clear proof, if such were needed, that faulting and unequal subsidences of the rock have had nothing whatever to do with the formation of the great hollow.

Another striking circumstance in connection with Scottish lakes is this—their dimensions are almost always proportionate to the extent of the drainage-system in which they occur. If the valley in which any particular rock-bound lake appears should be an important one, draining a wide tract of elevated ground, the lake is sure to be long and deep; if the valley be of inconsiderable extent, the rock-basin it happens to contain is certain to be proportionately unimportant. In other words, where large glaciers are known to have existed, we find large rock-basins, while in valleys which have been occupied by inconsiderable glaciers, the rock-basins are small.

These remarks on Scottish rock-basins would be incomplete if no reference were made to the fiords or sea-lochs so abundantly developed along the west coast. The hollows occupied by these arms of the sea are simply submarine continuations of land-valleys, which, as everyone knows, stretch into the country for a less or greater distance from the head of every fiord.

If the reader will glance at the sketch-map of Scotland, he will observe that while freshwater lakes are plentifully present on the eastern slopes of the great watershed that runs from the head of Loch Shin to the hills above Loch Linnhe, there are comparatively few on the other side, but we have great sea-lochs instead. Now each of these submerged land-valleys contains at least one rock-basin, so that if the land were only to be elevated sufficiently, we should find in that region an exact counterpart of the appearances that present themselves on the eastern slopes of the watershed, namely, deep mountain-glens with rock-bound lakes.

The Amiralty charts are excellent maps of the sea-bottom, and afford clear and definite ideas of its physical features. The tracings given are taken from the reduced Admiralty chart of the west coast of Scotland. One of these (Plate IX.) shows Loch Broom, and Little Loch Broom, with Gruinard Bay. This part of the coast has been selected for no other reason than simply because it happens to come nicely within the compass of one of these pages. Almost any other sea-loch would have served my purpose equally well—some of them, indeed, would have done better, as for example, Loch Long, Loch Fyne, or Loch Sunart.

It will be observed, upon glancing at the chart, that the upper reach of Loch Broom, between Corrie Point and the head of the loch, rests in a distinct basin, the lower lip of the basin opposite Corrie being reached at a depth of 11 fathoms, and its deepest part, 26 fathoms, occurring near Lacmelm. There appears to be a second basin between Corrie Point and the mouth of the loch, but it is not so well marked. Little Loch Broom, however, is an admirable example. At the mouth of this loch the underlying rock comes actually to the surface in Ardross Rock, and between this point and the shores we have the maximum depths of 10 and 26 fathoms respectively. Yet the soundings half way up the loch show a depth of no less than 57 fathoms. Beyond the mouth of the loch the water deepens somewhat gradually until a depth of 119 fathoms is attained, beyond which it shallows again to 34 fathoms. Now it is worthy of remark that no part of the North Minch, on which Gruinard Bay opens, is anywhere deeper than some 50 or 60 fathoms, except immediately opposite the mouths of the great sea-lochs that open out from the mountain-valleys of Harris and Lewis, and the mainland. The 100-fathom line is only reached when we get beyond the Outer Hebrides altogether. Yet it is no uncommon thing to get greater depths than this in many of the sea-lochs and sounds. In the Inner Sound of Raasay, for example, we find depths of 100, 128, and even in one place of 138 fathoms! (See Plate X.) Thus, were Scotland to be lifted out of the sea

PLATE LX.

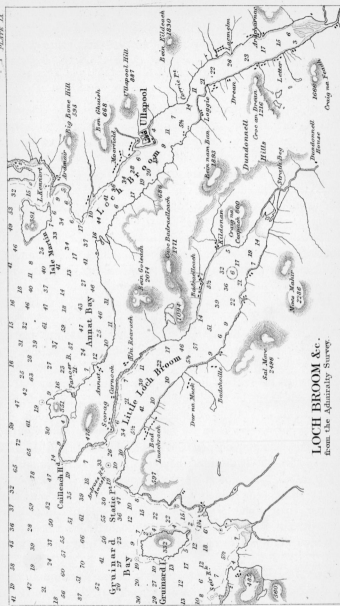

LOCH BROOM &c.
from the Admiralty Survey.

J. Bartholomew, Edin.

To face page 280

PLATE X.

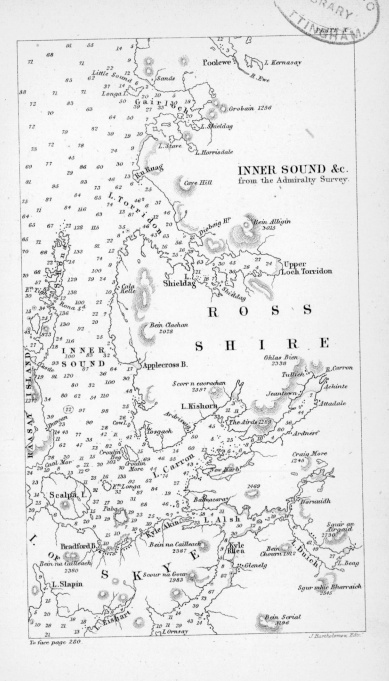

INNER SOUND &c.
from the Admiralty Survey.

Poolewe
L. Kernasay
R. Ewe
Sands
Little Sound
Longa I.
Gairloch
Grobain 1256
L. Shieldag
L. Stave
L. Horrisdale
Rh Ruag
Cave Hill
L. Torridon
Diobaig Hᵗ
Bein Alligin 3015
Upper Loch Torridon
Cala Kelle
L. Shieldag
Shieldag

R O S S

S H I R E

Bein Clachan 2028
Castle
INNER SOUND
Applecross B.
Ghlas Bien 2338
Tullich
R. Carron
Scorr n caorachan 2597
Jeantown
Achinte
Attadale
L. Kishorn
The Airds 1289
Ardnerf
Ardrisaig
Cowl.
Fosgach
Craig More 1245
Croulin Beg
Croulin More
L. Carron
New Harb⁴
Eⁿ Longa
Duncan
Caol Mor
Scalpa I.
Paba
Balmacaray
Dornaidh
1469
Kyle Akin
L. Alsh
Squir an Argoid 2730
Bradford B.
Bein na Cailleach 2387
Kyle Rhea
Bein Chourn 1912
L. Duich
L. Beag
Bein na Cailleach 2380
S K Y E
Scour na Gour 1983
Glenelg
Sgur mhic Bharraich 2545
I. OF
L. Slapin
L. Eishart
Bein Scrial 3196
I. Ornsay

RAASAY ISLAND
Rona sᵈ

To face page 280.
J. Bartholomew, Edinʳ

for 100 fathoms, all the islands would be connected with the mainland, and numerous lakes would exist to mark the sites of the sea-lochs, one of which, lying between Raasay and Ross-shire, would reach as much as 528 ft. in depth.*

Here then is the singular fact that the deepest portions of the Scottish seas lie close in shore ; nor in the vast [majority of cases can there be any doubt whatever that these deep submarine hollows are true rock-basins. In many cases, indeed, the soundings actually prove this. Still some may think that since we do not actually see the lower lips of these basins, it is at least doubtful whether they really consist of rock. Might not the lower lips be formed of mud or sand ? We know that the sea has the power of heaping up banks of these materials across the mouths of estuaries ; might not this be the explanation of the basins in our sea-lochs ? Now there are many reasons which could be given to show why it is in the highest degree improbable that banks of the kind required would always accumulate in such places. But it is not necessary to go into this question, for it is quite evident, upon a little reflection, that even if the sea had the power to heap up, and were now actually engaged in heaping up banks across the mouth of every sea-loch on the coast, still this would not help us to explain the matter any better. For, assuming this to be the case, we should be compelled to admit, first, that the beds of all the sea-lochs did at one time fall away gradually from their present extreme depth up to and even far beyond the 100-fathom line ; in other words, that the floor of the sea sloped persistently outwards from the greatest depth reached by the fiords. So that if the land had then been elevated above the waves there would have appeared mountain-valleys containing no lakes, but showing rivers that flowed on uninterruptedly up to and even far beyond the edge of what is now termed the Scottish submarine plateau. But this plateau is not known to be breached by any such profound submarine valleys. Then, in the second place, we should be forced to hold the extravagant belief that the sea had filled up all these deep hollows with accumulations of sediment varying in thickness from 30 or 40 to considerably more than 100 fathoms, but had left the shoreward portions

* See Map showing Physiography of Western Scotland, Plate XII.

of its bed pretty much as they were before submergence ensued; that, in short, only the lower reaches of the submarine valleys had been silted up, the platform of sand and mud stopping abruptly opposite the mouths of the sea-lochs, and not a few of the sounds! Into such absurdities do we land ourselves if the rock-bound nature of the basins in the sea-lochs be denied.

Fortunately, however, there is at least one sea-loch of the rock-bound character of which we have ocular demonstration. I refer to Loch Etive. This loch, as the chart (Plate XI.) will show, contains two basins, the lower one of which extends from Connel Ferry to near Taynuilt, the upper one from this place to the head of the loch. At Connel Ferry the passage is very narrow, and the rock so near the surface that at half-tide the water rushes over the reef with the roar of a cataract. The sight of the seething white water will, I should think, be enough to convince even the most sceptical that, above the ferry, Loch Etive is a true rock-basin. It will be observed that the greatest depth attained in the lower basin is 35 fathoms; in the upper basin we have a depth of not less than 76 fathoms. Here then we have a double rock-basin, the bottom of which is rather more than 400 ft. deeper than its lower lip.

Now while such deep submarine rock-basins can be traced in all or nearly all the sea-lochs, it is remarkable that no such basins occur opposite a low flat stretch of country. For example, along the western shores of Lewis, in which part of the island there are no deep valleys, we find that the sea-bottom inclines very gradually outward; and the same is the case off the low-lying districts on the eastern sea-board of Scotland. There seems to be an obvious connection, therefore, between submarine rock-basins and sea-lochs, just as there certainly is between sea-lochs and mountain-valleys. Nor, if we admit that rock-basins, filled with fresh water, have been scooped out by glaciers, can we, as I think, escape the conclusion that the submerged rock-basins have had precisely the same origin; for the presence of the sea is a mere accident. We know for a fact that all those sea-lochs were once filled to overflowing with ice, and rock-basins occur just in those places where from theoretical considerations they

PLATE XI

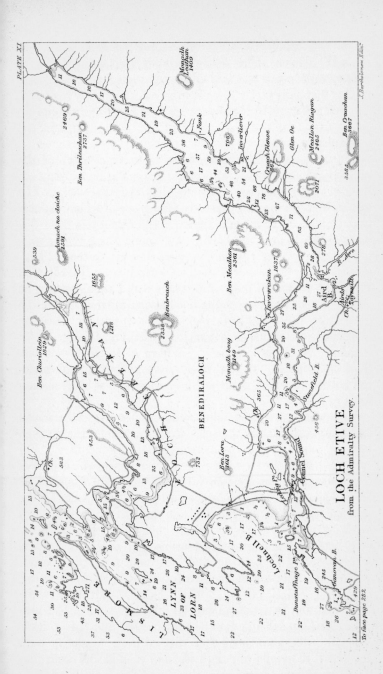

LOCH ETIVE
from the Admiralty Survey.

ought to appear. An attentive examination of the physical features of the fiords, and a careful scrutiny of the Admiralty charts, will show that whenever the opposite shores* of a fiord approach each other so as well-nigh to separate the water into two separate sheets, two distinct rock-basins are almost invariably the result. This appearance is well explained by the erosion theory, but is inexplicable otherwise. When glacier-ice filled such a fiord, it would be strangled in the narrow pass, and the motion of the ice advancing from behind would be impeded. Hence there would be a heaping up of the glacier, and intensified pressure upon the rocky bed would produce its natural effect—increased erosion.

At the same time, not a few double rock-basins are to be explained in another way. Each basin has probably been scooped out at a different period. During the advance of the glaciers there may have been—there most likely were—long pauses ; each pause, if of sufficient duration, being marked by the formation of rock-basins. When, again, the glaciers began to retire, the same set of circumstances might well recur— pauses might take place, and basins be again deepened. Moreover, owing to the nature of the ground and the character of the drainage-system, one may be quite sure that a glacier would tarry much longer in some reaches of its valley than in others. Hence we might naturally expect the valleys often to contain more rock-basins than one. If the larger fresh-water lakes were drained, we should in all probability find that some of them would show separate basins, analogous in a measure to the upper and lower basins of Loch Torridon, Loch Cairn-Bahn, and others. Even as it is, however, many valleys do contain more than one lake. Good examples occur in the region of the Trosachs. Again, in the valley of the Tummel we have Loch Lydoch, Loch Rannoch, and Loch Tummel. Farther north, in the valley of the Conan, we come upon the wild Loch Fannich and, lower down, Loch Luichart. The valley of the Doon, in Ayrshire, contains the loch of the same name and Bogton Loch, which last, although now much silted up and of little extent, is yet proved to be a rock-basin,

---

* I refer, of course, to promontories of solid rock. Where a lateral stream enters a fiord, a spit of low land frequently projects for some distance into the water, but that is a very different matter.

from the fact that the soft watery mud of its alluvium broke into some coal-workings in the neighbourhood, at a depth considerably below that of the rock, which comes to the surface, and crosses the valley a mile or so farther down.

So long a time, indeed, has passed since the glaciers vacated the valleys, that streams and rivers, by carrying down and depositing gravel, sand, and silt, have often obscured the original rock-bound character of the lake-basins, and in several cases have even entirely obliterated them, so that we find broad flat meadows where lakes formerly existed. As an instance of a partially obliterated rock-basin, I may refer to St. Mary's Loch, in the south of Scotland, the depth of which has been ascertained to be at least 120 ft. At its outlet the whole valley is paved with gravel, but a series of borings made across the bottom of the valley at this place struck the rock at depths varying from 24 to 53 ft. The present bed of the lake is therefore 67 ft. at least lower than the lip of the buried rock at the point of outlet; what thickness of superficial materials may be lying upon the rocky bed of the lake has not been ascertained.*

Of rock-basins completely obliterated, many examples might be given. There is one at the head of the Manor Water, in Peeblesshire. Another fine instance occurs in the valley of the Talla (same county), where an ancient lake once occupied the whole bottom of the valley from Talla Linnfoots for nearly two miles down. The higher valleys of the Cheviot Hills afford examples of the same phenomena. But, as might have been anticipated, the rock-basins that are so silted up are usually of small extent.

* For these data I am indebted to the kindness of Messrs. A. & A. Leslie, C.E., Edinburgh.

CHAPTER XXIV.

ROCK-BASINS OF SCOTLAND—*Continued.*

Fiords plentiful along west coast, but not so on east coast.—Depths in the Friths of east coast.—Examples of *fiord-basins.*—Examples of *deflection-basins.*—Union of the two groups; examples.

SOME years ago I was struck with the fact that the deepest parts of the Scottish seas appeared precisely in those places where a glacialist who held Professor Ramsay's views might readily have expected to find them. Not only did deep rock-basins occur in all the sea-lochs or fiords, but they also made their appearance again and again off the coasts of many islands in such positions as could not but be highly suggestive to a glacialist. In connection with these facts it was also singular to observe that, while deep submarine hollows were so abundantly developed along the wild western shores of Scotland, they were almost entirely wanting in the corresponding latitudes on the other side of the island. And, then, one could not fail to notice that, with the exceptions of the Friths of Forth, Tay, Inverness, Cromarty, and Dornoch, no fiord-valleys open out upon the German Ocean, and no such islands as the Inner and Outer Hebrides appear off the east coast. Fiord-valleys and islands abound in the west, and there rock-basins are numerous; hardly any fiord-valleys or islands exist in the east, and there submarine hollows are rarely to be found. As far as I can make out from the Admiralty charts, only one deep submarine basin occurs along the whole stretch of coast-line between Duncansby Head and Berwick, and that is in the upper reaches of the Frith of Forth, between St. Margaret's Hope and a point east of Kinghorn and north-east of Inch Keith. The hollow is a long narrow trench, gradually opening out as it shallows to the north-east of Inch Keith. It is deepest near Inch

Garvie, where its bottom is 246 ft. below the surface of the sea, or 186 ft. lower than the lip of the trench. It shallows passing east, but deepens again to 168 ft. between Inch Colm and the Oxcars Rocks, shallowing once more, and again deepening to 138 ft. before it finally shelves away. It is certain, however, that this basin must at one time have been more extensive. Immense quantities of silt and sand are borne down into the estuary of the Forth, and great banks of sand and mud have accumulated, especially in the upper reaches of the estuary. There cannot be much doubt, therefore, that the submarine hollow has been greatly silted up.[*]

No hollow so deep appears in any of the other friths that open into the German Ocean, but each is characterised by the presence of great banks of sand and mud, which in many cases impede navigation. In the Frith of Tay the mud-banks are specially noticeable; above Dundee the Frith at low-water shows little more than a series of slimy banks, with winding water-lanes; and below Dundee, at the mouth of the estuary, the mud and sand are pushing out seaward, so as to form a well-defined submarine delta. In short, it is evident that all the friths on the east side of the island have been and are still being gradually silted up. Yet we may still trace elongated hollows in these friths. There is one 48 ft. deep opposite Broughty Ferry; two occur in Beauly Loch, 108 ft. and 72 ft. deep respectively; Cromarty Frith is 120 ft. deeper than the sea outside, and although Dornoch Frith is very shallow, it is still 36 ft. deep above the Bar, which is only 12 ft. below the sea.

To return to the west coast: I would first direct the reader's attention to the general slope of the sea-bottom, as represented upon the map (Plate XII.), which has been reduced for me by my friend and colleague, Mr. R. L. Jack, from the Admiralty charts of the west coast of Scotland.[†] It will be observed that (putting rock-basins for the moment out of account) the bottom of the sea in the North Minch falls away towards the north, a river being inserted to show the direc-

[*] In the borings made for the projected bridge across the Forth, a mile above Blackness Castle, the mud and clay lying upon the bottom of the Frith were found to vary in thickness from 90 up to 176 ft.

[†] *Scotland, West Coast*, from surveys by Captains Robinson, Otter, and E. J. Bedford, Commanders Wood, Thomas, and other officers; *Ireland, East Coast*, from surveys by Capt. Beechey and others. Nos. 2,365 and 1,824.

tion the drainage would take were an elevation of the whole west coast, to the extent of 600 ft. to supervene. Between the north end of Skye and the Shiant Isles the soundings indicate the existence of a ridge which would form a low watershed between the country of the North Minch and that lying to the south. The configuration of this latter, however, is exceedingly irregular, and it is difficult to ascertain from the charts in what direction the lakes in the Little Minch would drain; most likely, however, it would be south-west into the large lake which is represented as sweeping from South Uist round Barra Head, and sending a river out to the sea. West from the Island of Islay another stream is inserted to show the slope of the land in that direction. It must not be supposed that these rivers are put down at random. The charts have been closely followed, and it is believed that the lines indicated are as near as possible those that would be taken by the streams and rivers upon an elevation of 600 ft. A greater number might have been inserted, but it was thought better to give only such as would suffice to indicate the general slope of the sea-bottom.

A glance at the map will show that the chief submarine basins occupy certain well-defined positions, and form two distinct groups. The first group embraces what may be termed *fiord-basins.* Enough has been said in the preceding chapter regarding the rock-hollows which are known to occur in our sea-lochs. These of course agree in direction with the sea-lochs, with which they are sometimes almost co-extensive, as in the case of Loch Fyne; or entirely so, as in the case of Loch Etive. But an examination of the Admiralty charts proves the existence of numerous submarine basins which lie beyond the sea-lochs, and run parallel to the course of sounds, channels, and straits. As examples we may take the basins of Raasay Sound, the Inner Sound, Sleat Sound, the Passage of Tiree, the Frith of Lorn, and Jura Sound. Now, these basins occur in what are simply the continuations of fiord-valleys. If the land were elevated for 600 ft. it would be seen that all these "Sounds" and "Passages" only formed the lower reaches of mountain-valleys. The Sound of Jura, for example, would appear as a wild mountain-valley continuous with that of Loch Craignish. In the same manner,

Sleat Sound would be continuous with the valley that now holds Lochs Alsh and Hourn. And each of these valleys, as the map shows, would contain deep freshwater lakes. We may therefore define the *fiord-basins* as those hollows which occupy the beds of, and extend in the same direction as, submerged mountain-valleys. They therefore follow the general slope of the sea-bottom, as the map itself sufficiently indicates.

Reasons have already been given for concluding that the rock-basins in our sea-lochs were excavated by glaciers which once filled all those now submerged land-valleys. We may next examine one or two of the rock-basins that occur in the sounds and straits, for the purpose of ascertaining whether appearances are such as to indicate a similar origin for them.

The map represents a large lake as occupying the sites of Raasay Sound and the Inner Sound, and stretching northwards to a point opposite Loch Broom. This is one of the deepest areas on the west coast of Scotland, the lip of the submerged basin being 50 fathoms, and its deepest part no less than 138 fathoms below the surface of the sea. Were the land to be sufficiently elevated, we should have here a freshwater lake 88 fathoms, or 528 ft. in depth; so that, even were the land to be upheaved for 600 ft., the bottom of the Raasay Lake would still be 38 fathoms below the level of the sea. Its deepest part trends along the east coasts of Raasay and Rona, and it shallows gradually away towards the north; that is to say, it is deepest where the channel is narrow—while, on the contrary, it begins to shallow as it expands into the North Minch. Now, if we examine the map of glacial striæ, we shall find that this large submerged basin was at one time occupied by a massive glacier that flowed in precisely the same direction as the trend of the basin itself, that is towards the north. Note further, that the striæ on the shores of Lochs Carron and Kishorn show that the glacier-ice which once filled those lochs spread over the low grounds of Skye between Broadford and Loch Eishart, where also it has left marks of its passage. This was doubtless at the same time that Raasay Sound and the Inner Sound were choked with glacier masses streaming outwards from Skye, Gairloch, Loch Torridon, and Loch Carron itself. For the reasons given in the preceding chapter, the erosion produced by this ice would be most excessive where the latter was strangled or compressed and heaped up. Consequently we find that it is between the mainland and the islands of Raasay and Rona that the basin attains its greatest depth. As the glacier crept out into the Minch it had room to expand, and therefore its erosive action became weaker in that direction.

I have selected for illustration one of the simplest cases. When we come to examine other fiord-basins, we not infrequently find that they are mixed up with a set of basins which cannot be said to coincide with mountain-valleys. These form our second group, one or two simple examples of which I shall describe first, and thereafter point out how the two groups sometimes coalesce.

The basins of the second group not infrequently extend at right angles to the trend of the fiord-basins, and are most typically developed along the inner shores of islands, especially when these are placed opposite the mouths of sounds and sea-lochs. As good examples, I may mention the great series of basins that stretch along the inner shores of the Outer Hebrides. For reasons which will be given presently, these may be conveniently termed *deflection-basins.*

A good example of a deflection-basin will be observed circling round the north of Rum. It reaches its greatest depth opposite Loch Eishart, where the excavation on the sea-bottom is as much as 74 fathoms, the bottom of the basin being 139 fathoms from the surface. Now it is certain that this is precisely where, during the climax of the glacial epoch, there would be immense erosion caused by the stemming of the ice that streamed out from the Coolin Mountains and Loch Eishart. Note how the basin is continued into Canna Sound, where it attains a depth of more than 50 fathoms, its bottom being 130 fathoms below the surface of the sea. A similar deep excavation makes its appearance between Eigg and Rum, which has an actual depth of not less than 48 fathoms, although the bed of the sea is only 86 to 88 fathoms deep at that place. Although this latter basin is separated from the one lying north of Rum, they were doubtless formed by the same glacier-mass, which, splitting upon Rum, would pour round that island, and exert excessive erosive power in the channels that separate Rum from Eigg and Canna.

Let us take another example. Mention has already been made of the deep basin that extends north from the Inner Sound into the North Minch, where it ends against the Shiant Isles and a bank known to fishermen as the Shiant East Bank. It will be observed that facing the end of the Raasay basin (which is a fiord-basin), another deep submarine hollow extends itself along the shore of the Long Island, opposite Loch Shell. This, there can be no doubt, belongs to our group of deflection-basins. When the ice which ploughed out the Raasay basin flowed out so far as to reach the Shiant East Bank, it would have a tendency to creep along the general slope of what now forms the bed of the sea; that is, it would trend towards the north. But as the whole of the North Minch became at the same time choked with glaciers descending from the wilds of Sutherland, it is evident that its passage in that direction would necessarily be blocked up. It would therefore be compelled to abut upon Lewis. Now we know that the ice which filled the North Minch attained so great a thickness that its upper strata were enabled to overflow the whole of Lewis from south-east to north-west, to a height of not less than 1,300 feet, and probably even higher than that. This is shown by the abundant traces of glacial erosion all over the island. But while the upper strata of ice were grinding across Lewis, there would necessarily be an "undertow" tending along the coast both to the north-east and the south-west. The greatest pressure would be exerted close in shore, where the high ground opposed the direct passage of the ice; and hence deflection-basins would be scooped out in such places. The process, indeed, would be precisely the same as in the case of Rum. The map represents a whole series of similar basins, extending along the inner margin of the Outer Hebrides. None of these are fiord-basins, but off the mouth of Loch Dunvegan, in Skye, there appears to be a union of basins belonging to both groups. South of Benbecula, however, the hollows which trend along the coast of the Hebrides seem certainly to be deflection-basins. This will become apparent when we reflect that, during the climax of the glacial epoch, the comparatively open space lying between Benbecula, South Uist, and Barra, on the one hand, and Skye, Rum, Coll, and Tiree, on the other, must have been filled with glacier-ice. From Loch Bhracadail, Loch Eynort, Loch Bhreatal, and Loch Scavaig, thick masses descended and became confluent with the ice that carved out the deep rock-basin lying north of Rum. At the same time glaciers streaming out from the Kyles of Skye, Loch Hourn, and Loch Nevis united in Sleat Sound, and swept past Eigg in the same general direction, namely towards south-west by west, until the *mer de glace* abutted upon the Outer Hebrides. Here, then, there would be intense grinding power exerted ; and while the upper strata of the ice would overflow in a westerly or north-westerly direction such portions as were not too lofty, the lower strata of the glacier-mass would sweep south-west by south, until, as the ice rounded the opposing high ground, it found freedom to extend itself more to the west, and so to shelve off into deep water. Thus the trend of many of the submarine basins, as shown upon the map, indicates the direction followed by the undertow of the great *mer de glace*, and will not always be found to run parallel with the marks of glacial erosion upon the contiguous land. For example, the deflection-basins lying off the east coast of Lewis trend from south-west to north-east, whereas the glacial markings on the land go across the island from south-east to north-west.

The two groups of basins which I have thus briefly described frequently become confluent, as one would naturally have expected. The upper reaches of Loch Carron, for example, occupy a fiord-basin, but where the hollow expands from the Kyles of Skye to north-west it forms a deflection-basin ; it is along its lower margin, indeed, where this hollow attains its greatest depth. If the land were elevated for 600 feet we should find the sea-bottom deeply scooped and hollowed in front of all the islets that stood right in the way of the ice-flow. But the map only shows such hollows as would form rock-basins and become freshwater lakes. Yet if we examine the Admiralty charts, we shall observe that a deep horse-shoe-shaped excavation would circle round the north end of Eigg, being evidently the work of the ice that came down Sleat Sound, and so with other islets; but when these are not very high, the erosion in front of them has been less excessive. In short, if the sea-floor were exposed to view, we should find that wherever abrupt ground rose opposite the mouth of a mountain-valley, a hollow of greater or less depth would circle round it like a collar. The island of Arran would afford a splendid example; the island of Mull, opposite Loch Linnhe, would be another hardly less striking; so would Rum, Eigg, Coll opposite the Sound of Mull, and many others. Thus the two groups of basins ever and anon coalesce, and in fact graduate into each other. Nevertheless, they must be distinguished, for while the fiord-basins invariably indicate the direct route taken by the *mer de glace*, the deflection-basins frequently indicate only the trend of the undertow, the upper strata having often overflowed the opposing land, and so swept on in the original direction.

But the most striking example of the union of *fiord-* and *deflection-basins* is afforded by the deep hollows that lie in the Sound of Jura, the North Channel, and the Irish Sea. Between Knapdale (Argyleshire) and the island of Jura, it will be observed that an elongated basin extends from Loch Craignish down the Sound of Jura, and is continuous with a great hollow that stretches south-east and south by the North Channel into the Irish Sea, and terminates at a point between Carnarvonshire and county Wicklow. In the first edition of this work, I described the Jura basin as a fiord-basin, separated from the deflection-basin that lies north of Rathlin Island; but an examination of the latest issue of the Admiralty chart of the "East Coast of Ireland" (No. 1,824) shows that the two basins are confluent, and that the lip or edge of the great submarine hollow is marked by the 50-fathom line. The deepest part of the Jura portion lies between Loch Crinan and a point nearly opposite the extreme south end of Jura Island. In this long narrow section the depths are very irregular; in fact, the hollow here consists of a string of small rock-basins, ranging from 83 to 110 fathoms in depth, the lip of the basin itself being 50 fathoms from the surface; so that in actual depth, the upper reaches of the basin attain, at the most, 33 to 60 fathoms. From the south end of Jura the basin widens out, and as it does so it gradually shallows, attaining, however, an exceptional depth (70 fathoms) immediately opposite the north point of Gigha Island. Now these appearances are precisely such as might have been expected ; the narrow and deep portions of the basin occur just in those places where the erosive power of the ice would be greatest ; and, on the other hand, the basin shallows as the fiord-valley opens out, for the simple reason that there the ice had room to extend itself.

When, during the climax of glacial cold, the confluent ice-masses were enabled to encroach still farther upon the bed of the sea, the Scottish *mer de glace* advancing upon the coasts of Antrim and Donegal became confluent with the Irish ice-sheet. This is well shown by the manner in which the glacial markings in the extreme north of Ireland turn away towards the west and south-east, instead of pointing right out to sea. The Scotch ice split upon Ireland, and flowed westward into the Atlantic, and south-east by the North Channel into the Irish Sea, and was continuous with the ice that overflowed the Isle of Man from north-east to south-west.

Since there can be no question that the Irish coast deflected the ice-current that streamed towards it from Scotland, there must have been great erosion upon the bed of the sea adjoining Ireland, and we ought to find there great hollows corresponding to the deep submarine troughs that occur along the inner margin of the Outer Hebrides, and in other similar positions. A glance at the map will show that precisely the same appearances recur off the Irish Coast. Opposite Rathlin Island we find a depth of not less than 133 fathoms ; the dotted line upon the map enclosing all the area which is at, or over, 100 fathoms from the surface. It is evident that this deep part of the great submarine hollow does not rest in a fiord-valley like that which now forms the Sound of Jura ; there is no sea-loch or deep land-valley opening out upon it from the Irish Coast. If excavated by ice, that ice could not have flowed from Ireland. There can be no doubt that we have here an excellent example of a *deflection-basin ;* for it is just opposite Rathlin Island that the immense glacier-mass discharging by the

Sound of Jura, met with resistance to its progress. Rathlin Island, in fact, behaved like a large boulder in the bed of a stream ; it stemmed the current, which was thus forced to flow east and west, and the usual result followed, a hollow was dug out in front. If the linear trend of the *fiord-basin* in the Sound of Jura indicates the former path of the glacier that formed it, not less does the crescent-shaped *deflection-basin* at Rathlin Island point out where the ice-current divided to flow in different directions.

But, as I have said, the Jura basin and the hollow in front of Rathlin Island are only the deeper portions of one great submarine trough, the lip of which is formed by the 50-fathom line. Nearly midway between the Wigtownshire coast-line and the Irish coast, the Admiralty chart shows a long trench which runs parallel to the shores of the adjacent countries. This trench reaches the depth of 149 fathoms, and is deeper by about 70 fathoms than any part of the great submarine hollow between the deflection-basin of Rathlin Island, and the termination of the great hollow itself in the Irish Sea. It is just where this deep excavation exists that the erosive power of the ice would be most excessive, as my colleague, Mr. J. Horne, has pointed out.* For the Scotch and Irish ice, uniting on the bed of the Irish Channel, must have been mutually subjected to intense compression and constriction ; and such increased constriction means of course greater pressure, and, consequently, more intense erosion.

The great hollow, as we trace it south, gradually shallows to a depth from the surface of 52 fathoms at a point opposite Lambay Island, after which it again deepens to 84 fathoms, and finally shelves off at a depth of 50 fathoms. Taking the lip of the trough at 50 fathoms from the surface, we find that the extreme depths appear in the Sound of Jura (70 fathoms) ; opposite Rathlin Island (83 fathoms) ; in the Irish Channel, between Wigtonshire and the opposite coasts of Ireland (99 fathoms) ; and midway between Dublin Bay and Holyhead Bay (34 fathoms). Let the reader note the fact that the greatest excavation upon the sea-bottom opposite the west coast of the Northern Highlands is 528 ft. in

† *Trans. Geol. Soc. Edin.*, vol. ii. pt. iii. 1874.

the Sound of Raasay. This great depth is exceeded by the hollow in the Irish Channel, for if the whole area of the British Islands were elevated so as to convert the adjoining seas into dry land, we should find an elongated lake extending from the Scottish Highlands southwards to the region between Wales and Wicklow county in Ireland, a length of not less than 240 miles, with a maximum depth of 594 ft.

Besides the groups of basins now described, a number of small ones are indicated upon the map as scattered about at a distance both from the fiord-valleys and islands. These are comparatively shallow, scarcely exceeding seven or eight fathoms in depth, and not often attaining even that. As a rule, their longer axis coincides in direction with what appears to have been the path of the *mer de glace.* Similar small hollows often occur in low-lying tracts on the land, as, for example, in the low grounds of Lewis, where they are seen to coincide in direction with the lines of glacial erosion. Some of these are rock-basins, and others are mere depressions in the glacial deposits.*

In fine, it seems to me that the distribution of submarine basins round the coasts of Scotland strikingly confirms the conclusions we had arrived at from an examination of the glaciated aspect of the land itself; namely, that the whole country—with the exception, perhaps, of the higher hill-tops —was at one time deeply smothered in ice, which flowed out from all the sea-lochs, overflowing the islands off the coasts, and only stopping at last in the deep waters of the Atlantic. And it is no less evident, to my mind at least, that the remarkable distribution of deep submarine hollows can only be accounted for by Professor Ramsay's theory of the glacial origin of rock-basins.

* I ought to mention that, owing to the small scale of the map, Plate XII., it has not been possible to show many of the submarine hollows which are indicated by the Admiralty charts; only those have been noticed which could be adequately represented.

CHAPTER XXV.

POSTGLACIAL AND RECENT DEPOSITS OF SCOTLAND.

Raised beaches.—Faintly-marked terraces, &c., at high levels.—Platforms of gravel, &c.—Platforms and notches cut in rock.—Raised beaches at mouth of Stinchar, at Newport, and Tayport.—Highest-level beaches belong to glacial series.—Evidence of cold climatic conditions during formation of some postglacial beaches.—Oscillations of level.—Raised beaches at the lower levels. —Human relics in raised beaches.—Proofs of oscillations of level.—Submarine peat-mosses, &c.—Blown sand.

THE accumulations which must next engage our attention carry on the story of the past from the close of the glacial epoch to the present; they are, therefore, termed by geologists the postglacial and recent formations, and comprise raised beaches, blown sand, peat-mosses, and alluvium. These will be described in the order they are here mentioned, not because that order is strictly chronological, but simply for convenience' sake. When the conditions of their accumulation have been ascertained, we shall be in a better position to discuss the question of their relative age.

In Chapter XXII. we considered the subject of certain beds containing marine organisms, and were enabled to come to these conclusions, namely, that in late glacial times Scotland was submerged to some extent below the waves, and that during this submergence the temperature of our seas was somewhat arctic. We found reasons for concluding that after the ice-sheet melted back the sea probably encroached to a height of one hundred feet or so above the present coast-line. During interglacial times the submergence was certainly much greater, for we find marine clays with shells at a height of 526 ft. above the present sea-level, and the actual submergence may have greatly exceeded that amount. No undoubtedly postglacial marine deposits have been met with above a height of 100 ft., but we find now and again in maritime districts, up to a height of several hundred feet, more or less well-marked shelves or terraces which have been excavated in the solid rock. These appear to indicate old sea-margins, but the higher ones at least probably belong to interglacial times. If they had been formed in postglacial times we ought certainly to have found some traces of them in the interior of the country ; yet I have never met with any such raised beaches in the inland districts. Dr. Chambers, in his "Ancient Sea-Margins," has given a number of instances of what he took to be old sea-beaches at heights approaching, and even exceeding, 1,000 ft. But none of these, I fear, can be relied upon as evidence of wave-work. The shelves on the Eildon Hills and the West Lomond Hill are cases of atmospheric erosion, and similar markings occur on every hill-side where the rocky strata are horizontal or approximately so. The examples quoted by the same author from the upper reaches of the valleys of the Clyde and Tweed are, some of them, flutings formed by the action of ancient glaciers, others are merely river deposits, while very many of the terraces at much lower levels, as for example those at Peebles, Kelso, &c., are also of fluviatile origin. Again, the Parallel Roads of Glen Roy, which have formed so fruitful a source of controversy, are no longer recognised as ancient sea-margins, but as lake-terraces. Indeed, when we consider the conditions under which the great glaciers disappeared, we cannot but be chary of ascribing any deposits met with in the interior of the country to the action of the sea. Beds of gravel, sand, and silt occur in such extraordinary positions in the Alps and other highly glaciated regions that we may well pause before deciding upon the marine origin of any such unfossiliferous deposits occupying similar positions in our own country. I do not, however, assert that the submergence in late glacial and postglacial times cannot have exceeded 100 ft. or thereabout ; all I mean to say is, that at present we have no certain evidence of any greater submergence than that : the exact amount has yet to be ascertained.

If we have thus reasonable doubts as to the marine origin of such shelves and terraces as may sometimes be detected in the interior of the country, we can have little hesitation in ascribing to the action of the sea those platforms of rock, and more or less broad terraces of silt, sand, and gravel which in so many places skirt the coasts. The terraced deposits are often plentifully stocked with the shells of the common littoral molluscs, and the whole aspect of the accumulations leaves one in no doubt as to their being ancient sea-margins. When such a terrace is followed inland from the coast it is usually found to abut more or less abruptly against a steeply-sloping bank or a well-marked cliff of hard rock, at the base of which we may often observe caves and hollows which are evidently the work of the sea.

As might naturally be expected, the raised beaches at the lowest levels are the best preserved—those at the higher levels occurring often in mere patches, and being hardly apparent except to a trained eye. These last have been modified and to a large extent obliterated by the grinding of the latest ice-sheet, and since then ordinary atmospheric action has so told upon them that their sharper outlines have frequently been smoothed off, and the terraced appearance well-nigh obliterated. This is especially the case where the shores are abrupt and rocky, and present bold cliffs to the sweep of the waves. Yet even on such rugged promontories we may occasionally detect shelves hewn into the seaward slopes of the hills. It is difficult indeed to perceive these when we are actually upon the ground, but when we retire to some little distance, so as to catch the profile of the land, they are then seen to form prominent platforms and notches. Some admirable examples of the kind occur along the bold coast-line in the south of Ayrshire, particularly on the high grounds that face to the sea at the mouth of the river Stinchar; others are noticeable on the shores of Fife, as near Elie. They may also be seen again and again on the rugged coasts of the western islands. The most continuous succession of shelves and terraces which I have observed at any one part of the coast, occurs between Newport and Ferryport-on-craig (Frith of Tay). The lower terraces at those places consist of gravel and sand—the higher ones being excavated in the solid rock. They are seven and perhaps eight in number—their levels being respectively 25, 50–54, 75–78, 100, 145–150, 250, 290, and 350 ft. above mean water; the last-mentioned one, however, is very faintly marked. Similar shelves and terraces occur at the same or approximately the same levels, and also at intermediate levels, at many places both on the west and east shores of central and southern Scotland. The higher ones all belong to the glacial and interglacial series; but even in those at the lowest levels we have indications of a somewhat colder climate than the country now experiences. And probably, when all the raised beaches have been examined in sufficient detail, it will be found that the retreat of the sea in postglacial times was not continuous, but interrupted by occasional pauses, and perhaps by occasional re-encroachments. There are indications of this even in some of the higher postglacial terraces. Thus, near Trinity (Frith of Forth), at a height of 70–80 ft. above the sea, Dr. Chambers observed a bed of peat under 10 ft. of sea-sand—the peat containing the remains of trees that were rooted in an underlying stratum of blue clay.* Facts of a similar kind have been noted not far from the same place ;† and the inference is that after the sea had so far retired, and vegetation had covered the country, there was a relapse to the former conditions, and the sea again advanced for some distance upon the land, until a bed of sand was deposited above the peat and prostrate trees. A much more striking example of this oscillation of the sea-level is furnished by certain facts connected with the latest raised beaches, as I shall now proceed to point out.

When we get down to levels below 60 ft. we find that both on the east and west coasts of central and southern Scotland there are two well-marked raised beaches, the upper of which occurs at a height varying from 45 ft. to 55 ft. or thereabout above the present sea-level. This old beach often extends continuously, and with some breadth, for considerable distances, but as a rule it appears for the most part only here and there in what seem to have been once sheltered bays. Nevertheless, on projecting promontories we not infrequently find it represented by a shelf cut in the solid rock. The terraced deposits consist principally of gravel and sand, and frequently contain shells belonging to existing British species, associated with which there have occurred certain shells that seem to be now restricted to

---

* *Ancient Sea Margins*, p. 17.   † *Op. et. loc. cit.*

more northern latitudes.* It is in this same terrace that the earliest traces of man appear to have been recognised. In the parish of Dundonald, Ayrshire, a rude ornament made of cannel coal was found at a height of 50 ft. above the sea-level, resting upon boulder-clay, and covered with gravel containing marine shells.† This evidence is perhaps slight, but it seems doubtful whether the human relics which have been disinterred from marine deposits so abundantly at lower levels than 50 ft. may not in reality sometimes belong to the age of the 45–55 ft. beach, or even to earlier times still : of this, however, more anon.

But by far the best preserved and most interesting of the old raised beaches is that which occurs at a height of 25–30 ft. above the present mean-tide mark in the Friths of Tay, Forth, Clyde, and Solway, and generally both on the east and west coasts of central and southern Scotland. When traced north-east to Aberdeen, it appears, according to Mr. Jamieson,‡ gradually to lose in elevation until it sinks to a height of only eight or ten feet above high-water. Along the steep and rocky sections of the coast this raised beach exists only as a narrow shelf hewn into the solid rocks, and in not a few exposed places it seems to be entirely absent. But wherever the land falls away to the sea in a long gentle slope the 25–30 ft. beach is usually well-marked, forming a broad terrace that may sometimes extend inland for a distance of several miles. Of this nature are the great carse-lands of the estuaries—the Carse of Gowrie, the Carse of Falkirk and Stirling (Plate XIII.), and the broad flats through which the Clyde flows in its lower reaches, are all raised beaches or terraces. So constantly present is this strip of flat land round the coasts that there are very few sea-port towns and villages in Scotland which are not built upon it.

The silts, clays, and sands, &c., of which this beach is composed, have, in many places, yielded abundance of shells —all of which, without a single exception, are still living round the coasts. But, besides shells, there have also been

---

* Mr. Gwyn Jeffreys, *British Association Reports*, 1862 ; A. Geikie, "On the Glacial Drift of Scotland," *Trans. Geol. Soc. Glas.*, vol. i. pt. ii. ; the latter author suggests that possibly these more northern forms may have been washed out of deposits of glacial age.

† *Antiquity of Man*, p. 61.

‡ *Quart. Jour. Geol. Soc.*, 1865, p. 191.

The Carse of Stirling: a raised beach, or estuarine flat. (By B. N. Peach.)

To face p. 300.

found the skeletons of seals and whales. The latter were
got in the Carse of Stirling at a height of twenty or twenty-
five feet above the present tide, and at a distance of several
miles from the sea. Along with one of the skeletons (discovered in 1819, during the famous improvements on Blair-
Drummond Moss), a perforated lance of deer's horn was
obtained.* Again, on a later occasion (1824), a similar
implement, evidently intended for a harpoon and still retaining part of the handle, was found associated in the same way
with another skeleton of a whale.† But these are not the
only traces of man which the alluvial deposits of the low-
lying carse-lands have yielded. A canoe, hollowed out of a
single oak-tree, and measuring 36 ft. in length by 4 ft. in
breadth, was exposed to view in the Carse of Falkirk by the
undermining of its banks by the river Carron. It lay at a
depth from the surface of 15 ft., and was overlaid with
successive layers of clay, shells, moss, sand, and gravel.‡
Another canoe was dug up near Falkirk at a depth of 30 ft.
from the surface.§ In the 25–30 raised beach of the Clyde,
at and near Glasgow,‖ at least twenty canoes have been discovered at various times, while digging foundations for houses
and in cutting drains. Most of these are formed of single
trees; others indicate greater skill in construction—one being
built of several pieces of oak, but without ribs—another
having its base and keel formed of a single oak, to which
were attached ribs, planks, and a prow with a high cut-water.
In another specimen of these ancient craft a circular hole in
the bottom was plugged with *cork*—pointing, as some antiquaries have suggested, to intercourse with Spain or southern
France ; but cork is light, and may have floated to the
shores of the Clyde. A beautifully polished stone implement
was found in the bottom of an old canoe, discovered so far
back as 1780, while digging the foundation of Old St.
Enoch's Church, Glasgow. The only recorded instance of

* *Edin. Phil. Jour.*, vol. i. p. 395; *Ibid.* vol. xi. pp. 220, 415; *Memoirs Wer-
nerian Society*, vol. iii. p. 327.
† *Memoirs Wernerian Society*, vol. v. p. 440.
‡ *Bibliotheca Topog. Brit.*, No. 2, part iii. p. 242.
§ *Beauties of Scotland*, vol. iii. p. 419.
‖ See Chapman's *Picture of Glasgow*, p. 152; Chambers's *Ancient Sea-Margins*,
p. 203; J. Buchanan's *Glasgow, Past and Present ; Trans. Geol. Soc. Glas.*, vol. iii.
p. 370.

the occurrence of human remains at any considerable depth in the old carse lands is that of a skull, which was dug up, in 1843, 21 ft. below the surface at Grangemouth.

No decided traces of ice-action have been detected in the deposits belonging to the 25-30 ft. raised beach. It is true that, in the clay-pits on both sides of the Forth at this elevation above the sea, contorted bedding is a common occurrence, but these contorted clay-beds belong unquestionably to the late glacial series*—the 25-30 ft. beach is merely cut into them, and now and again the gravel and sand of the old beach may be seen lying upon the denuded clay-beds, which have evidently suffered considerable erosion. Here and there large boulders rest upon the raised beach, but they have plainly been derived from the denudation of the boulder-clay. Boulders are scattered along the present beach in exactly the same way. The observer has, therefore, to be on his guard lest he should include among the deposits belonging to the 25-30 ft. beach every superficial accumulation that may chance to occur at that elevation. He must always remember that the beach is not entirely a terrace of deposition—but over wide districts is merely a shelf, broad or narrow as the case may be, cut out of pre-existing deposits of clay, sand, and gravel, and sometimes out of solid rock.

Before leaving the subject of these raised beaches, it must be mentioned that beds of peat containing trunks and roots of trees frequently occur underneath the deposits of the carse-lands, and submerged peat-mosses and ancient forests appear at many places round the coasts, as will be more particularly described in the next chapter. There can be no doubt that these indicate an old land-surface that existed prior to the deposition of the carse-clays. They therefore prove that the see-saw movement of which there are some traces in the higher raised beaches, was repeated at a later stage. The sea retreated until all the area now covered by the carse-clays was converted into dry ground. Trees then flourished and decayed, and were eventually submerged, and buried under-

* No hard and fast line can at present, or probably ever will be, drawn between the glacial and postglacial deposits—for the one must shade into the other. The deposits laid down during the last submergence of 100 feet, were, of course, eroded and partially re-arranged as the land again emerged above the waves.

neath great deposits of silt and sand. Then, finally, the land
emerged and the sea retired to its present level.

Now, since the peat and trees occur at the bottom of the
carse-clays, and are usually found overlying glacial deposits,
it is clear that, so far as direct evidence goes, they must be
older than the 25-30 ft. raised beach, and they may be, and
probably are, older than the 45-55 ft. beach. When the sea
stood at a height of 50 ft. above its present level—or, if the
reader prefers it, when the land stood just so many feet
below that datum-line—clay and silt must have accumulated
in our estuaries and bays just as it did when the land had
risen some 25 ft. higher. Indeed, if it be true, as some
evidence would lead one to infer, that glaciers may still have
lingered on at the heads of some of the higher valleys even
after the 45-50 ft. beach began to be formed, then the rivers
would bear seawards a much greater quantity of fine silt than
they could at a later date, when the glaciers had dwindled
down to utter insignificance, or even disappeared altogether.
And it does seem reasonable, therefore, to hold that some
part at least of the carse-clays was laid down upon the sea-
bottom at a time when the waves beat along the 50 ft. level.
From which it would follow that the bulk of the buried and
submerged peat-mosses belongs to a period anterior in date
to either of those two raised beaches: that, in short, the
mosses indicate a submergence and subsequent emergence of
50 ft. and more since the time that they and the trees which
they enclose grew green upon the land. It seems also probable that some of the primitive canoes may have sailed in
the waters of the Clyde when the sea reached not 25 or 30,
but 45 or 55 ft. higher than now.

Of the *Blown Sands*, which are met with here and there
along the coasts, it hardly falls within the scope of this work
to say more than a few words. They occur generally on low-
lying shore-lands, and very often at or near where a large
river enters the sea. They frequently form long chains of
dunes that extend parallel to themselves and the coast-line.
The Tent-Moor, between Tayport and the mouth of the Eden,
is the best example of the kind which I have seen. The
ridges there are wonderfully persistent and well-defined. In
other places, as at Stevenston on the Ayrshire coast, they

form irregular hummocks and banks. Some of the most extensive accumulations are found along the shores of the Moray Frith, and Mr. Jamieson thinks that these have probably some connection with the rivers entering the sea in their neighbourhood—the sands of Culbin, for example, having been derived in great measure from the sand brought down by the Spey, the Findhorn, and the Nairn.* But in many instances they appear rather to be derived from the denudation of pre-existing drift deposits. Such is certainly the case with those on the shores of Ayrshire and the Frith of Forth. So much is this so, that it is often impossible to draw a line upon the map to indicate what is true recent blown sand and what is drift belonging to the glacial series. Blown sands are certainly very often connected with the great river-valleys, but this appears in most cases that I have seen to be due to the fact that those river-valleys contain abundant gravel and sand deposits of glacial age which, upon the low coast-lands at their mouths, become exposed to the combined action of the sea and the wind.

* *Quart. Jour. Geol. Soc.* 1865, p. 192.

CHAPTER XXVI.

POSTGLACIAL AND RECENT DEPOSITS OF SCOTLAND—
Continued.

Peat-mosses, their composition.—Trees under peat, their distribution.—Submerged peat-mosses of Scotland, England, Ireland, Channel Islands, France, Holland.—Loss of land.—Continental Britain.—Climatic conditions.—Causes of decay and overthrow of the ancient forests.—Growth of the peat-mosses.—Climatic change.—Decay of peat-mosses.

EVERYONE is familiar with the fact that very large areas in Scotland are covered with more or less thick coatings of peat. These are not confined to any particular region, but they certainly occur in greatest abundance in upland and highland districts, where the soil is frequently obscured over many square miles in extent.

That a peat-moss is entirely composed of vegetable matter I need hardly say—that it has been formed by the growth and decay of successive generations of plants no one doubts: and these plants, moreover, as is well known, are still indigenous to the country. Such being the case, there may seem to be no difficulty in understanding how it comes to pass that we have peat-mosses. The plants which go to form these turbaries are still growing, and if we only allow them sufficient time, no doubt they will give rise to more peat-mosses. But when we begin to look a little more closely into the matter, we find that we cannot settle the question quite so easily. It is well known that underneath the bogs and peat-mosses, roots, trunks and branches of forest-trees and shrubs occur in great profusion. Here, then, is a difficulty. This buried timber assuredly marks the sites of ancient forests. How, then, did the peat come to overwhelm them? To discover this, it is obviously necessary that we should first endeavour to ascertain what kinds of trees are buried

X

under the peat, and how they are distributed through the country.

The Scottish "mosses" have yielded oak, pine, birch, hazel, alder, willow, juniper, &c.—all of them species which are even now indigenous to the country. There would appear, however, to be an interesting exception to the rule, for it is said, on good botanical authority, that the cones of *Abies picea* (silver fir) have been dug out of the peat in Orkney— a tree which is common in Norway, but not now indigenous to Scotland. From the position occupied by the buried trees, it is positively certain that they actually grew in place. The stools are rooted in the old soil; the trunks, branches, twigs, and even the leaves, lie all about. Nay, more than this, each species is found rooted upon that particular kind of soil which it is known to prefer : thus pines occupy the lighter gravelly soils, and oaks the heavier clays. Again, we find that the pine predominates in high-level mosses, while the oak abounds most in the bogs of the lower grounds.

Then, as regards the distribution of the ancient forests, it is no overstatement to say that they occur everywhere. I know of but few areas of peat-moss in which they have not been detected ; and this is not peculiar to the mainland, but even characterizes the little outlying islands. The visitor to Lewis is startled to find amidst the blank desolation and sterility of its extensive moorlands, the trunks of full-grown trees, consisting of oak, alder, birch, and especially Scotch fir. Now, the only trees in the island are those which Sir James Mathieson has, at great expense, reared around his residence. Yet, in some of the islands of the Outer Hebrides, a few stunted stems of hazel, birch, and mountain-ash may occasionally be seen clinging to the rocks, in places which are beyond the reach of sheep and cattle. The bare islands of Orkney and Shetland have also at one time supported large trees, while of the mainland itself it is difficult to say what district has not waved with greenery. The bare flats of Caithness, the storm-swept valleys of the Western Highlands, the dreary moorland tracts of Perthshire and the north-eastern counties, the peaty uplands of Peeblesshire and the Borders, and the wilds of Carrick and Galloway have each treasured up abundant relics of a bygone age of forests.

It would seem also that some of our trees had a greater vertical and horizontal range in old times than they have now. Mr. Watson gives 600 yards and upwards as the height reached by the Scotch pine at present. But he "has seen also small scattered examples at 800 or even 850 yards of elevation." These last, however, he thinks had probably been planted. "But that the pine," he continues, "has grown naturally on the Grampians at an equal elevation in former ages, is rendered certain by the roots still remaining in the peat-mosses of the high table-lands of Forfar and Aberdeen at 800 yards and upwards."* Again, in Glenavon, Banffshire, there are peat-mosses nearly 3,000 ft. above the sea, with abundant roots of the pine ;† and in the north of England they have been met with at a similar height.‡ The Scotch pine now ranges from Perthshire into Sutherland within lat. 56°-59°, but in ancient times it must have grown indiscriminately throughout the length and breadth of Britain, since we meet with it in many of the English mosses, as well those of southern as of northern districts.

The common oak has a similar wide diffusion in the peat-mosses, and the same remark applies to other species. Nothing indeed is more common than to meet with buried trunks of very large dimensions, occupying levels and positions which are now in the highest degree unfavourable to the growth of timber ; and this not only in the interior parts of the country, for great trees are frequently dug out of peat close to the sea-shore.§

But one of the most noteworthy points in connection with the peat-mosses remains to be mentioned. They are frequently found to pass below the level of the sea. This peculiarity has been observed in many places all round the coasts. It is needless to describe these submerged forests in detail, but I may note a few localities where they have been seen. On the coast of the Bay of Skaill (Orkney) an acre of peat-moss containing roots and trunks of fir-trees was exposed

---

* *Cybele Britannica*, vol. ii. p. 409.
† Sinclair's *Statistical Account of Scotland*, vol. xii. p. 451.
‡ Mr. Wynch, quoted in *Cybele Britannica, loc. cit.*
§ *Edinburgh Philosophical Journal*, vol. xvii. p. 53; see also *Philosophical Transactions*, vol. xxii. p. 980 ; and the *Statistical Account of Scotland* (Old and New), *passim*.

during a storm by the washing away of the superincumbent sand.* Again, on the north coast of the island of Sanday (one of the Orkneys) decayed roots of trees are seen at ebb tide upon the beach at Otterwick Bay,† and the like occurs in the bay of Sandwick, another of the same group of islands.‡

In the sea at Lybster, and under the sands of Reiss in Caithness, my colleague, Mr. B. N. Peach, tells me he has seen sunk peat with large trees.

A number of years ago, while some improvements were being made in the harbour of Aberdeen, a good many trunks of oak of large size were dug up, and their position showed that they had not been brought down by the river, but had grown where they were found.§ In the parish of Belhelvie, in the same county, peat-moss occurs under the sea-level, and is covered to a depth of ten or twelve feet with sand. Oak-remains appear in this peat, and from the fact that during storms large cubical blocks of peat are often cast on shore, it seems probable that the peat-moss and its buried forest extend for some distance out into the bay.‖

In the Carse of Gowrie it is well known that trunks of oak, willow, and other trees lie buried at depths varying from twenty to twenty-seven and even to forty feet. All these are really at or below the sea-level, for the surface of the carse does not rise more than twenty to thirty feet above that datum-line. At the Braes of Monorgan and Polgavie, the river Tay has cut down through the carse-land and exposed a bed of peat four feet thick, containing trunks of oak, fir, alder, and birch, the roots of which penetrate an old soil. This peat, which now forms the bed of the river, is buried below some seventeen feet of alluvial matter, throughout which a good deal of vegetable débris occurs; towards the top of the section, cockles, mussels, and other sea-shells make their appearance. It is said also that in sinking wells in the carse-land, " deers' horns, skulls, and other bones " have frequently been found, along with the remains of the trees mentioned above.¶

At Flisk, on the south side of the Frith of Tay, submerged

* *Edin. Phil. Jour.,* vol. iii. p. 100.
† Sinclair's *Statistical Account,* vol. vii. p. 451; Barry's *Orkney Islands.*
‡ *New Statistical Account.* § *Ibid.*
‖ *Ibid.* ¶ Sinclair's *Statistical Account,* vol. xvi. p. 556.

peat-moss has been traced along the beach in one place for a distance of three miles, and in another for no less than seven miles. It contains hazel and hazel-nuts, and what appears to be alder, and the roots are said to occur in places at ten feet below the limits of the full tide.* A thin bed of peat, also, may be seen at low water on the shores of the Frith of Forth, a little to the east of Largo.

In the islands of the Hebrides the same phenomena may be studied. At Pabbay, for example, peat with large trees is exposed at ebb of the spring tides, and on the coasts of Harris, wherever a high bank has been undermined and cut back by the sea, a rich loam or black moss is discovered. And this is by no means peculiar to Harris, but characterizes all the low-lying sandy shores of the Long Island,† as in North Uist and Vallay, at both of which places submarine peat and trees occur.‡ Again, on the north-west coast of Tiree, and here and there in Coll, the same appearances recur. §

Nor are similar phenomena wanting along the western shores of the mainland, for trees and peat have been found under low-water mark at Loch Alsh;∥ while at Oban the bottom of the harbour, which is not less than twenty fathoms deep, is said to be covered with peat in some places.¶

The phenomena of drowned trees and peat-mosses are by no means confined to Scotland. They appear quite as constantly in England** and Ireland,†† nor are they absent on the further side of the English Channel. Sunk forests abound along the coasts of Brittany, Normandy, and the Channel Islands, where trees have been observed at a depth which could not have been less than sixty feet below high-water. Similarly, off the shores of Holland, Holstein, Sleswig, and Denmark, submarine peat-mosses occur.

Now these facts enable us to conclude that the sea has within geologically recent times made considerable encroachments upon the land. It is quite clear that our shores and

* *Trans. Roy. Soc. Edin.*, vol. ix. p. 419.
† Sinclair's *Stat. Acc.*, vol. x. p. 373.　　‡ *Ibid.* vol. xiii. p. 321.
§ *Edin. Phil. Jour.*, vol. vii. p. 125.　　∥ *Op. et. loc. cit.*
¶ Dr. Anderson's *Practical Treatise on Peat-moss*, p. 150.
** *Philosophical Transactions*, vol. xxii. p. 980; vol. l. p. 51; vol. lxxxix. p. 145; *Philosophical Journal*, April 1828; *Quart. Jour. Geol. Soc.*, vol. vi. p. 96.
†† Jukes' *Manual of Geology*, p. 740.

the opposite coasts of the Continent have, at some period of
the past, extended much farther seaward. We infer this not
only from the facts connected with the submerged mosses,
but also from the large size of the buried trees of the maritime districts. In most of the islands it is impossible for
trees now to attain to respectable dimensions, unless they are
carefully protected and looked after. When the buried
forests of the Hebrides and Orkney and Shetland Islands
were growing, no doubt the land stood at a relatively higher
level and the sea at a greater distance.

But more than all this, peat has been dredged far out in
the German Ocean and the English Channel; and freshwater and littoral shells have been dredged in deep water at
distances of fourteen and forty miles from the nearest land.*
Add to these cases the frequent occurrence of mammalian
remains—bones and tusks of the mammoth—which have
been obtained often at a considerable distance from the English coast, both in the North Sea and the English Channel,
and we shall hardly escape from agreeing with Mr. Godwin-
Austen and Mr. Trimmer, who have inferred that at no
distant date, geologically speaking, the bed of the North Sea
was a great undulating plain traversed from south to north
by a mighty river, which carried the tribute of the Thames,
the Rhine, and other streams, and poured in one magnificent
flood into the Northern Ocean.

At this period the British Islands were, in all probability,
joined to each other, stretching farther westwards than now
into the Atlantic; even reaching, perhaps, to the edge of the
100-fathom plateau. We cannot of course positively assert
that this last was the case, but a full consideration of the evidence in all its bearings, leaves one hardly any room for
doubt. Botany, zoology, and geology alike seem to require
a continental Britain to explain the facts. The plants and
animals that now clothe and people our islands have been,
in large measure, derived from the Continent, and some land-
passage was needed in recent times for them to cross by.
The geological evidence proves that a much larger area of
land must certainly have existed; and if the bed of the sea
were only to be elevated so far as to expose to the light of

* *Quart. Jour. Geol. Soc.*, vol. vii. p. 134; *Ibid.* vol. xxii. p. 160.

day all the peat which has been reached in dredging and sounding, Britain would immediately become part and parcel of the Continent ; for our seas are very shallow, no part of the German Ocean, the English Channel, or the Irish Sea being anywhere so deep as Loch Lomond. An elevation of from twenty to thirty fathoms would drain nearly all the German Ocean between England and the Continent, and twenty fathoms more would lay dry the same sea between Scotland and Denmark. The average depth of the Irish Sea is not more than sixty fathoms, and that of the Minch does not exceed the same depth. By an elevation of only some 400 ft., every little islet off our coasts would unite with the mainland, and the mainland with the Continent. Such a degree of upheaval, however, is not absolutely required to explain the phenomena of the submarine forests : 250 or 350 ft. would perhaps suffice.

The character of the buried timber indicates pretty clearly the kind of climate experienced at that time in Britain. It is impossible to look at the thick bark and the tough resinous wood of the bog-pines, without feeling sure that the winters then were much colder than they are now. A rigorous climate is required to produce the best pine-wood, and it has frequently been observed in the north of Scotland that trees grown in the most exposed situations show the reddest wood and the thickest bark. Yet pines dug out of mosses in the south of England compare favourably with the best timber in the old pine forests of Rothiemurchus. This of itself is enough to show that our climate has greatly changed within comparatively recent times.

But again, the presence of large oaks buried in peat, at heights and in situations that would now be considered most unfavourable to their growth, bespeaks the former prevalence of somewhat warmer summers. In short, we are led to con- clude that the seasons during the growth of the ancient forests were more strongly contrasted than they are now. Such conditions would naturally follow upon the union of Britain with the Continent. With broad wooded plains sub- stituted for the German Ocean and the Irish Sea, and with a wider spread of land along our western sea-board, it can hardly be doubted that, other things being equal, our climate would be greatly affected, so much so as to approach in character to that of Germany.

We have now to inquire what it was that caused the decay and overthrow of the ancient forests, and induced the growth of peat-mosses instead.

It has been surmised by some writers that much of the old timber may have been blown down, and they have referred to the fact that all the trees in some peat-mosses often lie in one direction, as if they had met their fate at one and the same time.* The woods, as we know, grew thick and close, the trunks rose tall and straight, and their roots were fewer and not so widely spreading as they would have been had the trees grown in isolated positions. Hence, when a breach was once effected by the overthrow of the sturdier trunks that guarded the outskirts of the forest, the destruction of the less firmly-rooted timber, it has been thought, would speedily follow. Doubtless many acres may have been desolated in this way. But it seems extravagant to infer that all the buried timber met its fate after this fashion. We cannot suppose the peculiar position of the trees to be in every instance the result of violent storms. Trees are usually bent over in some particular direction by prevailing winds, and when any cause leads to their overthrow, whether it be natural decay or otherwise, they naturally fall as they lean.

Other causes of destruction have been suggested, such as lightning, and what are known in America as ice-storms. Neither of these causes can be quite ignored, yet they can hardly have been other than partial in their operation.

But when we come to ask what share man has had in the work, we find that he has been a far more potent agent of destruction than any of the causes yet referred to. Besides the evidence of his hand afforded by the charred wood under peat, we sometimes come upon marks of adze and hatchet.

The earliest historical accounts of North Britain have afforded abundant food for controversy to antiquarians, but

---

* *Highland Society's Prize Essays*, vol. ii. p. 19 (Old Series); Rennie's *Essays on Peat-moss*, p. 31; Sinclair's *Stat. Acc.* vols. iv. p. 214; v. p. 131; and xv. p. 484; *New Stat. Acc. Paisley* and *Carluke.* Vide also, for similar phenomena in English and foreign peat-mosses, *Phil. Trans.*, vol. xxii. p. 980; Rennie's *Essays*; Degner, *De Turfis*, p. 81.

when the geologist has gleaned together the few descriptive remarks which occur here and there, in the pages of Tacitus, Dion Cassius, Herodian, and others, he will find that his knowledge of the physical aspect of Scotland does not amount to much that is very definite. He will learn, however, that Caledonia was notorious on account of its impenetrable forests and impassable morasses. But the precise extent of ground covered by these woods and marshes must always be matter of conjecture. The forest-land known as *Sylva Caledoniæ* appears to have stretched north of the wall of Severus, but south of that boundary large forests must have existed ; indeed, down to much more recent times, many wide districts of southern Scotland could still boast of their woodlands. Of the nature of those waste plains, described by the ancients as full of pools and marshes, we can have little doubt, although we cannot of course pretend to point out their particular site. Those who have traversed the central counties of Scotland must have been struck with the numberless sheets of alluvium which everywhere meet the eye, betokening the presence, in former days, of so many little lakes. In Bleau's Atlas, many lochans appear in spots that have long ago come under the dominion of the plough. These, however, must form but a small proportion of the lakes which have been drained since the time of the Romans. Such inconsiderable peaty lochans were not likely to merit particular mention by those who had gazed on the Alpine lakes, save as they became vexatious interruptions to their progress through the country, and surrounded, as many of them in all probability were, with treacherous morasses, the words of the old historians appear to have been descriptive enough of certain ample areas in the Scottish Lowlands.

It seems to have been the common practice of the Romans to cut down the trees for some distance on either side a "way," to prevent surprise by the enemy. Several old "ways" have been discovered on the clearing away of mosses, and in their neighbourhood lie many trunks of trees, bearing evidence of having fallen by the hand of man. The presence of Roman axes and coins leaves us in no doubt as to who the destroyers were. But it is quite evident that such embedded relics do not enable us to fix the age of a peat-moss. They merely tell us that the origin of the peat cannot date back beyond a certain period, but may be ascribed to any subsequent time. Hence it is impossible to say what amount of waste we are to set down to the credit of the Romans. Some authors have, perhaps, been too ready to exaggerate the damage done by the legions. The buried forests which can be proved to have fallen before Roman axe and firebrand are not many after all ; but we may reasonably suppose that these form only a portion of the woods which were cleared at that time.

We have, however, what appears to be direct evidence to show that some regions had been divested of their growing timber before the Roman period ; for, if Solinus may be trusted, the Orkneys were, in the days of the Romans, bare and bleak as they have been ever since. He says, " They are three in number, and contain neither inhabitants nor woods ; here and there they bristle with shaggy copse and herbs, but, for the most part, all they show is bare sand and rock." A patriotic Orcadian might insist that the statement " three in number " renders what follows untrustworthy ; and perhaps he might prefer the testimony of Ossian, who, in his poem of " Carric-thura," says of some island in the group, "a rock bends along the coast with all its echoing wood." According to Torfaeus (historiographer to the King of Denmark),* the condition of the Orkneys in the year 890 agreed with the description given by Solinus.† For at that time Einar conferred a great boon upon his countrymen by teaching them the use of peat for fuel—there being then, as Torfaeus says, no woods in the islands. Yet it is well known that the peat-mosses of the Orkneys, and even those of the Shetlands, contain the remains of considerable trees.

My limits will not permit me to consider in detail accounts of the condition of the Scottish forests in times subsequent to the Roman period. Any reference by the chroniclers to the state of the woodlands is only incidental, and perhaps not always to be relied upon. It is interesting, however, to learn from Boethius that the *horrida Sylva Caledoniæ* had

---

* Torfaeus wrote about 1690. He was a native of Iceland, and died in 1720.
† Solinus is supposed to have written about A.D. 240.

in his time become mere matter of history.* He further tells us that Fifeshire had formerly been well wooded (in the times of some of his early Scottish kings) ; but "it is now," says his old translator, "bair of woddis ; for the thevis were sometime sa frequent in the samin that they micht na way be dantit, quhill the woddis war bet down."† Again Boethius describes the island of Isla (whose peat-mosses contain roots and trunks of trees) to be an island rich in metals which could not be wrought on account of the want of wood.‡

After the period to which Boece refers, any allusions to the aspect of the country are best sought for in cartularies and such records. For the rights acquired by monasteries over various forests throughout the country, these cartularies afford abundant evidence. Chalmers§ has enumerated many instances of special grants by kings and barons "of particular forests in pasturage and panage, and for cutting wood for building, burning, and all other purposes ;" and Mr. Tytler‖ has added to the list. It need hardly be remarked that the greater part of these woodlands has long disappeared. And yet the old cartularies "abound with notices of forests in every shire during the Scoto-Saxon period." I have not hesitated to quote the authority of those records, and the opinions of two such learned and correct writers as Chalmers and Tytler. No one can deny that the evidence of the cartularies is in favour of a better wooded condition for the country than now obtains. But we must guard against the mistake of supposing that all the area embraced under the designation of a "forest" was covered with forest-trees. And there can be little doubt that both Chalmers and Tytler read the cartularies in the light of the facts which are disclosed by the peat-mosses. The trunks of pine, oak, ash, and other hard timber dug out of the mosses, were regarded

---

* If this had not been the case, he would surely have quoted a less ancient authority than Ptolemy for the site of the ancient forest. See *Cosmographie and Description of Albion.*

† *Croniklis of Scotland,* chap. xi.

‡ Bellenden's version of the passage is characteristic. He says, Isla is "full of metallis, gif thair wer ony crafty and industrius peple to win the samin ;" but he quietly drops all allusion to the want of wood in the island.

§ *Caledonia,* vol. i. p. 792, &c.

‖ *Hist. of Scot.,* vol. ii. chap. ii. third edit., and the authorities there quoted and referred to.

as proofs that the regions indicated by the cartularies were in reality the sites of great forests at the time to which those records refer. But it is probable, nay in many cases quite certain, that much of this buried timber belongs to a more remote period. But even with this reservation, Scotland, down to the fourteenth century, would appear hardly to have merited the description given by Æneas Silvius at a later date. During the civil commotions of the country,* and the long wars with England,† much wood seems to have been destroyed, and the gradual progress of cultivation also began to encroach upon the forest-lands. The great number of salt-pans that were early established in Scotland, and the right which the proprietors usually obtained to cut the requisite firewood from the forests of the country, was another cause of destruction, and much timber disappeared in this way from the maritime districts. But although wood appears to have been the fuel commonly employed in the manufacture of salt, yet it is not unlikely that peat may also have been burned in some cases. It is certain, at least, that peat was a common enough fuel in David I.'s reign, and that‡ "petaries became frequent objects of grant to the abbots and convents during the Scoto-Saxon period." This fact ought perhaps to be looked upon as a farther proof of the increasing decay of the forests.

But by far the most remarkable testimony to the bare condition of the country is furnished by the Acts of the Scottish Parliament. From the times of the first James, stringent acts were adopted by successive Parliaments,§ having for their

* Foredun relates that Robert the Bruce defeated the Earl of Buchan near Inverury, and ravaged the district with fire. The marks of fire are said to be visible on the trees in the peat-mosses of that neighbourhood. Sinclair's *Statistical Account*, vol. xx. p. 144.

† Knighton mentions that in the reign of Richard II., the English, under the Duke of Lancaster, besides firing the forests, employed eighty thousand hatchets in the work of their destruction.

‡ *Caledonia*, vol. i. p. 793.

§ See *Acts of Scottish Parliament*. The more interesting acts referring to the state of the woods were passed as follows :—James I., Second Parliament, A.D. 1424 ; James II., Fourteenth Parliament, A.D. 1457 ; James IV., Sext Parliament, A.D. 1503 ; James V., Fourth Parliament, A.D. 1535 ; Mary, Sext Parliament, 1555 ; James VI., First Parliament, 1567, Sixth Parliament, 1579, Eleventh Parliament, 1587. It is curious to notice how, from the time of James I., the penalties imposed upon the destroyers of wood increase in severity. Pecuniary fines are succeeded in time by stocks, prison, or irons ; the culprit is to be fed on bread and water during confinement, and to be scourged before parting from his jailers. The climax is reached in the following act, which became law object the preservation of the woods. Æneas Silvius (after-wards Pope Pius II.), who visited this country about the middle of the fifteenth century, relates: "We have seen the poor people almost naked, who came to beg at the doors of the temples, receive for alms pieces of a stone, with which they went away contented. This kind of stone, being impreg-nated either with sulphur or some other combustible material, they burn instead of wood, of which their country is destitute."* Such a statement regarding the bare condition of the country might have been thought somewhat exaggerated, for it is the testimony of a visitor from more favoured climates ; but its truth is curiously illustrated by an Act of Scottish Parliament, passed in the reign of James IV.—"Anent the artikle of greenewood, because that the Wood of Scotland *is utterly destroyed*, the unlaw theirof beand sa little : Therefore, &c.†

There are, of course, numerous traditions regarding the former wooded condition of various districts from which the trees have long since been stripped. Many of these refer to some of those woods which I have already mentioned, as being frequently named in the cartularies and similar records.

Another line of evidence is supplied by local names ; but into this subject I cannot enter here.

The short outline of historical facts now given seems to prove:—

1st. That when the Romans entered Britain they found the surface of the country to some extent covered with forests, but diversified in many places with bogs and marshes.

2nd. That to this period we must refer the destruction of some portions of the ancient forests, whose remains are dug out of the peat-mosses ; but what amount of damage the woods then sustained we have no means of ascertaining.

3rd. That from the time which elapsed after the departure of the Romans down to the eleventh century we have no certain records referring to the state of preservation of any part of the Scottish woods, unless we except the statement of

in 1587:—"Whatsoever persone or persones wilfully destroyis and cuttis growand trees and cornes, sall be called therefore before the Justice or his deputes, at Justice Airs, or particular diettes, and punished therefore to the death, as thieves."

* *De Europa*, cap. 46. † Sext Parliament, A.D. 1503.

Boethius, who tells us that Fife had in a great measure been divested of its forests by some of his early Scottish kings.

4th. That from the eleventh to the thirteenth century, and down even to later times, there appear to have been still considerable areas of forest-land, the rights to which were frequently granted to ecclesiastical communities and others.

5th. That during these centuries much forest was thus cleared and brought under cultivation; that at the same time woods were exhausted by building and burning, more especially as fuel for the salt-works; while extensive tracts were displenished and laid waste during times of war and civil strife.

6th. That from the time of James I. there appears to have been a progressive decay of the remainder of the Scottish woods.

There can be no doubt, then, that man must be credited with no small share in the work of destruction. It may be questioned, however, whether he was, after all, the chief agent. Certain considerations would seem to show that too much has been reckoned up against him.

We have seen that the general character and distribution of much of the timber in our peat-bogs points to the former prevalence of a somewhat excessive climate, and I have sought to connect this period with that continental condition of Britain which geologists are generally agreed did obtain within comparatively recent times. Now, when our area once more became insular, it is almost needless to say that this change would react upon the climate—the winters would become milder, and the summers cooler. The trees in what are now the maritime districts, would soon succumb to the influence of the sea air. Thus, wide areas along the coasts, and in the islands of Orkney, Shetland, and the Hebrides, would be displenished. The trees, falling to the ground, would obstruct the surface-drainage, and thus give rise to marshes in which the bog-mosses would speedily multiply, until, by-and-by, they overwhelmed the prostrate timber, and covered the whole with a mantle of growing peat. Nor can it be doubted, that, on the moist hill-tops, and in many places in the interior of the country, similar changes would come about.

It is a mistake, however, to suppose that peat-moss always overlies a prostrate forest. There are cases where no trace of wood can be detected. Peat of this description is not uncommon in the upland districts of the south of Scotland, where it frequently clothes the tops and slopes of considerable hills to a depth of from 6 to 12, and even 16 ft. Here, then, there are no trees to account for its presence. Again, in the mosses of the higher hill-tops, when trees do occur, they are of small size—mere brushwood, in fact, the overthrow of which, we can hardly think, would have done much in the way of collecting moisture for the support of the bog-mosses.

From a consideration of these and other points, it seems not unreasonable to suppose that the decay of the woods and the growth of the peat were both alike to some extent induced by a change of climate. Insulation would render the country less capable of supporting an exuberant forest-growth, and would at the same time increase the moisture of the atmosphere, and thus favour the spreading of the bog-moss and its allies.

As the beginning of these changes carries us back far beyond the earliest dawn of history, it follows that much of the peat and buried timber of our country may be of great antiquity. And, indeed, in the cases of many mosses, we seem more likely to err in ascribing too recent than too early a date to the period of their formation. We cannot estimate the time which has gone by since the Western Islands supported those timber-trees, the remains of which are dug out of the mosses. It is highly probable, that, at the period in question, those islands were joined with the mainland, and shared a continental climate. To the same date we may refer much of the buried timber of the Orkney and Shetland Islands. Again, the more elevated peat-mosses of the country must have been among the first to be formed; for, any change from a continental to an insular state would tell first upon the trees that grew along the sea-board, and at the higher elevations of the land. It seems reasonable, therefore, to conclude that, long before the Romans set foot in Britain, the overthrow of timber and the growth of peat-moss had made considerable progress; that, in short, the Caledonian Wood was but the relics of that great forest which in former ages had spread over all the area of these islands and the German Ocean.

Farming operations have encroached, and every year are continuing to encroach, upon the moss-lands. But a very long time indeed will elapse before the great "flow-mosses" or quaking bogs, some of which exceed 40 ft. in depth, shall be improved out of existence. Draining, however, has done much to stop the growth of peat in many places, and is destined to do still more. I feel sure, from what I have myself seen, that the general decay of the peat-mosses (I refer more especially to those on flat hill-tops and sloping ground) far exceeds the rate of growth. Frost and rain are breaking down the peat and washing it rapidly away, and in many cases only a few shreds have been left scattered here and there over the tops and slopes of the hills. Under present climatic conditions, the eventual clearing of all these high grounds is only a question of time. This change must, no doubt, be attributed, in large measure, to improved systems of drainage, but it seems not improbable that it may also in some degree be due to a lessened rainfall—the mosses not receiving so much moisture as they did in former times. But, for obvious reasons, this would be a very difficult matter to prove.*

* For general information on Scottish peat-mosses consult Rennie's *Essays on Peat ;* Aiton's *Treatise on the Origin, Qualities, and Cultivation of Moss-earth ;* and Steel's *History of Peat-moss.* Dr. Anderson's *Practical Treatise on Peat* is a whimsical attempt to prove that peat-moss is a plant *sui generis !* [The account of the Scottish peat-mosses given above is condensed from a paper by the author communicated to the Edinburgh Royal Society (*Trans.* vol. xxiv. p. 363, 1866). Recently Mr. Axel Blytt, a Norwegian naturalist, has come to similar results from an examination of the flora and the peat-mosses of Norway. Some account of his conclusions will be found in chapter xxxii.]

CHAPTER XXVII.

POSTGLACIAL AND RECENT DEPOSITS OF SCOTLAND—
Continued.

Action of the weather on rocks.—Erosion by running water.—Postglacial erosion insignificant in amount as compared with denudation during last interglacial period.—Recent river-terraces.—Silted-up lakes.—Marl-beds.—Organic remains in freshwater alluvia.—Human relics.—Conclusions regarding succession of events in postglacial times.—General summary of glacial, interglacial and postglacial changes.

THE great erosion caused by the continuous grinding of gigantic masses of ice—the rounded outline given to crags and hills—the scooping-out of deep basins in solid rocks—and the accumulation of thick and wide-spread deposits of till—seem, by comparison, so immensely more important than the results effected by the action of rain and frost, as at first sight to render these somewhat insignificant. A little reflection, however, will serve to dispel this notion, and show us that, even in the absence of snow-fields and glaciers, the waste of the land by the other atmospheric forces must be enormous.

Let us recall the appearance presented by the Scottish mountains—bold hummocky masses of rock, for the most part, but often bristling with splintered crags and shattered precipices. See how frequently the hill-tops are buried in their own ruin, and how the flanks are in many places curtained with long sweeps of loose angular blocks and rubbish, that shoot down from the base of cliff and scaur to the dark glens below. All this is the work of rain and frost. When the whole country was swathed in snow and ice, the hills and valleys no doubt experienced considerable degradation from the grinding action of the confluent glaciers ; but then, on the other hand, frost was debarred in large measure from carrying on its usual work of destruction—for only a very

Y

few of the highest mountains then lifted their heads above the level of the far-extended *mer de glace.* Glacial erosion during these conditions was, no doubt, excessive; but we must remember that the continuous grinding of a glacier upon its bed produces less effect than the simple action of the frost upon such rocks as are exposed above its surface. Consequently under extreme climatic conditions, the greater the area of bare rock, the more considerable will the waste be; the moraines of small glaciers being proportionately larger than those of more important ice-flows. Thus, long after the glaciers of Scotland had dwindled down to comparative insignificance, the waste amongst the mountains must still have been prodigious. The extreme cold of those old times has long since passed away, but even now, when no persistent snow-fields exist, the havoc effected by frost is yet very considerable.

Then, again, we have to bear in mind that the whole surface of the country is being subjected to the abrading action of running water. Under the influence of rain, soil is continually travelling down from higher to lower levels; rills and brooklets are gouging out deep trenches in the subsoils and solid rocks; streams and rivers are constantly wearing away their banks and transporting sediment to the sea. The gravel and sand and silt that pave the numerous water-courses, are but the wreck and ruin of the land, and it is easy to see, that, since the close of the glacial epoch, immense quantities of material have been thus abstracted from the country. The streams and rivers have been working deeper and deeper into the bottoms of the valleys, and leaving behind them terrace after terrace of alluvial detritus to mark the different levels at which they formerly flowed. And if we tried to estimate the amount of material which has been thus cut out of the valleys and carried seawards, we should no longer feel inclined to undervalue the erosive power exerted by running water. But we should not have proceeded far in our investigations before we became aware of the fact that, great as this erosion has been since glacial times, it is yet insignificant as compared with the vast denudation which was effected during the last stage of the glacial period, that is, during the accumulation of the gravel and sand that were

laid down in the final retreat of the glaciers. It was then
that the till and other glacial deposits were swept out of the
valleys, and the solid rocks themselves deeply incised.
During the succeeding period of partial submergence, the sea no doubt eroded the superficial materials here and there, and scarped out
shelves on the slopes of the hills in maritime
districts, but its work was chiefly that of re-
arranging and re-assorting—the clearing-out
of the valleys, many of which had been choked
up with débris by the glaciers, was well-nigh
exclusively effected by the great rivers and
floods of the last glacial period.

In the annexed diagram (Fig. 53) I have
indicated the relative positions occupied by
the modern or recent river deposits, and those
that belong to the era of the receding glaciers.
The solid rock is shown at *r r*; the till at *t t*;
the glacial river gravels at *g g*; and the recent
deposits at *a a*. These appearances compel us
to infer, first, that till not only covered the
side slopes, but also cumbered the bottom of
the valley to a considerable depth. Then came
the final stage of the last glacial period, with
its big rivers, which ploughed out the till and,
as they deepened their channels, clothed the
sides of the valleys with gravel and sand.
Finally, the rivers became much reduced in
volume, and began to re-excavate the glacial
gravels and sand; and as they cut their way
into the bottom of the valley, successive terraces of alluvial gravel, sand, and silt, were left
fringing the valley slopes, as shown at *a a*.

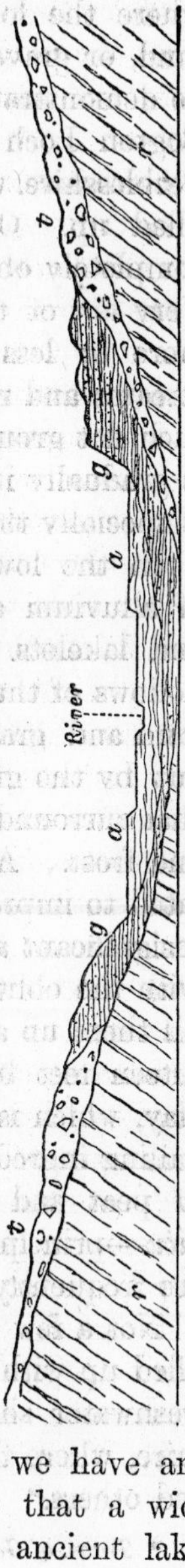

I have described the various kinds of lakes
that exist in Scotland, and have shown how
not a few of these have been silted up by
the streams since glacial times. Such filled-up
lakes are probably far more numerous than we have any
idea of—for it is always difficult to prove that a wide
flat of alluvial ground marks the site of an ancient lake.

Fig. 53.—Diagrammatic view of glacial and postglacial river-gravels: *t*, till; *g*, glacial gravels; *a*, recent alluvium.

The barriers that formerly held in the water become obliterated, either by being swept away, or buried deeply under
recent deposits.   Such is the case with not a few rock-basins,
where the lower lip of rock is often concealed below silt,
sand, or gravel.   And it is only by boring that this fact can
be demonstrated.   I have referred to two such cases, namely,
Bogton Loch near Dalmellington, and St. Mary's Loch in
Peeblesshire, which are two rock-basins in the course of being
filled up.   Others, again, as I have remarked, have been
completely obliterated by the pouring into them of sediment.
Very few of the freshwater lakes and sea-lochs do not show
more or less extensive flats opposite the mouths of the
streams and rivers that flow into them ; and even where no
such flat ground appears, the soundings yet show that a delta
is gradually increasing below the surface of the water.   This
is specially the case, of course, when the lakes are deep.

In the lowland districts there are numberless little sheets
of alluvium and peat that mark the sites of shallow pools
and lakelets.   Many of these, especially in Ayrshire, rest in
hollows of the till, and some in superficial depressions of drift
sand and gravel.   They have not been silted up by streams,
but by the gradual washing down of the banks and slopes
that surround them, under the long-continued action of rain
and frost.   And, indeed, I know hardly anything more calculated to impress one with the importance of these apparently
insignificant agents of waste, than the phenomena connected
with the obliterated lakelets referred to.   The deposits that
fill them up are often several yards in thickness, twelve and
fifteen feet being no uncommon depth.   Loam and loamy
clay, which is sometimes used for brick-making, are the prevailing ingredients, but these often contain intercalated beds
of peat and decayed trees, which have evidently grown *in
situ*—principally willows and alders, but at the bottom oaks
are frequently found rooted in the subjacent glacial clays.

Not a few old lake-beds are found to be in large measure
filled up with marl, consisting of the remains of innumerable
freshwater shells.   Many examples of this occur in Forfarshire, where they were long ago studied by Sir Charles Lyell
and others.[*]

* *Trans. of Geol. Soc.*, vol. iv. p. 305.   *Ibid.* Second Series, vol. iii. p. 73.

Now in these alluvia, both lacustrine and fluviatile, mammalian remains have frequently been discovered. Among other forms we get *Bos primigenius, B. longifrons,* wild boar, red deer, fallow-deer, roebuck, elk or moose-deer, Irish elk, reindeer, goat, wolf, wild-cat, fox, beaver. The *Bos primigenius,* or urus, is now extinct, but is believed to be represented by the white cattle of Chillingworth and Hamilton, and our present domestic breeds. *Bos longifrons* is also extinct, but from it some of our domestic cattle may have descended.

The true elk (*Cervus alces*) which ranges over the northern regions of America and Asia, from latitude 45° northwards to the shores of the Arctic Sea, but in Europe does not come farther south than the 64th degree of latitude, wandered in postglacial times over all Scotland, its remains having been found in recent deposits, as well in northern and central as in southern counties.* But there appears to be only one instance on record where remains of the Irish elk have occurred in recent deposits, namely, in a marl-bed at Maybole in Ayshire.† The reindeer is also rarely met with, but there can be no doubt that it likewise was a native of Scotland‡ in postglacial times ; some writers, indeed, relying on a statement of Torfaeus, think that it may have survived in the extreme north down to the twelfth century. Wolves and beavers, though no longer natives of Scotland, were certainly so within historical times. Of the other animals mentioned, nothing need be said here ; they are all forms eminently characteristic of a temperate climate.

It is remarkable that nowhere in the recent deposits of Scotland have we any trace of the great pachyderms, so frequently met with in certain river-gravels of England and the Continent. All the remains of the mammoth yet detected have appeared either in beds that underlie or are intercalated with the till, or else they have occurred in the actual till itself. There is a vague mention of the horn of a rhinoceros having been dug up in marl at the Loch of Forfar,§ but I fear no reliance can be placed upon it.

* *Proceedings of the Society of Antiquaries of Scotland* (Dr. J. A. Smith), vol. ix.
† *New Statistical Account of Scotland,* vol. v. p. 353.
‡ *Proc. Soc. Antiq. Scot.,* vol. viii. p. 186.
§ *Edin. Phil. Journal,* vol. viii. p. 397 ; *Memoirs Wernerian Society,* vol. iv. p. 582, vol. v. p. 573.

The oldest relics of man in Scotland consist of stone implements. They turn up everywhere, and to give merely a list of the places where they have been detected would be to enumerate every district in the country, not even excepting the outlying islands. They occur either at the surface of the ground or embedded below peat, and in recent alluvial deposits, and they frequently appear associated with the remains of some of the animals referred to above. We cannot assign them to an older date than the Newer Stone period of archæologists, not a single relic of the Older Stone period having yet been met with north of the Tweed.

Having now finished our very rapid survey of Scottish postglacial deposits, I shall endeavour, in a few words, to summarise the results obtained.

During the deposition of the clays and sands with ice-floated stones and northern shells, the land, as we have seen, stood relatively at a lower level than now. But the period of submergence was passing away ; slowly and gradually the sea retired, leaving behind it, as the land emerged, certain shelves and terraces to mark the height at which its waves had formerly rolled. This recession of the sea appears to have been occasionally interrupted ; nay, it even happened that sometimes the water regained a part of the territory it had lost, and spread its sediment over the site of prostrate forests. A good deal of ice seems to have been floating about in Scottish seas, for rafts, and, perhaps, bergs stranded in the shallow waters of the estuaries, and threw into confusion the fine silts and clays that were there accumulating. Often, too, they dropped stones and boulders as they floated along, and these became embedded upon the floor of the sea. In this way pieces of chalk, which may have come from Denmark or the north of Scotland, were covered up in the clay at Barry and Portobello. At this time glaciers still lingered in our mountain-valleys, and the rivers, turbid with silt, carried down great quantities of shingle and sand to the low grounds, and poured their muddy waters into our sea-lochs and estuaries.

The sea continuing to retire, the British Islands became at last united to the Continent. We have no positive evidence as to the character of the climate which then prevailed in our area, but it could hardly have been other than excessive and quasi-continental. Edward Forbes considered* that our country at that time was in the condition of the barren grounds of North America—bare and treeless—and inhabited by reindeer, Irish elk, uri, bears,† foxes, wolves, hares, cats, and beavers. It is almost certain, indeed, that a bare and treeless state must have preceded the age of forests, but it would be hazardous to assert that trees did not exist in Britain before the German Ocean became for the last time converted into dry land. The remains of trees occur in Scottish postglacial beds that are most probably of older date than the latest continental condition of Britain. It would appear, therefore, that trees existed in Scotland before the bed of the German Ocean was uncovered. Whence these were derived we can only conjecture ; most likely, however, they came from England, and if so, this would indicate that England was joined to the Continent at an earlier period than Scotland. But, however this may have been, we know that the whole of the British area became at last one magnificent forest-land, continuous across the bed of the German Ocean with the great forests of northern Europe. Scotland at this time was inhabited by numerous races of wild animals, many of them now locally and some wholly extinct. The reindeer, elk, wolf, beaver, &c., have disappeared from the country ; the ancient wild bovidæ now only live in our domestic breeds, and the Irish elk is extinct. It was, probably, during this last continental condition of the country that the men who used the polished stone implements entered Scotland. They were a race of hunters and fishers, and seem to have frequented the neighbourhood of rivers and lakes, living a life not unlike that of the Indians in what were once the woody wildernesses of Canada. The climate would appear to have been somewhat excessive, the winters being considerably colder, and the summers, perhaps, a little warmer than at present—at least, on what is now the eastern side of our island.

How long this continental condition lasted we cannot even

---

* *Memoirs of the Geological Survey,* vol. i. p. 397.
† Species of bear appear to have been got in true postglacial deposits in Ireland, but nowhere in Scotland.

conjecture. We only know that, after it had endured for a considerable time, the sea once more began to encroach upon the land, and at last Britain became an island. The sea advanced until the water-line reached some fifty or sixty feet above its present level, and then a considerable pause supervened. Man still inhabited the country, casting his nets in the lakes, and sailing about the sea-coast in his canoes hollowed out of single oaks. Again the sea retired, and once more paused when it had fallen to twenty-five or thirty feet above its present level. The arctic mollusca that once lived around the shores had now vanished, and the present fauna occupied their place. But the seas were, perhaps, even then a little colder than they are now; as would seem to be indicated by the presence in the carse-clays of the stranded whales, which belong to the large Greenland species.

The final retreat of the sea to its present level brings us down to recent times, after which it falls to the archæologist to continue the strange story of the past.

So many points of evidence have now been adduced, that it will be well, before we address ourselves to the study of the glacial deposits of other countries, to reckon up here in a few paragraphs what appears to have been the general succession of geological changes in Scotland from the advent of the Ice Age down to recent times.

1. The till or boulder-clay, with its intercalated beds, indicates a vast lapse of time, during which there were several revolutions of climate—how many, we do not know.

2. The beds of till point to intense arctic conditions having prevailed at the time of their formation.

3. During the climax of glacial cold, glaciers not only filled the mountain-valleys to overflowing, but coalesced upon the Lowlands, and creeping outwards, occupied all the shallow seas around the shores. Only the tips of the highest hills peered above the *mer de glace*, which became confluent with the ice-fields of Ireland, England, and Scandinavia, and terminated as a great wall of ice, beyond the shores of the Outer Hebrides, in the deep waters of the Atlantic.

4. The accumulations of silt, clay, sand, and gravel, with land-plants and mammalian remains, and the similar deposits with marine shells, all of which beds are intercalated in the

till, clearly show that the intense arctic cold which covered the country with an ice-sheet was interrupted, not once only, but several times, by long continuous ages of milder conditions. Some of these periods may have been warmer than others, just as some of the glacial periods may have been colder.

5. A land-surface seems to have existed in the last interglacial period. The land at that time was dotted with freshwater lakes, and clothed, to some extent, with vegetation, which supported several species of mammals. Submergence next ensued, and the sea drowned the country to a depth of not less than 526 feet. This is the greatest height at which sea-shells have been met with in the glacial drift of Scotland. The submergence, however, may have greatly exceeded 500 ft., and marine interglacial beds may yet be found at higher levels. Some of the faintly marked terraces of erosion met with at high levels in maritime districts probably belong to this date.

6. So far as direct evidence goes, we cannot say that Scotland during any one of the interglacial periods was characterized by a warmer climate than is now enjoyed in the forest regions of high latitudes in America.

7. Considering the sorely wasted appearance of the interglacial deposits, and keeping in view the nature of the conditions under which they have been preserved, it would be rash to conclude that they contain a complete record of the changes which ensued during interglacial times, or that we are entitled to argue, from the few fossils yielded by them, that the climate of the interglacial periods was never positively warm.

8. The most recent deposits of till indicate, for the last cold period of the glacial epoch, an ice-sheet of less thickness than that underneath which the bottom or oldest accumulations of till were formed. During the last cold period the confluent glaciers cleared out the marine deposits laid down in preceding interglacial times, and incorporated these with their *moraine profonde*. This is the origin of most of the shelly tills or boulder-clays.

9. Certain deposits of boulder-clay at low levels and in maritime districts were accumulated during the final recession

of the ice in the last cold period. They indicate a time when the confluent glaciers had greatly diminished in thickness and extent, but were still broad enough to cover all the Lowlands. The sea followed after the retreating ice, but how far it encroached upon the land we cannot say. The boulder-clays belonging to this period occur only a few yards above the present sea-level, and the submergence was probably very limited. The glaciers ere long ceased to reach the sea, and began to deposit their gravelly moraines upon the land. Perched blocks and erratics were stranded on the mountain-slopes and on the lowland hills at ever-decreasing levels as the ice melted away.

10. The sand-and-gravel drift overlying the till and boulder-clay was carried down from the melting glaciers, and deposited upon the low grounds. These deposits, therefore, indicate the further retreat of the ice, and the amelioration of the climate. It was during this period that the greatest erosion of the older glacial deposits ensued ; the large rivers then occupying the valleys not only swept down the morainic matter which marked the retreat of the local glaciers, but ploughed into the till or boulder-clay, and scoured that deposit out of the valleys.

11. High-level terraces of angular shingle and earthy sand mark the sites of old glacial lakes formed at this time by the damming-up of lateral valleys from which the ice had melted away. To the same period belong many interrupted shelves and terraces of more or less well-rounded gravel with sand and clay, which seem to have accumulated between the margins of the ice and the hill-slopes that rose above its level. Many gravel-and-sand ridges (kames) of the low grounds seem to have been formed in subglacial water-courses ; others graduate into true moraines and mark the terminal fronts of the decaying glaciers. Erratics were often carried down the valleys by river-ice in summer-time, and distributed over the inundated low grounds ; others travelled upon the surface of the retreating glaciers, and, falling over their terminal fronts, dropped upon the surface of the gravel-and-sand mounds that were slowly emerging from underneath ; yet others mingled with the gravel and shingle of terminal moraines.

12. Certain deposits of sand, clay, and mud, with northern species of shells, arctic seals, &c., which occur along the shores of estuaries and in maritime districts, indicate a submergence of some 100 ft. or thereabout. At the time of their accumulation local glaciers existed in the mountain-valleys, and some of these may even have reached the sea in certain fiords of the west coast. Ice-rafts, and perhaps icebergs, floated in the sea, distributing erratics, and occasionally running aground and confusing the beds of silt and clay that gathered there.

13. The sea now commenced to retreat, the various pauses in the emergence of the land being marked by the formation of successive raised beaches, which are better preserved than certain higher-level shelves excavated in the solid rock of maritime districts during the last interglacial period of submergence (see par. 5).

14. Britain became continental by the conversion of the German Ocean into dry land. At first, probably, bare and treeless, it eventually passed into the condition of a great forest-land. The climate was continental, and the fauna temperate and cold-temperate. Men who used polished stone implements then lived in Scotland.

15. Submergence once more ensued. The destruction of the forest-lands and the increase of peat-mosses dated its commencement from this period. Climate insular, but colder and more humid than at present.

16. Final emergence and formation of the low-level raised beaches.

17. The present.

CHAPTER XXVIII.

GLACIAL DEPOSITS OF ENGLAND.

Necessity of comparing deposits of different countries.—Glaciation of mountain districts of England and Wales.—Unfossiliferous till, its character.—Direction of ice-flow in the north-west districts.—Lower boulder-clay of Lancashire, Cheshire, &c.—Middle sand and gravel.—Upper boulder-clay.—River gravels.—Morainic débris.—Succession of changes.—Lower and middle glacial series of East Anglia.

NO one who shall endeavour to trace the origin and history of the drift accumulations within any particular area need hope to do so satisfactorily without continual reference to the superficial phenomena of contiguous regions. Individual sections, however clear and apparently consecutive they may be, yet do not contain all the truth ; and it would be ridiculous to suppose that the drifts of any limited locality tell one everything that he might hope to learn of the physical history of the Ice Age. Two observers who should restrict their examinations, the one to a mountainous district, the other to low-lying tracts at a distance from the hills, would be sure to form very different ideas of what the glacial epoch really was. One might be all for glaciers—the other all for icebergs. The earlier students of the Scottish glacial deposits held that the whole island had been swept from north-west to south-east by an ice-laden ocean current, and they pointed triumphantly to the direction followed by the rock-striations and the till in the great midland valley as conclusive proof of their theory. But had they been as well acquainted with the Southern Uplands and the Northern Highlands as they were with the low grounds of the Lothians, this iceberg theory would probably never have been advanced. It is only when the geologist has gone over a sufficiently large tract of country and studied its superficial accumulations at all levels, in lowlands and mountains alike, that he can safely generalise. He will not, however, fully appreciate the results obtained if he ventures to ignore what other workers are doing elsewhere in the same field of inquiry. When he compares his own conclusions with those of others, he will often find reason to hesitate and proceed with caution, where, previously, he may not have perceived any difficulty. On the other hand he will not infrequently have his own inferences strengthened, and here and there catch a hint that may enable him to see newer and deeper meanings in his facts than he had any idea of before. Certain it is that we shall never acquire a proper knowledge of the physical changes that supervened during the glacial age, until the records of that age have all been correlated and compared. But what a vast amount of work remains to be done before this can be adequately accomplished! Nevertheless, some approximation towards it can be—ought to be, indeed—attempted. A great deal has already been learned. The general succession of events that marked the progress of the Ice Age in widely-separated countries has been more or less clearly made out, and it becomes, therefore, a matter of importance to inquire how far the conclusions so arrived at harmonize with each other. If they shall be found to tally as closely as could have been expected, we shall have so far a guarantee of their accuracy, and be enabled, as we shall afterwards see, to form some definite opinion as to the succession of changes that followed upon the close of the glacial epoch. In this and succeeding chapters, then, I shall attempt, with what success I may, to compare the results obtained in Scotland with the conclusions arrived at by English, Irish, and foreign geologists.

So long as the observer confines his attention to the mountainous districts of England, he will experience no difficulty in detecting the traces of former extensive glacial action. He will find both in Wales and the Lake district, that the mountains frequently show that peculiar flowing and rounded contour which is so characteristic a feature of ground over which land-ice has passed. In the valleys he will see polished and striated surfaces of rock, and heaps of morainic deposits; and the presence of numerous true rock-basins will farther conspire to assure him that the influences under which Scotland assumed much of its most characteristic scenery, have also had no small share in designing, or at all events in adding some of the latest and finest touches to, that beautiful picture of hill and dale and lake that so charms one in Cumbria and Wales.

But when we leave the hilly districts and begin to traverse the broadly undulating low grounds, the evidences of old ice-action become obscure and hard to read. And our difficulties increase the farther we recede from the mountains. The tough and firm rocks of Cumbria and Wales are replaced as we travel outwards from these centres by rocks less capable of retaining any ice-markings which may at one time have been graven upon them. Add to this the great thickness of superficial materials, underneath which the strata in the low-grounds are frequently buried, and the confused and intricate appearance often presented by these drifts, and it will be admitted that the geologist who sets for himself the task of unravelling the evidence, so as to educe a clear and consecutive story, has no easy work to accomplish. Not the least perplexing part of his task will consist in attempting to discover the meaning of the terminology employed by different observers. Similar deposits he will find are known under different names; while under one and the same designation accumulations are described which are certainly not the same, but in some cases as wide apart as they could well be.

The English glacial deposits are typically developed in two regions: 1st, in the region of Wales and the north-western counties; and 2nd, in East Anglia and Yorkshire. It will be most convenient to treat of these two districts separately. My limits, however, will not allow me to do more than trace the general succession established or in process of being established by English geologists. For convenience' sake I take first the north-western district.

The oldest deposit which has yet been recognised in this part of England, is a more or less tough stony clay that answers precisely to the typical unfossiliferous till of the Scottish Lowlands. It is quite unstratified, save here and there where the included stones show a rude kind of arrangement, similar to that which I have described as occasionally visible in the till of Scotland. Like the latter it also contains in places thin irregular seams and amorphous patches of earthy sand and gravel, while its colour varies according to the district in which it is found. Thus it may be yellowish brown, grey, dark blue, or red—the colour evidently depending upon that of the rocks from the degradation of which it has been derived. So far as yet known it would appear to be unfossiliferous. The stones are angular, blunted, striated, smoothed and polished—the more compact and finest-grained rocks receiving the best dressing. Moreover they are scratched most markedly in the line of their longest diameter—irregular-shaped stones not being striated in any one direction more than another. In these and other items this till tallies precisely with that of Scotland.

It rests usually upon a smoothed and striated pavement of rock, but sometimes the strata are bent over, crushed, and broken underneath, and their fragments commingled with the till.*

An examination of the rock-striations proves conclusively that from all the valleys of Wales and the Lake district, there formerly issued great streams of ice, which coalesced to form one gigantic confluent glacier. Mr. Tiddeman has shown † that the general trend of this ice-sheet in North Lancashire and adjacent parts of Yorkshire and Westmoreland, was towards the south or south-south-east, across deep valleys and over hills of considerable elevation. And he justly infers from this fact that some barrier existed in the Irish Sea which prevented it following the natural slope of the ground towards the south-west. This barrier was the ice deriving from the Lake mountains. But if so, then some other barrier must have ponded back the latter also ; for had not such a barrier existed, the glaciers of Westmoreland and Cumberland would have found for themselves a more direct route to the sea than they appear to have done. The cause of this deflection was undoubtedly the presence of the

---

* Mr. J. C. Ward describes the till of the northern part of the Lake district as a "stiff clay stuck full of smoothed and scratched stones and boulders, and unstratified. It occurs every here and there in small patches among the mountains, in rock-sheltered spots, and may frequently be seen in the valleys, either by itself or underlying a more gravelly deposit." This latter he describes as consisting of "subangular gravel (very rarely containing beds of sand) in a clayey matrix, with large boulders in and upon it. It sometimes passes down into the till, and either forms sloping plateaux running up the valleys (as the till alone sometimes does) or wide spreads of a more or less moundy appearance." *Quart. Jour. Geol. Soc.*, vol. xxix. p. 422. For further information on the Lake district see Mr. Ward's papers, *Op. cit.*, vol. xxx. p. 96, and vol. xxxi. p. 152.

† *Quart. Jour. Geol. Soc.*, vol. xxviii. p. 471.

massive ice-sheet that streamed from the south of Scotland, and had sufficient power to deflect the ice creeping out from Ireland. Such being the case it is not surprising to learn that the Isle of Man [*] and Anglesea [†] afford evidence to show that the united glaciers or ice-sheet actually overflowed both these islands. Mr. J. G. Goodchild has shown [‡] that the Scotch ice ascended the valley of the Eden in Cumberland, its path being marked not only by the presence of glaciated rock-faces, but also by boulders in the drift which have been transported from the high grounds in the south of Scotland. These he has traced up to the top of Stainmoor, across which the united Scotch and Lake-district glaciers must have flowed in a general easterly or north-easterly direction. Mr. Goodchild also mentions the fact that great quantities of Scotch drift "have gone over the watershed between the Eden and the South Tyne eastward to the North Sea." I have already stated (see p. 181) that the ice which flowed down the valley of the Tweed from west to east was compelled to turn gradually away to the south-east as it neared the English border, so as to overflow Northumberland in a direction parallel to the coast-line. The Cheviot Hills appear to have been smothered in ice, for I found till with striated stones here and there on the very watershed. Nevertheless they divided the ice-flow, for all the valleys on the Scotch side are glaciated from south to north in the direction of their trend, while the English slopes of the hills are marked in the opposite direction. Here and there, however, we get evidence to show that ice passed across some of the lower heights of the dividing ridge from one country into the other, boulders from the English side being scattered over the upper reaches of one or two of the Scotch valleys.

At low levels in Lancashire and North Wales the unfossiliferous till is overlaid by another stony clay, which, how-

[*] *Guide to the Isle of Man*, (Rev. J. G. Cumming), p. 249. See also an excellent paper by Mr. J. Horne, "A Sketch of the Geology of the Isle of Man," *Trans. Geol. Soc. Edin.*, vol. ii. part iii. Mr. Horne shows conclusively that the island has been glaciated by ice that moved outwards from the mainland over the bed of the sea.

[†] Professor Ramsay has recently endeavoured to prove that the hollow occupied by the Menai Straits has been scooped out by the action of the great ice-sheet that streamed outwards from Scotland and the Lake district. See *Quart. Jour. Geol. Soc.*, vol. xxxii. p. 116.

[‡] *Quart. Jour. Geol. Soc.*, vol. xxxi. p. 55.

ever, differs markedly from the till it rests upon. According to Mr. De Rance,* it is a stiff reddish-brown clay, containing a vast quantity of packed stones and boulders that vary in size from fragments a quarter of an inch thick or so up to blocks measuring four yards across. At least 70 per cent., he tells me, are striated, but many have been more or less water-worn between the periods of scratching and deposition. The deposit shows sometimes faint indications of bedding, and contains such shells as *Tellina Balthica, Cardium edule, C. aculeatum, Psammobia ferroensis, Turritella terebra,* &c., and Mr. De Rance informs me that he has also obtained spiculæ of sponges. He calculates that 94 per cent. of the stones and boulders do not belong to the drainage-area in which any given section of the deposit appears; and he has not met with the clay at a greater height than 150 ft. above the sea.

Above this boulder-clay come considerable depths of sand and gravel—200 ft. in places. They are well-bedded, and have been traced from near the sea-level up to heights of 1,200 ft. (Macclesfield), and even of 1,300 ft. (Moel Tryfan). As the boulder-clay does not rise more than 150 ft. above the sea, it is evident that the sand and gravel beds must overlap that deposit. Here and there they have yielded marine shells, many of which are still living in British seas, but upon the whole the fossils indicate colder conditions than now obtain in the Irish Sea; conditions, however, which were far from approaching those of which the Scottish shelly clays are memorials.

Resting upon the marine sands † we find yet another stony clay—the so-called "upper boulder-clay" of Lancashire and North Wales. Mr. De Rance describes it as closely resembling, in the region between Ulverstone and Manchester, the lower boulder-clay (with shells) "in its physical character, chemical composition, included erratic fragments, and the species of shells of mollusca found in it. Both clays contain more Silurian erratics in the north-west and more Carboniferous erratics in the south-east of Lancashire; both are of a

* *Quart. Jour. Geol. Soc.*, vol. **xxvi.** p. 641.
† Mr. Hull was the first to point out this succession: *Memoirs of Lit. and Phil. Soc. of Manchester,* 1865, p. 449.

dull Indian-red-coloured tint." Here and there faint indications of bedding may sometimes be observed, and sometimes the clay contains lenticular layers of sand, "but the pebbles and boulders are imbedded pell-mell and at all angles in the mass." The base of the clay is generally a bed of "marl," of tolerably hard consistence ; stones are not common in it, but all are much glaciated, being highly polished and intensely scratched ; minute fragments of shells are common ; and the clay has a deep chocolate-colour. Higher up stones are common, but less glaciated, and the clay is of the usual red colour." * East of Blackpool the deposit has an average thickness of 30 or 40 ft. "Fragments and occasional perfect specimens of several shells of mollusca occur, including *Turritella terebra, Cardium edule,* and *Tellina Balthica.*" †

In other places, according to Mr. Mackintosh,‡ the upper boulder-clay contains "rather few stones, and exceeding few large boulders," and is extensively used for brick-making. Where I have myself seen it, it looked not unlike some of the stony brick-clays of Scotland. The stones were scattered sparsely through the deposit, and were not so closely aggregated as in the more common type of boulder-clay or till. I did not, however, notice any trace of bedding, and it is evident from Mr. De Rance's account that the deposits seen by me were not exactly typical of the normal character assumed by this upper boulder-clay, which appears to be as good till as much of that which occurs in the maritime districts of Scotland.

According to Mr. Mackintosh, the upper boulder-clay "seldom rises higher than 400 ft. or 500 ft. above the sea." A shelly till occurs at Mottram (Manchester) at 568 ft. above the sea.

In the north-western districts of England, then, we have clearly three stony clays—the lowest one of which appears to be destitute of organic remains, while the two overlying masses contain here and there a few shells which are chiefly broken and fragmentary. One might have doubted indeed

---

* *Quart. Jour. Geol. Soc.*, vol. xxvi. p. 649.

† *Memoirs of Geol. Surv. of England and Wales,* Explanation of Sheet 91, S.W., p. 8; see also *Op. cit.,* Exp. of Sheet 90, N.E.

‡ *Geological Magazine,* vol. ix. p. 190.

whether the lower shelly clay and the unfossiliferous till were not one and the same deposit, but Mr. De Rance tells me that east of Little Orme's Head, Llandudno, the whole series is shown in one and the same section as follows :—

4. Upper boulder-clay.
3. Middle, sand, and gravel.
2. Lower boulder-clay, resting on a denuded surface of
1. Unfossiliferous till or boulder-clay.

Enough has been said in regard to the conditions under which the unfossiliferous till of the Lake district of Wales has been laid down. My colleagues, Messrs. Tiddeman, Ward, and Goodchild, have brought forward indisputable evidence to show that an ice-sheet radiated outwards from the mountains of the Lake district, and became confluent with a similar mass of glacier-ice that crept outwards from Scotland and greatly modified the course followed by the ice that had its origin in England. In the sequel I shall mention some considerations that seem to lead to the inference that before the first great ice-sheet overflowed the British Islands our country stood at a higher level, and it is quite possible that in those preglacial times the Irish Sea may have had no existence. If this were so it would account for the fact that the oldest till is quite destitute of marine remains, even when it occurs in close proximity to the sea, as at Little Orme's Head.

Mr. De Rance has suggested that the lower boulder-clay with shells may have been deposited along the seaward edge of the ice-sheet at a time when this was melting away. It is more probable, however, that this boulder-clay has originated in the same way as the Caithness till, and that, as Mr. Tiddeman remarks, the shells have been introduced by the ice-sheet working over an old sea-bed and pushing marine sediment and organic remains on to the land.[*]

It is now generally admitted that the middle sands and gravels indicate a great recession of the confluent glaciers consequent upon a change of climate. These deposits rest directly upon the lower boulder-clay when that is present, and the latter often shows a much denuded surface underneath the sands. So far as direct evidence goes, we cannot

* *Quart. Jour. Geol. Soc.*, 1872, p. 486.

assert that the sea followed immediately upon the disappearance of the ice-sheet by which the lower boulder-clay was amassed. There is a distinct break between the two deposits —the one rests unconformably upon the other.

The upper boulder-clay, which at one time I was inclined to think was chiefly of marine origin, has in all probability been formed much in the same way as the lower boulder-clay. It indicates the incursion of the last ice-sheet, and may be the equivalent of much of the unfossiliferous till of the mountainous and hilly districts of the interior.

The stony clays and middle sands of this region of England seem therefore to afford us evidence of the following changes : *first,* a period of excessive glaciation, when an ice-sheet covered all Wales and northern England,—before this ice-sheet appeared the land may have stood higher relatively to the sea than at present ; *second,* a great recession of the ice, accompanied with or followed by the submergence of the area now covered by the Irish Sea ; *third,* a new advance of the ice-sheet which flowed over the bottom of the sea and mingled marine deposits and their organic contents with its bottom-moraine ; *fourth,* a disappearance of intense arctic conditions, accompanied or followed by denudation of the old bottom-moraines,—for aught we can tell, a wide land-surface may have existed at this period ; *fifth,* a gradual depression of the land to a depth of 1,300 ft. or thereabout during comparatively mild conditions of climate ; *sixth,* a reappearance of arctic conditions and the last incursion of a great ice-sheet.

Considerable accumulations of fluviatile gravel occur in the valleys of Wales and the Lake district, often at great heights above the present rivers. This gravel, when traced up stream, becomes coarser and earthier, and not a few of the stones even show faint traces of striæ. As we follow it still farther into the mountains, it appears to pass into, or at least it cannot be distinguished from, morainic débris. Opposite the mouths of some of the mountain-valleys great deposits of hummocky angular and sub-angular gravel and hillocks of sand make their appearance, but elongated ridges of gravel and sand, like the more marked kames of Scotland, are either absent or of uncommon occurrence.

Lastly, I would refer to the immense quantities of morainic

matter, and the numerous *blocs perchés* * which are found in almost every valley in the Lake district and in Wales. This angular earthy débris hangs on all the hill-slopes, and gathers on all the bottoms of the valleys. Towards their upper reaches it often takes the form of low mounds and ridges—the lateral and terminal moraines of small local glaciers. But the terminal moraines of the great glaciers that ground out the rock-basins of such lakes as Llanberis, Coniston, and Ulleswater, and which may, at one time, have cumbered the valleys just below the lakes, have disappeared.

I have shown that in Scotland much of the moraine-matter that occupies the mountain-valleys cannot be referred to the latest local glaciers. The terminal moraines of the last glaciers are restricted to the higher mountain-valleys, and even in many cases to the upper reaches of these; but much farther down the valleys, and at levels on the hill-slopes which the latest local glaciers never attained, great masses of true moraine-matter exist. To what age do these masses belong? Certainly not to the period of the unfossiliferous bottom till or boulder-clay, but, as I have tried to make clear, to the great recession of the ice-sheet that followed upon the deposition of the youngest boulder-clay—to a time when the ice had shrunk back from the sea into the mountain-valleys, where it existed as a series of gigantic local glaciers.

Such are the kind of glaciers which Ramsay describes as having occupied the valleys of Wales † after the great submergence, and glaciers of a like extent are required to explain the phenomena of the low-level morainic gravels of the Lake district, which appear to be direct successors in time of the upper boulder-clay of the districts of Lancashire and North Wales. This, in other words, implies that the ice-sheet crept gradually back from the sea, until, at last, its moraines began to be deposited upon the land. It then broke up into separate glaciers, which filled all the mountain-valleys, and from which, especially in summer-time, great rivers carried

* These erratics have travelled outwards from the mountains in precisely the same directions as that followed by the great glaciers; nevertheless, many geologists consider them to have been carried by ice-rafts and not by glaciers.
† *Quart. Jour. Geol. Soc.*, 1851. See also *The Old Glaciers of Switzerland and North Wales*.

down to the low grounds vast heaps of gravel and sand. Slowly the glaciers retreated until at last they vanished away, leaving behind them little hummocks of moraine matter near the heads of the mountain-valleys to mark the spots where they made their final stand.

In the account given of the Scottish drifts I have pointed out the evidence which has led me to recant the views I formerly held as to the marine origin of certain kames, and to conclude with Mr. Jamieson that there has been no great submergence of the land since the disappearance of the last ice-sheet. As the sand-and-gravel hummocks in and opposite the mouths of the old glacier-valleys of England and Wales come under the same category as the similar mounds of drift in Scotland, I must hold that there is no proof of any great submergence having occurred in England either, at the time referred to. The phenomena receive a much better explanation and we get rid of many difficulties by adopting the view of the morainic and torrential origin of the later drifts as described in Chapters XIX.—XXI.

When we pass to the other side of England, we find, as in the district we have just been considering, several stony clays and intervening beds of sand and gravel. From this circumstance some geologists have surmised that the East Anglian boulder-clays and associated beds are the precise equivalents of those of Lancashire and North Wales. There are certain facts, however, which, as Mr. S. V. Wood, jun., has pointed out, render this extremely improbable, if, indeed, they do not disprove it altogether.

But, before quoting what Mr. Wood has to say upon this interesting subject, I may first give a short outline-sketch of the deposits met with in the eastern part of England, arranging them in their order as ascertained by Mr. Wood and his associates, the Rev. J. L. Rome and Mr. F. W. Harmer.

Along the cliffs of the Norfolk coast at and near Cromer, magnificent sections of drift deposits are exposed. These have been long famous among geologists, and must ever be looked upon with interest, inasmuch as we obtain from them the only reliable evidence as to the kinds of plants and animals that clothed and peopled Britain in the old pre-glacial ages.

The cliffs show the following succession, beginning at the top :—

6. Sand and rolled gravel.
5. Contorted drift, with masses of marl and chalk.
4. Boulder-clay with erratics.
3. Fluvio-marine gravel, sand, and clay, or "laminated series" of Gunn, including seams of so-called "Crag" in places = Bure Valley beds of S.V. Wood, and Westleton shingle of Prestwich.
2. Forest-bed.
1. Sand, gravel and loam (Norwich Crag Series).
   Chalk.

The beds marked 1 contain a mingling of land and fresh-water shells along with many marine species, and bones of extinct mammalia. They thus indicate fluvio-marine conditions, having been laid down at or near the place where a river entered the sea. It is remarkable that, while all the land-and freshwater-shells belong to still living species, 18 out of 124 of the marine mollusca are extinct. Another point of interest consists in the fact that, among the fossils a number of northern forms occur. This Norwich Crag series thus points to the gradual approach of cold conditions, but it is in deposits of still earlier age that we are to look for the first hint of what was afterwards to happen in Britain.

On top of the Norwich Crag series comes what is called the forest-bed. This consists of a mass of vegetable matter, showing stumps of trees standing erect, with their roots penetrating an ancient soil. Associated with this old forest, for such undoubtedly it is, occur the remains of many extinct species of mammalia, commingled with others that are still living, and some of which are even now indigenous to Britain. Of these animals may be mentioned the hippopotamus, three species of elephant, including the mammoth, two species of rhinoceros, bear, horse, Irish deer and several other species of deer, beaver, wolf, &c.

The forest-bed is overlaid with alternations of freshwater and marine deposits, showing that the physical conditions which obtained before the trees began to grow had returned. Great quantities of vegetable débris occur in these beds, indicating the breaking up of the ancient forest-bed ; and it is worthy of note that the climate appears to have been then becoming colder, for Mr. Nathorst, a Swedish geologist, detected in the "laminated series" certain truly arctic plants.*

The accumulation next in order points to a still further increase of cold conditions.

The Cromer till or boulder-clay differs considerably from what is recognised in Scotland as typical till; for not only are its included stones and erratics much less numerous, but the clay itself is not infrequently laminated. It is generally of a dark dingy grey or bluish colour, and is often tough and tenacious, as much so indeed as some of the tough till in the north of England or in Scotland. The stones are scattered somewhat sparingly through the mass as a rule, although now and again they are more abundant, but never, as far as I could see, so closely aggregated as in the ordinary till of Scotland and the north. They are also as a rule small, from stones the size of one's fist down to mere pebbles; but boulders two or three feet and more in diameter are not uncommon, and in some places these and erratics of yet larger dimensions are even plentiful. The most abundant boulders I saw were chalk and flint; but one could note also fragments of Oolitic and Carboniferous rocks, and some of red sandstone. Blocks of blue basalt-rock, very like the igneous masses that intersect the coal-fields in the north, were somewhat common, while amongst the less frequently occurring varieties were pink granite, quartzite, greywacké, and porphyrite, the last mentioned exactly resembling some of the porphyrites of the Cheviot Hills. Many of the blocks are well striated. The stones and boulders are scattered higgledy-piggledy through the clay, and show no traces of any arrangement whatever. Here and there I picked out of the clay bits of broken shells, which occurred in precisely the same way as the fragmentary shells in the boulder-clays of Lewis. Towards the top the clay becomes distinctly bedded, and seems here and there to interosculate with, and to shade up into, the overlying "contorted drift;" at other times, however, the line of separation between the two deposits is sharply defined. Lower down the traces of bedding become indistinct, and the clay appears in some places to be amorphous. Lenticular and irregular patches, and sometimes considerable beds of

* *Antiquity of Man*, p. 261.

sand and gravel, are now and again intercalated in the clay.

The " contorted drift " consists for the most part of a kind of brick-earth, yellowish brown in colour ; but sand is often plentifully present, and now and again the beds are more or less gravelly.   The whole series is laminated and well bedded,

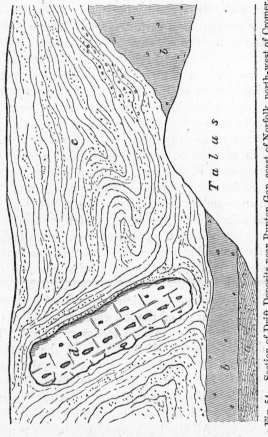

Fig. 54.—Section of Drift Deposits near Runton Gap, coast of Norfolk, north-west of Cromer. *a*, false-bedded fine yellow sand ; *b*, dark, blue silt or clay = so-called " Cromer Till ;" *c*, " contorted drift " of brick-earth, silt, sand, and gravel ; *d*, large erratic of chalk with flint nodules.

save here and there where the brick-earth seems to be amorphous.   The drift displays wonderful contorted bedding, the contortions often affecting the whole thickness of the deposit, and even disturbing the underlying boulder-clay. Stones occur scattered through the brick-earth, and here and there large transported masses of chalk and marl make their appearance. One of these masses, according to Mr. Wood, measured no less than 800 ft. and upwards in length, and 60 ft. in height. West of Runton Gap a number of these huge erratics appear in the sea-cliffs, one of them being shown in the accompanying rough sketch taken in April of the present year (1876). The contorted drift contains marine shells, most of them rolled and worn ; but perfect valves are occasionally met with, Mr. Wood having obtained from the centre of one of the contortions a perfect valve of *Tellina Balthica.**

At the top of the Cromer cliffs appear here and there considerable masses of sand and rolled gravel with marine shells. Mr. Wood has pointed out that these deposits rest upon a highly eroded surface of the contorted drift, an appearance which was very noticeable when I visited the sections.

The facts so briefly indicated above, and which the reader will find much more fully displayed by Mr. Wood and his coadjutors in their numerous papers,† point clearly to the following succession of changes. We have, first, evidence of a preglacial land-surface which supported a vigorous forest-growth and an abundant mammalian fauna. The "laminated series" next affords indisputable proof of a gradual submergence when what had been forest-land became the bed of an estuary. As that submergence increased the climate appears to have become colder, as is shown by the presence of the boulder-clay with its scratched stones. At that time glacier-ice must have occupied the high grounds of Britain, and even covered large areas of the low country, pushing out to sea and covering the bottom with stones and mud. In no other way does it seem possible to account for the appearances presented by the Cromer boulder-clay. Several geologists have expressed their belief that icebergs at this period set sail from Scandinavia and dropt erratics over the sunken area in England. But I could find nothing in the Norfolk cliffs to favour this view. All the boulders of crystalline rocks that came under my notice might quite well have been derived from Scotland and the north. There is no evidence from

* *Geological Magazine,* vol. viii. p. 408.
† See *Geol. Mag.,* vol. v. p. 452; vol. vii. pp. 17, 61; vol. viii. pp. 92, 406 ; vol. ix. pp. 153, 171, 352 ; "Supplement to Crag Mollusca," *Palæontographical Society,* vol. xxv.; *British Association Report,* 1868 ; *Quart. Jour. Geol. Soc.,* vol. xxii. p. 546; vol. xxiii. p. 89; vol. xxiv. p. 146; vol. xxv. p. 446.

which we can infer even approximately the depth of the sea
during the deposition of the Cromer boulder-clay. It seems
to have been laid down at or near the terminal front of some
great ice-sheet deriving from the north—its stratified appearance indicating quiet deposition in comparatively undisturbed water. No very large masses of chalk or marl occur
in the boulder-clay, although towards the top one may note
now and again boulders of chalk of considerable size. The
absence of large angular erratics indicates probably that all
the chalk high grounds of Yorkshire were smothered in ice
during the accumulation of the clay. Their abundant presence, however, in the overlying contorted drift, shows that
the chalk hills were now so far exposed as to allow of the
fall of large masses upon the surface of the melting ice.
The contorted drift itself is proof that the ice-front had
retreated from the Cromer area. It is worth noting that in
Scotland and the North, and, as we shall see presently,
in Norway and Sweden, in Switzerland, and in North America also, we invariably find that the accumulation of stony
clays or tills has been followed by the deposition of great
masses of sand, gravel, shingle, and erratics. In Scotland
we prove that the sand and gravel series is of morainic
and torrential origin and points to the action of excessive
floods ; in that country, however, the last ice-sheet melted
away upon a land-surface. But the contorted drift of Norfolk contains marine shells, and there is every reason to
believe, therefore, that the melting of the first great ice-sheet
in Eastern Anglia took place in the sea. During the period
of intense cold, when the underlying Cromer boulder-clay was
being formed, there would be only a slight melting of the ice
superficially, and comparatively little water would flow out
from underneath its terminal front. But when thaw set in
then the whole surface of the ice would be abundantly washed
by the water set free during the short but exceedingly warm
summers, and the result would be the descent of great torrents
by cleft and chasm to the bottom of the ice, the consequent
denudation of underlying morainic matter, the sweeping out
of much water-worn material and its distribution over the bed
of the sea. From the terminal point of the retreating ice-
sheet large icebergs, freighted with huge masses of chalk and

marl, ever and anon broke away, and, running aground, pushed up, twisted, and contorted the stratified deposits that were gathering upon the sea-bottom.

The beds now referred to form what Mr. Wood terms the "lower glacial series." It will be observed that the contorted drift is covered with sand and gravel. These are part of a great series of sand-and-gravel beds, which Mr. Wood considers to be marine, and designates the "middle glacial." They are clearly of younger age than the deposits just described, as is proved by their position, and also, as it would seem, by their fossil contents. But they are upon the whole unfossiliferous, and in the few cases in which they have yielded marine fossils these are somewhat rolled. Mr. Wood, however, does not believe the shells are derivative, but really pertain to the deposits in which they occur. The shells exhibit a preponderating southern aspect, and a considerably milder condition of climate than obtained during the deposition of the underlying contorted drift.

The same geologist has clearly shown that prior to the accumulation of his "middle glacial" series the "lower glacial" beds were "enormously denuded and swept away, the part remaining being furrowed into valleys, some of them 150 ft. deep."[*]

If we are to place any reliance at all upon the evidence derived from fossils, we must admit that Mr. Wood's "middle" and "lower glacial" series cannot possibly represent the middle sand and gravel and lower boulder-clay of Lancashire, nor can they be the equivalents of any portion of the shell-bearing clays of Scotland. The fossils belonging to the deposits in the north-west of England and in Scotland have a decidedly northern aspect—that is to say, the more characteristic and typical shells belong to species which are even now living in the adjacent seas or in more northern latitudes. On the other hand, the shells of the East Anglian so-called "middle" and "lower glacial" series have, as Mr. Wood has shown, a preponderating southern aspect—the great majority occur in the Crag, or, in other words, were denizens of the seas during preglacial times, and of these a number are either unknown now as living species, or as living nearer than

* *Geol. Mag.*, vol. viii. p. 407.

the Pacific. The results obtained during the late deep-sea dredgings should, of course, make us cautious as to deciding whether a species is extinct or not. It may eventually turn out that many, or even all, the shells obtained from the East Anglian deposits are really living in some hitherto unapproached region of the seas. But even bearing this contingency in mind, it appears to me that we cannot but admit with Mr. Wood, that his lower and middle glacial series are older than any of the shell-bearing deposits belonging to the glacial formation in other parts of Britain.

CHAPTER XXIX.

GLACIAL DEPOSITS OF ENGLAND—*Continued.*

The great chalky boulder-clay of eastern and south-eastern counties.—Mr. S. V. Wood on its origin.—Its formation by land-ice.—Mr. S. B. J. Skertchly on the boulder-clay of midland and eastern counties.—Drift phenomena in the south-west, south, and midland districts.—"Northern drift," its origin.

THE great chalky boulder-clay which covers such extensive areas in Essex, Hertford, Bedford, Cambridge, Suffolk, Norfolk, and Lincoln, has been shown by Mr. Wood * to be of more recent date than his middle glacial series ; and this is a most important point to have ascertained, as we shall see presently. The boulder-clay in question is an unstratified mass of pale dirty grey clay, more or less abundantly crammed with fragments of chalk and flint. Amongst these may often be detected stones which have come from greater distances, such as Oolitic fragments, white sandstone, basalt-rock, quartz, granite, and other crystalline rocks. None of the stones appears to be water-worn, save such as may have been derived from gravelly beds in the Tertiary formations, their general appearance being similar to that of erratics in the till of Scotland and North of England : they are blunted and subangular, often well smoothed, and frequently striated. Now and again lenticular beds and patches of sand and gravel occur in the clay, just as in the Scotch till. Traces of bedding in the

* The great chalky boulder-clay forms Mr. S. V. Wood's "Upper Glacial Series." I think his classification of the drifts of the eastern counties is excellent ; and, after visiting many of the localities described by him, I have been able to confirm, to my own satisfaction, the succession which he and his coadjutors, Messrs. Rome and Harmer, have sought to establish. At the same time, I think their nomenclature is, unfortunately, misleading, since one is apt to suppose that their "Upper Glacial Series" represents the close of the glacial period, whereas it is the product of the most intense glaciation experienced in these islands. There are younger deposits of boulder-clay, as will be pointed out farther on, each of which indicates the presence of an ice-sheet, not so extensive, indeed, as that underneath which the chalky boulder-clay accumulated, but still big enough to cover all Scotland and the north of England.

mass are very rare, according to my colleague Mr. Whitaker, and are chiefly noted towards the bottom of the deposit. This "bedding," such as it is, appears to be defined by mere local changes of colouring. Here and there, however, the clay contains at its base irregular layers of gravel, which sometimes attain a thickness of several feet. In the same position beds of laminated brick-clay also occasionally occur. These and the gravel-beds are usually inferred to belong to the so-called " middle glacial series," which is said therefore to contain here and there one or more intercalated beds of boulder-clay. From what I have seen of these beds myself, however, I cannot agree with this classification. The brick-clays and gravel-and-sand beds evidently form part and parcel of the great chalky boulder-clay, and are quite analogous to the similar beds which are found underlying and intercalated with the Scotch till. So strongly indeed do the laminated brick-clays which are associated with the chalky boulder-clay resemble those which occur now and again in and below the Scotch till, that I fully expect to hear some day that they have yielded both mammalian bones and vegetable remains.* The gravel-beds associated with the base of the boulder-clay do not differ, as I have said, from like deposits that occur as lenticular beds in and under the Scotch till, of which they clearly form a part.

In a number of good sections which I visited under the guidance of my colleagues, who are at present engaged in geologically surveying the East Anglian districts, I noticed that the clay was as hard and compressed as any till I have seen, and here and there it appeared to be squeezed down into underlying strata of chalk and other rocks. It is of very variable thickness, being sometimes only a few feet, and at other times swelling out to a depth of 100 ft. or more. The junction-line between it and the underlying strata is always more or less well defined, but every one who has studied it has been struck with the unevenness of the surface upon which it rests—for while here and there it may repose upon a level platform over a considerable area, it ever and anon

* At one of the pits near Ipswich, where these laminated clays are worked, and which I visited in company with my friend, Mr. Whitaker, we were informed that pieces of wood were found at or near the bottom of the clay—a statement which I hope Mr. Whitaker may be able to verify.

cuts deeply down into the strata underneath. Very frequently it seems to cut out all the earlier drift deposits so as to repose directly upon older Tertiary or Cretaceous deposits. I may add that the deposit has not been traced farther south than the heights overlooking the valley of the Thames.

In the eastern part of Yorkshire, more especially Holderness, and the Vale of York, extensive areas are more or less thickly strewn with boulder-clay. The drift of this district has been described by Professor Phillips,[*] who mentions the occurrence of two boulder-clays separated by an intervening series of sand and gravel, as follows :—

Upper boulder-clay, south of Bridlington . .	{ Brown clays, with fragments. Sands and gravels (irregular). Brown clays, with fragments.
Middle gravels	Gravel, sand, &c.
Lower boulder-clay	{ Blue clay, with chalk and flint, and fragments of distant rocks.
"Bridlington Crag," of undetermined age .	{ A limited sandy mass, unconformed to the boulder-clay above it, and rich in marine shells, mostly of existing species and indicating a cold climate.
Basement bed, or lower gravels . . .	{ Fragments of chalk and flint with boulders of distant origin.

More recently [†] the drifts of this area have been examined in detail by Messrs. S. V. Wood and Rome, and correlated with the glacial deposits of East Anglia, &c. The divisions recognised by them are as follows, the beds being mentioned in descending order :—

  e Hessle boulder-clay.
  d Hessle gravel.
  c Purple clay, including "Bridlington Crag."
  b Gravel, &c.
  a Chalky boulder-clay.

The chalky boulder-clay answers in every respect to the great chalky boulder-clay which has already been described, and there can be no doubt that the one is merely the continuation of the other. Messrs. Wood and Rome describe it as "a lead-coloured clay abounding in chalk-débris, accompanied by stones and boulders from all sorts of rocks." It "rises up in only a few parts of the coast, and is overlapped in every direction by another thick bed of boulder-clay (*c*) to which in most of its exposures it presents a very denuded

---

  [*] *Illustrations of the Geology of Yorkshire,* 1875 [last edit.].
  [†] *Quart. Jour. Geol. Soc.,* vol. xxiv. p. 146.

surface, rising up beneath it in bosses, and in some places divided from it by the beds marked *b*." At Dimlington I noticed that this lead-coloured till was not only very tough and well-charged with stones, most of the harder ones of which showed glacial striæ, but it was also quite unstratified. Here and there, however, there occurred lenticular and irregular layers and patches of shingle, gravel, sand, &c., just as in the typical Scotch till. Now and again I also observed that peculiar "curled arrangement" of the stones in the clay which has been described in connection with the Scotch till, and which points to the *moraine-profonde* origin of the deposit. The same curious relation between the size of the stones, and the coarseness of the striæ imprinted upon them, likewise obtains in the chalky boulder-clay of Holderness.

According to Mr. Wood the great chalky boulder-clay is the product of an ice-sheet—a view which my own observations compel me strongly to support. I differ from Mr. Wood, however, both in regard to the extent of this ice-sheet and to the mode in which its *moraine profonde* was formed and accumulated. He believes the latter to have been extruded upon the sea-bottom by an ice-sheet which broke off in bergs along the southern slope of the Lincolnshire wolds, by which means the subglacial débris of the chalk Wolds was distributed over all the submerged part of England down to the northern brow of the Thames valley. It would lead me into details for which I have no space, were I here to attempt a minute criticism of Mr. Wood's views for the purpose of showing how inadequate they are to explain the phenomena, and I wish as much as possible to avoid a controversial tone. The kind of ice-sheet which he supposes to have existed in the Wolds, and of which he has ventured to give a sectional representation, is, I believe, a physical impossibility. He seems to have been considerably influenced in forming his opinion of the origin of the East Anglian boulder-clay by his inability to conceive of the formation underneath land-ice of a bottom-moraine. And yet all the appearances connected with the chalky boulder-clay conspire to assure us that such was indeed its origin. I could see nothing in it to distinguish it from the till of Scotland, or the tough clay with striated stones which covers such wide areas in the low grounds of

Switzerland. It is just as good and genuine a till as one could hope for : there is nothing whatever about it to indicate former marine action—the intercalated and interrupted beds and patches of sand, gravel, and laminated clay which now and again appear being precisely similar to those that occur in the boulder-clay of the north of England and Scotland : while the distribution and transport of its included fragments clearly indicate that these have been brought by a great stream of land-ice flowing in some determinate direction, and have not been dropped at random over a sea-bottom by the eccentric action of icebergs and ice-floes.

Although the land-ice formation of the chalky boulder-clay thus appears to me to be so very obvious, yet there are some geologists who still maintain that it owes its origin in some mysterious way to the action of icebergs which sailed over a large part of England during a period of depression ; no one, however, as far as I know, has ever entered so far into details as to show in what precise manner the deposit could have been formed by icebergs. My friend and colleague, Mr. S. B. J. Skertchly, who has surveyed wide areas of this drift in the eastern and midland counties, is very decidedly of opinion that icebergs have had nothing whatever to do with it, but that its formation must be ascribed to land-ice. The facts upon which he bases his conclusions are much the same as those which have led Swiss, Scandinavian, and Scottish glacialists to hold the ground-moraine origin of their unstratified clays with striated stones ; but as some of our fellow-hammerers in England are not quite "educated up" to these views of the origin of their chalky boulder-clay, it may be well to allow Mr. Skertchly to state his case here. He has been good enough to supply me with some notes on the drift deposits of the eastern and midland counties which are so interesting in themselves, and so pertinent to the question of the origin of the chalky boulder-clay, that I have much pleasure in making room for them.

Mr. Skertchly says : "The district to which the following notes refer is over 2,000 square miles in extent, and lies within the counties of Lincoln, Rutland, Leicester, Northampton, Huntingdon, Norfolk, and Suffolk. The Fenland itself occupies parts of all the above counties excepting

Rutland and Leicester, and embraces an area of over 1,300 square miles, all of which, with very trifling exceptions, is covered with Post-tertiary deposits.

" The lie of the older rocks must be briefly described before entering upon the questions relating to the newer beds. The strike of the Oolitic rocks is roughly north and south, as is also that of the Cretaceous beds along the south and east of the Fenland ; but upon the north, in Lincolnshire, the strike assumes a westerly trend so as to overlap the Oolitic beds. The two great clays, the Oxford and Kimeridge ** (which throughout this area come together in consequence of the local absence of the Coral Rag), underlie most of the Fenland, the former capping the ground to the west thereof, while the latter takes the ground on the north-west and south-west. The Gault Clay is found beneath the Fens in parts of Cambridgeshire and Norfolk only, and the Chalk underlies very little of the area, but bounds it on the south, east, and north-east.

" Confining our attention for the present to the Chalk, Kimeridge Clay, and Oxford Clay, we find that the boulder-clay lying upon these rocks partakes of their physical character. Thus upon the Chalk the boulder-clay is very chalky, and indeed in some places, as at Mareham-le-Fen in Lincolnshire, and Thetford in Norfolk, it is almost entirely made up of that substance ; at the former place it is quarried and burnt for lime, and at the latter the presence of seams of clay and ice-scratched flints alone enables us to discriminate between it and the Chalk beneath. The Kimeridge Clay is darker than the Oxford Clay, and we accordingly find the boulder-clay which reposes upon the former is darker than that which lies upon the latter. Where boulders are rare it is sometimes very difficult to distinguish the boulder-clay from the older rocks.†

" I have chosen these examples as being most readily observed around the Fens. But similar remarks apply to all other formations upon which I have mapped boulder-clay. For example, the light-blue Upper Lias Clay of Leicestershire impresses its character upon the boulder-clay which overlies

---

* See Table of Formations, Appendix A, for geological position of these and other Oolitic and Cretaceous beds.

† It is difficult to express this forcibly enough in a few notes ; examples and localities could be multiplied *ad infinitum*.

it, and the other members of the Liassic group where they are in force behave in a similar manner. The great Lincolnshire (Inferior) Oolite limestone around Melton Mowbray yields so large a quantity of material to the boulder-clay there that I have been in doubt as to whether the deposit might not be faulted limestone.

" These peculiarities are at once, and correctly, expressed by the statement that the ingredients of the boulder-clay are for the most part supplied by rocks, upon or near which it reposes. That this is actually the case, and not an accident of colour, is further attested by the included fossils ; *Gryphœa dilatata* and *Belemnites Owenii*, for example, are abundant upon the Oxford clay, and *Ostrea deltoidea* upon the Kimeridge Clay. It rests with the upholders of the marine theory of this boulder-clay to explain by what " selective affinity " icebergs shed Oxford Clay detritus chiefly upon Oxford Clay, and so on with other rocks.

"By a happy accident it can, however, be proved that much of the boulder-clay around Brandon has been formed in that immediate vicinity, that it has not moved more than a few miles, and that the material has never been exposed to the free action of the weather. Brandon is the seat of the gun-flint industry, and from neolithic * times flint has been uninterruptedly mined for in the neighbourhood. The beds of flint are five in number, and each possesses peculiarities which render its recognition easy. These layers of flint are quite local, not exceeding in area ten square miles. The flint to be available for gun-flint making must be perfectly sound, and pure in colour. An exposure to the weather for a few months entirely spoils it. Now in the boulder-clay near Brandon, large pieces of each of these kinds of flint are found measuring occasionally as much as a yard over. They are perfectly striated ; but the coats have suffered hardly any diminution of thickness, and the stone is as sound and the colour as good as in that freshly dug from the flint-pits ; indeed they are actually used by the flint-knappers. These flints can only have been derived from the immediate vicinity ; it is clearly impos-

---

* The age during which the ancient inhabitants of Britain used weapons and implements of stone comprises two periods ; viz., the Old Stone or Palæolithic, and the New Stone or Neolithic periods. See Chapter xxxvii.

sible that they should have been dropped by icebergs, for the glacier from which the berg broke away must have occupied the same *dry* ground as the iceberg *floated over* and *melted upon!* and it is equally impossible that the flints should have formed part of a lateral moraine, or they would have become shattered by exposure to the weather.* The only explanation which accounts for their presence and condition is that they formed part of a ground-moraine beneath an ice-sheet.

"While engaged in mapping the Oölitic rocks of North Northamptonshire, Lincolnshire, Rutland, and Leicestershire, we often met with a very puzzling phenomenon which now appears very easy of solution. From the Inferior Oolite to the Cornbrash the beds there consist of intercalated beds of clay

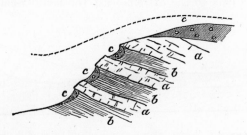

Fig. 55.—Drift sticking to clays. *a, a, a,* limestone; *b, b, b,* clays; *c, c, c,* boulder-clay; *dotted line,* indicates the original contour of boulder-clay.

and limestone averaging say fifteen feet in thickness. The boulder-clay has suffered considerable denudation, and is frequently absent from the narrow outcrops of the limestones but present upon the clays, so that we used jokingly to say "the boulder-drift sticks to the clays." The appearance is represented in the annexed cut. The hard limestones stand out and the soft clays have been worn away. I know of no other power than a grinding and scooping one which could have cut out the Oolite clays and filled the hollows up with boulder-clay. Of course ordinary atmospheric action would wear away the rocks in the same manner, but here everything tends to show that the scooping was contemporaneous with the filling up, and if icebergs or ordinary glaciers had done

* Many of these flints were dug last summer (1875), and the exposure to a single season's frost has rendered them unfit for flint-knapping: how then could they have withstood exposure to the rigours of arctic winters upon the surface of glaciers?

the work they would have left different tool-marks. The original contour of the boulder-clay is shown by the dotted line, and it is only in consequence of the subsequent denudation that the phenomenon in question is revealed.

" There is a remarkable modification of the law, that the physical character of the boulder-clay is dependent upon that of the subjacent rocks—a modification which evidently cannot be explained on the marine theory, nor yet on that of local glaciers. This is the invasion of the outcrop of one rock by the boulder-clay which is composed of some other rock lying to the north-east.[*] This is best observed on the northern border of the Fens, where, in consequence of the overlap of the Cretaceous beds their strike runs in a north-west direction. Upon the Chalk to the extreme east the boulder-clay is very

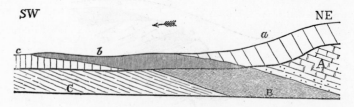

Fig. 56.—Exaggerated diagram-section showing the relation of the boulder-clay to the subjacent rocks in Lincolnshire.

A, Cretaceous ; B, Kimeridge Clay ; C, Oxford Clay ; *a*, very chalky boulder-clay ; *b*, dark blue Kimeridge-like clay ; *c*, light-blue Oxford-like clay.

chalky, and it maintains this character across the narrow Greensand outcrops on to the Kimeridge Clay. We then get a deposit composed chiefly of Kimeridge Clay, and this is continued in like manner on to the outcrop of the Oxford Clay, when the boulder-clay assumes the character of that rock, as shown in the subjoined very exaggerated diagram-section. This peculiar arrangement can only be explained by supposing the ice-sheet to have flowed from the north-east to the south-west, that is to say *inland from the coast.* In this it agrees with the ice-marks along the north-eastern shores of Britain generally.

" I thought at one time that the chalk-surfaces beneath the boulder-clay might yield us ' ice-pavements ' similar to those found in the glaciated Palæozoic regions to the north.

[*] See *ante*, p. 73.

These I have not yet found, for the chalk was too soft to resist the grinding pressure of the ice, and consequently there is generally no sharp line of demarcation between it and the boulder-clay, but the former is broken up and mixed with sand and clay, forming a peculiar material locally known as *dead-lime*, which, I believe, is unknown in the south of England. This dead-lime passes insensibly into solid chalk below, and into boulder-clay or palæolithic gravel (as the case may be) above; thus affording another proof of the local nature of the glacial clay. It is mostly composed of shattered chalk, and averages about three feet in thickness, and the marly cream-coloured portions form irregular-shaped pockets surrounded by the white dead-lime. Flints are abundant in it when the chalk beneath is flint-bearing, but in other cases

Fig. 57.—Relations of the dead-lime, boulder-clay, and edge-ways flints.
a, boulder-clay; *b*, cream-coloured pockets of dead-lime; *c*, white dead-lime; *d*, edge-ways flints; *e*, solid chalk.

they are rare or wanting. It is a significant fact that these flints seldom lie in a natural position, or as they would fall under the influence of gravity alone, but stand on end, or as the workmen say *edge-ways*. The general appearance is shown in the following figure, which forcibly suggests a motion from north-east to south-west. Many sections, however, do not bring this out so clearly, because they are not in the right direction; but, so far as my observations have yet gone, the phenomena are pretty general. The edge-ways flints are quite un-weathered, and are often used by the flint-knappers.

"All of the above peculiarities are explicable solely on the land-ice theory, and are absolutely antagonistic to the marine hypothesis; hence, even if they stood alone they would yet be sufficient to negative the latter. But an equally powerful argument in favour of the land-ice origin of the boulder-clay is furnished by a consideration of the heights to which that deposit extends. Icebergs are merely fragments broken from the terminal fronts of glaciers which protrude into the sea, and the material they transport is part of that which has fallen upon the surface of the parent glacier, or which has become frozen into its base. To produce iceberg boulder-drift two things are essential, namely, gathering-grounds from which the boulders are derived, and sufficient depth of water to float the bergs over the *highest* point upon which their burden is deposited. It follows from this that the material composing such boulder-clay must have been derived from rocks lying *in situ* at a higher level than the boulder-clay attains. Now the boulder-clay under consideration has received the name of the ' great chalky boulder-clay '—*great*, because of its wide-spread extent, which is not less than 3,000 square miles and probably much more, and *chalky* because it is throughout characterized by the presence in greater or less abundance of fragments of chalk. It caps all the high grounds of the eastern and midland counties, attaining an elevation of at least 500 feet above the sea-level, and it is also found (at Boston) 600 feet below that level. Now we may be sure that if it be iceberg-drift, there must exist an extensive gathering-ground of Chalk having an elevation of more than 500 feet. But where is it ? Certainly not in western Europe, for the Chalk does not attain so great an elevation except in a few isolated spots. It is clear that a few scattered islands could never feed the great glaciers whose fragments formed the chalky boulder-clay, and hence we may at once dismiss the marine theory on the ground that the rocks which supplied the material of the boulder-clay would be almost entirely submerged beneath a sea capable of floating icebergs over hills 500 feet above the present sea-level.*

" I think it quite unnecessary to add more facts to prove that only the land-ice theory can account for the phenomena of the boulder-clay of this district, and should not have dealt with them at so great a length had not recent writers taken

---

* The Oxford and Kimeridge Clays, which supply so large a bulk of the boulder-clay, would be *entirely* submerged.

it almost for granted that the marine theory would alone
'hold water.'

"The boulder-clay, however, like its relative the Scottish
till, is not one and undivided, but contains intercalated beds
of sand and stratified clay and loam in places. They are,
however, so precisely similar to the Scotch intercalated beds
that I will only give three sections for comparison.

"The first is at Little Bytham in Lincolnshire, where the
section is as follows :—

	ft.
Boulder-clay, thickness unknown, say	30
Sand and gravel	16
Boulder-clay	33
Sand and gravel	88
Boulder-clay	
	167

"The second section is from a boring at Boston, and is
remarkable for the thickness of the beds and the depth to
which they descend, the top of the section being only 20 ft.
above the sea :—

	ft. in.
Fen-beds	24 0
Boulder-clay	440 0
Sand, gravel, and clay	14 0
Clay	7 0
Coarse gravel	5 6
Boulder-clay	19 6
Coarse gravel	19 0
Clay	7 0
White sand	11 0
Brown loam	6 0
	553 0

"The third section is at Elvedon Gap, near Thetford, in
Norfolk, and is taken in the centre of a basin-shaped depression in the Chalk, which basin the recent beds fill up :—

	ft.
Sand lying unconformably upon, and cutting into, the subjacent bed	3
Boulder-clay	6
Grey clay	4
Blue clay	12
Rock formed of cemented loam	2
Laminated and contorted loam	3
Very fine gravel, stratified and contorted, with seams of loam	4
Loam as above	4
Boulder-clay	2
Gravel	2
Chalk	
	42

" The similarity of these sections to many of those described from Scotland in the earlier part of this work is very striking, and obviates the necessity for further description."

From the fact that the great chalky boulder-clay extends much farther south than any other member of the glacial formation, we may infer that it marks the epoch of greatest cold. The extreme limit reached by the ice-sheet underneath which this ancient till accumulated has been the subject of considerable discussion. We know that it must have reached at least to the edge of what is now the Thames valley, and the probabilities are that it even extended farther. But while in the north we have little difficulty in tracking the course of the great confluent glaciers, we find, as we approach the southern counties, that the marks by which we had learnt to track the spoor of the ice gradually fail us. We have no longer the well-known glaciated outline which is so marked a feature in the north ; undulating hilly tracts there are, but we look in vain for *roches moutonnées* and striated rock faces. Instead of hard sandstones, limestones, gray-wacké, and igneous rocks, we now meet with more or less crumbling calcareous strata, clay-beds, soft sandstones and other incoherent or semi-indurated masses, which if they had ever been glaciated, could not have retained for any lengthened period the outline impressed upon them.

Nevertheless, even in such unlikely districts, evidence of what appears to be old ice-work is not wanting. Thus in the neighbourhood of Bath, Mr. Charles Moore has noticed [*] that the surface of the stiff clays of the Lias shows, whenever the overlying gravel-drift has been removed, " deep and long-continued furrows," such as might have been the result of ice-action. Farther south Mr. W. C. Lucy has noted [†] distinct traces of glaciation in West Somerset, at Minehead and Porlock ; and Mr. C. W. Peach informed Dr. Croll that he had observed a well-striated rock-surface on the Cornwall coast, near Dodman Point. It is remarkable, however, that south of the Thames we meet with no undoubted boulder-clay. We cannot therefore positively assert that the great ice-sheet, underneath which the chalky boulder-clay of York-

[*] *Bath Natural History and Antiquarian Field Club*, 1869.
[†] *Geological Magazine*, vol. i., Decade ii., p. 255.

shire and the eastern counties originated, ever advanced farther south than the valley of the Thames. The evidence, however, leads us to infer that during the climax of glacial cold, a portion of the great ice-sheet that covered Wales and the north streamed south by the valley of the Severn into the Bristol Channel.

More than this : when we track out the spoor of the old ice-sheet by means of the erratics which lie scattered over its former path, we find that these lead us in Northumberland from north-west to south-east, while along the eastern slopes of the Pennine chain the ice-flow is generally from west to east. Coming farther south the erratics lead us towards the south and then south-west into the midland districts, and so on to the Cotteswold country and the Bristol Channel. Evidently the midland counties have been crossed by an ice-sheet that flowed from the north-east, and the explanation of this apparent anomaly is probably that which has been suggested by my colleague Mr. R. L. Jack. He points out that during the climax of the Ice Age, the ice deriving from the south of Scotland and the north of England must have been compelled by the Scandinavian ice-sheet, which filled the bed of the German Ocean, to hug the English coast and eventually to sweep across the whole breadth of the island in a south and south-westerly direction. The ice descending to the east from the Pennine chain was thus forced to turn round as it approached what is now the sea-board and so to flow away to south and south-west. Thus it is that boulders derived from Scotland and the north of England are now found scattered over Yorkshire and the counties to the south. And if, as I believe was the case, the deflection of the Scotch ice took place in the Moray Firth, then the *mer de glace* that overflowed the East Anglian counties may actually have streamed first out of the northern glens of the Grampians. Dr. Croll has even ventured to affirm that the south-east part of England must have been overflowed by the great Scandinavian ice-sheet that crossed Denmark. He believes that the ice was so thick that it must have continued on its course towards the west, filling up the bed of the English Channel so as to become at last confluent with the gelid mass which at the same time occupied the bottom of the Bristol Channel. There is no

direct proof, however, to show that the ground south of the
Thames valley was ever covered with land-ice.   But so great
has been the denudation of the country since the climax of
the Ice Age, that even if the ice-sheet had overflowed the
Downs we could hardly expect to meet now with very strong
marks of its former presence there. · Nevertheless, erratics
and gravel of rocks foreign to the district ought certainly to
have been sprinkled about in sufficient quantity to have at-
tracted the notice of geologists, and that these are not forthcoming is proof presumptive that the ice-sheet terminated
somewhere in the region now watered by the Thames.

The disappearance of this great *mer de glace* was doubtless
accompanied by excessive floods and torrents due to the rapid
melting of the snow and ice and to heavy downfalls of rain in
summer.   We might expect therefore to meet with the
evidence of such floods in the presence of more or less
tumultuous accumulations of gravel, shingle, and boulders.
And such certainly are not wanting.   Buckland, Conybeare,
Sedgwick, Phillips, and the early observers were much struck
with the great quantities of shingle and the numerous erratics
that strew the midland districts, and which occur even farther
south, as in Cornwall and Devon.   And they probably came
very near the true explanation of the facts when they attributed the transport of the materials to the action of great
debacles.   The "drift" in question is certainly not marine,
for it contains no trace of marine organisms, and no one has
succeeded in showing how it could have been formed by the
action of ordinary rivers.   It sweeps up and over considerable
hills, and occurs on the tops of plateaux, and on the dividing
ridges of separate river-basins.   Mr. Lucy has met with
"northern drift" at a height of upwards of 600 feet above
the sea among the Cotteswolds.*   In fact, it is from the very
circumstance that the gravels do occur in such anomalous
positions that they received the name of "hill-gravels" from
Professor Phillips.   Speaking of the drift pebbles in the
Cotteswold country and in the wide depressed and elevated

* See *Proceedings of the Cotteswold Club*, April, 1869; on the same subject, see
also *Quart. Jour. Geol. Soc.* (E. Hull), November, 1855; "Geology of the Country
round Cheltenham," *Mem. Geol. Survey*; *Geology of Oxford and the Valley of the
Thames* (Phillips); *Reliquiæ Diluvianæ*; *Quart. Jour. Geol. Soc.* (T. Belt), vol.
xxxii., p. 80, and the references there given.

regions round Oxford, he says their appearance does not at first view suggest that they have been transported by floating ice. "Their actual distribution is due to watery movement on the surface where they rest. If icebergs brought these materials they seem to have left no definite trace of their passage. Still less do we perceive the marks of glacial friction on the surfaces where the pebbles rest. Yet the sudden changes of level and nature of materials of these deposits in particular limited and especially high situations— red northern drift, flint masses of every shape and various sizes, sometimes with unworn chalk, in separate patches or layers—give occasion for the opinion that something of ice action and currents, less continuous than ordinary streams, and less expanded than lake fluctuations or tidal swellings, must be called in to account for these facts." * All the phenomena referred to here, and the appearances described by other observers of the "northern drift" in central and southern England, receive as it seems to me a simple explanation if we conceive of the gravelly drift having been laid down during the retreat of the great ice-sheet. At that period there must have been in summer-time floods of water escaping from the melting ice which would scatter, more or less confusedly, the morainic materials brought down underneath, embedded in, and resting upon the ice. It is not necessary, however, to suppose that the larger erratics have been carried along by such débâcles into their present positions; they would simply be left lying upon the ground as the ice melted away. Thus after the ice had vacated the country this "northern drift" would be found scattered promiscuously over hill and valley. That the deposit is not now more continuous than we find it arises from the fact that a very great degree of denudation has been experienced since the time of its formation, as every student of glacial geology well knows.†

* *Geol. of Oxf. and Thames Val.*, p. 462.
† Some further remarks on the great chalky boulder-clay will be found towards the close of the next chapter.

CHAPTER XXX.

GLACIAL DEPOSITS OF ENGLAND—*Continued*.

Glacial deposits of Yorkshire, &c.—Stratified deposits between chalky till and overlying boulder-clay.—Purple boulder-clay.—Hessle gravel, &c.—Hessle boulder-clay.—Phillips on age of mammalian remains of Yorkshire.—Age of deposits in Victoria Cave, Settle.—Cause of the different colours, &c., of the Yorkshire boulder-clays.—Contrast between glacial deposits of north and south.—Plateau gravel.—Physical features of North and South contrasted. —Summary.

THE labours of Messrs. Wood and Rome have shown that after the deposition of the chalky boulder-clay in south-east Yorkshire and Lincolnshire, there supervened a period during which considerable denudation took place. Hollows were then scooped out in the chalky boulder-clay, and from certain regions the whole deposit was cleared away, and the underlying solid rocks were scarped and denuded before the accumulations presently to be described were laid down. In the hollows of the chalky till appear now and again beds of gravel and sand and occasionally layers of clay with sandy partings. At Dimlington I observed that these beds attained a considerable thickness, and consisted of a lower series of laminated gutta-percha clays with fine sandy partings, which varied in thickness from a foot or less up to ten feet, and an upper set of fine current-bedded yellow sands, with occasional gravelly layers that ranged from six to fifteen feet in thickness. The series, however, is very inconstant, and is often totally wanting. Professor Hughes obtained sea-shells from the cliff at Dimlington which were probably derived from the horizon of these stratified beds. Sea-shells of a markedly arctic character have also been obtained from a similar position at Bridlington. According to Phillips the latter shell-bed was covered unconformably by the purple boulder-clay, which is precisely the case with the stratified deposits at Dimlington—they rest upon chalky boulder-clay and are covered by purple boulder-clay. It is worthy of note that the so-called "Bridlington Crag" contains some five species of molluscs which are not known as living forms. As a rule, however, the beds between the chalky till and the purple clay are unfossiliferous, and it is by no means improbable that although they occur on the same geological horizon they may yet be neither strictly contemporaneous nor exclusively marine. I believe that much of the denudation that befel the chalky till before the accumulation of the purple boulder-clay took place may have been subaerial. The great ice-sheet that once reached south as far as the valley of the Thames may have vanished in the light of day from the whole sur-face of England, leaving its morainic débris exposed only to the action of the atmospheric forces. No marine deposits with arctic shells either cover it or are associated with it in East Anglia, and until unequivocal evidence of the former presence of the sea is forthcoming it seems more reasonable to hold that the denudation of the chalky till that preceded the deposition of the overlying purple clay was mainly effected by the subaerial forces. The shell-beds at Bridlington and Dimlington occur close to the sea and indicate no great sub-mergence, and I think it will eventually be shown that they are much more closely connected with that period of cold during the climax of which the purple clay was deposited than with the preceding cold era of the chalky till. In short, the beds lying between the two boulder-clays in question indicate a complete break in the succession, and point, as I believe, to an interglacial mild period; a conclusion which will appear not unreasonable after we have concluded our review of all the evidence bearing upon the glacial succession in the north-east of England.

Purple boulder-clay.—This deposit attains a considerable thickness and, according to Messrs. Wood and Rome, covers a wider area in Yorkshire than any of the other superficial deposits. It is believed by these geologists to be of marine origin, partly because it contains beds of sand, gravel, &c., which have yielded sea-shells, and partly from the peculiarity of its distribution. The shell-beds, however, occur apparently at the base of the purple clay, and no more prove that stony clay to be marine than the shell-beds in the Scottish till prove the latter to have been accumulated in the sea. Again, the peculiar distribution of the purple boulder-clay, so far from favouring the marine theory of that clay's origin, seems to me to militate strongly against it. But let me first give a short description of what seem to be the chief characteristics of the purple clay.

In Holderness the purple clay is quite unstratified and generally tough—quite as much so in many places as the chalky boulder-clay. Its prevailing colour is a purplish brown, and hence it well deserves the name applied to it by Messrs. Wood and Rome ; now and again, however, one may notice irregular areas of dark greenish or bluish grey and dull leaden grey clay completely enclosed in the ordinary purple clay and forming part and parcel of the same deposit. The stones are of all sizes from mere grit up to blocks several feet in diameter, and they are scattered in the usual pell-mell manner throughout the deposit, in which they lie at all angles without any reference to their shape. Now and again, however, I noticed that close to the bottom of the clay the stones, which were often large, lay horizontally upon the subjacent chalky till, forming a kind of rude pavement of coarse shingle and boulders. Most of the stones and boulders which were capable of receiving and retaining striæ were more or less well glaciated—and many of the finer-grained rocks, such as limestones, were just as well striated as any specimens to be seen in tills elsewhere. Amongst the rocks represented I noticed the following :—

Chalk, most abundant.
Oolitic limestone, and other rocks.
Dark blue Liassic rock with fossils.[1]
Red sandstones, various shades from pale reddish grey to dark chocolate probably Triassic and Lower Carboniferous.
Magnesian limestone.
White and yellow sandstones, probably Carboniferous.
Carboniferous limestone, pretty common.
Carbonaceous shale.
Basalt-rocks, like that of "whin-sill," and other intrusive masses in the northern coal-fields.
Diorite, perhaps from dyke in Silurian rocks of the north-west.
Porphyrite, various kinds, both fine-grained and coarsely crystalline, and amygdaloidal; all of them may have come from the Cheviots, where rocks of precisely the same character are found.
Greywacké, fine-grained and coarse varieties, all Silurian.
Pebbly conglomerate, like "Haggis-rock" of Scotch Silurians, from which it may have come, by way of the Tyne Valley.
Granite, pink.

Syenite, pink, probably from dyke in Silurian strata.
Pink felstone with blebs of quartz; like intrusive rocks that occur in Silurian strata.
Lydian-stone.
Porcellanite.
Quartz.

The stones are quite of the usual blunted and subangular form, and the larger the stone the coarser are the striæ. Here and there lenticular beds and irregular patches of gravel, &c., occur, and sometimes these look as if they had been rolled over upon themselves. The thickness attained by the clay is very variable—in some places it appears to be 60 feet and more.

It rests either upon the *interglacial beds* already described or upon chalky till, or when this is absent the chalk itself forms its pavement. At Dimlington it forms here and there a very irregular junction with the chalky till which it has caught up in large masses and incorporated. It cuts down into the latter deposit again and again, and the *interglacial beds* are squeezed and confused here and there, and often abruptly truncated. In short, all the appearances which I have referred to so often as characteristic of a true *moraine profonde* may be studied to admiration in the purple boulder-clay of Holderness.

Messrs. Wood and Rome have pointed out that this purple boulder-clay with chalk extends all the way north to Flamborough Head, where it is overlaid by a purple boulder-clay which contains no chalk. In other words, they proved that the chalky purple clay is restricted to the area occupied by Cretaceous rocks and does not extend north of that area, while the chalkless purple clay is chiefly confined to the region that lies to the north of the chalk Wolds of Yorkshire, although it does invade the Wolds to some extent and even appears on the southern slopes of these uplands. All these appearances are readily explicable on the land-ice theory. It is obvious, indeed, that the ice-sheet which formed the purple boulder-clay must have flowed from the north, and this explains why it is that the chalky clay should only occur in the region occupied by the chalk. But as the boulder-clay was always being rolled forward underneath the ice, it is equally evident that boulder-clay resulting from the tritura-

tion of the rocks that lie to the north of the Wolds, and in
which no chalk could occur, would eventually be dragged forward and compelled to overlap upon the chalk.   To account
for the absence of chalk débris in the boulder-clay lying
here and there upon the Wolds Mr. Wood is driven to infer
that none of that chalkless clay was deposited "until, by the
complete submergence of the Wold, all source of chalk débris
had been removed."   He thinks that the chalky part of the
purple clay was laid down at a time when ice covered the
Wold, and that this ice continued to envelop the ground
until the extremity of the submergence succeeded in floating
it off, so that chalkless clay drifting from the north came to
be deposited over that part of the drowned Wold country
which had been formerly occupied by ice.   This view appears
to me beset with difficulties on all sides.   Putting out of
account the impossibility of an ice-sheet (of the kind desiderated by Mr. Wood) continuing to occupy the trivial Wold
heights during any considerable depression of the land, and
banishing from our minds all the evidence which the clays
(as well those with chalk as those without it) furnish as to
their true morainic origin, we may well ask how it came to
pass that with a barrier of ice stretching across the Wolds
there yet happened to be such a plentiful deposition of
northern stones and débris immediately to the south of it.
And if it be replied that these stones and débris were continually travelling from the north underneath the ice and
being extruded upon the sea-bottom at the ice-front, then we
may again ask why chalk débris did not likewise continue to
be extruded upon the Wolds until the ice had entirely melted
back from these heights.   But without entering further into
controversial matter, I merely leave the evidence to speak
for itself.   The view of the land-ice origin of the purple
boulder-clay which I support has at least the merit of sim-
plicity, and it does not necessitate the occurrence of so many
elevations and depressions of the land—oscillations of
level for which no unequivocal evidence has yet been
adduced.   None of the appearances described by Messrs. Wood
and Rome and observed by myself refuse to be explained by
the theory I hold.   The more plentiful occurrence of boulders
in the lower part of the purple clay is by no means peculiar

to that deposit, and it is difficult to see how it can favour any theory of its marine origin. So far as my own observations go I find that boulder-clay is frequently more stony below than above : often, indeed, the bottom portion of a mass might be described as a coarse boulder-agglomerate. But one can understand why large blocks and boulders, and even stones of smaller size, should often tend to gather thickly towards the bottom of a subglacial mass which was kneaded and rolled forward under an ice-sheet.* Nor is the comparative paucity of boulders in some parts of the purple clay without a parallel in other tills, which have without doubt been formed by the grind of land-ice. Those in the north of England and Scotland are sometimes free enough of stones to be worked for brick-making, and the same is now and again the case with the till of other well-glaciated regions.

The most reasonable inference from the phenomena now described and commented upon seems to be that we have in the beds that overlie the great chalky boulder-clay evidence not of a gradually ameliorating climate, but of a succession of climatic changes. The great chalky boulder-clay tells us of an intense arctic climate, during the continuance of which an ice-sheet covered all the British Islands and was continuous with a similar mass, underneath which, as we shall see by-and-by, Scandinavia and a large part of northern Europe lay buried. Then came a time when this mighty ice-sheet melted away and left the ground cumbered with the loose gravel and shingle which the great floods that resulted from its dissolution scattered over the low grounds. To what extent the ice-sheet then retreated we cannot yet tell. We have no evidence to show that it might not have melted entirely away ; all we know is that its bottom-moraine was very highly denuded, and even the solid rocks upon which that moraine reposes suffered likewise very considerable erosion before the next scene in the strange history was acted. It is highly probable that most of this denudation was the work of subaerial forces —of rain, frost, and rivers. But eventually a time came when the sea appears to have occupied a somewhat wider area in Yorkshire than it now does. At that time shells which indicate a very cold climate lived round the Yorkshire coast.

* See *ante,* p. 69.

B B 2

The climate became still more severe, until eventually another
big ice-sheet (that of the purple boulder-clay), extending
from the northern districts, covered all Yorkshire and swept
south into Lincolnshire. Further south than this its moraine
has not been recognized. The next deposits will show us what
happened in Yorkshire after this last-mentioned ice-sheet
melted away.

   Hessle gravel and sand.—According to Messrs. Wood and
Rome the beds so called have "a considerable but not uniform
development under the Hessle boulder-clay"—a deposit which
falls to be described presently. I suspect, however, that the
"Hessle gravel," like the beds which occupy a similar position
between the chalky and the purple tills, have really been
deposited at different times, and under considerably different
conditions. The researches of Mr. Wood and his coadjutors
Messrs. Rome and Harmer have demonstrated that prior to
the deposition of the Hessle gravel all the older drifts had
undergone very extensive erosion. The whole of the region
under review appears to have been worn and furrowed—valleys having been excavated through the drift down into the
underlying Secondary strata—before the Hessle beds began
to be formed. This points to the long-continued action of the
subaerial forces. It is impossible to believe that the great
denudation in question could be due to other than river-
action. Whatever view we take of the mode of origin of the
purple boulder-clay we must admit that after its deposition a
land-surface existed, and that rivers then took their way to
the sea, and hollowed out most of the valleys that still form
the lines along which the drainage of that part of England is
effected.

   The Hessle gravel-beds are seen under boulder-clay at
Hessle Cliff in the chalk-quarry and in the railway cutting ;
they are also well exposed in some gravel-pits near Burstwick : they appear at Paul Cliff on the Humber ; and deposits
occupying the same position occur again and again in the
wonderful section laid bare by the sea along the whole coast
of Holderness. The beds are remarkable for having yielded
at Kelsea Hill and Paul Cliff a littoral marine fauna, comprising amongst other shells the famous *Cyrena fluminalis*—a
shell which we shall afterwards find is associated in certain

old valley-gravels in the south of England with mammalian remains and ancient human implements. Professor Phillips also mentions the occurrence below the boulder-clay at Hessle of remains of horse, mammoth, ox, and deer.* A detailed account of the deposits exposed in the gravel-pits near Burstwick village, on the line of the Hull and Withernsea Railway, has been given by Professor Prestwich,† to which the geological reader may refer for a list of the shells discovered. Amongst these shells "there is not only," as Messrs. Wood and Harmer remark, "an absence of the specially arctic and American forms which characterize the Bridlington beds, but also of those characteristic Crag forms *Tellina obliqua* and *Nucula Cobboldiæ.*" The shells indicate a climate not colder than the present. But the chief point of interest is undoubtedly the occurrence in the beds of *Cyrena fluminalis* and mammalian remains.

Without going farther than the Hessle beds themselves we can infer from them that the ice-sheet, underneath which the purple boulder-clay was formed, had entirely vanished—arctic conditions having given place to a temperate climate when the land supported a varied mammalian fauna. And not only so but we may also conclude that after the disappearance of the ice-sheet in question there must have been a much wider expanse of land than now. This is evident, for the valley of the Humber and many of its tributaries were scooped out of the older drifts before the deposition of the Kelsea Hill beds, and this of course implies that the sea was much farther away from the Yorkshire coast than it is at present. The presence of sea-shells in the beds near Burstwick, however, clearly shows that eventually the sea gained upon the land : and during all the time these changes were taking place the climate appears to have continued mild and temperate.

Hessle boulder-clay.—I come now to describe the youngest, and certainly not the least important, of the Yorkshire boulder-clays. This clay is well exposed at Hessle, and it also appears capping the cliffs along the Holderness coast. But the most interesting sections which I have seen are those exposed in the large ballast-pit at the side of the railway, one mile

* *Geology of Yorkshire*, 3rd edit.   † *Quart. Jour. Geol. Soc.*, vol. xvii. p. 446.

east of Burstwick.   This is the Kelsea Hill section described by Professor Prestwich, and subsequently by Mr. Wood and his coadjutors.   The latter geologists describe the Hessle clay as being a genuine boulder-clay of a foxy red colour, and less tenacious character than the purple boulder-clay.   According to them it varies in thickness " from 10 to 20 ft, and may be said to wrap the whole of Holderness and East Lincolnshire like a cloth, spreading over and enveloping the denuded edges of the basement and purple clays, and beyond them extending some way over the Chalk itself, reaching up the eastern slope of the Wolds to elevations approaching 150 and perhaps even 200 ft. but not now maintaining any constant elevation ; " they have also shown, as I have mentioned above, that the deposit is certainly posterior in date to the valley-system of the region in which it occurs, for it seems to clothe hill and valley alike.   The same observers are likewise of opinion that the Hessle boulder-clay is of marine origin, and has been derived chiefly from the denudation of the purple boulder-clay, at a time when ice formed along the shore and floated out to sea stones and boulders.   The clay, they think, indicates a depression of the land, not exceeding perhaps " 350 or 400 ft. anywhere in Yorkshire, and dying off to nothing in southern Lincolnshire."

I am sorry to appear so antagonistic to the views of geologists, for whose labours I have sincere respect, and whose classification of the drifts of the eastern districts of England must be accepted as indicating the true succession.   But a personal examination of the deposits has left me no alternative but to reject their interpretation as inadequate.   The Hessle boulder-clay yields no proof of a marine origin, but is as much a *moraine profonde* as the purple boulder-clay or even as the great chalky till itself.   This is proved not only by the character of the clay, but also by the mode of its occurrence.

At Hessle Cliff the clay is reddish brown, and very tough, quite as much so indeed as many portions of the purple clay or great chalky till.   The stones which it contains are small as a rule, but I noticed a number exceeding 5 and 6 in. in length, and one boulder measured 1 ft. 8 in. across.   Most of the stones which are of such a kind as to receive and retain striæ are well-striated, and the limestone fragments were quite as distinctly smoothed and scratched as any in the typical tills of more northern districts. They had certainly not been subjected to any rolling and abrasion subsequent to the period of their glaciation—but the striæ were as fresh and sharp as those upon the stones of the Scotch and other well-marked tills. They lay also at all angles in the unstratified clay, and were scattered higgledy-piggledy through that deposit in the usual way. Here and there, moreover, could be seen little patches of gravel and sand in the clay, of precisely the same character as those to which reference has been so frequently made in preceding descriptions of till. At one place in the same quarry I observed boulder-clay resting directly on the chalk without the intervention of any "Hessle gravel," and the appearances there were highly suggestive. The colour of the clay was duller and more of a dirty brown colour, owing to the greater quantity of chalky stuff diffused through it. The chalk below was much shattered and rose up as it were in irregular broken hummocks into the clay, the lower portion of which was crammed with angular blocks and débris of the rock. These were so closely set that in some places they formed quite a breccia, and one could even push one's hand into the interstices between the blocks—appearances which are closely paralleled by the coarse débris and breccia of angular blocks which now and again occur underneath the till in Scotland, especially when the pavement-rock is a much-jointed sandstone. The upper part of this clay had been removed by the quarrymen, and I cannot positively assert therefore that it may not be some fragmentary portion of either the purple boulder-clay or the chalky till. But as neither of these deposits appears in any other part of the large openings at Hessle, I think it is more likely to be a bottom portion of the Hessle boulder-clay itself : on this, however, I lay no stress.

In the sea-cliffs along the coast the clay is well-developed, in some places attaining a thickness of 20 and even of 30 ft. Beds of gravel and sand of very variable character, and not reaching a thickness of more than a few feet, often separated it from the underlying purple clay, but not infrequently these were wanting, and the red Hessle clay then rested directly on the latter—the junction-line being often irregular. The stones were as usual small, but fragments several inches in diameter were common, and occasional boulders, 18 in. and 2 ft. across, now and again occurred. Sometimes the stones are so sparsely present that the clay is worked for brick-making, just as is the case with the upper boulder-clay of Lancashire, &c. There is no trace of bedding in the deposit, and nothing whatever appears from which one could infer its marine origin. Stony clays which have been deposited in water invariably present more or less well-marked stratification—the beds being often beautifully laminated. Numerous examples of such stratified stony clays occur in the glacial series (arctic shell-beds) of Scotland, and the Cromer clay exhibits similar appearances. One looks in vain, however,

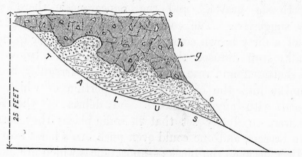

Fig. 58.—Section in ballast pit, Kelsea Hill ; June, 1876.
s, surface soil ; h, Hessle boulder-clay ; c, sand and gravel, with *Cyrena fluminalis*, &c. ; g, commingling of beds h and c.

in the Hessle boulder-clay for any such signs of aqueous deposition. Although not so well charged with stones as the two older boulder-clays of Yorkshire, it is nevertheless just as tumultuous a mass as either the purple clay or the great chalky till.

So far, then, as an inspection of the Hessle clay goes, there are strong grounds for believing that clay to be the direct pro-duct of land-ice. This conclusion, moreover, is forced upon us when we examine more attentively the junction between the clay and the underlying Hessle gravel-beds. This is nowhere better seen than in the ballast-pit at Kelsea Hill. Here the unstratified red boulder-clay is seen resting upon deposits of gravel and sand which are full of current-bedding. When

Mr. Prestwich visited the section in 1861 this superposition of the clay does not appear to have been visible, but in 1867 Mr. Searles Wood found that the continued excavation of the "ballast" had laid bare a most instructive section which showed the boulder-clay resting upon the stratified deposits along nearly the whole face of the wide cutting. This summer (1876) when I examined the section I saw that it had evidently been materially altered from the time when it was visited by Mr. Wood. All round the pit the clay occupied the top of the cutting, but it formed now and again a very irregular junction with the underlying deposits. In Fig. 58 the clay is shown at *h*, where it attained a thickness of 15 ft. or thereabout. It was of the usual character. It will be seen that the junction between it and the underlying beds, *c*, is most irregular. At *g* the clay was confusedly mixed with the gravel. Near the junction there was no trace of bedding in the gravel, but gradually, as one receded from the clay, bedding became distinct—the deposit being thickly charged with the old river shell, *Cyrena fluminalis*, and other species.

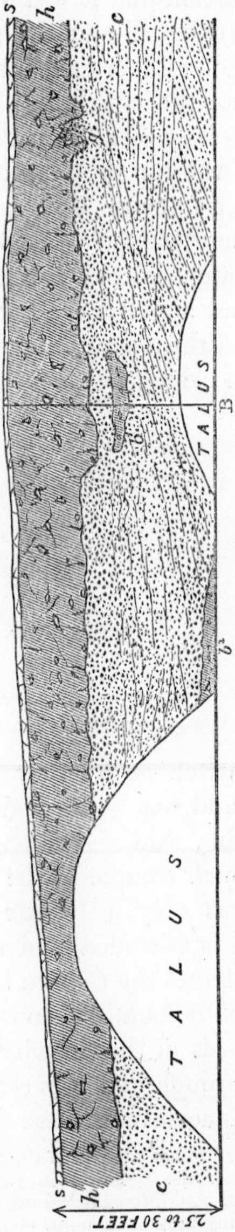

But still more remarkable phenomena appeared on the southwest side of the pit where the men are at present working. At that place the annexed section was very clearly exposed,

Fig. 59.—Section in pit at Kelsea Hill; June, 1876.

s, surface soil; *h*, Hessle boulder-clay; *c*, *Cyrena* beds; *b¹*, intruded mass of Hessle boulder-clay; *g*, commingling of beds *h* and *c*; *b²*, boulder-clay, probably connected with *h*; *A—B*, line of diagram-section in Fig. 60.

(Fig. 59). As before, h represents the boulder-clay and c the gravel and sand beds which are locally full of shells. The junction-line it will be observed is irregular, and at one place (g) the till and the gravel become commingled. At b^1 an irregular layer of boulder-clay of precisely the same character as the overlying Hessle clay makes its appearance, which I at once saw must be connected in some way with the mass at the top of the section. The gravel between the bed b^1 and the main bed h was much confused, and in fact hardly any trace of stratification was visible. All round the lower patch, indeed, the gravel was amorphous. From these and other appearances I inferred that the two beds were connected in the manner shown in the annexed diagram. (Fig. 60.)

Upon asking the men how they explained the occurrence

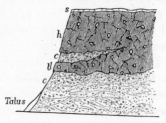

Fig. 60.—Diagram section across the cutting at *A—B.* as shown in Fig. 59.
h, Hessle boulder-clay; c, *Cyrena* beds; b^1, intruded tongue of h.

of the patch at b^1, they informed me that it was only a "leg" and was connected with the stuff at the top—from which they said several such "legs" had come and had given them much trouble in the working. The patch in question, then, was only a tongue of boulder-clay which had been injected or intruded under the pressure of a superincumbent ice-sheet into the *Cyrena* beds below. Similar appearances are occasionally found in connection with the intercalated and subjacent beds of the Scotch till—tongues of till being squeezed down through and between the yielding deposits over which the subglacial mass was rolled and pressed.[*] At b^2 (Fig. 59),

[*] In my brother's paper on the " Phenomena of the Glacial Drift of Scotland " (*Trans. Geol. Soc. Glasg.*, vol. i., part 2) will be found a section of contorted beds of sand and clay (Medwin Water) which shows a similar intercalated bed of till. This bed, my brother thought, might have been floated as a boulder, and dropt into its present position. I believe, however, that it has been injected under pressure in the manner described by the same author in his account of the till and stratified beds at Chapelhall, near Airdrie.

another apparently separate mass of boulder-clay is seen, which at first I thought must be a different bed altogether from that at the top. It was harder and tougher than the clay at *h*, and also of a darker and duller hue, being more of a greyish brown than a red. It closely resembled that part of the clay at Hessle Cliff, which rested immediately upon the chalk. I was told, however, that it also was connected with the mass at the top. Unfortunately the pit face where this junction was said to have been visible was quite covered up, —the portion concealed by the talus being relatively wider than I have shown it in the sketch-section. The men assured me that at that place there was no "ballast" at all, but the clay occupied the whole face of the cutting from top to bottom. I was further informed that "large bones and horns" had been got at various times from the gravel, but they could not tell me what had become of them now ; most of them it seems were purchased by gentlemen who had occasionally visited the pit.*

Now these sections seem to me to prove that the Hessle boulder-clay is beyond doubt a true *moraine profonde*. And this being so, a most important point in the history of the glacial epoch is established by direct proof—this, namely, that the *Cyrena fluminalis* which occurs in valley-gravels in the south of England, associated with human implements and mammalian remains, and the presence of which has been usually looked upon as a proof of the postglacial age of the deposits in which it appears, did really live during interglacial times.

We have now learned, then, that after the mild conditions of climate, which followed upon the disappearance of the purple-clay ice-sheet, had passed away, there supervened once more an intense arctic climate. An ice-sheet again enveloped the north and crept south over Yorkshire down into Lincoln-shire ; but all trace of its southerly termination, like that of the purple-clay ice-sheet, is now lost under the wide post-glacial flats of that county. It is unlikely, however, that

---

* Should this chance to meet the eye of the enthusiastic gentleman who him-self superintended the extraction of a bone, or horn, from the gravel under the clay, I hope he will be induced to send some account of his discovery to the editor of the *Geological Magazine*. It will be a pity if this and other "finds" at Kelsea Hill are not chronicled, because, as we shall see presently, a great deal rests upon their evidence.

this last ice-sheet reached so far south as that underneath which the purple clay was formed.

Professor Phillips was of opinion that the mammalian relics found at Hessle under the boulder-clay, as well as those got in the famous Kirkdale Cave, are all of preglacial age. He distinguished three periods, each marked by characteristic features :—

1st. Preglacial land, occupied by lion, hyæna, mammoth, rhinoceros, &c.

2nd. A period during which glacial waters were rising and falling. The deposits of clay, gravel, &c., of this period enclose remains of animals of the first period, which are often worn.

3rd. Postglacial land. No great Carnivora, no great Pachydermata living, the terrestrial surface abounding in cervine and bovine quadrupeds.*

There can be no doubt, however, that the Hessle gravel with its mammalian remains is not only not preglacial, but was laid down during mild conditions of climate long after the intensest cold of the Ice Age had passed away. Phillips, however, was not far from the true explanation. He saw clearly that the mammalian remains of undoubted postglacial age—those, namely, that occur in lacustrine and fluviatile deposits which are clearly subsequent in date to all the boulder-clays and glacial drifts, present a complete contrast to the fauna of Kirkdale Cave, and the animals whose relics are found underneath or intimately associated with the drift gravels and stony clays. This remarkable conclusion deserves particular note, for it is quite in accordance with all that we know of the glacial and postglacial deposits of Wales, the north part of England generally, and Scotland. In all those regions the freshwater postglacial deposits have yielded only cervine, bovine, and other quadrupeds, most of which are still indigenous to these islands, while the great carnivores and pachyderms are conspicuous by their absence. The Hessle gravel, with its mammalian and molluscan remains, is clearly of interglacial age, and since the overlying boulder-clay is the most recent deposit of that kind in the north-east of England, we must conclude that the mammoth and its

* *Geology of Yorkshire* (1875), p. 170.

congeners, whose relics occur in the Hessle beds, lived in that part of England during the last interglacial period.

Professor Phillips's views as to the preglacial age of the old mammalia of Yorkshire have recently received strong support from the discoveries made in Victoria Cave, near Settle, as reported on by my friend and colleague Mr. Tiddeman.* In this cave occur the bones of the old mammalia, comprising elephant (*E. antiquus and primigenius*), hippopotamus, rhinoceros (*R. hemitœchus* and *tichorhinus*), bear (*U. spelœus* and *ferox*), bison, *Cervus elaphus*, &c., and associated with these have also been found a human bone—"a fibula of unusually clumsy build, and in that respect not unlike the same bone in the Mentone skeleton." Resting upon the deposit in which these relics lie entombed are laminated clays, and clay containing scratched stones—accumulations of undoubted glacial origin. Mr. Tiddeman concludes that the ossiferous bed is of preglacial age, and that the absence of the old extinct mammalia from the valley-gravels of the neighbourhood is due to the grinding action of the old ice-sheet which once enveloped the country, and scoured out all the loose superficial accumulations that lay in its path.

I quite agree with Mr. Tiddeman that the notable absence of the old mammalia is to be accounted for by glacial erosion —indeed I advanced that view very strongly a number of years ago—but, as I shall point out more fully in the sequel, the evidence does not entitle us to hold that the deposits of the Victoria Cave are necessarily of preglacial age. I hardly think we can put them farther back than the early stages of the last interglacial period—in short it seems most reasonable to include them with the mammalian remains of the Hessle gravel beds.

I have extended these remarks on the drifts of Yorkshire to a greater length than I at first intended, but the novelty of some of the facts must be my excuse for this prolixity. Before I pass on to another subject, however, there are one or two remarks that I wish to make in regard to the conditions under which the three stony clays of Yorkshire were respectively accumulated.

* "Report of the Victoria Cave Exploration Committee," *Brit. Assoc. Rep.*, 1873-74-75; *Geological Magazine*, vol. x. p. 11; *Nature*, vol. ix. p. 14.

The oldest till (great chalky boulder-clay) of that county evidently owes its origin to an ice-sheet that exerted more grinding force than the smaller sheets that succeeded in later cold eras. During the climax of glacial cold, when the Scandinavian ice-sheet strongly opposed the passage of the British ice out to sea, the ice that overflowed the Yorkshire Wolds and the country to the south, streamed inland towards the south-west, and as it went on its way its *moraine profonde* naturally became chalkier, seeing that its path lay for so many miles over the area occupied by Cretaceous strata. In Holderness, although it contains upon the whole more chalk than the overlying purple clay, yet the quantity of that material is not so great as to entitle the deposit to be called a "chalky boulder-clay." Moreover, fragments of northern rocks in the clay are much more numerous in Holderness than in the regions farther south.

The purple boulder-clay is the product of a smaller ice sheet, and its colour I think is due primarily to this fact. When the ice which formed it flowed towards the south the great Scandinavian ice-sheet still opposed itself to the free passage of the British glaciers, but as these latter were now of less consequence than during the climax of glacial cold, it is reasonable to infer that the Scandinavian ice-sheet also had in like manner lost much of its importance, and was therefore unable to exert the same degree of pressure upon the ice-sheet that covered the northern parts of Britain. The latter would consequently be able to flow out farther than before towards what is now the bed of the German Ocean, and hence the débris of the New Red Sandstone strata of the valley of the Tees and the Vale of York would be pushed farther eastward, and so give a colour to the *moraine profonde* that was forming over the Wolds.

In like manner during the accumulation of the Hessle boulder-clay, which took place under a yet smaller ice-sheet, not only would the débris of the soft red Triassic rocks continue to give a tone to the subglacial moraine stuff then forming, but the purple boulder-clay itself would here and there be highly denuded and its materials re-arranged and incorporated in the newer formation.

There are many other interesting topics which are suggested by the appearances presented by these boulder-clays of Yorkshire. I would specially point to the fact that as we trace the deposits northwards, the triple series, with its intercalated and separating accumulations of gravel, sand, &c., becomes less well marked, until when we get well into Northumberland and Scotland we find only one marked deposit of till, with here and there underlying shingle and gravel, and only now and then some fragmentary portions of earlier boulder-clay making their appearance below the latest accumulations of that kind. In Holderness, as we have seen, the great chalky till is much denuded under the purple clay, and eventually disappears altogether, the latter forming then the basement deposit. North of Flamborough Head,—at Speeton, Filey, Scarborough, and Whitby—the boulder-clay everywhere, according to Phillips, occurs in two layers, separated by gravels and sands or sands only,* and these two boulder-clays, we can hardly doubt, are the representatives of the purple boulder-clay and Hessle clay of Holderness. I have not traced the beds, however, into the district described by Phillips, and cannot therefore be certain that this is the case. I believe, however, that the Hessle boulder-clay is represented by the reddish clay with stones that occurs in the valley of the Tees near Croft. From this point as we trace it north it gradually loses its reddish colour, becoming grey, and tougher, and more thickly charged with stones and boulders, until we approach the region occupied by the Carboniferous strata, when it begins to assume a dull leaden grey or blue hue, and to pass erelong into one of the most strongly pronounced kinds of till that we find in Britain, as in the immediate vicinity of Durham. In this region there seems to be only one boulder-clay, although if the district were closely searched I have no doubt that traces of an older till would be met with.

Now these appearances admit of a simple explanation. It will be noticed that the glacial series is most complete in the districts that are farthest removed from the great centres of glaciation. The ice-sheet underneath which the great chalky boulder-clay accumulated seems gradually to have lost much of its erosive power as it crept south towards the valley of

* *Quart. Jour. Geol. Soc.*, vol. xxiv. p. 254; *Geology of Yorkshire.*

the Thames. Thus we find that in Yorkshire the chalky till
rests directly upon the Chalk ; but as we trace it southwards,
certain underlying beds of sand and gravel begin to appear.
These, however, are not continuous, being ever and anon
abruptly cut out by the clay. But as the southern districts
of East Anglia are approached, the beds in question assume
a greater development, and the chalky till rests upon them
continuously over considerable areas—the junction-line
between the two being often wonderfully even. Similar
appearances characterize the purple boulder-clay. The ice-
sheet, underneath which that clay was formed, dug out and
incorporated with its own subglacial débris the ground-
moraine of the preceding cold period. And the destruction
of the latter was most complete in the north, where the ice
was thickest and moving faster than in the region farther
south. As the ice-sheet of the purple clay approached its
termination, it was not only thinner but it also moved more
slowly, and hence its erosive power was not so great. So
in like manner when that ice-sheet had melted away, and when
the last warm interglacial period had also come and gone, and
the final ice-sheet descended from the north, the same more
or less complete destruction befel the purple boulder-clay (or
its representative) and the interglacial deposits in those districts which lay farthest to the north. As this last ice-sheet
crept south it likewise lost in erosive power, and was often
unable to do more than roll its subglacial moraine over the
surface of the older drifts. When we come to describe the
American glacial deposits we shall meet with similar remarkable phenomena, and find that towards the termination
reached by the latest ice-sheet of that region, the ice seems
also to have over-ridden the older drifts without entirely
destroying or re-arranging them.

Plateau gravel.—Under this term Mr. Wood has described
certain unfossiliferous gravels which cap some of the high
grounds, and have an extensive spread in West Norfolk.
They are composed chiefly of rolled flints, and appear to be
younger than the great chalky boulder-clay. Similar thick
beds of gravel occur on the chalk Wolds of Yorkshire, and
seem to bear a like relation to the purple boulder-clay of that
region. Is it not highly probable that these are related to

the clays in the same way that the drift gravels of Scotland are related to the till—that they were formed during the dissolution of the ice-sheets ? I have not seen the gravel-beds on the Wolds of Yorkshire, but as we follow the glacial deposits north of the Tees, we meet now and again with heaps and spreads of sand and gravel, resting either on rock or till, which are certainly the counterparts of the Scotch gravel-and-sand or kame series. It appears most probable that the coarse gravels that cover much of the low grounds in Yorkshire, and some of which even reach to considerable heights, were laid down during the retreat of the last ice-sheet. When that latest sheet was melting away, it is evident that the Vale of York would be abundantly swept by heavy floods, and this will go a long way to account for the fact, upon which Messrs. Wood and Rome insist so much, that the country on the west side of the Wold has been stript of its glacial deposits. From the nature of the ground, however, it is evident that the deposition of glacial drift on the western slopes of the Wold could never have been so great as that which took place on the lee-side. Till would accumulate to the south of the chalk escarpment, while little or none would be permitted to gather on the *stosseite* which was exposed to the full force of the ice flowing from the north and north-west.

Before concluding what I have to say about the glaciation of England, there is one important point to which I would direct the special attention of geologists. According to my view of the origin of the English drifts, it ought to follow that the district lying to the north of a line drawn roughly from Chester to the Humber, should exhibit much stronger marks of glaciation than are to be met with in the midland and southern districts. Indeed so very long a time has elapsed since the disappearance of the great ice-sheet underneath which the chalky boulder-clay was formed—so many climatic changes have supervened since then, during which the northern area was more than once subjected to severe glaciation, while the central and southern districts experienced only subaerial denudation—that we should hardly expect to find in the latter districts either glacial striæ or *roches mou-tonnées*. And this is, to a very large extent indeed, quite

true. In the region referred to crags and escarpments are
the rule, wherever the rocks are of such a nature and
structure as to admit of their formation ; in short, the marks
left by the old ice-sheet, have been almost entirely obliterated,
and the country has resumed what I may call its natural
features—that surface-configuration, namely, which is determined by the varying character of the strata as they " weather" and moulder away under the touch of the atmospheric
agents. But no sooner do we enter upon the region to the
north than all at once the long well-marked escarpments
either disappear or are very feebly represented, while the
flowing outline so characteristic of a country over which land-
ice has recently prevailed becomes strongly marked.

This contrast between the surface features of the midland
districts and those of the northern counties has not escaped
the notice of my friend, Professor A. H. Green; indeed it was
he who some years ago first drew my attention to it; and
since then I have had several good opportunities of studying
the appearances referred to. Mr. Green wrote to me in 1873
as follows :—" I have been much struck since I have been
working on the Lower Carboniferous rocks of this neighbourhood [Cockermouth], by the miserable character of their
escarpments as compared with those of the corresponding
rocks in the centre of England. In Derbyshire, North Stafford-
shire, South Lancashire, and South Yorkshire, the escarpments are magnificent,—great craggy precipices of rock, up
to 50 ft. in height, running in unbroken walls for miles, so
that you could map the whole country by their aid alone,
without seeing a single section. As you come northwards
the escarpments grow more fragmentary, till here there is
scarcely anything deserving the name of an escarpment to be
seen,—none at all on the low ground, and in exposed situations only a few fitful and mostly feeble features. I have
been quite staggered sometimes to find the junction of a sandstone or limestone bed with underlying shales take place
without any change whatever in the slope of the ground. I take
the meaning of this to be that here the escarpments, which must
once have existed, have been planed clean away by the ice-
sheet, and that it is only in the higher grounds, where subaerial denudation acts more energetically, that they are begin-

ning to be formed afresh. But I cannot understand how it comes to pass, if the centre of England had been smoothed down in the same way, that there has been time in that region for the subsequent formation of escarpments so much larger than those hereabouts—more especially as the rainfall is certainly greater here than farther south. *Ergo* I more than ever suspect that the ice-sheet never spread much farther south than Leeds and Liverpool." The true explanation of the contrast in question, however, is I believe that which I have already given—namely that the northern districts have been not only more frequently, but also more recently subjected to glacial erosion than the midland counties.

In bringing this short discussion of the English drift deposits to a close, I may briefly sum up what I take to be the general succession of events, so far as this is illustrated by the glacial accumulations. In the sequel we shall see that the history of these drifts necessarily involves that of certain ancient freshwater gravels in the midland and southern counties, which have yielded remains of extinct mammalia and relics of man ; but for the present these freshwater gravels must be left entirely out of account.

1. *The Forest Bed of Cromer Cliffs.*—This appears to be the only undoubted relic of the old preglacial land-surface which has been preserved. Its organic remains indicate a climate somewhat like that of the present, and allow us to speculate upon the geographical condition of our island in preglacial times. The general character of the flora and fauna put it beyond doubt that a land-passage must have existed between Britain and the continent in preglacial ages, so as to allow of the immigration of the plants and animals whose remains occur under the glacial deposits of the Norfolk coast. The purely geological evidence points in the same direction. In Chapter XII. I have given some account of certain old preglacial water-courses which occur in Scotland, buried under considerable accumulations of drift materials. These channels evidently owe their origin to the action of rivers, which scooped them out at a time when the land stood, relatively to the sea, not much less than 300 ft. above its present level. Similar buried river-channels are known to occur in England ; thus it has been ascertained by numerous

borings and excavations, connected with the docks at Hull and Grimsby, that the preglacial bed of the Humber lies buried under upwards of 100 ft. of drift accumulations. So also the preglacial bed of the Yare at Yarmouth is actually more than 100 ft. below the present sea-level. The ancient river-course, known to the miners of the Durham coal-field as the "Wash," has been traced underground for a distance of fourteen miles, from Durham to Newcastle, and its bed, where it enters the Tyne, is not less than 140 ft. below the sea-level. Indeed it must appear evident on reflection that all our rivers which enter the sea over a bottom of thick mud, silt, and sand, must at one time have flowed at a much lower level—in other words it is clear that since the preglacial era there has been a very considerable loss of land. The time was when our rivers excavated their channels in older Tertiary, Secondary, and Palæozoic strata. After that came the glacial period, when the old channels became choked up with drift, which at the lower levels of the land has not yet been cleared out, even in cases where the postglacial river-courses follow precisely in the track of the preglacial channels—the latter being buried of course at a considerable depth under the former. In the low-lying districts of Britain we may feel sure that when a river flows over a rocky bed, the latter cannot be of preglacial age, but has been hollowed out for the most part in postglacial times.

The phenomena of such ancient river-courses clearly indicate therefore that the land now stands not less than about 300 ft. below its preglacial level. The actual loss, however, is probably a good deal more than that. In my description of the Scottish sea-lochs, it was incidentally stated that these occupy submerged land-valleys. This must be apparent to any one who has paid even the slightest attention to the physical contour of the country. Rivers have flowed down these old drowned valleys in days long anterior to the glacial period. Indeed we know that some of them date back to an age as remote as that of the Old Red Sandstone. Some geologists hold that the fiord-valleys have actually been excavated by glaciers—but if so, such glaciers cannot possibly have belonged to the Ice Age of which these pages treat. I think it is highly probable that glaciers may have aided in the erosion of the Highland glens and fiords at many different epochs in the past—but you must first have valleys before you can have valley-eroding glaciers. Streams and rivers, therefore, aided by frost, must have initiated the scooping out of the mountain-valleys; and we have every reason to believe that all the fiord-valleys and glens of the Highlands had assumed very much their present appearance before the advent of the Ice Age. The erosion they experienced during that age, although *absolutely* great, was yet *relatively* inconsiderable.

Now there are certain considerations which lead to the belief that in preglacial times the Highland fiords may have existed as dry valleys. In Lewis, as we have seen, there are two kinds of till or boulder-clay—one in which broken shells occur, and another which not only contains no shells, but is harder, sandier, and much less argillaceous. We may also remark that no broken shells have yet been detected in any portion of the ancient bottom till of Scotland. I have already given my reason for holding that most of the till or boulder-clay that now occupies the actual surface in Scotland belongs to the last cold period of the Ice Age; and the advent of the final ice-sheet was preceded, as we have seen, by a considerable submergence of the land, during which species of arctic and northern shells lived in the Scottish seas. We have further learned that the marine deposits containing these shells were ploughed into by the latest ice-sheet, and confusedly intermingled with its ground-moraine. Reflecting upon these facts one cannot help surmising that the reason why no broken shells occur in the bottom till of Lewis may be owing to the circumstance that in those early days the area occupied by the Minch was in the condition of dry land, so that when the ice streamed out of the mountain districts of Ross-shire, there were neither marine glacial mud nor sea-shells for it to incorporate with its moraine. Of course I do not wish to lay too much stress upon this inference, but I suggest it in order that geologists may consider whether it may not throw some light on the conditions that obtained in Britain in preglacial and interglacial ages. It is worth noting in this connection that the great chalky boulder-clay has only at rarest intervals yielded shell-fragments, although the ice-sheet which formed it must have flowed partly over the bed of the North Sea. Yet the more recent boulder-clay which covers broad areas in Northumberland and Durham contains broken shells, pretty widely disseminated through its mass in some places. Can it be possible that when the great ice-sheet, to which the chalky boulder-clay is due, crept into England, the British Islands formed part of a great continent, and that this is the reason why the chalky boulder-clay contains no fragmentary marine organisms, save such as may have been derived from some of the older drift deposits? However that may be, we know that the latest ice-sheet which overflowed Scotland, did enter the sea and mix up marine deposits with its moraine. Thus it was that the silt and shells lying on the bed of the Minch were pushed up and over the north end of Lewis; and so also was it that Caithness received the spoils of the Moray Firth. Now if in preglacial or early glacial times the Minch had any existence, it does seem curious that we should not find some evidence of this in the bottom till of Lewis—for the ice which laid it down certainly overflowed the island from the south-east.[*]

Upon the whole, therefore, while we are quite sure that in preglacial ages, Britain stood higher relatively to the sea than at present, we yet cannot assert that this elevation was more than would suffice to join our islands to the continent. But so far as the evidence goes, it does seem most likely that what are now inland seas existed in preglacial times as dry land. In place of fiords the west of Scotland probably showed wild mountain-valleys, that opened out upon an undulating table-land above which rose the rugged heights of Harris and Lewis. At this time also it is highly probable that no German Ocean existed, and the English channel may also have been in the condition of dry land. We have therefore a picture of old preglacial Britain forming part of the European continent, and supporting a vegetation similar to that which

---

[*] This evidence, of course, is only negative, and it might easily be pointed out that while there is proof to show that immediately before the appearance of the last ice-sheet, Scotland was submerged to a depth of more than 500 feet, yet the upper boulder-clay of that country rarely contains broken shells, save in maritime districts. Why, we may ask, does not the upper boulder-clay of the central lowlands (a great proportion of which must have been submerged before the last ice-sheet overflowed Scotland) contain broken shells, and afford other indications of the latest confluent glaciers having usurped the bed of the sea? That is a very hard question to answer, and I fear we must wait some time yet for an adequate solution of the difficulty.

still characterizes our land and the corresponding latitudes of Europe. At that distant date our mammalian fauna included many species which are now extinct—among these were three of elephant, two of rhinoceros, the hippopotamus, two species of bear, a tiger, (*Machairodus latidens*) the urus, the great Irish deer, and a number of other forms of deer. Associated with these animals were not a few species which still survive, although some are now locally extinct, such as the wolf and the beaver, while others are yet indigenous, such as fox, roe deer, red deer, common mole, common shrew, and water-rat. Our shores were then visited by the narwhal, the walrus, and the whale.

2. *Fluvio-marine Series.*—The arctic plants found in these beds afford evidence of the incoming of cold climatic conditions. It is clear also that the sea was gaining upon the land.

3. *Cromer Clay* points to the near vicinity of a great ice-sheet which deployed upon the bed of the sea, and extruded there its morainic mud and stones.

4. *Contorted Drift* indicates a recession of the ice-sheet, and the presence of a sea in which icebergs floated and grounded.

5. *Sand and Rolled Gravel.*—As these deposits rest often in hollows eroded in the till and underlying beds, it follows that a period of considerable denudation must have preceded their deposition. It is quite possible that a land-surface may have existed prior to the formation of the " sand and rolled gravel," and much of the sand and gravel, which is for the most part unfossiliferous, may be of torrential or fluviatile origin. But since marine shells make their appearance here and there, it is inferred that the sea covered wide areas in eastern England during the accumulation of the beds in question. Climate temperate.

6. *Great Chalky Boulder-clay of East Anglia, &c., and Unfossiliferous Bottom Till of Cheshire, &c.*—Severe glacial conditions obtained during the formation of this deposit. The ice-sheet extended south as far as the heights overlooking the north bank of the Thames, and was continuous with that which covered all the midland and western districts of the country. The confluent glaciers deriving from the Lake

district united with the ice from Scotland, and flowed south over the bed of the Irish Sea, after which they were forced to encroach upon the low grounds of Lancashire and Cheshire, and eventually to sweep south by the Severn Valley into the Bristol Channel.

7. *Northern Drift with Erratics.*——The coarse gravel and débris with erratics which cover wide areas in the midland and southern counties, are probably of much the same age as the chalky boulder-clay of East Anglia. They point to the dissolution of the ice-sheet, and the consequent deposition of more or less tumultuous heaps and spreads of stones and shingle, with which erratics were necessarily associated. Sometimes this drift is found resting upon boulder-clay, but frequently the latter is absent, having probably been denuded.

8. *Beds above the Chalky Boulder-clay.*——These are unfossiliferous and are most likely of freshwater origin. Indeed they may belong to the same period as the gravel of the "northern drift." Before their deposition the chalky boulder-clay had been greatly denuded.

9. *"Bridlington Crag" Beds* clearly indicate very cold climatic conditions, and a certain degree of submergence of the land.

10. *Purple Clay of Yorkshire, Lower Boulder-clay of Lancashire, Cheshire, &c.*——Advance of an ice-sheet which reached as far south at least as Lincolnshire in the east, and the valley of the Severn in the west.*

11. *Hessle Gravel, Middle Sands, &c., of Lancashire, &c.,* and probably also some portion of the loose surface-gravels with erratics in midland districts. Disappearance of the ice-sheet, climate mild. Several pachyderms and carnivores lived in Yorkshire at this time. These terrestrial conditions were followed by submergence——the land sinking in Wales for 1,300 ft.——and a subsequent re-elevation.

12. *Hessle Boulder-clay, Upper Boulder-clay of Lancashire, Cheshire, &c.*——Latest advance of the ice-sheet.

---

* It is not unlikely that some of the so-called "great chalky till," in regions further south than are reached by the purple clay, may really be of the age of the latter. As the ice-sheet of the purple clay flowed southward over the Chalk, the purple colour of the clay would eventually disappear.

Thus from the time of the preglacial-forest-bed of Norfolk down to the latest advance of the glaciers, we seem to have evidence of several great oscillations of climate, which might be tabulated thus :—

Preglacial mild period	Forest-bed, &c.
First glacial period	Cromer clay and contorted beds.
First interglacial mild period . .	Sand and rolled gravel above Cromer clay.
Second glacial period	Great chalky boulder-clay, &c.
Second interglacial mild period .	{ Beds between great chalky boulder-clay and purple clay.
Third glacial period	{ Purple clay; lower boulder-clay of Lancashire, &c.
Third and last interglacial mild period .	{ Hessle gravel; middle sands, &c., of Lancashire.
Last glacial period	{ Hessle clay; upper boulder-clay of Lancashire.

It will now be seen why I object to the nomenclature adopted by Mr. S. V. Wood. The Hessle boulder-clay in his classification becomes " early postglacial," although the evidence shows that during its accumulation England was passing through severe glacial conditions—conditions which were not so severe, however, as those which gave rise to the formation of the preceding purple boulder-clay of Yorkshire. Holding the views that are stated above it seems to me that the term *postglacial* is misleading, and I would therefore suggest the following modification of Mr. Wood's nomenclature :—

PREGLACIAL :—
    a Forest-bed of Norfolk.
EARLY GLACIAL :—
    b Cromer clay and contorted drift.
MID-GLACIAL :—
    c Sand and gravel beds of East Anglia = Mr. S. V. Wood's "middle glacial."
    d Great chalky boulder-clay; bottom unfossiliferous till of north-west; "northern drift."
    e Sand, gravel, and clay, with shell-beds of Bridlington and Dimlington.
    f Purple boulder-clay of Yorkshire; lower shelly boulder-clay of north-west.
LATE GLACIAL :—
    g Hessle gravel and *Cyrena* beds ; middle sands of north-west.
    h Hessle boulder-clay ; upper shelly boulder-clay of north-west.*

* It would be useful to have some short names to distinguish the various members of the drift mentioned in this table. Thus we might have one name to include the purple boulder-clay of Yorkshire and the lower shelly boulder-clay of Lancashire; one also to embrace the Hessle boulder-clay and the upper shelly boulder-clay of the north-west; and so on with the other sub-divisions. The beds marked *b* might be termed simply *Cromer drift ; c, East Anglian sands*, or some such name ; *d, bottom till*, or *main till ; e, Bridlington beds*, or *Dimlington beds*— the latter being preferable; *f, middle till ; g, Hessle*, or *Lancashire, beds ; h, upper till.*

CHAPTER XXXI.

GLACIAL DEPOSITS OF IRELAND. — POSTGLACIAL BEDS OF ENGLAND AND IRELAND.

Unfossiliferous till.—Morainic débris.—Lower boulder-clay.—Interglacial marine sands, &c.—Upper boulder-clay.—Eskers.—High-level marine terraces.—Summary.—Postglacial deposits of England and Ireland.

NO part of the British Islands exhibits better than the wilder parts of Ireland the extreme effects of glaciation. In the rugged western districts of Galway and Mayo especially, rounded and well-rubbed rocks and heaps of glacial deposits occur everywhere. The striæ upon the rocks, and the direction in which the till has travelled, mark out clearly the path taken by the great sheet of ice which wrapped up Ireland even as it enveloped Scotland.

The oldest glacial deposit recognised by the Irish geologists is a tough stony clay similar in all respects to the Scottish till. This is the chief drift of the central plain of Ireland. It usually lies upon a smoothed and striated surface of rock, and the stones which it contains are more or less blunted and well glaciated. Occasionally it contains nests or lenticular beds of sand and gravel, and sometimes of fine laminated clay. Not infrequently the deposit is arranged in a series of broad parallel ridges and banks, the trend of which has been ascertained to coincide precisely with the direction taken by the old ice-flows.[*]

Morainic débris occurs in great abundance in the hilly tracts, covering the slopes and bottoms of the valleys, in the

---

[*] See this beautifully shown upon the map accompanying a paper *On the General Glaciation of Iar-Connaught and its neighbourhood*, &c., by Messrs. Kinahan and M. H. Close. For detailed information on the Irish glacial deposits, the reader must consult the publications of the Geological Survey, and papers by Messrs. Kinahan and Close in the *Dublin Quarterly Journal of Science*, in which he will find references to other authorities on the subject.

lower reaches of which it appears frequently to graduate into coarse gravels.

In the north-eastern districts of Ireland it is interesting to find a series of gravel and sand beds resting upon and covered by stony clay.* These intercalated beds contain a number of sea-shells belonging, for the most part, to species now living, but indicating somewhat colder conditions than obtain at present in the neighbouring seas. Professor Hull believes these beds to be the equivalents of the middle sand and gravel series of the north-west of England. He also correlates with the same beds certain gravels at Wexford, described by Professor Harkness as underlying a mass of boulder-clay. But an examination of the fossils by Mr. A. Bell,† seems to show that this latter correlation cannot be maintained, but that the Wexford beds belong most likely to some part of the older glacial series of East Anglia, as defined by Mr. Wood and his associates.‡ With regard to the drifts of the northern and central districts, however, there can be no doubt that we have the Lancashire type very well displayed. Mr. E. T. Hardman has recently described§ a number of sections where the triple series is admirably shown. This arrangement holds good all through the counties of Tyrone, Armagh, and in such parts of Derry as Mr. Hardman is acquainted with, and he thinks that "the drift of the more central parts of Ireland, especially that of the Queen's County, Carlow, and Kilkenny, is equally susceptible of a tripartite arrangement." The section of the drift deposits in Dublin county, cited by Professor Hull, also affords clear proof that two boulder-clays separated by intervening marine gravels are characteristic of the drift in that neighbourhood. The annexed section has been kindly sent to me by Professor Hull. It shows how the three members of the drift have been deposited on an inclined bank of limestone and subsequently denuded.

The great elongated ridges of gravel called eskers, and the

---

* Professor Harkness, *Geological Magazine*, vol. vi., p. 542 ; Professor Hull, *op. cit.* vol. viii., p. 294.

† *Geological Magazine*, vol. x., p. 447.

‡ I would not myself lay much weight in this case upon the palæontological evidence, but it is difficult to believe that the last ice-sheet advanced so far south as Wexford. And as the probabilities are against it having done so, I think the geological evidence, so far as it goes, supports the palæontological.

§ *Jour. Roy. Geol. Soc. of Ireland*, vol. iv. (new series), p. 73.

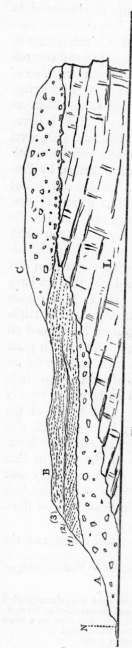

Fig. 61.—Section at Kilkenny Marble Quarries.

A, Lower boulder-clay, with large blocks of limestone and grit; 25 to 35 feet thick.

B, Middle (interglacial) gravels { 3, Limestone-gravel and sand, stratified . . . } 10 to 25 feet thick.
{ 2, Bed of loamy sand }
{ 1, Earthy gravel, current-bedded, pebbles waterworn }

C, Upper boulder-clay; brown clay with subangular and rounded boulders; 20 to 25 feet thick.
L, Limestone.   N, Valley of the River Nore.

widespread deposits of similar materials which are met with so abundantly, especially in the central parts of Ireland, have long been famous. They are remarkable for being frequently dotted over with large erratic blocks. The origin of the eskers has long been a debated question. There can be little doubt, however, that they have been formed in the same way as the gravel ridges of the Scottish Lowlands, and the åsar of Sweden (see p. 407). Like these the eskers are also unfossiliferous. Mr. Kinahan strongly upholds their marine origin. I was formerly of the same opinion, but having since seen reason for believing that the sea has had no share in the formation of the Scotch gravel ridges, which are in the same category as the Irish eskers, I now look upon the latter as having been heaped up principally by the action of subglacial waters during the final melting of the confluent glaciers.

On the sea-coast and in the interior of the country, sand-hills are very frequently found heaped up at or near the mouths of valleys. In the neighbourhood of the sea they form undulating dunes, which are continually being influenced by the winds. Mr. Kinahan was, I believe, the first to point out their connection with the valleys. He tells us that they not only occur at or near the mouths of the valleys, but the greater and more extensive the valley, the greater, he says, is the accumulation of sand. He considers that the sand of which these hummocks consist was originally brought down by rivers at a time when glaciers occupied the valleys * —an inference which is strongly supported by the appearance of similar phenomena in Scotland. The same author has described the occurrence under the till in Ireland of what he calls "preglacial drift," which occasionally contains the remains of trees.†

Gravel beds with marine shells have been traced in Ireland up to a height of 1,235 ft. on Montpelier Hill.‡

The general succession of events during the glacial epoch would seem therefore to be closely analogous to those experienced in the north-west of England—viz. :

1st. A period of intense arctic cold, during which the whole island was wrapped in ice that coalesced with the *mers de glace* of England and Scotland. Underneath this ice the land was highly glaciated, and the till was formed. The Wexford beds may indicate a genial interglacial period, like that of the first interglacial period of East Anglia.

2nd. The shrinking back of the ice-sheet, and the stranding of erratics and deposition of coarse moraine-matter.

3rd. Submergence of the land ; deposition of the middle sands and gravels of the central and northern districts, and formation of the high-level marine terraces ; climate temperate.

4th. Return of arctic conditions of climate, accompanied probably by re-elevation of the land ; re-advance of the ice-sheet, which ploughed up the middle sands and gravels to a great extent and incorporated their débris with its bottom-moraine; climate temperate; deposition of upper boulder-clay.

5th. Melting of the ice-sheet ; stranding of *blocs perchés,*

---

* *Geological Magazine,* vol. viii. p. 155.
† *Dublin Quarterly Journal of Science,* vol. vi. p. 249.
‡ *Explanation of Sheets* 102 *and* 112 (*Geological Survey Maps*), p. 67.

and deposition of coarse morainic débris in mountain-valleys ; scattering of erratics over the low grounds from the terminal front of the melting ice, formation of the eskers and much of the "limestone gravel," of the centre of Ireland, and of the sand-hills opposite the mouths of hill-valleys.

The postglacial alluvial deposits of Ireland and the north of England have yielded similar results to those of Scotland. In Lancashire and Cheshire, for example, where large areas are covered by the upper boulder-clay, the postglacial accumulations which overlie the former never yield palæolithic* implements nor any of the old pachyderms and carnivores with which, as we shall presently see, palæolithic man was contemporary. The oldest human relics met with in that district are of neolithic age. An excellent account of the postglacial deposits of western Lancashire and Cheshire has been given by Mr. C. E. De Rance,† from whose paper I quote the following section :—

		Feet.
1. *Bithinia-tentaculata* sand		2—4
2. Peat. This bed occasionally appears to have formed a cultivated surface before the deposition of the sand		1
3. *Tellina-balthica* sand, with seams of bluish clay. This is apparently the seam in which Mr. Ecroyd Smith has recorded the presence of Saxon and Roman coins		2
4. Peat. The representative of the thick peat of Lancashire and Cheshire		3
5. Bluish-grey clay, the upper portion of freshwater origin . . .		3
" " " the lower portion marine, and containing *Scrobiculariæ*		1
6. Peat, with a few stumps of trees with their roots in boulder-clay .		1½
7. Boulder-clay. From half-tide to the lowest water-mark.		

Mr. De Rance correlates the historical periods with the geological deposits as follows :—

Recent to Norman conquest .	.	*Sand dunes.*
Danes and Saxons . .	.	B.-tentaculata *sand.*
Saxons . . .	.	*Peat and made earth.*
Saxons and Romans .	.	Tell-balthica *sand.*
Romans and Celts . .	.	*Main peat.*
Celts . . .	.	" " *lower portion.*
Neolithic-weapons race‡	.	*Lower blue silt.*
No trace of man . .	.	Lowest peat.

If now we glance at the postglacial deposits which overlie the youngest boulder-clay of the north-east of England, we

---

* For some account of palæolithic and neolithic implements, &c., see Chapter xxxvii.

† *Quart. Jour. Geol. Soc.*, 1871, p. 655.

‡ In Mr. De Rance's paper, "Palæolithic" appears here by a slip of the pen. The relics, he tells me, are unquestionably *neolithic*.

find a similar absence of palæolithic implements and no trace
of the extinct pachyderms and carnivores.   The accumulations
of later date than the Hessle boulder-clay comprise lacustrine
marls with *Cyclas,* gravel and sand, laminated clays, and peat
with remains of oxen, deer, &c.   The postglacial beds of Ireland tell the same tale, and all that need be remarked about
them, therefore, is simply this, that they indicate a gradual
amelioration of climate from cold-temperate to the present
temperate conditions.   The land animals obtained in or below
peat-mosses, &c., comprise the brown bear, the grisly bear, the
Irish elk, the bison, bovidæ of extinct species, horse, wolf,
fox, beaver, hare, &c.   And, just as in Scotland, the polished
stone implements used by primeval tribes are everywhere
scattered about both in England and Ireland—the latter
country being especially rich in these interesting memorials of
our lowly civilised predecessors.*

* I discuss the age of the ancient river-gravels with human implements and
mammalian remains met with in south of England, in Chapter xxxvii., *et sqq*.
The postglacial deposits referred to above are those which can be clearly shown
to be of that age from their superposition upon accumulations belonging to the
close of the glacial epoch.   As the ancient river-gravels in the south do not occupy
this position, their age cannot be ascertained in so simple a manner; and, therefore, it is more convenient to treat of them separately.

CHAPTER XXXII.

GLACIAL DEPOSITS OF SCANDINAVIA.

Extensive glaciation of mountainous and northern regions throughout the northern hemisphere.—Glaciation of Norway, Sweden, and Finland.—Lower and upper till of Sweden.—Interglacial freshwater deposits.—Till of Norway.—Åsar. —Erratics on åsar.—Clays with marine arctic shells.—Contorted bedding, &c.—Postglacial deposits with Baltic shells.—Moraines.—Succession of changes.—Southern limits of glaciation in northern Europe.—The "great northern drift."—Theories of the origin of the åsar.—Summary.—Peat-mosses and buried forests of Norway.

IF the British Islands, which are now in the enjoyment of a mild-temperate climate, have beyond doubt experienced in ages that are past the utmost severity of arctic and glacial conditions, it would only be reasonable to infer that other regions of the northern hemisphere should give evidence of having likewise been at the same time characterized by a rigorous climate. It is, *à priori*, in the highest degree improbable that a great ice-sheet should have enveloped a large part of our country, while other areas situate in similar or nearly similar, latitudes escaped. On the contrary, the observer who knew nothing whatever of the geological records of any country save his own would be justified in believing that the evidence gathered in Britain alone is enough to convince one that during the intense cold of the glacial epoch the temperature of the whole northern hemisphere must have been similarly affected. Geological investigations have clearly shown that such was really the case.

In Scandinavia and northern Europe generally the evidence in favour of arctic conditions having formerly prevailed is overwhelming. So likewise in Switzerland the proofs of this are everywhere patent. But not only were the snow-fields and glaciers much larger at one time than now—they even existed in some mountain districts which at present lie far below the limits of perpetual snow. In the Northern Apennines and the Apuan Alps are found the moraines of extinct glaciers which must have attained a considerable size.* Again, there are distinct traces of glacial action at the foot of Morvan, a hill on the confines of the Department of Yonne ; nay, there is even, according to M. Collomb, evidence of a glacier having moved in the direction of the valley of the Seine, before that valley had come into existence. In the Black Forest, the Vosges,† and the volcanic mountains of Auvergne, we find ancient moraines ; and similar relics of old ice-action have been noted in the valleys of the Cevennes and the hills of Lozère. The Pyrenees, whose puny glaciers are confined to the higher mountain-slopes, and do not now descend into the valleys,‡ appear at one time to have been covered with great snow-fields, from which large glaciers streamed outwards, and even in some cases debouched upon the plains. Old moraines now covered with vegetation, and *roches moutonnées* rising behind quiet villages, and occasionally crowned with some church or chapel, are familiar scenes in many of the valleys on the French side of the mountains. Along their southern slopes similar traces of ancient glacial action have been observed, especially in Galicia, by the late Casiano de Prado. Farther south, in the Sierra Guadarrama,§ to the north of Madrid, the same geologist has detected evident marks of old glaciers, and described great deposits of loam, sand, and gravel which have been laid down by rivers escaping from masses of melting ice. Nay, even as far south as latitude 37° the former existence of glaciers in the Sierra Nevada has been proved by the researches of MM. Schimper and Collomb ; and so on with most, or perhaps all, the hillier regions in Europe, great snow-fields existed where now there are none, and the present ones are merely the insignificant successors of mighty ice-sheets which have long since melted away.

* Stefani : *Bolletino del R. Comitato geologico d'Italia,* 1874.

† An excellent account of the old glaciers of the Vosges is given in Hogard's *Coup d'Œil sur le Terrain erratiques des Vosges,* 1851 ; see also an interesting paper on the same subject by M. Ch. Grad, *Bulletin de la Société géologique de France,* Tom. i. (3 série) p. 88. Professor Ramsay was the first to detect traces of glacial action in the Black Forest.

‡ " Glaciers actuel et Période glaciaire " (Martins), *Revue de deux Mondes,* 1867 and 1875.

§ *Descripcion fisica i geológica de la Provincia de Madrid* (Don Casiano de Prado), p. 164.

As we pass out of Europe we are met with the evidence of similar changes. According to Mr. Palgrave the mountains in the provinces of Trebizond and Erzeroum have at one time nourished very large glaciers, which have left their moraines in the valley of the Chorok—a district which is certainly very far from being glacial now.* The valleys of the Caucasus have also brimmed with ice; † the present glaciers are comparatively small. Traces of glacial action have been noticed among the Atlas mountains,‡ and the cedars of Lebanon, as Dr. Hooker § tells us, grow upon old moraines. The great glaciers of the Himalaya have in past times attained gigantic proportions,‖ and in parts of Asia where there are now no glaciers at all, one may yet readily trace the marks of their former action. Thus in North China huge boulders are found scattered over the valleys, often at considerable distances from the mountains; ¶ nor are rock-basins wanting, especially in that rough undulating country which is passed through on the route from the Great Wall to the Siberian frontier.**

---

* *Nature*, vol. v. p. 444; vol. vi. p. 536.

† *Travels in the Central Caucasus and Bashan* (Douglas W. Freshfield).

‡ *A Journey to Morocco and the Ascent of the Great Atlas* (G. Maw), p. 19.

§ *Natural History Review*, January, 1862.

‖ Of the Sind valley Mr. Drew (*Jummoo and Kashmir Territories*, p. 220) says: "The whole valley from Harō (and perhaps from lower still) upwards to the source of the Sind River (south-east from the Drās Pass) was filled with ice, making a glacier forty miles in length. This is not much greater than glaciers we shall come to in Baltistan, but it contrasts strongly with the small glaciers remaining at high levels in the hollows of these mountains. Of these small separated glaciers there are still over thirty in the basin of this river." See also pp. 282, 327, 372. The same author shows that ice must at one time have filled the valley of the Nubrā River at Charāsa to a depth of 4,000 or 4,500 feet. With such a thickness of ice at this point, he believes the glacier "must have reached to the Shayōk valley, and there probably joined with other ice masses, and it may have extended far away down," p. 278. Nubrā River drains from the Karakoram mountains, and from the summit ridge of the Karakoram to the junction of the Nubrā River with the Shayōk is upwards of seventy miles. At present the main glacier at the head of the Nubrā valley is only some twenty miles long, and the largest glacier in Baltistan (Karakoram) hardly exceeds thirty-five miles in length.

¶ See Williamson's *Journeys in North China*. Describing the country between Si-gnan and Toong-kwan (Shensi) the author says:—"For many miles the country was like one continued splendid park, with knolls and lawns and winding paths, leading round some huge fantastic boulder, which had descended from the mountains which lay contiguous on the south," vol. i. p. 387. Again: "We found the country (north-east corner of Shang-Tung) strewn with huge boulders of various sizes, looking like so many cattle at rest with elephants around them," *op. cit.* p. 189. See also pp. 429, 430, where the author describes conical hills and ridges crowned with huge boulders. These were probably *roches moutonnées*, or moraines.

** "In all these instances the depressions are entirely in the solid rock, and vary in size from a few yards to several thousand feet across. They have the

In North America the evidence in favour of intense glacial conditions having formerly prevailed is overwhelming. From the shores of British Columbia* to the borders of the Atlantic and from the coasts of the Arctic Ocean down to the latitude of New York, ice-marks are everywhere; while in mountain regions even farther south, as in the Sierra Nevada † of California, the morainic débris of great glaciers lies scattered over the lower reaches of the valleys.

Having assured ourselves that a glacial or arctic climate did within comparatively recent times characterize a very large area of the northern hemisphere, it becomes a matter of no little interest and importance to inquire whether we can detect in foreign glacial deposits any proofs of that remarkable succession of changes which, as we have seen, may be traced in the drifts of our own country. With this view, I propose to give a short sketch of the glacial phenomena of the better-known regions—viz., Scandinavia, Switzerland, Italy and North America.

I have already had occasion to mention the great ice-sheet that enveloped Scandinavia, and to point out that it in all probability coalesced with that of Scotland upon the floor of the German Ocean. No grander display of ice-action could one wish to see than that which the fiords and fiord-valleys of Norway present. The smoothed and mammillated mountain-slopes, the rounded islets that peer above the level of the sea like the backs of great whales, the glistening and highly-polished faces of rock that sweep right down into deep water, the great perched blocks, ranged like sentinels on jutting points and ledges, the huge mounds of morainic débris at the heads of the valleys, and the wild disorder of crags and boulders scattered over the former paths of the glaciers, com-

appearance of having been produced by erosion, and not by sinking." Richard Pumpelly, " Geological Researches in China, Mongolia, and Japan," *Smithsonian Contributions,* 1866.

* *Quarterly Journal of the Geological Society* (Bauerman), 1860, p. 202; see also *American Journal of Science,* vol. c. (1870), p. 318, where Dr. R. Brown shows that British Columbia, Vancouver's Island, Washington Territory, and the Queen Charlotte Islands, all exhibit fine rock-striations and scattered erratic blocks. Some American geologists had previously held the opinion that the glacial formation disappeared west of the Rocky Mountains.

† For a lively account of that region, see Clarence King's *Mountaineering in the Nevada.* Some suggestive notes on the glaciers of the Sierra Nevada by Mr. John Muir, of Oakland, California, will be found in the *Proc. of the Amer. Assoc. for the Advance. of Science,* 1874.

bine to make a picture which no after amount of sight-seeing is likely to cause a geologist to forget. The whole country has been moulded and rubbed and polished by one immense sheet of ice, which could hardly have been less than 6,000 ft. or even 7,000 ft. thick.*

The Gulf of Bothnia appears to have brimmed with ice, which pressed up against and even in some places overflowed the lofty Norwegian frontier, through the valleys of which it found its way into the North Sea.† Mr. Törnebohm, of the Geological Survey of Sweden, informs me that the glacier-carried erratics of Jemtland clearly show that the ice has passed from east to west—that is, right against the slope of the land; and, according to Keilhau, similar blocks which could only have come from Sweden are now found in Trond-hjems-fiord. The most remarkable circumstance in connection with some of these blocks consists in the fact that they occur at a considerably greater height than the rock from which they have been derived. Thus at Åreskutan, Törnebohm found blocks at a height of 4,500 ft. which could not possibly have come from any place higher than 1,800 ft.

How far south the Scandinavian ice-sheet extended we cannot tell. We know that it not only filled the Gulf of Bothnia, but occupied the whole area of the Baltic Sea, over-flowing the Åland Isles, Gottland, Öland, Bornholm, and Denmark, and passing south-east over Finland into Russia, across Lake Onega, Lake Ladoga, and the Gulf of Finland.‡ [See map.] But its farthest limits have not been determined, and that for a very good reason, as we shall see presently. The direction of the glaciation in the extreme north of Scandinavia, the peninsula of Kola, and north-eastern Finland, demonstrates that the great *mer de glace* radiated outwards from the high grounds of Norway and Sweden, flowing north

---

* Mr. Amund Helland in his paper "Om Mægtigheden af Bræerne i Norge under Istiden," (On the thickness of the glacier-ice in Norway during the glacial epoch), *Geologiska Föreningens i Stockholm Förhandlingar*, 1874, Band II., No. 6, states that the height reached by the ice-scratches in the Sognefjord indicates a thickness of from 1,700 to 1,800 metres; in Hardangerfjord of 1,200 metres. These, of course, are minimum thicknesses.

† See Hörbye's *Observations sur les Phénomènes d'Erosion en Norvège*, where the striæ are indicated as crossing the watershed between the two countries.

‡ Professor Nordenskjöld, *Beitrag zur Kentniss der Schrammen in Finland*, Helsingfors, 1863; for direction of Norwegian glaciation, see Hörbye's work, *op. cit.;* for that of Sweden, consult the maps of the Geological Survey of that country.

and north-east into the Arctic Ocean and east into the White
Sea, and thus clearly proving that northern Europe was not
overflowed by a vast ice-cap creeping outwards from the North
Pole, as some geologists have supposed.*

The oldest of all the glacial deposits of Sweden is till,
which, in a more or less continuous sheet, covers all the low
grounds. It usually lies upon a polished and striated surface
of rock, but occasionally thick beds of sand come between it
and the underlying rock. It "consists of two distinct layers,†
the lower of which is generally darker in colour, and contains
fewer big stones than the upper. Both, however, have evidently been formed in the same way, and may be considered

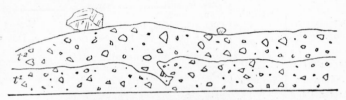

Fig. 62.—Upper and lower till in railway cutting in Wermland.
(A. E. Törnebohm.)

true *moraines de fond.* There is usually a sharp line of
demarcation between them, and in some places the lower till
has been partly broken up and denuded before the upper till
was deposited." ‡ The Swedish geologists have no doubt
whatever that these masses and sheets of till were formed
and accumulated by land-ice, exactly in the same way as our
own till. Moreover, the fact that their lower till exhibits
such marked evidence of denudation underneath the upper
and overlying mass, " seems to point out," says Törnebohm,
" that during the glacial epoch there was a great interval of

* Of course I do not deny that the Polar lands to the north of Europe were
encased in ice during the climax of glacial cold, but I can see no evidence whatever that any European land was ever impinged upon by polar ice, much less
overflowed by it. All the glacial phenomena of the British Islands and Scandinavia can be quite well accounted for by such confluent glaciers as we know
covered these countries. The direction of the glaciation and of the transport of
boulders and drift put this beyond reasonable doubt.

† In central Sweden three kinds of till are distinguished by Mr. Otto
Gumælius, the lower of which he thinks was formed when the ice-sheet was
advancing, while the two upper ones were deposited during its retreat. "Om
mellersta Sveriges glaciala Bildningar,' *K. Svenska Vet.-Akad. Handlingar*, 1874.

‡ Mr. Törnebohm, in a letter to the author. See *On Changes of Climate
during the Glacial Epoch,* p. 24. He says: "The till is often so hard and packed
that it is easier to break the stones that are in it than to dislodge them."

comparatively mild climate, during which the ice retreated to the mountains; the land, however, was not at this time submerged. When the ice-sheet once more overspread the country it would obliterate any freshwater deposits that might have been laid down in the interval." Traces of glacial freshwater beds, however, are not wanting — Mr. Nathorst having detected these some years ago in Scania. The beds referred to contain plants which, according to Mr. Nathorst, indicate a climate as severe as that of northern Norway. The same geologist gives the following table as embodying the results of his investigations into the glacial and interglacial deposits of Sweden and Denmark :—

POST-GLACIAL FORMATIONS
- *Peat* with
  - Quercus sessiliflora, Q. robur.
  - Pinus sylvestris.
  - Populus tremula, Betula nana.
- *Clay* with
  - Betula nana, Salix herbacea, S. reticulata, Dryas octopetala, Cytheridea torosa, Limnea limosa, Pisidium, Anodonta, Salix polaris.

GLACIAL PERIOD . . . . *Glacial Deposits. Boulder-clay.*

INTERGLACIAL *Clay* with
  - Salix polaris, Dryas octopetala, Limnea limosa, Pisidium, Anodonta, Cytheridea torosa.

GLACIAL PERIOD . . . . *Glacial Deposits. Boulder clay.* *

Mr. Holmström has also described similar deposits as occurring at Klågerup, in Scania, in the following descending series :—

> Yellow till with scratched stones.
> Brown sand and yellow glacial freshwater clay.
> Grey marly sand.
> Blue glacial freshwater clay.
> Blue till with scratched stones.

The freshwater clays have yielded—1st. (Shells) *Pisidium pulchellum* (Jen.); *P. obtusa* (Pfeiff); *P. Henslowianum* (Jen.); *Anadonta anatina; Limnæa lagotis* (Schr.); 2nd. (Plants) *Dryas octopetala, Betula nana.* From these facts Mr. Holmström considers that he has evidence of an interglacial period. He says the lower blue till is very thick, and extends almost continuously over the whole country. It points, as he thinks, to the former existence of an extensive *mer de glace* which covered the whole land, destroying all life. The shells and plants found in the freshwater clays must therefore, according to him, have come in from the south when the ice retired. Then afterwards, at a later period, some local glaciers crept down from the great mass of

---

* *Kongl. Vetenskaps-Akademiens Förhandlingar,* 1873. No. 6.

ice that still lingered in the north, covering with morainic matter the freshwater clays which, during the interval, had accumulated in pools upon the surface of the older till.[*] More recently Mr. E. Erdmann of the Geological Survey of Sweden has described [†] the occurrence of interglacial sand and clay in the till or boulder-clay of Scania. He believes he has evidence to show that there were more interglacial periods than one, for several interglacial deposits separated by intervening masses of till occur one above another. In one of the interglacial beds freshwater shells were detected : this bed was covered by 70 feet of boulder-clay.

In Norway a deposit of till also occurs ; it does not, however, cover so wide an area as in Sweden, but appears often of considerable thickness in sheltered places, as on the lee-side of crags and rocky knolls.[‡]

Resting sometimes on till, but oftener, perhaps, upon solid rock, appear certain great natural embankments, or long winding ridges, which are known in Sweden as åsar.[§] They generally rise abruptly to a height that may vary from 50 to 100 ft. above the average surface of the ground. Sometimes, however, they reach as much as 180 ft., while now and again they sink to 30 or 20 ft., or even disappear altogether below newer deposits. Their sides have an inclination of from 15° to 20°, but occasionally as much as 25° or even 30°, and the two declivities very rarely slope at the same angle.[||]

Often beginning in the interior of the country, the åsar follow the valleys down to the low coast-land, across which they pass as well-defined ridges out to sea, after a course of not infrequently more than a hundred English miles.[¶] In the mode of their distribution they show a striking resemblance to river courses, as will be seen from the

---

* Öfversigt af Bildningar från och efter istiden vid Klågerup i Malmöhus lan (L. Holmström) ; *Kongl. Vetenskaps-Akademiens Förhandlingar*,' 1873, No. 1. I am indebted to Mr. Törnebohm for calling my attention to these interesting observations. For an interesting account of stratified beds, underlying and intercalated with Swedish till, see a paper by E. Erdmann, *Geol. Fören. i Stockholm Förh.*, Bd. i. p. 210.

† *Geologiska Föreningens i Stockholm Förhandlingar*, Bd. ii. p. 13.

‡ *Iagttagelser over den postpliocene eller glaciale Formation* (Sars and Kjerulf).

§ As singular, åsar plural ; similar ridges in Norway are termed *Raer*.

|| *Exposé des Formations quaternaires de la Suède*, par A. Erdmann, pp. 40, 61.

¶ Erdmann mentions as examples, Upsala ås, which is about 200 kilometres in length ; Köping ås, very nearly 240 kilometres ; Enköping ås, 300 to 340 kilometres ; Badelunda ås, about 300 kilometres. *Op. cit.* p. 44.

accompanying sketch-map, on which the black lines represent the åsar.*

At greater heights than 300 ft. above the sea these remarkable ridges are, as a general rule, confined to the valleys, but at lower levels they seem to be tolerably independent
of the present configuration of the ground. They are met
with at all levels up to and beyond 1,000 ft.† The materials

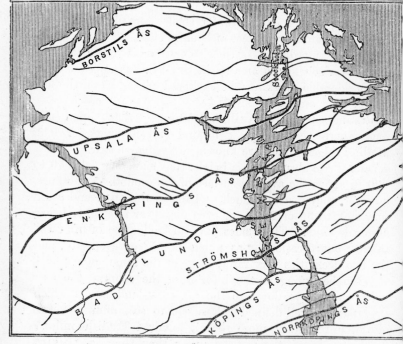

Fig. 63.—Map of Äsar in basin of Mälar Lake.

of which they are composed may consist either of coarse
shingle, or of pebbly gravel, or of sand, or it may be made
up of all three. In some parts of a ridge shingle and gravel
predominate, in others sand is the principal ingredient. In

---

* The map is from a paper by A. E. Törnebohm in *Geol. Fören. i Stockholm
Förh.,* Band I. No. 4, and is meant to illustrate an ingenious theory advanced by
that geologist in explanation of the åsar.
† The highest mentioned by Erdmann occurs at Herjeådal, between 1,300 and
1,400 ft. above the sea, but Mr. Törnebohm informs me that in the mountain-
valleys of the north they go up to elevations of over 2,000 ft.

one place the stratification will be distinct, in other places obscure, and not infrequently false-bedding appears.

In many respects then the âsar seem analogous to the British eskers and kames. These deposits have yet another character in common—they are unfossiliferous. For, as we shall see immediately, the shells which have been described as occurring in the âsar, do not properly belong to them.

Erratic blocks are frequently found perched upon the top of an âs, or plentifully sprinkled along its sides, and sometimes also they occur in the interior, especially towards the top, or at the base.

A fine glacial clay containing arctic shells* often covers the slopes of the âsar. The same clay also forms deposits of considerable thickness, especially on the low grounds upon the borders of the Baltic and the North Sea. Traced inland it gradually gives place to sand and gravel. Here and there immense accumulations of shells of northern and arctic species† flank the hill-slopes, and have been dug for making lime and other purposes, just as we in this country quarry chalk or limestone. At the hill of Capell-backen, near Uddevalla (207 ft. above the sea), they were energetically digging the shells in Linnæus's time, and the same heap is being quarried now.

Frequently the shelly clays exhibit disturbed and contorted bedding, and they often contain large erratics. The greatest height at which shell-bearing beds have been obtained is some 600 ft. above the sea.

The beds next in succession consist of marl, clay, sand and gravel. They contain numerous shells of Baltic species, and large erratics often rest upon them.

In the interior of the country well-marked moraines are not very common. Some fine examples, however, are occasionally met with. Thus the southern part of Lake Wener is crossed by three parallel terminal moraines.‡ Moraines also occur in the mountain-valleys of Sweden, and are well marked in those of Norway.§

---

* The shells belong to such genera as *Yoldia, Saxicava, Leda, Cyprina, Arca, Natica, Astarte,* &c.

† The highest of these great shell-banks is that at Gustafsfors, near Westra Silen Lake, 500 ft. above the sea. (The Swedish foot is ⅓th less than the English.)

‡ Mr. Törnebohm is my authority.

§ See the paper by Sars and Kjerulf already cited.

The annexed diagram shows the mutual relations of the Swedish deposits, and will help to make the preceding notes more intelligible.

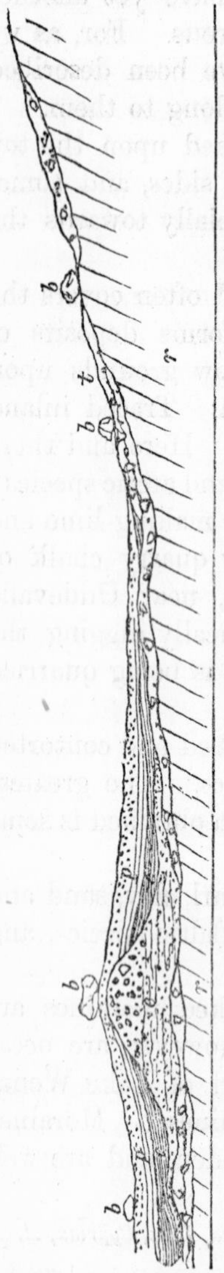

Fig. 64.—Swedish deposits: *t*, till; *c, âs; c*, shelly clay, &c.; *p*, postglacial deposits; *b*, erratics; *r*, underlying rocks.

The succession of changes thus indicated would appear to be as follows :—

1. Period of intense arctic cold, with a vast *mer de glace* covering the country (lower till).
2. Intervening period of milder conditions, when the ice-sheet drew back to the mountains.
3. Return of the ice-sheet (upper till).
4. Retreat of the ice-sheet ; stranding of *blocs perchés ;* great rivers carrying down immense quantities of sand and gravel ; formation of âsar.
5. Submergence of land, and deposition of shelly clays, &c. ; climate arctic; abundance of floating ice.
6. Gradual re-elevation of the land ; climate changing from arctic to temperate.

How far south the Scandinavian ice-sheet extended has not been determined. When we pass beyond the limits of Scandinavia and Finland into the low grounds of northern Russia and the great plains of Germany, we encounter vast accumulations of sand and gravel dotted over with blocks and boulders, all of which have come from the north. Erratics from Finland and Lapland are widely scattered over Poland and Russia, and fragments of rock broken from the mountains of Norway and Sweden strew the surface of Denmark, Holland, and northern Germany. Underneath these deposits the solid rocks disappear, and we have, therefore, no means of asceraining, with any approach to certainty, the extreme limits reached by the continental ice-sheet. It is by no means improbable, however, that it may have stretched nearly as far south as the great "Northern Drift" extends.

In its general character this Northern Drift very much resembles the remodelled drifts of the British Islands and Scandinavia—the eskers, kames, and åsar. It often forms undulating hills and mounds, which bear on their tops and slopes large boulders and angular erratics. Here and there in East and West Prussia it is said to have yielded shells, but certainly the great bulk of the deposit is quite unfossiliferous, and it is possible that these shells may belong to some more recent overlying formation ; just as the shells which were formerly believed to occur in the åsar, are now known to be of later date and to lie in beds that rest upon these peculiar ridges.*

The general unfossiliferous character of the Northern Drift would be inexplicable if we could believe that the materials of which that drift is composed were deposited upon the bottom of what was once open sea. But for this supposition there are really no good grounds. We have seen that the materials of which the kames consist were laid down by the swollen rivers that flowed underneath and issued from the last ice-sheet. In like manner the åsar of Sweden would appear to be of freshwater and subglacial formation ; and that the great bulk of the Northern Drift of Europe, consisting as it does of boulder-clay, gravel, sand, and erratics, was deposited by an ice-sheet, and the water escaping from it, may safely be inferred.

The remodelled aspect of some of this drift in Northern Germany, however, and the presence of sea-shells seem to show that after the ice-sheet had retreated and left the ground covered with boulder-clay, sand, gravel, erratics, and moraine-matter, a process of submergence ensued. Diluvial sand and gravel would now be subjected to the action of the sea. Step by step the land disappeared, but to what extent the submergence reached has been a much-disputed question.

---

* See a paper by G. Berendt, "Marine Diluvialfauna in Ostpreussen zweiter Nachtrag zur Diluvialfauna Westpreussens," *Zeitschrift der deutschen geologischen Gesselschaft*, Bd. xxvi. p. 823.

Some geologists who maintain that the åsar are banks heaped up by the sea, insist that Sweden sank to a depth sufficient to allow of the formation of the highest of these ridges, which would give a depression of not less than 2,000 ft. Others, again, think the absence of shells from the åsar is proof that these ridges cannot be of marine origin, and since sea-shells are nowhere found in Scandinavia at a greater height than 600 ft. or thereabout above the sea, they would limit the depression to that amount.*

The whole question thus turns upon the origin of the åsar. How were they formed? Scandinavian geologists are now generally agreed that the ridges in question are not marine. It is hard, indeed, to understand how sea-currents of any kind could form a series of long ramifying banks like those shown upon the sketch-map. Quite recently Mr. A. E. Törnebohm advanced a theory on the subject which I may here briefly describe.†

His belief is that the åsar are ancient river-courses, and he makes pointed reference to their peculiar riverlike ramifications. In those valleys which contain the åsar detached patches of sand are sometimes found, perching high on the side slopes. These patches, according to him, are the wreck of a great deposit of sand, which at one time filled the valleys from side to side. While the valleys were still filled with this thick bed of sand, rivers began to flow just as they now do, and cut their way down into the sand. The running water carried along with it coarse sand and gravel, and deposited these on the beds of the rivers, which thus became paved with coarser materials. By-and-by this state of things changed —denudation set to work upon the whole deposit, and removed the fine sand, but had not power to carry away the coarse gravel which had filled up the old river-courses. This gravel, therefore, remained behind, and very frequently has protected a considerable thickness of underlying sand. The

* The old beach-lines of the Norwegian coast have long been objects of interest to geologists, and have frequently been described. The most recent information about them is given in a paper by H. Mohn, " Bidrag til Kundskaben om gamle Strandlinier i Norge," *Nyt Magazin for Naturvidenskaberne*, 1876. In this paper the levels of the various beach-lines in a number of the most important fiords are compared with each other.

† See foot-note, *ante*, p. 408.

annexed woodcuts, which are taken from Törnebohm's paper, will further illustrate his meaning.

Fig. 65 shows the section of a valley partly filled with sand, *s*, in which is cut the river-bed, paved with coarse sand and gravel, *b*. Fig. 66 represents the aspect of the valley after denudation has removed the greater portion of the sand, patches of which are seen at *a, a*. At the bottom of the valley the river-gravel rests upon some depth of sand, forming together an ås, *b*.

The close connection between the åsar of the valleys and those that strike across the low country, clearly shows that in both districts they must have been formed in the same way. As an example, Mr. Törnebohm cites the åsar that occur in the basin of the Mälar Lake. (See the map, p. 408.) To apply his explanation to the åsar of that region, it is necessary to suppose the Mälar basin to have been filled up with sand and mud, through which the rivers, coming from

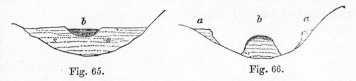

Fig. 65.   Fig. 66.

the melting *mer de glace*, cut their way to the sea. After the rivers had thus coursed across the broad deposits of sand which are inferred to have covered so large a part of Sweden, a movement of subsidence ensued, the land sank down, and the Mälar basin became converted into a shallow sea. During this depression the fine sand which was unprotected was washed away, and thus the åsar were formed. It is difficult, however, to comprehend how such immense deposits of sand and clay could have been removed so completely, while, at the same time, the supposed river-beds were left intact ; for some of the åsar are all but continuous throughout the whole of their course. Had this been their origin, surely one might have expected to find these ridges more frequently interrupted than is the case, and many miles of them often swept away.[*]

[*] Most of them, indeed, are more or less interrupted with gaps, but these are not so wide as to make it a difficult matter to identify the different parts of the same ås. Badelunda ås is, one might say, all but continuous for a distance of more than 160 English miles.

Mr. Törnebohm, who is one of those who consider that the land was not submerged more than 600 ft. or thereabout, is of course compelled to assume that the åsar above that level owe their origin to the action of rivers. And there can be no doubt, indeed, that streams flowing across a broad terrace will clear out hollows and leave intermediate banks or ridges of more or less prominence. There is great difficulty, however, in conceiving how stream-action could so denude a terrace as to leave nothing but a great central ridge extending for many miles along the course of a valley.

Robert Chambers, who examined some of the åsar many years ago,[*] at once recognised their strong similarity to our kames and eskers, and formed the opinion that they were probably marine, as M. Ch. Martins[†] was the first to suggest. This opinion, however, I believe Dr. Chambers subsequently changed; at all events he held latterly that the Scotch kames were of morainic origin.

What appears to be by much the most satisfactory explanation of the åsar has been recently worked out in a very interesting manner by Mr. David Hummel, of the Geological Survey of Sweden.[‡] Among the phenomena which Mr. Hummel specifies as specially suggestive of the origin of the åsar, are the frequent passage of the gravel of the åsar into true morainic matter (a passage which one can trace not only along the sides of an ås, but also in the direction of its trend); the appearance of angular blocks and gravel in the heart of well water-worn gravel; the less rounded aspect of the stones in the upper part of an ås; the existence of beds of well-rounded stones underneath true *moraines de fond;* the confused and dislocated appearance of the bedding sometimes noticeable in the interior of an ås; the general agreement that obtains between the trend of the rock-striations and the direction followed by the åsar, which seems to point to both phenomena being due to one and the same cause. We are further reminded of the fact that although the deposits in the interior of an ås are often beautifully strati-

---

* *Tracings in the North of Europe* 1850, p. 238, *et passim; Edinburgh New Philosophical Journal,* 1853.

† *Bulletin de la Société géologique de France,* 1845, 1846.

‡ "Om Rullstensbildningar" (Sveriges geologiska Undersökning); *K. Svenska Vet.-Akad. Handlingar,* 1874.

fied, they yet contain no fossils, while the exterior deposits, those which rest upon the flanks of the åsar, are often full of shells, &c. Again, we are to bear in mind that such stratified deposits were rarely formed before the accumulation of the åsar, which is in strong contrast to their frequent occurrence, in certain localities, after the åsar had come into existence. In fine, the facts seem to Hummel to indicate the agency of running water, and the direct action of glacier-ice; and he comes to the conclusion that the åsar have been formed in tunnels underneath the dissolving ice, by running water, introduced through crevasses, &c., acting upon the ground-moraines of the great confluent glaciers which covered Sweden during the glacial epoch. As the ice followed the general slope of the ground, so also the direction of the subglacial streams was necessarily determined by the contour of the underlying rock-surface. Thus we find that the chief åsar coincide in direction with the trend of the glacial striæ. Not infrequently, however, they follow another direction than that taken by the ice, the course pursued by the subglacial waters conforming in all cases to the slope of the ground, while the ice-sheet accommodated itself only to the *general* or *average* slope of the surface over which it moved. This theory obviously accounts for the passage of the åsar gravel into morainic matter, and for the fact that the gravels in the upper portion of an ås are not usually well rounded. It likewise explains the occasional occurrence of angular blocks in the interior of the åsar, the blocks having been introduced through crevasses, or melted out of the ice itself, and then dropt from the vault of the subglacial tunnel upon the bed of the stream. The contorted and interrupted bedding sometimes noticed in the heart of an ås is no doubt due to the crushing force of the ice during an occasional collapse of the tunnel. This theory (which to some extent resembles Mr. Goodchild's view of the origin of drift-deposits in general) throws much light upon the origin of the kames of Scotland, as I have endeavoured to show in Chapter XXI.*

* Dr. N. O. Holst has proposed yet another explanation of the åsar (see *Geol. Fören. i Stockholm Förh*. Band iii., No. 3). According to him the åsar have been formed in superficial channels licked out of the ice-sheet by the water derived from the melting of the inland ice. The materials, he believes, were obtained from the melting ice in which they had lain embedded. This explanation occurred

The erratics that occur on the tops and slopes of the âsar have in most cases been dropt into their present position from the front of the ice, during the final disappearance of the great glaciers. It is a prevalent belief, at least in this country, that the Northern Drift which covers such a large area in the low grounds of northern Germany is of marine origin, and that the erratics which are so plentifully sprinkled over its surface were deposited there by icebergs which set sail from the mountainous parts of Scandinavia during some period of great submergence. But, as we have seen, the Swedish and Norwegian geologists can find no traces of a greater degree of submergence than some 600 ft. or thereabout. Nor does it seem at all necessary to invoke the aid of the sea to account for the presence of the hills and undulating tracts of sand with erratics of northern Germany. If the great Scandinavian ice-sheet actually invaded and covered that region, it must have left behind it when it disappeared deposits of precisely the same character as those which are now so conspicuous there.

The sea-shells, however, which at rare intervals have been obtained from the diluvial sand of Germany, seem to indicate a certain degree of postglacial submergence, something like that which is shown, by the shell-beds that abut upon and overlie some of the low-level âsar of Sweden, to have obtained in the north. The submergence of the Scandinavian peninsula began and reached its climax at a time when arctic mollusca lived in the neighbouring seas. By-and-by, however, these departed, and their place was taken by the present fauna. From the presence of erratics resting upon beds which are full of shells belonging to the living Baltic fauna, we gather that large ice-rafts still sailed about in that sea during postglacial times ; and it is quite possible that many erratics may have been dropt over the low grounds of northern Germany at the same period : although most of the erratics of that region were most probably left there upon the

to me some years ago, but I rejected it then for these reasons: 1st. Because the âsar, eskers, and ridgy kames are not so continuous as they must have been had they been formed in superficial river channels ; and, 2nd, because we have no reason to believe that the ice of the old extinct glaciers was more thickly charged with débris than the present ice-sheets of arctic and antarctic regions. Did space permit I might mention other objections, but Dr. Holst's suggestive paper has only reached me while these pages are passing through the press.

retreat of the Scandinavian ice-sheet. Even in our day floating ice continues to scatter stones over the bed of that sea, and sometimes immense rafts are driven ashore, causing great damage. During the winter of 1862-63 a vast pile of ice was cast ashore on the southern coast of the Gulf of Finland, overwhelming many dwellings and whole forests. When this ice had melted away stones and blocks were found piled in great quantities upon the ground. The change from arctic to temperate conditions has thus been less complete in Scandinavia than with us.[*]

An examination of the flora of Norway enabled Mr. Axel Blytt [†] some time ago to come to the conclusion that the present peculiar distribution of Norwegian plants has been brought about by a succession of humid and dry periods. Having subsequently learned that I had previously inferred from the phenomena of the Scottish peat-mosses that a humid climate succeeded in postglacial times to an age of forests, he was induced to study the peat-bogs of his own country, with a view to discover whether the results he had already obtained would be supported or not by that line of evidence. He has not yet completed his observations, but so far as he has gone, he finds abundant corroboration of the truth of his views. The facts mentioned by him in connection with the peat-bogs of Norway are much the same as those I have already described when treating of the Scottish peat-mosses, and he

---

[*] The gradual change from arctic to temperate conditions is well seen in the shell-beds of Norway, as Sars has shown. He has also pointed out the curious fact that certain species of molluscs occur in these shell-beds which are now restricted to seas farther south, ranging from England to the Mediterranean; while others again now living off the Norwegian shores occur also in the Mediterranean, but are not met with in intermediate regions (*Iagttagelser over den postpliocene eller glaciale Formations*, p. 56). Mr. Gwyn Jeffreys, as is well known, noted similar facts at Uddevalla, *British Association Report*, 1863. Similar facts again have been observed in connection with the glacial and postglacial deposits of Britain and Ireland. We have no doubt still much to learn concerning the natural history of glacial, interglacial, and postglacial seas. But it already appears that there were several great changes in the distribution of the marine fauna of north-western Europe during the glacial epoch. I would ask palæontologists whether the occurrence of southern forms in late glacial times (arctic shelly clays) is not further proof that a mild climate of long continuance supervened after the retreat of the great ice-sheet which preceded the extreme submergence in Wales, Scotland, and Ireland. These southern forms I would take to be relics of the fauna that tenanted our seas during the climax of the last mild interglacial period. See the question of this last warm interglacial period discussed in Chap. xxxvii., *et sqq*.

[†] *Essay on the Immigration of the Norwegian Flora during alternating Rainy and Dry Seasons;* Christiania, 1876.

comes to the same conclusions—namely, that the buried forests indicate a continental climate, while the bogs that cover them point to the former prevalence of a humid insular climate. And since he meets with several successive buried forests occurring one above another and separated by intervening beds of peat, he is strongly inclined to think that there may have been a number of alternating dry and rainy periods in postglacial times.

CHAPTER XXXIII.

GLACIAL DEPOSITS OF SWITZERLAND.

No trace of sea-action or of floating ice.—Erratics of the Jura.—Glaciers of the
Rhine and its tributaries.—Glacier of the Rhone.—Moraine-profonde in
Dauphiny.—Moraine-profonde of Swiss low grounds.—Ancient alluvium or
diluvium overlying moraine-profonde.—Interglacial deposits of Dürnten, &c.
—Morainic débris, &c., overlying interglacial deposits.—Reasons why the
moraines of the second great advance of glaciers are large and well-preserved.
Postglacial deposits.

THERE is no region where the marks left by the gigantic
glaciers of the Ice Age, have been more assiduously
studied than in Switzerland. Besides the many eminent
native geologists who have devoted themselves to this subject,
hosts of enthusiastic visitors from a distance, some of them
men of great distinction, have won for themselves scientific
laurels amongst the glaciers of that beautiful country. For
us especially the Swiss glaciers, ancient and modern alike,
have many valuable lessons. Geologists in this country are
frequently puzzled to decide what part of the glacial phenomena here ought to be ascribed to the action of land-ice, and
what portion must be assigned to rafts and bergs. In Switzerland nowadays there is no such difficulty. Glacialists are
unanimous in considering that all the marks of old ice-action
in that country have been produced entirely by glaciers.
Rock-scratching on the grandest scale—striæ running across
the tops of considerable hills—erratics which have crossed
deep broad valleys, often for great distances, and stranded at
last on steep mountain-slopes—till, formed and accumulated
under ice (a process which some geologists even yet cannot be
persuaded has ever taken place), may all be studied to the
greatest advantage in Switzerland. It is not my purpose,
however, to dwell much upon these matters. The object I
have in view is simply to point out the succession of the
glacial deposits, for the purpose of instituting a comparison
between these and glacial accumulations elsewhere.

The Jura Mountains, as every one knows, extend in a long series of parallel ridges from south-west to north-east, between the valleys of the Rhone and the Rhine. From the base of these mountains the low grounds of Switzerland roll themselves out to east and south-east until they sweep up against the great barrier of the Alps. Now upon the southern flanks of the Jura we find numerous scattered blocks and boulders, all of which have been carried from the Alps across the intervening plains, and left where we now see them. Some of the blocks are of enormous dimensions : many contain thousands of cubic feet, and not a few are quite as big as cottages. Indeed one of them——the great granite-boulder of Steinhoff ——might be compared, as Mr. Maclaren has remarked, to "a goodly-sized house of three storeys." Such blocks have been observed on the Jura at a height of no less than 2,015 ft. above the surface of Lake Neuchâtel, or 3,450 ft. above the sea ; and from this elevation downwards they are strewn in greater or smaller numbers along the whole mountain-slope that faces the Alps.

Towards the north-east, where the Jura begins to lose in height as it approaches the valley of the Rhine, we find the erratics scattered not only along the southern slopes, but even over the tops of the mountains. According to Swiss geologists these erratic blocks and boulders have been carried down from the Alps on the surface of a mighty *mer de glace*, underneath which the whole of the central low grounds were at one time buried. This vast sheet of ice, not less than 3,000 ft. in thickness, stretched continuously outwards from the Rhone Valley, and abutted upon the Jura, the higher ridges of which rose above its level. Other gigantic glaciers descending the valleys of the Rhine and its tributaries, became confluent with the glacier of the Rhone, and each of these carried its quota of rubbish and boulders, which it stranded along the slopes of the mountains.

When the Rhone glacier advanced across the plains of Switzerland and abutted upon the Jura, it was of course compelled to flow south-west and north-east along the flanks of that range.* That portion which crept towards the north-

* The great ice-stream that pressed upon the Jura must have exerted very considerable erosive power along the base of these mountains, just as we have

east coalesced with the glaciers of the Aar, and its tributaries, and these last again with the great glacier of the Rhine. How far, then, to the north did this vast ice-flow extend? Its limits in that direction are at present unknown. The old moraine-matter has been traced down to the Rhine at its confluence with the Aar, but beyond that, the track of the ice has not been followed. No one, however, can believe that the great glacier stopped abruptly on the banks of the Rhine. The mass of ice which overtopped the Jura and flowed down the Frickthal to the Rhine, must of necessity have continued its course much farther. Nor when we remember that at this very time the Black Forest also had its great glaciers, can we doubt that the ice of that region was confluent with the Swiss *mer de glace.*

Passing north-eastward from Waldshut and Schaffhausen on the Rhine the moraine-matter of the ancient glaciers has been traced continuously into the valley of the Danube as far north as Riedlingen. From this point its northern boundary forms a rapidly undulating line that sweeps away to the east by Buchau, Kellmünz, Mindelheim, and the Ammer See. It crosses the valley of the Isar a little above Munich, descends the valley of the Inn as far as Braunau, and reaches down that of the Traun to within ten miles of Linz on the Danube. It short, it is evident that great glaciers have issued in old times from all the Alpine valleys that open to the north, so as to become confluent on the low grounds at the foot of the mountains and form one *mer de glace* that stretched continuously from the valley of the Rhone onwards into Austria.

That part of the Rhone glacier which flowed to the south-west, was not until recently thought to have extended beyond some twenty miles below Geneva. But quite lately the path of the old ice-stream was followed by MM. Falsan and Chantre,[*] from Geneva as far as Lyons, passing by Seillon, Châtillon,

seen was the case in Scotland, where, in front of the islands and high grounds that opposed the advance of the ice, deep hollows were scooped. We are not surprised, therefore, to find similar hollows at the base of the Jura—the lake-basins of Neuchâtel and Brienne, namely. The trend of these lakes corresponds with that of the great glacier that flowed towards the north-east.

* According to these geologists, all the plain of the Dombes and lower Dauphiné is covered with the *moraine profonde* of the Rhone and its tributaries. *Bull. de la Soc. géol. de France,* tome xxvi. 2e Serié, 1868 ; *Bibliothèque Universelle* (1872), vol. xliv. p. 46; *Nature,* vol. viii. p. 468.

Aars, and Sattonay, and even farther south to Valence in the department of Drome—that is to say, about 130 miles as the crow flies from Geneva. On its way it overflowed the rubbish heaps of limestone blocks brought down by the local glaciers that descended from the valleys of Savoy, and deposited above them its own moraines of crystalline rocks. What a picture does this give us of the old Ice Age! Truly if Scandinavia and Britain had then their great enveloping *mer de glace*, central Europe was not much behind with its colossal glaciers; a stone dropped upon the Rhone glacier at its source might in those days have been carried upwards of 270 miles before it reached the end of the ice-flow. In comparison with this what are the present glaciers of the Himalaya and the Karakoram, the very largest of which attains a length of only thirty-five miles?[*]

But erratic blocks and loose rubbish strewed along the mountain-slopes are not the only deposits which these great glaciers accumulated. In the low grounds of Switzerland[†] we get a dark tough clay packed with scratched and well-rubbed stones, and containing here and there some admixture of sand, and irregular beds and patches of earthy gravel. This clay is quite unstratified, and the strata upon which it rests frequently exhibit much confusion, being turned up on end and bent over, exactly in the same way as the rocks in this country are sometimes broken and disturbed below till. The whole deposit has experienced much denudation, but even yet it covers considerable areas, and attains a thickness varying from a few feet up to not less than thirty yards. At Dürnten a shaft was sunk in it to a depth of thirty feet without reaching the bottom.

[*] It would seem that during a comparatively recent period the desert of Sahara was submerged, recent marine shells having been found widely distributed over its surface, and embedded at some depth in the sand. It is highly probable that, as Escher von der Linth has suggested, this submerged condition of the Sahara obtained during the glacial epoch, and that much of the moisture which then fed the great snow-fields of the Alps was brought by the prevalent winds flowing from Africa across the Sahara Sea and the Mediterranean.

[†] For descriptions of the ancient *moraine profonde* of the plains of Switzerland see Necker's *Etudes géologiques dans les Alps;* and A. Favre's *Recherches géologiques dans les Parties de la Savoie,* &c., tome i. chap. iv. Some of the best sections of this stony clay or till which I have seen are exposed in the steep banks of the river Arve, a little above Carouge, where a thickness of 80 or 90 ft. is seen. The included stones and boulders at that place were beautifully striated, especially those of limestone. Considerable masses of rolled stones, gravel, and shingle, were enclosed in the tumultuous unstratified till.

The Swiss glacialists believe this deposit to be the material that gathered underneath the great *mer de glace,* and hence they term it *grund-moräne* or *moraine profonde.* That it has been subjected to great pressure is evident from the exceedingly stiff and compact nature of the clay, in which, as in other particulars, it closely resembles, as indeed it is the counterpart of, the Scotch till.

I have mentioned the fact that the *grund-moräne* has suffered much denudation. Resting upon its eroded surface we find sand and gravel, and the same deposits are spread far and wide over the low grounds, attaining often a great thickness, and frequently rising to considerable heights. These constitute the ancient alluvium of Swiss geologists. When they are traced from the low grounds up to the base of the Alps they generally become coarser, and show many angular stones, especially at or near the bottom.* Of course they do not cover the ground continuously ; in many places, indeed, they are absent altogether.

The origin of the ancient alluvium is sufficiently obvious. When the great glaciers were retiring and leaving trains of blocks and boulders upon the mountain-slopes at ever decreasing heights, they by-and-by came to shoot their rubbish upon the low grounds. Streams of water issuing from the melting ice then washed these moraines down, rounded the angular stones, and spread sand and gravel far and wide. The ancient alluvium, therefore, is exactly the counterpart of those great accumulations of sand and gravel, which occur so abundantly in and at the mouths of our own mountain-valleys. There seems, however, to be an entire absence of such conspicuous gravel ridges as the åsar of Sweden, the eskers of Ireland, and certain of the kames of Scotland.

The beds which I have now to refer to, carry the story still farther on, and are of much interest and importance.

At Dürnten and Wetzikon in the canton of Zurich, certain seams of lignite have long been worked, and in the canton of St. Gall, similar seams occur at Utznach and Mörschweil, on the Lake of Constance. The lignite at these different places is believed to be the same, or at all events to have been accu-

* Carl Vogt's *Lehrbuch der Geologie und Petrefactenkunde,* third edition, vol. ii. p. 36.

mulated at approximately the same time. It varies from two to five feet, and even occasionally reaches a thickness of twelve feet. It appears to be made up chiefly of peat-forming plants. Like much more recent peat-mosses, it also contains numerous remains of trees, such as pines, oaks, birches, larches, &c. From an examination of these remains Professor Heer has concluded that the climate of Switzerland during the formation of the lignite was similar to what it is now.

Associated with this ancient peat-moss are found the bones of the elephant (*E. antiquus*), a species of rhinoceros (*R. Merkii*), the urus or great ox, the stag (*Cervus Elaphus*), the cave-bear, and the elk. In addition to these fossils a number of insects are found whose shining wing-cases speckle the upper surfaces of the beds. Some of the coleoptera described would seem to be now extinct.

But the same lignite has recently yielded a much more remarkable "fossil" than any of those just mentioned. Dr. Scheuermann of Basle noticed on one occasion a number of small pointed rods that lay side by side, closely embedded in the lignite, and he at once handed the block containing them to Professor Rütymeyer, who has since published * an account of his observations. It seems that the sticks are four in number, and afford distinct evidence of having been cut and pointed by the hand of man. There are evident marks moreover of a string having been wound tightly round them at one part. The inference is that the rods "formed a portion of rough basket or wattle work." There can be no doubt whatever that this bit of man's handiwork was embedded in the lignite, of which indeed it formed a part as much as any of the other vegetable remains, by which it was surrounded. The rods were distinctly compressed or flattened, and they did not differ either in texture or colour from the wood which is usually found in the lignite.

Such, then, is the general character of the lignite. At Dürnten it rests immediately upon a layer of fine yellow sand and clay, beneath which comes an unknown thickness of *grund-moräne*.† Overlying the lignite we find a considerable

* "Spuren des Menschen aus interglaciären Ablagerungen in der Schweiz," *Archiv für Anthropologie*, Bd. viii., Heft 2, 1875. See also *Nature*, vol. xiii. p. 130.

† *Die Urwelt der Schweiz*, p. 486. It was at Dürnten where they drove a shaft

thickness of gravel and sand arranged in beds, which are surmounted with several large alpine erratics.*

Now from these facts we gather that the great *mer de glace* eventually vanished from the low grounds, and the glaciers shrunk back again into the deep mountain-valleys. The climate grew as mild as it is at present. Oaks, pines, and other trees overspread the ground, many large animals entered Switzerland, and man himself became a denizen of the "Alpenländer." That this condition of things must have endured for a long time no one can doubt. Nor could the change from the intense glacial climate of the great *mer de glace* have been other than gradual. The glaciers would slowly retire, and many ages would elapse before the conditions became such as to induce the growth of oak-trees. After the genial climate that nourished these trees had lasted for untold centuries, the cold again increased. Slowly the glaciers crept down the valleys. Little by little, year by year, they continued to advance until at last, escaping from the mountain-valleys, they deployed upon the low grounds. And now, encroaching upon, and eventually occupying the basins of the Alpine lakes, they crept out from these and piled up great end-moraines upon the low grounds beyond.

But the erratic blocks that overlie the lignite beds are not the only evidence of this second advance of the glaciers. That the ice after retiring from the Jura to the mountain-valleys did again invade the low country, had been inferred before the interglacial character of the lignite beds was discovered. It had been known for years that the first ground-moraines and ancient alluvium were overlaid by newer ground-moraines, terminal moraines, and alluvium ; the meaning of this having been pointed out by Morlot as far back as 1854.† It was extremely satisfactory, however, to get the further evidence supplied by the lignite beds, as it enabled

---

in the *grund-moräne* to a depth of 30 ft., and were prevented from going farther by an influx of water.

* Near the village of Hermance, on the borders of the Lake of Geneva, there is an interesting section showing a bed of turf (with trunks of trees and recent species of land and freshwater shells) which overlies a blue tenacious clay with scratched stones, and is covered with reddish clay containing erratic blocks and a little gravel. None of the blocks in this upper clay are striated. A. Favre, *Recherches géologiques,* &c., tome i. p. 71.

† *Bulletin de la Société vaudoise des Sciences naturelle,* 1854, iv. pp. 39, 41, 53, 185; *Edinburgh New Philosophical Journal,* 1855, p. 14.

geologists to appreciate more fully what the retreat and advance of the glaciers really meant.

A similar succession of deposits has been detected by Professor Hanns Höfer, as occurring in Carinthia. In the lower reaches of the valleys of that region ground-moraine is well developed, and perched blocks and erratics are found at great elevations, while the glaciated aspect of the mountains further shows that the valleys at one time must have brimmed with ice. Overlying the ground-moraine come massive deposits of river-gravel, &c. (near Klagenfurt), which have yielded remains of the woolly rhinoceros, the steinbock (*Ibex cebennarum*), and *Bos taurus*. These freshwater beds Professor Höfer correlates with the gravel beds that immediately overlie the Dürnten lignites (corresponding to the *Interglaciale Geröllbildung* of Heer). A younger series of large moraines met with in Carinthia near the Raiblersee, and in the Möll and Malnitzer Valley, he considers to be the equivalents of the great moraines of the "second glacial period" in Switzerland.*

The glaciers of the second period, although of very much larger dimensions than their puny descendants of to-day, yet were themselves but pigmies as compared to the gigantic ice-flows of the first period. Nevertheless, strange to say, while the end-moraines left by the former are large and well defined, those of the latter do not exist, or exist only in the form of scattered blocks. For this apparent anomaly several reasons may be given. In the first place we have to consider that during the melting of the great *mer de glace* that filled to overflowing the low grounds of Switzerland, the rivers must have been enormously swollen, and excessive denudation of the moraines would necessarily follow. Next we have to take into account the greater antiquity of the deposits belonging to the first period. So long a time passed between the date of their formation and that of the second set of moraines, that we should naturally expect to find the latter in a better state of preservation than the former. Again, it is very doubtful whether the end-moraines of the first period were much larger or even as large as those of the second. The moraines

* "Studien aus Kärnten": *Neues Jahrbuch für Mineralogie, Geologie, und Palæontologie*, 1873, p. 128.

of a small glacier, as Mühlberg * has well reminded us, are
larger in proportion than those of an ice-stream of greater
pretensions.   During the first period an immense frontage of
rock disappeared below the ice, and was thus prevented from
showering down its debris.   In the second period, however,
the glaciers did not reach nearly so high upon the sides of
their valleys, while the snow-fields were less continuous, and
thus a much greater area of rock was exposed to the action
of the frost.   Yet, further, we cannot tell whether or not the
glaciers of the first period remained long stationary when they
had reached their maximum size.   But we know that those
of the second period did.   Finally, when we consider that the
end-moraines of the former were dropped upon the bottoms
of two of the largest river-valleys—those of the Rhone and
the Rhine—it does not appear at all improbable that much
of the morainic debris may yet be lying concealed below the
deep and widespread deposits of loam (loess), through which
the present rivers make their way after escaping from Switzerland.

The change from the last glacial conditions to the present
climate appears to have been gradual ; the glaciers retiring
slowly up the valleys, but perhaps occasionally advancing
for a short distance, during some exceptionally severe year.

The mammalian remains met with in postglacial deposits
in Switzerland, belong for the most part to the same species
and genera as those which characterize similar deposits in
Ireland, Scotland, and north of England.   Thus we get the
bison, extinct bovidæ, several species of deer, &c., and also
the mammoth and the woolly rhinoceros.   Human relics
likewise occur plentifully in the postglacial beds, but none of
these go back to an older date than the newer stone period of
archæologists.

* *Ueber die erratischen Bildungen im Aargau,* &c., p. 85.

CHAPTER XXXIV.

GLACIAL DEPOSITS OF NORTHERN ITALY.

MM. Martins and Gastaldi on moraines of Dora Baltea, &c.—So-called pliocenic
sands and alluvia of Piedmont.—Shells of the pliocene sands.—Great
moraines not the equivalents of the Swiss till or ground-moraines.—Post-
miocene denudation in the valley of the Po.—Pliocene shells and striated
stones in same deposit.—Views of Professor Stopanni, M. Desor, and Signor
Gastaldi.—Observations and views of Professor Rütymeyer.

UST as in Switzerland we have central low grounds, with
the Alps rising in the south and the Jura in the north, so
also in Italy we find the great plains of Piedmont and Lombardy flanked by the Alps on the one hand, and bounded by
the hills of Turin and the northern spurs of the Apennines
on the other. With two exceptions, every great valley that
opens out from the Alps upon the plains of northern Italy
contains a lake, as is the case with similar valleys in Switzerland. The two exceptions referred to are the valleys of the
Dora Riparia and the Dora Baltea.

Thus, at the first glance there appears to be a broad
general resemblance between the regions on both sides of the
Alps. The geologist might therefore expect to meet with a
like similarity in the glacial phenomena of the two regions;
and up to a certain point his expectations would no doubt be
realised. But when he came to correlate the Swiss with the
Italian deposits, he would find the task by no means so easy,
and the resemblance between the two not nearly so striking
as he anticipated. So long as he confined his attention to
the mountain-valleys, he would observe precisely the same
appearances as present themselves in the mountain-valleys of
Switzerland. Rounded and polished rocks, morainic débris,
and perched boulders he would see everywhere; and at the
lower ends of the great lakes he would encounter huge
terminal moraines. But out upon the broad plains he would

find only wide-spread deposits of gravel and loam, the stony glacial clay so often met with upon the low grounds of Switzerland nowhere appearing upon the plains of northern Italy.

Of all the glacial deposits of Italy, perhaps the most striking are the moraines of the Dora Baltea. They form a huge semicircular embankment opposite the mouth of the large valley of Aosta, and some idea of their vast extent may be gathered from the simple statement that they rise out of the plains of Piedmont as steep hills, to a height of 1,500 ft., and even in one place to very nearly 2,000 ft. Measured along its outer circumference,* this great morainic mass is found to have a frontage of at least fifty miles, while the plain which it encloses extends for some fifteen miles from Andrate southwards, with a breadth of about eight miles. Two lakelets (the largest of which is little more than two miles in length by one in breadth) occur within the moraine.

MM. Martins and Gastaldi have shown† that the moraine-matter rests upon beds of coarse gravel, and that these again repose upon deposits of sand, and the succession given is as follows :—

3. Moraine.
2. Alpine diluvium.
1. Marine sands.

The upper deposit (No. 3) forms the great bulk of the semicircular range of hills above referred to. It exactly resembles the moraines of the Swiss Alps, being composed of a pell-mell heap of angular blocks and débris, with some admixture of earth and sand.

The bed (2) also answers precisely to those wide accumulations of gravel which cover so large an area in the low grounds of Switzerland. It shows no trace of fossils, and the rounded stones of which it consists have evidently been derived from the Alps. None of these stones is striated, and no angular blocks occur among them.

The underlying marine sands contain a number of fossils,

* That is from Andrate by Mongrando, Saluzzola, Cavaglia, and Caluso to the bridge over the Chiusella.
† *Bulletin de la Société géologique de France*, tom. vii. 2me serie, p. 554; Professor Favre's *Recherches géologiques*, tom. i. p. 169. The moraines of northern Italy are described by several geologists, as by Sig. Omboni (*Atti della Soc. Ital. di Scienzi naturali*, 1861) and by M. Mortillet *op. et loc. cit.*

many of which belong to species still living in the Mediterranean. Out of ten shells which are said by MM. Martins and Gastaldi to be characteristic of these sands, eight are even now denizens of the neighbouring sea, one is doubtful, and only one is said to be extinct.

Resting upon the sands occurs here and there an ancient alluvium, which is considered by Martins and Gastaldi to be of older date than the Alpine diluvium. This deposit has yielded remains of the mastodon, the rhinoceros, the hippopotamus, the elephant, along with recent land and freshwater shells. The bottom of the marine sands is not always seen; in some places, however, these beds may be observed resting upon the solid rocks of the Alpine districts, while in other places they repose upon certain loose accumulations of older Tertiary age. According to some Italian geologists, both the marine sands and the alluvium with bones belong to the Pliocene period, and are considered therefore to date back to preglacial times.

In a recent publication,[*] however, Signor Gastaldi explains that he has termed these bone-bearing beds "*pliocenic alluvia*," not so much because he wished to make them a constituent part of the Pliocene formation, but rather to discriminate them from the Alpine diluvium, which of course is a later accumulation. Besides the "pliocenic alluvia," there occur at various places in northern Italy, as in the environs of Carignano, at Lanzo near Stura; at Gifflenga in the valley of the Cervo; at Boca, Maggiora, &c., certain beds of lignite which the same eminent observer is inclined to consider as being the precise equivalents of the ossiferous alluvia; and he quotes the opinions of MM. Comalla and Stoppani, who have no hesitation in saying that the lignites of Leffe (Gandino), in which occur remains of the elephant (*E. meridionalis*), the beaver, the emys, (not distinguishable from the recent *Cistudo europea*), deer, and goats, really belong to postpliocene, and not to Pliocene times. In short, as Professor Gastaldi remarks, the lignites rest upon Pliocene deposits, and are covered by diluvium, and thus occupy the same relative position as the Swiss lignites (Utznach, Wetzikon, &c.), which,

* "Appunti sulla Memoria del Sig. J. Geikie, *On Changes of Climate, &c.*" *Atti delle Reale Accademia delle Scienze di Torino*, vol. viii. Aprile 1873.

it will be remembered, lie at the base of the Alpine diluvium.

But while Professor Gastaldi is clearly of opinion that the Italian and Swiss lignites belong to one and the same age, he does not agree with Professor Heer that the Swiss lignites are interglacial, and objects to the suggestion which I had ventured to make,* namely, that the ossiferous beds of northern Italy mark an interglacial period. I feel somewhat sure, however, that if Professor Gastaldi were to study the Swiss deposits, he could come to no other conclusion than that arrived at by the eminent Swiss botanist. It is beyond question that the Swiss beds rest in some places upon true glacial deposits, upon unmistakable ground-moraine—*i. e.* clay holding scratched stones and boulders. If, therefore, the Italian lignites be of the same age as those of Switzerland, they can only be referred to interglacial times. It is true that, so far as is known, no glacial deposits underlie the Italian lignites ; but the same is the case with not a few of the Swiss lignite beds, as for example those at Utznach, where the beds rest directly on highly disturbed deposits of Miocene age. The mere absence of underlying moraine-matter is no proof, therefore, that the Italian lignites are of preglacial age ; the Swiss lignites were supposed to be so, until at Wetzikon and Dürnten they were found to repose upon a true erratic deposit belonging to post-pliocene, or glacial times.

In the publication referred to I not only suggested the interglacial age of the ossiferous alluvia of Piedmont, but I even went so far as to state that the underlying marine sands might probably prove eventually to belong to interglacial times also. I was quite aware that this suggestion would appear bold to Italian geologists, and it was not without some trepidation that I ventured to express my views upon the subject. Nevertheless, holding as I did and still do, decided convictions concerning the great interval of time represented by the Swiss lignites, and by their equivalents, in northern and western Europe, I was prepared to risk the charge of boldness, in the hope that the whole subject would be thoroughly ventilated. In this hope I have not been disappointed. Signor Gastaldi, in a most interesting com-

* *On Changes of Climate during the Glacial Epoch.*

munication to the Academy of Sciences, Turin, has taken up the question. After giving his arguments the careful study which they deserve, I am compelled still to dissent from his views, which I the more regret as it may appear presumptuous in me—whose personal acquaintance with northern Italy has only been obtained during a few short holiday excursions—to differ from the opinion of one who has made that region a lifelong study. The question, however, is not one of the geological succession of strata. There is no dispute as to what relative position the "marine sands" of Piedmont occupy. They are clearly of older date than any recognizable morainic or diluvial deposits in northern Italy; and if it were simply a question of local geology, one could have no good reason for doubting their preglacial age. But then the question is not one of local geology alone; the Italian deposits must be considered in the light of the evidence derived from contiguous regions. If it be true that certain oscillations of climate accompanied the deposition of the glacial deposits and their equivalents in every region of the northern hemisphere in which these accumulations have been studied, it is not unreasonable to hope that in Italy also we shall find some indications of the same great world-changes. What then, let us ask, is the evidence furnished by the "marine sands" of Piedmont? Do they afford us any definite proof that they are of preglacial age?

Of the shells which occur in these sands a certain percentage are not known as living species. The great majority, however, still occupy European seas. My friend Mr. Etheridge, who has been kind enough to examine for me some lists of the fossils obtained from the marine sands which are exposed here and there at the base of the Alps between Lake Maggiore and the Ticino, tells me that in his opinion these deposits do not date back to so old a time as the Pliocene beds of England. It is difficult, however, to ascertain the proportion of living to extinct species in the Italian Pliocene, and the results obtained during the recent dredging cruise of the *Porcupine*,[*] make it doubtful whether many of the shells which are now only known in a fossil state in these Italian Tertiaries may not eventually prove to be still living species.

* *Depths of the Sea*, p. 183 et sqq.

Signor G. Michelotti, well known for his works on the Pliocene and Miocene faunas of Piedmont, examined for Professor Gastaldi a series of fossils from the marine sands at the base of the Alps, and informed him that not a single characteristic Miocene shell appeared amongst the number.[*] But even if it should eventually prove that the extinct or apparently extinct species in the so-called Pliocene sands at the base of the Alps are in the proportion of 20 or 30 per cent., still that will not prove these deposits to be of preglacial age. Nay, it would not even follow from this that the yellow sands of Piedmont were accumulated at the same period of time as those English deposits that contain a similar percentage of apparently extinct species. The mode adopted by M. Deshayes and Sir Charles Lyell for ascertaining the relative antiquity of Tertiary deposits is no doubt most excellent, so long as the deposits we examine happen to form a more or less continuous series, and are confined to some definite geographical area. The Norwich Crag, for example, contains about 18 per cent. of extinct or apparently extinct species of sea-shells. Now, if certain other English Tertiary deposits are found to contain a greater percentage of extinct forms than this, it is legitimate to infer that these must be older than the Norwich Crag, just as on the contrary we should consider those beds to belong to later times which happen to exhibit a smaller number of extinct species; for as Sir C. Lyell remarks, "the greater number of recent species always implies the more modern origin of the strata." But when we pass into a different geographical area, it is evident that although we there detected superficial accumulations in which the proportion of extinct to recent species was the same as in the Norwich Crag, still it would not follow that these accumulations had been deposited at the same time as the English beds referred to. We have to take into consideration the fact that marine faunas must in the course of time be subjected to very different conditions, and that, owing to geological and geographical changes, species characteristic of certain areas may die out and become extinct at a more rapid rate than the contemporaneous life-forms of

[*] "Studii Geologici sulle Alpi Occidentali," *Mem. del R. Comitato Geologico d'Italia*, vol. i., 1871.

other regions. Hence, deposits laid down at one and the same time in different latitudes and in separated districts, may come to envelope and contain assemblages of shells amongst which the proportion of extinct to recent species may vary indefinitely. And the difficulty of identifying contemporaneous deposits becomes the greater the nearer these approach in age to recent accumulations. In short, it may well be that the Newer Pliocene of one country may be either older or younger than the Newer Pliocene of another. We may conclude, therefore, that the evidence supplied by the organic remains in the marine sands of Piedmont is not sufficient to prove that these sands are of preglacial age.

But it will be said that, since the sands in question are overlaid by the great moraines, they must necessarily date back to preglacial times. Now this would certainly follow, if it could be shown that these moraines mark the farthest limits reached by the glaciers during the climax of the glacial epoch. There are several considerations, however, which lead to the inference that the moraines referred to do not mark the southern limits of the ancient glaciation, but belong indeed to a more recent date.

On the north side of the Alps there is distinct evidence to show that Switzerland experienced at least two glacial periods, separated by an intervening period of milder conditions. During the first cold period the glaciers increased to such an extent that all the ice-streams issuing from the mountain-valleys coalesced upon the low grounds to form one gigantic *mer de glace* that rose some 2,000 feet high upon the flanks of the Jura. Towards the north-east, the ice would appear to have overflowed these hills, aud thereafter to have descended the Frickthal to the Rhine at a point some twelve miles below the confluence of that river with the Aar. How much farther west it may have gone we cannot say, but there is reason to believe that the Swiss *mer de glace* united with the glaciers of the Black Forest. Again, it is certain that from that part of the *mer de glace* which flowed to the south-west a great glacier crept outwards upon the plains of France, over the dreary Dombes, and descended the valley of the Rhone, as far at least as Valence, in the department of Drome.

Now it will readily be admitted that during the greatest extension of the ice on the north side of the Alps, gigantic glaciers must at the same time have filled all the mountain-valleys of northern Italy. In proof of this, we are referred to the great moraines of the Dora Baltea and those of the Dora Riparia, and the similar heaps of débris which occur at the lower ends of all the great Italian lakes—Orta, Maggiore, Lugano, Como, Lecco, Isea, and Garda. These moraines indicate, no doubt, the former presence of very large ice-streams, yet it is hardly conceivable that they can be the equivalents of the old *grund-moränen* of the Swiss low grounds. When we picture to ourselves the condition of Switzerland and the adjoining tracts of France and Germany during the climax of glacial cold—when we think of the Rhone glacier after its egress from the low grounds of Switzerland, flowing for 130 miles out upon the plains of France—when, further, we conceive of its northern branch uniting with the glaciers of the Rhine and its tributaries, and thereafter pouring over the end of the Jura to coalesce with the ice-fields of the Black Forest, it is impossible to believe that on the southern side of the Alps the glaciers could have been, comparatively speaking, so insignificant, that they never succeeded in getting well out of their mountain-valleys. The more southerly latitude of Italy will not enable us to explain this anomaly.

It is perfectly true that the present glaciers on the south side of the Alps are quite insignificant when compared to those occupying similar positions in Switzerland, and during the climax of the glacial epoch it is more than likely that the Swiss glaciers would much surpass those of Italy in importance. Still, those geologists who consider that Sahara existed at that time as a vast inland sea, will perhaps admit that the difference between the climates of the opposing slopes of the Alps would not then be so marked as it is now. We may, indeed, believe that the Italian glaciers would be arrested in their downward course sooner than those of Switzerland, yet the vast extent of the latter indicates a former intensity of cold which must needs have given rise to glaciers in Italy of even greater magnitude than those that occupied the lake-basins, and dropped their superficial moraines on the low grounds beyond. In short, we are led to infer that when the Rhone glacier was depositing its moraines in the plains of France, the glaciers of the Dora Riparia and Dora Baltea must have advanced far beyond the mouths of their mountain-valleys, and may have even traversed the plains of Piedmont, and abutted upon the hills of Turin.

I am well aware that there are no deposits on the plains of Piedmont which can be referred to this great extension of the glaciers, and so far there is no direct and positive evidence in favour of such an extension. But the great valley of the Po, like that of the Danube, and that of the Rhine between the Vosges and the Black Forest, is everywhere covered by river deposits of comparative recent origin. It is quite possible, therefore, that a deposit of *moraine profonde* or till may lie concealed at a greater distance from the Alps than the conspicuous moraines of the Baltea, &c. No inference can be drawn either one way or the other from the fact that no terminal moraines are known to occur farther south than the mouths of the Alpine valleys in Italy. Terminal moraines do not exist on the plains of Germany or the low grounds of France to mark the limits reached by the ice during the coldest period of the glacial epoch ; yet it is not unlikely that the Scandinavian ice-sheet reached into northern Germany, and the Rhone glacier certainly flowed south as far as the low grounds of Dauphiny.

The slopes of the Moncalieri-Valenza Hills are sprinkled with boulders and large erratics of Alpine rocks, which were at one time supposed to have been carried across Piedmont by the ice of the glacial epoch. But subsequent and more detailed observations* have led Gastaldi to the opinion that the blocks in question are merely the denuded wreck of certain great beds of conglomerate belonging to the Miocene formation. No one who has visited the ground is likely to dispute this conclusion. One sees embedded in the Miocene conglomerate large erratics of precisely the same character as those that are lying loose on the hill-slopes ; and the conclusion seems irresistible that these latter are but the relics of those portions of the conglomerate which the denuding

---

* "Sugli Elementi che compongono i Conglomerati Mioceni del Piemonte ;" *Memoria della Reale Accademia delle Scienze di Torino*, serie ii. vol. xx.

forces have carried away. At the same time, it must be remarked that if the glaciers, during the glacial epoch, ever did reach the Hills of Turin, the erratic blocks which they must then have left behind would now be indistinguishable from the denuded remains of the older erratic formation which Gastaldi has clearly shown to be of Miocene age.

While, therefore, it must be admitted that there is no positive evidence* to show that the Italian glaciers ever crept farther south than the limits reached by the terminal moraines which now circle round the mouths of the Alpine valleys, it is on the other hand equally true that no proof is forthcoming to show that they did not. We are not, however, without some indirect evidence in favour of the great extension which I have inferred.

Let me ask the reader to go back with me in imagination to the Miocene period—that period which preceded in time the Pliocene, and during which the great conglomerates of the Moncalieri Hills were deposited. At that time the Adriatic Sea extended up the valley of the Po, and in all probability communicated with the Mediterranean across that low range of hills which now serves to connect the Maritime Alps with the Apennines. The Alpine valleys then formed long fiords, and the waves rose high on the northern slopes of the Apennines. Such conditions were maintained during many long ages, so as to allow vast heaps of sediment to gather upon the bed of the old sea. In some places these accumulations now form considerable hills. We find them fringing the northern flanks of the Apennines,† and extending in unbroken succession from Moncalieri to Valenza, forming those great deposits of conglomerate (and associated beds of gravel, sand, and marl), of which I have already spoken. An examination of these deposits shows that they have been derived from the degradation of the Alpine mountains. The

---

* It seemed to me, however, that the mountains behind Nomaglio (Val d'Aosta) were glaciated at least half way up from the surface of the great lateral moraine to their summits. If this be so, then the glacier that flowed at that level must have attained greater dimensions than the glacier which brought down the lateral moraine that extends from Andrate to Cavaglia. The glaciation at the higher level was much less distinctly marked than that at and below the summit level of the moraines, indicating that the former was probably effected at a much earlier age than the latter.

† They occur also upon the southern slopes of that range, but I confine attention to the valley of the Po.

sea in which they gathered washed the base of the Alps, and extended into the great valleys. But although this must have been the case, yet it is remarkable that no trace of miocene deposits can be anywhere detected along that ancient coast-line between Lake Maggiore and the River Ticino. We cannot doubt that at the time the thick beds of conglomerate, gravel, sand, &c. (which are so conspicuous in the Moncalieri-Valenza Hills, and which occur in those hills at a higher level than the base of the Alps) were being deposited, similar materials were also gathering on the sea-bottom along the shores of the northern mountain-land. Yet no trace of these exists. Again, it is to be noted that while the Pliocene sands that fringe the Moncalieri-Valenza Hills rest upon deposits of Miocene and Eocene age, yet the Pliocene of the Dora Baltea and the Sessia recline upon the solid rocks of the mountains. It is clear, therefore, that before the Pliocene beds were laid down, the pre-existing Miocene and Eocene deposits had been removed. In short, it is evident that after the close of the Miocene period, and before the yellow marine sands of Piedmont were accumulated, there must have been enormous denudation along the base of the Alpine mountains. Whether this great erosion is to be referred in chief part to the action of gigantic glaciers I do not say, but it is difficult to find a simpler and more satisfactory explanation.

Reference has already been made to the fact that, with two remarkable exceptions, all the great mountain-valleys of northern Italy contain lakes at their lower ends. But no lake occurs at Rivoli, and no large sheet of water, but only two inconsiderable lakelets, appear opposite the mouth of the Val d'Aosta. Now, it does appear singular that just where we might have expected large rock-basins to appear, we should find nothing of the kind. If glaciers dug out the basins of Maggiore, Garda, and the other lakes in Italy, and those of Constance, Lucerne, Zurich, &c., in Switzerland, why should not the colossal glaciers of the Val d'Aosta and the Dora Riparia have excavated similar hollows near Ivrea and Rivoli? The answer is that they did do so, but the basins so scooped out were subsequently filled up again with aqueous deposits.

Since I ventured this suggestion to explain the absence of a rock-basin at Ivrea, Signor Gastaldi has reinvestigated the matter, and now gives it as his opinion that such a buried rock-basin does really exist, and that portions of it are still visible in the little lakes of Candia and Viverone. He thinks that the basin is of no great depth, as the rocks in which it has been excavated are of a more durable character, and must therefore have yielded less easily to erosive action than those which contain the great lakes of the other valleys of northern Italy. As the great glacier slowly retired up the valley of the Dora, the river swept down vast heaps of gravel, sand, and silt (diluvium), with which it gradually filled up the ancient lake.

To draw these scattered remarks together, I shall now, in a few paragraphs, endeavour to correlate the Swiss and Italian deposits :—

1. At the period of most intense cold all the Alpine valleys were filled with glaciers, which in some cases reached a depth of 2,000 ft., and even more. These coalesced upon the low grounds of Switzerland to form a great *mer de glace*, from which two principal ice-flows extended—the one into the valley of the Rhine, where it became in all probability confluent with the glaciers of the Black Forest ; the other into the low grounds of France, over which it advanced as far south as Valence, in the department of Drome, a distance of 130 miles, at least, from Geneva. At the same time, great glaciers swept northwards by such valleys as those of the Iller, the Lech, the Loisach, the Isar, the Inn, &c., and became confluent in Würtemberg and Bavaria ; while vast glaciers descended the southern valleys of the Alps into the plains of northern Italy. There is no positive evidence forthcoming to show how far the latter invaded these low grounds, but taking into consideration the colossal proportions attained by the glacier of the Rhone, it is not improbable that the Italian glaciers may have crossed the valley of the Po so as to abut upon the Hills of Turin, a distance from the base of the Alps of only 25 miles.

2. Owing to a change of climate, the ice gradually melted back until it had retired from the low grounds, and shrunk into the deep mountain-valleys. During this retreat great

perched blocks were stranded along the mountain-slopes, and masses of sand and gravel were strewn over all the low grounds to which the water from the melting ice had access.

3. The climate becoming still more ameliorated, Switzerland assumed a vegetation similar to that which now characterizes it; while at the same time the elephant, rhinoceros, urus, and other animals, became denizens of the country. On the south side of the Alps, similarly, a strong forest growth sprung up, and numerous mammalia inhabited the land. [The deposits containing these remains rest upon, and are therefore older than, certain beds of sand of marine origin, which Italian geologists recognise as being of Pliocene and preglacial age. The fossil contents of these sands, however, do not demonstrate their preglacial age. So far as direct evidence goes, there is nothing to show that the sands may not be, to some extent at least, of interglacial age.]

4. The climate again becoming cold, the glaciers began another advance. Large rivers flowed down the valleys, and distributed vast heaps of gravel and sand, just as they had done during the retreat of the earlier glaciers. These deposits gathered over the site of the ancient forests in Switzerland, and rested on the marine sands and ossiferous alluvia of Piedmont, spreading far and wide over the whole valley of the Po. Eventually, the glaciers themselves crept out upon the low grounds of Switzerland, overriding the river-gravels and ancient forests, and dropping their moraines often miles below the lower ends of the lakes, as at Spreitenbach, in the valley of the Limmat, and below Mellingen, in the valley of the Reuss. At the same time, the glaciers that occupied the Italian valleys deployed upon the low grounds at the base of the Alps, and deposited their moraines above the great gravel beds that rest upon the marine sands.

5. Finally, the glaciers again retired, until at last they assumed their present proportions.[*]

* The foregoing portion of this chapter stands as it appeared in the "Appendix" of the last edition—only a few trifling verbal alterations having been made. The succeeding paragraphs contain an account of some recent investigations which show that my conclusions as to oscillations of climatic conditions having obtained in northern Italy during the accumulation of the so-called Pliocene beds, are, to some extent at least, borne out. While the question is still *sub judice* I have not thought it advisable to incorporate the new material with the old, and have therefore merely summed up the results of the most recent observations in the paragraphs that follow.

Some recent anomalous discoveries in the neighbourhood of Como, which have given rise to considerable discussion in Italy, must be noticed here, as they may yet throw much light on the relation of the so-called Pliocene strata to the older glacial accumulations on both sides of the Alps. Towards the end of 1873 Dr. Casella of Laglio found in a gravel pit, near the station of Cucciago (Milan and Como Railway), a great many sea-shells of the same species as that occur in the Pliocene strata. This gravel pit lies within the great amphitheatre formed by the large moraines that rise to the south of Camerlata. Shortly afterwards similar discoveries were made by the Marchese Rosales-Cigalini, not far from the same place; at Ronco, namely, in the neighbourhood of Cassina Rizzardi. At this locality the shells were commingled in the same deposit with striated stones (some of which had been drilled by boring-molluscs), and with disc-shaped pebbles. Subsequently, during the operations connected with the new railway between Chiasso and Mendrisio, the cuttings exposed complete sections, not only of the moraines and the underlying Pliocene marl beds, but even laid bare the Cretaceous strata upon which the latter rest. Now in several of the sections thus laid open, Professor Stopanni[*] observed that striated stones were not confined to the moraines, but appeared likewise in the underlying Pliocene clay, which was well stocked at the same time with its characteristic shells.

No doubt is expressed by the Italian geologists that the shells really belong to the so-called Pliocene. Out of fifty-three species obtained from Cassina Rizzardi, the late Signor Spreafico[†] found that thirty-one were extinct, twenty were still living in the Mediterranean, and two in tropical seas; so that if we compare the shells with those that occur in the Subappenine strata, we connot refuse to class them as of the same age.

Professor Stopanni's observations are supported by those

---

[*] "Il mare glaciale a' piedi delle Alpi," *Rivista Italiana*, 1874; "Sui rapporti del terreno glaciale col pliocenico nei dintorni di Como," *Atti della Soc. Ital. di Scienzi Naturali*, vol. xviii., fasc. ii., 1875. An excellent résumé of the views held by Italian geologists is given in Prof. Rütymeyer's memoir, *Ueber Pliocen und Eisperiode auf beiden Seiten der Alpen*, Basel, 1876.

[†] "Conchiglie marine del terreno erratico di Cassina Rizzardi," *Atti della Soc. Ital. di Scienze Naturali*, 1874.

of a well-known Swiss savant, M. Desor, who, after a detailed examination, concludes* that the shells are not accidentally mixed with the moraine-matter, but that the molluscs actually lived and died where their shells are now found, and were buried under morainic débris dropt upon them by a glacier.

From these observations Stopanni and Desor infer that during the formation of the marine Pliocene the old Adriatic Sea covered all the low grounds of northern Italy, and extended into the deep valleys of the Alps, down which crawled large glaciers which eventually entered the sea and shot their moraines upon its bed. At the same time, according to Stopanni, the elephants, rhinoceroses, deer, and other animals, whose remains are found in the lignite of Leffe and other places, wandered along the shores of the old sea which then laved the foot of the Alps.

These views are opposed by Signor Gastaldi,† who points out with much force that throughout the whole of Piedmont the marine Pliocene deposits are separated from the overlying moraines, opposite the mouths of the Alpine valleys, by a great thickness of shingle and gravel beds which he calls "Alpine diluvium," and which he believes is unquestionably the product of river-action. The old lignite beds, he further maintains, are intermediate in age between the Pliocene marine beds on the one hand and the Alpine diluvium on the other. He is inclined to admit, however, that the intermingling of striated stones and Pliocene shells in one and the same deposit points to the former existence of glaciers, probably small ones, in the Pliocene age. But the advance of the great glaciers which threw down the huge moraines of Rivoli, Ivrea, Camerlata, &c., was separated from the period of the small glaciers of Pliocene times by a prolonged continuance of terrestrial conditions. The bed of the old Pliocene sea had been upheaved—a rich vegetation had covered the new land—elephants and their congeners had become denizens of Piedmont and Lombardy—then by-and-by a period of flooded rivers had supervened, and immense deposits of sand, gravel, and shingle had been swept down

---

* *Le Paysage Morainique*, Paris, 1875.

† "Sur les glaciers pliocenique de M. E. Desor," *Atti della R. Accademia delle Scienze di Torino*, vol. x.

the Alpine valleys and scattered far and wide over the plains of the Po,—all this had taken place before the last colossal glaciers deployed upon the low grounds of northern Italy.

Another objection which might fairly be urged against the conclusions arrived at by Stopanni and Desor is based upon the character of the marine fauna of the Pliocene. The shells, there can be no doubt, indicate a warm sea—warmer probably than the present Mediterranean. According to the researches of Signor F. Sordelli,* ninety-eight species have been recognised among the shells which occur in the morainic gravel and sand at Cassina Rizzardi, Ronco, and Bulgaro Grasso. Of these, forty-seven still live in the Mediterranean, two in tropical seas, while forty-eight are apparently extinct. Again thirty-two are common to the Atlantic and the Mediterranean, but only five of these range northwards, while twenty are found in tropical waters. Not one of them is arctic. While the genial conditions which are implied by such an assemblage of molluscs prevailed in the sea at the foot of the Alps, it is difficult to believe that colossal glaciers, at the same time invaded the old Adriatic, and dropt their morainic débris on the shells lying scattered over its bottom. We are reminded, however, that somewhat similar conditions obtain in New Zealand with its tropical-like vegetation, where considerable glaciers descend to the neighbourhood of the warm Southern Ocean. But to this it may be replied that the geographical conditions of Italy and New Zealand are very dissimilar. Waiving such an objection, however, we might still ask why it is that glaciers as large or even larger than the old ones of the Dora Riparia, the Stura, the Dora Baltea, &c., do not even now exist on the south side of the Alps; for these mountains are higher, relatively to the sea, by some 400 metres, than they were at the time the Pliocene marine beds of Lombardy were being deposited. Can it be believed that the mere submergence of the valley of the Po would suffice to feed the snow-fields on the south side of the Alps to such an extent as cause the glaciers to assume the gigantic dimensions reached by those which piled up the great moraines of Ivrea and other places ?

I come now to notice certain observations made by Pro-

* "La fauna marina di Cassina Rizzardi," *Atti della Soc. Ital. Sc. Nat.*, 1874.

fessor Rütymeyer,* during a recent visit to northern Italy. Unfortunately, the sections which were at one time well exposed at several spots between Cassina Rizzardi and Fino had been covered up before his arrival, but he was able to examine some sections at Ronco. He describes the deposits at one place as consisting of fine sand with layers of rounded stones that vary in size from pebbles like hazel-nuts and walnuts up to blocks one or two feet in diameter. Comminuted fragments of shells were scattered through all the beds, but were most plentiful in the sand. No scratched stones were observed; but the place was surrounded by moraines. At another place close to the last, he noted shells and " scratched glacier-stones, some of which had been drilled by boring molluscs." The whole country, Rütymeyer remarks, bears the impress of the former presence of glaciers in so apparent a manner that one cannot hesitate to attribute to these a chief part in that anomalous commingling of Pliocene shells and striated stones which has so puzzled geologists.

That the shells do not occupy the place where the molluscs lived and died is evident from the fact that they all exhibit more or less manifest traces of having been rolled about and brought from a distance; perfect shells are rare, and the stones bored by lithodomi have subsequently been a good deal worn and rubbed. The shells belong to species which, according to Sordelli, could not have lived together side by side in the same place where we now find them—for while some of the molluscs affected a clay bottom, others preferred rock, &c. What is still more worthy of note, the shells are filled with blue marl or clay—a deposit which does not occur in the neighbourhood—the matrix in which the shells now lie embedded consisting of sand. Sordelli is of opinion that the deposit in which the shells occur is re-modelled morainic matter. From these and other observations it is evident that the Cassina Rizzardi deposits have been derived from two sources—one being a littoral formation of Pliocene age and the other a glacial accumulation, whose constituent elements got mixed up at the time when the last great glaciers descended to the valley of the Po.

Rütymeyer describes a section exposed in the railway-

* *Ueber Pliocen und Eisperiode*, &c.

cutting between Mendrisio and Balerna where older Tertiary (Eocene) strata are capped by a thick mass of true moraine. This was a tumultuous accumulation of rolled stones of all sizes up to large boulders, many of them being smoothed and striated, embedded in a tough grey or blue and often red clay. This boulder-clay rested upon and appeared to graduate down into an unfossiliferous finely laminated clay which contained a few stones scattered through it. Although the leafy clay closely resembled a similar deposit containing Pliocene shells that lies at the base of the moraines of Pontegana on the banks of the Breggia, yet Rütymeyer could see no reason for concluding that the former was of Pliocene age. On the contrary, both the leafy clay and the overlying morainic matter appeared to him to be exclusively of terrestrial glacial formation. He concludes, therefore, that this well-exposed section lends no countenance to the belief that the great glaciers whose moraines now cumber the plains of the Po opposite the mouths of the Alpine valleys were contemporaneous with the old Adriatic Sea of Pliocene times.

In the same memoir he enters at length into the evidence furnished by the lignites and other mammaliferous deposits on both sides of the Alps for the purpose of ascertaining the relation borne by the Pliocene to the glacial epoch, and comes to the general conclusion that in the present state of our knowledge no hard and fast line can be drawn between these two periods. From early Pliocene times onward we have proofs of a continuity of terrestrial conditions over a wide region in Europe. And in the long lapse of time represented by the Pliocene and post-pliocene deposits—a period during which considerable changes in the mammalian fauna were taking place—glaciers now and again descended to the mouths of the great Alpine valleys. How well these conclusions harmonize with the results obtained from a study of our own glacial and interglacial accumulations will appear in the sequel.

CHAPTER XXXV.

GLACIAL DEPOSITS OF NORTH AMERICA.

Glaciation of the northern regions.—The Barren Grounds.—Profusion of lakes.
—Oldest glacial deposits.—Unmodified drift, or till.—Scratched pavements
in till.—Marine arctic shells in boulder-clay of maritime districts.—Interglacial deposits.—Extent of the glaciation of North America.—Views of
Dana, Winchell, and Newberry on the mode of origin of unmodified
deposits.—Whitney on "driftless area."—Interglacial age of "Forest-bed."
—Succession of changes after formation of Forest-bed.—J. D. Dana on the
floods in postglacial or late glacial times.—Drift of the forty-ninth parallel
not marine.—Gravel and sand mounds, ridges, &c.—Limits of submergence.
—Glacial lake-terraces in White Mountains.—Laminated clays with marine
arctic shells.—Local moraines.

IT would be interesting to ascertain how far the results
obtained from an examination of British, Scandinavian,
and Alpine glacial deposits, harmonize with what may be
learned from the records of the glacial epoch in other
European districts, as in the Pyrenees and the Carpathians,
but these districts have not yet been studied in sufficient
detail. The day is no doubt coming when it will be possible
to correlate the glacial deposits of such mountain areas with
those of better-known regions. Nay, the student of glacial
geology may even look forward to a time when it will be
possible to compare in detail the relics of the Ice Age that
are known to occur in northern Asia with the similar accumulations in Europe. But if we are as yet imperfectly
acquainted with the superficial deposits in the northern
latitudes of Asia, it is otherwise with those in the corresponding regions of North America. The literature of
American glacial geology is already very extensive, and every
year is adding to its bulk. Much light has been thrown
upon the whole question of these researches, and the conclusions arrived at must be carefully studied by geologists on
this side of the Atlantic if they would seek to gain an adequate conception of those great revolutions of climate that

supervened in our hemisphere during the glacial epoch. In the following slight sketch, however, I will not attempt to do more than place before the reader what seems to have been the general succession of events.

It is no exaggeration to say, that the whole surface of North America, from the shores of the Arctic Ocean to the latitude of New York, and from the Pacific to the Atlantic, has been scarped, scraped, furrowed, and scoured by the action of ice. The ice-worn rocks of Labrador, Canada, the Northern States, and British Columbia, have been examined and described by many specialists ; but, so striking are the appearances presented, that they have not failed to arrest the attention of other observers in those desolate regions of the far north which have been but seldom traversed. No geologist can read the accounts of the Barren Grounds to be found in the writings of Franklin, Richardson, Back, and others, without recognising everywhere the evidence of ancient glacier-action. If Richardson had been a professed glacialist, he could hardly have described in more expressive language the aspect of the ice-worn tracts traversed by him in company with the hapless Franklin.* Everywhere we meet with references to "round-backed ridges," "very obtuse conical hillocks," "bare, rounded masses of granite and gneiss," "land-locked sheets of water," &c. Many years afterwards, when this traveller once more threaded his way through the Barren Grounds, he did not fail to observe also the furrows and scratchings upon the harder rocks.† Another observant traveller, Captain Back, who followed the course of the Great Fish River (Back's River) down to the Arctic Sea, gives the following graphic sketch of a scene on the skirts of the Barrens : as a faithful picture of a highly ice-worn surface, it might have been drawn by a glacialist himself. "There was not the stern beauty of Alpine scenery, and still less the fair variety of hill and dale, forest and glade, which makes the charm of a European landscape. There was nothing to catch or detain the lingering eye, which wandered on without a check over endless lines of round-backed rocks, whose sides were rent into indescribably eccentric forms. It was like a

---

* *Narrative of a Journey to the Shores of the Polar Sea in the years* 1819-22.
† *Journal of a Boat Voyage through Rupert's Land.*

stormy ocean suddenly petrified. Except a few tawny and pale green lichens, there was nothing to relieve the horror of the scene." *

But the rounding of the rocks is not the only modification effected by the grinding of land-ice. Not only are sharp edges and projecting points smoothed away, but hollows are scooped out in the solid rocks. The lakes and sea-lochs of Scotland and Scandinavia, the innumerable lakes of Finland, and those of Switzerland and Italy, are both far outnumbered, and far surpassed in extent also, by the freshwater seas (for such not a few are) of North America. Lakes are profusely distributed over the whole vast tracts that drain into the St. Lawrence, Hudson's Bay, and the Arctic Ocean, and they are equally abundant in Labrador and Newfoundland. By far the great majority of these lakes must owe their origin directly or indirectly to the grinding power of ice—for they either rest in rock-bound hollows or are dammed back behind irregular ridges of glacial deposits.

But if the glaciated aspect of North America is only that of Europe on a larger scale, we shall find a no less close correspondence between the superficial accumulations of the two continents. The lowest glacial deposit recognised by Canadian and American geologists is "unstratified boulder-clay," "unmodified drift," or "hardpan." In some places this deposit is found to overlie beds of sand, gravel, and clay. Generally speaking, however, the "unmodified drift" appears to rest directly upon the rocks, which are polished and striated below it. But over wide regions in the Barren Grounds and Labrador, the lowest number of the drift series appears to be entirely absent, or rests in patches among the hollows of ice-worn hummocks and hills. Considerable tracts of it, however, seem to occupy the low grounds upon the western borders of Hudson's Bay.† In Labrador it appears not to be very plentiful. Dr. A. S. Packard says:—"Nowhere did I see on the coast of Labrador any deposits of the original glacial clay or unmodified drift. Upon the sea-shore it has been remodelled into a stratified clay; and the boulders it

* *Narrative of Arctic Land Expedition to the Mouth of the Great Fish River* p. 178.
† *Narrative of a Journey to the Shores of the Polar Sea* (Franklin and Richardson), p. 499.

once contained now form terraced beaches."* Professor Hind, however, mentions its occurrence capped by sand, and forming banks "rising seventy feet above the level of the Moisie River, twenty miles from its mouth." It is well developed in Canada, where, according to Professor Dawson, it assumes the character of a "hard grey clay, filled with stones, and thickly packed with boulders." The stones and boulders are often scratched, and the whole deposit is usually devoid of stratification.† Thick masses of it are encountered in Maine, where it presents precisely the same character as in Scotland, —a tough, unstratified clay, crammed with angular and sub-angular, smoothed and striated stones. In the State of New York it is described as "sometimes loose, but frequently partially aggregated by argillaceous matter, that renders a pick necessary to dig it."‡ Mr. Whittlesey also makes frequent reference to its occurrence in Michigan and Ohio, where it is described as a firmly-compacted "mixture of clay sand, and gravel, or fragments of rocks in a confused or imperfectly stratified condition, which is locally known as 'hardpan.'"§ A similar account is given of the Illinois glacial drift by Professor E. Andrews,‖ and, scattered through the various admirable Reports of the State Geologists, numerous descriptions will be found that tally with the foregoing. Professor Winchell describes the "hardpan" of the North-west States as "a heterogeneous mixture of clay and gravel-stones with boulders of northern origin. It is nearly impervious to water, and occasionally, but rarely, shows a rude arrangement in alternating bands, as if, in a plastic state, it had been folded upon itself." The contained boulders are almost always glaciated, and, although disseminated through the whole mass, are apt to be most abundant towards the bottom, where sometimes the boulders are exceedingly numerous and associated with much gravel. Occasionally the "hardpan" rests upon more or less regular boulder beds or accumulations of gravel and sand, and when such is

---

* *On the Glacial Phenomena of Labrador and Maine.*
† "Notes on the Post-pliocene Geology of Canada": *Canadian Naturalist,* New Series, vol. vi.
‡ *Geology of New York,* part iv. p. 160 (Prof. W. Mather).
§ *Smithsonian Contributions to Knowledge,* vol. xv.
‖ *American Journal of Science* (1867), vol. xciii. p. 75.

the case the underlying rock is not generally well glaciated. Sometimes lenticular masses of gravel, sand, silt, &c., are enclosed in the "hardpan." The general character of the deposit varies somewhat in different regions. Thus, for example, "in north-western Ohio it is very close and clayey, the upper part being free from boulders and stones. In central Minnesota, however, the stones and boulders are more generally disseminated throughout the whole, and it shows much more sand."*

The somewhat rare phenomena of "scratched pavements" in the till have also been observed in North America. Professor O. N. Stoddard refers to an excellent example in the till of Miami. The upper surfaces of the embedded stones were all striated in one and the same direction, but when the boulders were picked out of the clay, their other sides showed scratches running in different directions.†

In the interior of the country the "unmodified drift" is quite unfossiliferous, but in certain maritime districts it appears to have yielded marine organic remains. This, according to Principal Dawson,‡ is the case in the lower part of the St. Lawrence River. Farther up in the vicinity of Montreal, however, it has not been observed to contain fossils. From Professor Dawson's description of the fossiliferous stony clay, that deposit would seem to be analogous to the shelly boulder-clay of maritime districts in Scotland, and to the like accumulations in Ireland and England.

Another interesting feature in the American glacial deposits, is the occurrence of intercalated and subjacent fossiliferous beds. These are passed through frequently in sinking wells and pits, and in digging foundations. They occur chiefly in the North-western States—Illinois, Ohio, Indiana, Wisconsin, Iowa, and Minnesota. A few brief notes will illustrate the general phenomena.

Some of the most interesting discoveries of buried forests and forest débris have been made in Illinois. The following

* "The Drift-Deposits of the North-west" (N. H. Winchell), *Popular Science Monthly*, 1873; see also *Annual Reports of the Geological and Natural History Survey of Minnesota* for 1872 and 1873; *Report of the Geological Survey of Ohio*, vol. ii., chapter xxx.

† *American Journal of Science* (1859), vol. xxviii. p. 227.

‡ "Notes on the Post-pliocene Geology of Canada," *Canadian Naturalist*, New Series, vol. vi.

section, for example, was obtained* during the sinking of a coal shaft at the city of Bloomington in that State :—

		Ft.
1. Surface soil and brown clay	. . . . .	10
2. Blue clay	. . . .	40
3. Gravelly hardpan	. . . . .	60
4. Black mould, with pieces of wood, &c.	. . .	13
5. Hardpan and clay	. . . . .	89
6. Black mould, &c.	. . . . . .	6
7. Blue clay . . .	. . . . .	34
8. Quicksand, buff and drab in colour, and containing fossil shells		2
Clay shale (Coal-measures).		
		254

Similar phenomena have been noted by the State geologists in many other localities in the same region. Thus in Perry County Mr. Worthen describes the occurrence of a blue mud with leaves and sticks which occurs below the main mass of drift clay. " Its average thickness," he says, " cannot be definitely stated, for when it was found in digging for water the well was generally abandoned as soon as this deposit was reached, because the partly decomposed vegetable matter which it contained rendered the water unfit for use. It appears to be composed, in good part, of vegetable matter consisting of leaves and partially decayed wood, embedded in a muddy sediment, and has been penetrated in some places to the depth of five to ten feet. It usually lies at the bottom of the drift deposits, but at one point in Jackson County it was underlaid by a bed of sand two or three feet in thickness." In Woodford County a similar accumulation of peaty matter was found at a depth of about 65 ft. below 50 ft. of hardpan. From this fragments of wood were obtained which Professor Lesquereux identified as belonging to the following species :—American white birch, black or double spruce, American larch or tamarack, and one variety of cedar. Mr. Worthen states that in Perona a shaft struck a " black mucky soil with limbs of trees," at the depth of 145 ft. This peaty bed was two feet in thickness and rested upon boulder-clay. The overlying drift consisted of coarse sand, gravel, and boulders, and a clayey bed 48 ft. thick of alternating layers of sand and gravel with boulders. Many other similar references to the occurrence of peat and frag-

* *Geology of Illinois,* vol. iv. p. 179. The " shells " are of freshwater species.

ments of wood underneath or intercalcated among the drift deposits of Illinois, and sometimes occurring in the hardpan itself, are recorded in the reports of the Geological Survey.*

In the State of Indiana a mud bed filled with leaves, twigs, and trunks of trees, and locally known as " Noah's barn-yard," is frequently met with at various depths from the surface underneath the drift. In one place at least the peat contained numerous roots of trees, shrubs, &c. Professor Cox also mentions that in the north-west part of Dubois County "the remains of shrubs and grape vines of enormous growth, indicating perhaps the luxuriance of a warmer clime," were got at a considerable distance from the surface. It is worth noting that these old buried forests and peat-beds are found chiefly in the southern and central portions of the State. In the northern third portion of the State, Professor Winchell remarks, there is no record of the discovery of peat or vegetation in the drift in the reports of the State geologist since 1869.

The occurrence of vegetable remains in the drift deposits of Ohio was noted a number of years ago by Colonel James Whittlesey,† from whose paper I take the following section :—

ARTESIAN WELL, COLUMBIA, OHIO.

Surface 215 ft. above Lake Erie, and 780 ft. above tide.

	Ft.
1. Soil	4
2. Sand, gravel and boulders	10
3. Coarse sand	2
4. Blue clay and boulders	4
5. Fine quicksand	2
6. Blue clay enclosing a log	17
7. Hardpan	3
8. Quicksand	1
9. Hardpan to cliff limestone	37
	80

The reports of the State geologists of Ohio contain numerous descriptions of an ancient forest-bed or soil which occurs intercalated among the drift deposits. It occurs at a variable depth from the surface, say, from 10 to 90 ft., and is

* An excellent digest of all the recorded occurrences of "vegetable remains in drift deposits in the North-West," is given by Professor N. H. Winchell in the *Proceedings of the American Association for the Advancement of Science*, 1875.
† *Smithsonian Contributions to Knowledge*, vol. xv.

typically represented in the following section, which is given by Mr. Orton in his account of Clermont County :*—

4. *Surface clays*—generally *white*, sometimes blackened by swampy conditions, entirely free from gravel, from 1 to 8 feet in thickness.
3. *Yellow clays*—abounding with gravel, with occasional boulders often constituting the surface instead of No. 4. Thickness seldom exceeds 10 feet.
2. (*a*) *Forest-soil*—a stratum of carbonaceous clay, containing vegetable matter, as leaves and wood, with occasional beds of peat, and in some districts replaced by (*b*). *Bog iron ore bed* (*b*)—a seam of ochreous clays that pass into true ores, yielding over 40 per cent. of metallic iron. The last division ranges from 1 to 2½ feet in thickness, the former sometimes rises as high as 8 feet. Both divisions are sometimes absent.
1. *Blue boulder-clay or hardpan*, with occasional layers of sand intercalated, resting upon the rocky floor of the country.

The same observer has described† the nature of the Ohio river-bottoms (valley-drifts), which contain a forest-bed, seven feet thick, between two seams of ochreous gravel, at a greater or less depth from the surface. This buried land-surface he identifies with the " forest-bed " so commonly met with in the upland drift of Southern Ohio. In the " forest-bed " of the Ohio bottoms " the trunks and roots of trees, some of the latter *in situ*, twigs and branches, layers of leaves, ripened fruits, grasses, and sedges, are all clearly distinguishable. Several of the species of trees can be determined, some by their wood, others by their leaves and fruits. Among them may be named :—*Platanus occidentalis* (sycamore), *Fagus ferruginea* (beech), *Carya alba* (shell-bark hickory), *Æsculus glabra* (buckeye), *Juniperus virginianus* (red cedar). A cucurbitaceous plant, probably *Echinocystis lobata* (wild balsam apple), is also shown to have been abundant by its seeds, which are preserved in the clay." ‡

This forest-bed lies at a depth " of at least 20 ft., and sometimes even of 40 ft.," below the present bed of the Ohio River. The bones and teeth of mastodon and mammoth are said to have been obtained in close contact with the old forest, but these and all other mammalian remains are, according to Professor Orton, of very rare occurrence. " It is possible," he says, " that the ' chips ' and ' axe-marked ' stumps reported at various points in excavations in the drift beds attest the former presence here of the gigantic beaver,

* *Report of the Geological Survey of Ohio*, vol. i. (Geology) p. 440.
† *Op. cit.* p. 428.
‡ See also *American Journal of Science*, vol. c., 1870, p. 54.

now extinct—*Castoroides Ohioensis.* It was certainly a tenant of the State during the general period to which this old forest-bed must be referred." He concludes that the " forest-bed " in question marks an old land-surface, and that the plants of which it is composed, and which indicate mild conditions of climate, grew *in situ* during interglacial times. He is of opinion, moreover, that this interglacial stage " must have had an immensely long period for the accomplishment of the work which we are obliged to refer to it."

In some districts of Ohio the old forest seems to be almost everywhere present, although it is more frequently met with on the high plateaux than in the valleys. The deposits underlying the vegetable débris are usually discoloured for some distance down with vegetable mould, and contain, mingled with their own substance, quantities of leaves, branches, roots, and tree-trunks.

In the States of Iowa and Wisconsin a buried forest-bed has also been detected, some account of which has been given by Colonel Whittlesey in the paper already referred to.

Professor Winchell mentions the like occurrence of a bed of vegetation in the drift deposits of Minnesota. Thus in Fillmore County—a region of high prairie—the buried peat " underlies a gravelly clay, which contains boulders, and has the appearance of being the same as the glacier deposit, known as unmodified drift. The same underlies it. Some portions of the clay above the peat are reported to be blue, while the whole of that which underlies it is of a blue colour. The whole country is heavily covered with this drift clay, and some very large boulders of granite lie near the wells that have met this peat."

Sir William Logan mentions* the occurrence at Grand Sable, on the south shore of Lake Superior, of a layer of roots and limbs of trees, 12 or 14 ft. thick, resting on clay, and covered to a depth of 300 ft. with sand and gravel; and Professor H. Y. Hind notes a similar section at Toronto. Dr. Dawson also cites† the case of " a hardened peaty bed, which appears under the boulder-clay on the north-west arm of the River of Inhabitants in Cape Breton." " It contains

---

* *Geology of Canada*, 1863, p. 905.   † *Acadian Geology*, p. 63.

many small roots and branches, apparently of coniferous trees allied to the spruces."

It is curious to find that the geologists of Illinois, Indiana, and Ohio have different views as to the position of the old forest-beds. Thus Mr. Worthen, of Illinois, holds that there are two forest-beds—one of which underlies and is of older date than all the glacial deposits, while the other rests upon these, and is covered by the old river-loess. The geologists of Indiana apparently recognise only one forest-bed, and it underlies the drift. On the other hand, the geologists of Ohio assert that their forest-bed is intercalated between glacial deposits, for it rests upon tough boulder-clay which is full of striated stones, while over it come accumulations of clay, sand, gravel, and erratics. Again, in Minnesota, the forest-bed reclines upon a mass of blue boulder-clay with striated stones, and is overlaid by an upper accumulation of precisely the same kind of material.

Dr. Newberry mentions that in some places in Ohio the forest-bed is underlaid by laminated clays and beds of sand, &c. (Erie clay series), which overlie the usual unstratified boulder-clay or hardpan.

If American geologists are right in ascribing to the same age the buried forest-beds of Ohio, Indiana, Illinois, Minnesota, &c., then the different views held by some geologists admit of a simple reconciliation. The interglacial position of the Ohio and Minnesota peat-bed cannot be doubted, and there is nothing adverse to the buried forests of Illinois and Indiana being put in the same category. For the mere absence in these States of a boulder-clay below the ancient forest does not prove the preglacial age of the latter. It will be remembered that in Switzerland the interglacial lignites sometimes rest upon the bare rock without the intervention of any till. It is quite possible, therefore, that something of the same kind occurs in the North-western States of America, the interglacial beds occasionally reclining upon true glacial deposits, and at other times having the solid rock for their foundation.

Before proceeding further it may be well to ascertain what are the general conclusions arrived at by American and Canadian geologists regarding the primary or principal glaciation.   As far as I can gather their opinions, the belief in the former existence of a great continental glacier or ice-sheet appears to be almost universal ; among the most vigorous upholders of this belief being Professor Dana and the State geologists, whose intimate acquaintance with the facts upon which any theory must be based renders their authority peculiarly important.   It is true that Principal Dawson, of Montreal, still holds the opinion that the rock-striations and boulder-clay of Canada and the States represent the action and the droppings of icebergs, but his views have not of recent years been supported by any experienced transatlantic geologist.   The presence of sea-shells in the boulder-clay of the lower reaches of the St. Lawrence, upon which Principal Dawson lays special stress, is really no proof that the clay in question was deposited in the sea.   The shells may quite well have been introduced into the ground-moraine of the ice-sheet which passed up the Gulf of St. Lawrence, in the same way as has been suggested in the case of the shelly tills or boulder-clays of Scotland and England.

The only theory which seems to explain all the facts is that of a great ice-sheet, as first propounded by Agassiz.   In no other way can the glaciation of Canada and the New England and North-western States be accounted for.   The rock-striations* have been traced from the low grounds up to a height of 5,500 ft. (White Mountains), while drift has been followed to an elevation of 5,800 ft. (Mount Washington) ; but the mountain tops above this level appear not to have been subjected to glacial action.†   The moraine-matter of the ice-sheet is scattered over the British Provinces from

---

* It is noteworthy that in North America there are sometimes two or more sets of striæ and groovings.   In the district of Lake Superior, for example, there are traces of two distinct glaciations—the main or continental glacier having flowed from north-east to south-west, while the local and latest ice-flow was from north to south.   *Report on Lake Superior,* part i. p. 205; see also N. H. Winchell on "The Glacial Features of Green Bay," &c., *American Journal of Science,* vol. cii. p. 15.   "In western New York there is, in addition to the south-west system, a subordinate south system (Hall) ; and on Isle La Motte, in Lake Champlain, there are eight sets (Adams), although usually not over two or three in Vermont."   Dana's *Manual of Geology,* 1875, p. 531.   Near Lake Winnipeg and the Lake of the Woods there appear to be at least two sets of striæ, according to Mr. G. M. Dawson : *Quart. Jour. Geol. Soc.,* vol. xxxi. p. 608.   Some of these newer sets may have been produced when the great ice-sheet began to retire ; others may have been the work of the last period] of glaciation that followed upon the close of the forest-bed epoch.

† *Geological Survey of New Hampshire,* vol. i. p. 540.

Nova Scotia and Labrador westward towards the Rocky Mountains. Mr. G. M. Dawson, however, has brought forward[*] a number of facts to show that the ice-sheet which covered the Laurentian axis of Canada did not extend westwards to the Rocky Mountains, at least along the forty-ninth parallel. Boulders derived from the north-east were traced by him " to within about 25 miles of the base of the Rocky Mountains at a height of about 4,200 ft. The distance of these travelled blocks from the nearest part of the Laurentian region is over 700 miles." Quartzite drift derived from the Rocky Mountains occurs very sparingly over what Mr. Dawson calls "the second prairie level," and is not found over its whole area. The first recognisable fragments he met with occurred at a distance of " 580 miles from the Rocky Mountains, and over 200 from the nearest part of the Laurentian region." It is not until the third or highest prairie-plateau is reached that the quartzite drift becomes abundantly present ; and eventually as the prairie slopes up towards the Rocky Mountains " the drift is entirely composed of material derived from them." The Laurentian ice, therefore, did not impinge upon the Rocky Mountains, at least in lat. 49° N. Northern drift, however, has been traced " over all New England and part of Pennsylvania, and the States west, to the western limits of Iowa and Minnesota. Beyond the meridian of 98° W. in the United States it is not known. It has its southern limit near the parallel of 39°, in southern Pennsylvania, Ohio, Indiana, Illinois, and Iowa, while its northern is undetermined."[†] [Dana.] But from the writings of Richardson, Back, and other explorers, there can be no doubt that the whole of the great Barren Grounds to the shores of the Arctic Sea have been traversed by glacier-ice which must have been continuous with that which glaciated Canada and the States.

At the time this continental glacier occupied so wide an expanse in the north and north-east, large glaciers filled many of the valleys of the Rocky Mountains, even as far south as Colorado. Dr. Hayden tells us that "the Arkansas valley

---

[*] *Quart. Jour. Geol. Soc.*, vol. xxxi. p. 603.

[†] "South of the Ohio River it is hardly traceable; yet it is stated to occur near Ashland, in Boyd County, Kentucky. Few boulders are found about Baltimore and Philadelphia, and these not on the higher lands." Dana's *Manual of Geology*, p. 528.

was filled with one enormous glacier, and that extending from
it on either side of the gulches were branches of greater or
less magnitude." " The great branch-glacier of Lake Creek
must have been 1,500 ft. or more in thickness.   The
valley or gorge is nearly uniform in width, about one-fourth
of a mile, and the glacier must have ploughed its way along,
paring off a great thickness of the gneissic rocks on either
side and on the bottom, the low rounded remnants of which
can be seen cropping everywhere from the detritus.   The
sides of the gorge for 1,000 ft. to 1,500 ft. are worn
smoothly, and in some places immense blocks of granite
have been wrenched from their places and carried down the
channel, so that the sides look like a quarry.   The most
striking feature is the very smooth surface of the sides of the
gorge to so great a height, like glass." *   No wonder that
glaciers such as this should have scooped out the basins of
the lakes that occur in the same neighbourhood.   In Nevada,
Oregon, and California, Whitney and his associates have
shown that the mountain-valleys of those territories have all
supported great glaciers.   Even in the less elevated ranges
of the Southern States there are indications of local glaciers
having occupied the valleys, namely, in the Unaka Moun-
tains† (the range between Tennessee and North Carolina),
and in the Alleghany Mountains, West Virginia.   Nay, more
than this, Mr. Belt, in his interesing work, " The Naturalist
in Nicaragua," states that he found traces of considerable
glaciers in that country.

What a strangely arctic character must North America
have presented during the climax of the glacial epoch !   All
the ground east of the Rocky Mountains, from the shores of
the Arctic Sea down to the latitude of New York, appears at
that time to have been swathed in one wide sheet of snow
and ice.   The ridge of the Rocky Mountains, however, was
much too high to be overwhelmed, but enormous local glaciers
filled the deep valleys of that range and piled up great
moraines.   Indeed it is by no means improbable that the
vast ice-sheet of the north was fed in part by tributary
glaciers draining from the eastern slopes of these mountains.

* *Geological and Geographical Survey of Colorado*, 1873, pp. 54, 55.
† *Geology of Tennessee* (Safford), p. 438.

Beyond the limits reached by the ice-sheet all the mountain tracts, and even some of the less considerable hill ranges, appear to have nourished local or valley glaciers.

Professor Dana has estimated* the probable thickness attained by the ice-sheet in New England from the height reached by the rock-striations, and comes to the conclusion that it was not less than 12,000 ft. on the watershed between the St. Lawrence and Hudson's Bay. "Over the plateau on the northern borders of New England it was about 6,500 ft.; in the region of the White Mountains 5,000 ft.; along the sea-shore of Portland 4,100 ft., the whole height there being of ice; at the terminal cliffs, 500 feet above the sea-level, with the under surface of the glacier resting on the sea-bottom. The glacier probably extended in a southward direction at least 60 miles south of Long Island, where the depth of water is not over 250 ft.; and perhaps 30 miles beyond, where the depth is 600 ft., and then falls off abruptly." The height of the terminal cliff 90 miles south of Long Island could not have been less than 200 ft.

The general flow of the ice was from north-west, north, and north-east, but the form of the ground appears frequently to have given rise to local deflections, in which, as in many other respects, the phenomena closely resemble those which are characteristic of the ancient confluent glaciers of Northern Europe.

The pressure and abrasive power of the American ice-sheet must have been excessive—6,000 ft. of ice corresponding, according to Dana, to a pressure of at least 300,000 pounds to the square foot. It was underneath this heavy mass that the unmodified drift or boulder-clay was formed. American geologists are somewhat divided in opinion, however, as to the precise way in which that stony clay has been deposited. Dana thinks that the stones and earth which the glaciers bore along were contained in the ice itself. He says, "There was not only abrasion of the rocks beneath by the ice armed with stones in its lower surface, and also a crushing of softer kinds from mere pressure, but besides, a breaking and crushing of the ice itself against the obstacles in its course, and also a pressing of the plastic material down among all the

* *American Journal of Science and Art,* vol. v., 1873.

stones and gravel or sand ; and thus it was able to envelop
and take up into its mass the loose material. Further, the
ice of the ice-mass above must have been forced down into
all openings and crevices in the rocks, so that the glacier,
as it moved, had tremendous power in prying off and
abrading, and must have made boulders and gravel—its
chips—in immense quantities for transportation." Under
such conditions he believes the débris carried along would be
enclosed in the ice itself, "mostly within the lower 1,000 ft.,
and probably the larger part in the lower 500 ft." There are
several objections, however, which may be urged against these
views. In the first place, it is well known that the ice of
glaciers is, as a rule, remarkably free from contained blocks
and earth ; such impurities as do exist having for the most
part been introduced from above, and not from below. In
the next place, there are many phenomena connected with
the boulder-clay itself, which Professor Dana's theory does
not explain ; such is the occurrence of lenticular beds of
gravel, sand, and laminated clay, which are sometimes horizontal, and at other times much contorted and confused.
There is also the appearance which the boulder-clay itself
presents of having been folded back upon itself again
and again, as if it had been kneaded and rolled forward
bodily.

Professor A. H. Winchell, who apparently adopts Dana's
theory, or some modification of it, has given a very graphic
sketch* of the mode in which he conceives the unmodified
drift to have been deposited as the ice-sheet melted away.
In the far north, where the glacier was enormously thick,
the surface would be free from any impurities, but as it
thinned away towards the south its crevasses would begin to
reveal multitudes of rock-fragments and occasional bands of
dirt and gravel embraced in the solid ice ; until by-and-by,
as the glacier crept farther south, the débris would appear at
the very surface, the attenuated ice being there covered with
a pulpy earth mingled with stones and boulders. At the
limits reached by the ice, water flowing from the melting mass
would re-assort much of the moraine-matter, forming sand
and gravel beds, while the unassorted materials would remain,

where the ice had quietly "let them down," as boulder-clay or unmodified drift.

Dr. J. S. Newberry controverts Professor Winchell's views of the origin of boulder-clay,[*] and maintains that the deposit in question "must have accumulated at the margin of the glacier." This is the same view as that held by Mr. S. V. Wood and some other geologists in our own country. It fails, however, to account for many of the facts. The boulder-clay has evidently been subjected to great pressure, and has been pushed and rolled forward under the ice, as I have endeavoured to show in my account of the mode of origin of the Scotch till or boulder-clay.[†]

But although opinions thus differ as to the precise manner in which the old unmodified drift has been accumulated, geologists are at one in their belief as to its true glacial origin. Without going further, therefore, into controversial matters, we may proceed now to the next stage of American glacial history, namely, the disappearance of the ice-sheet.

Dr. Newberry has described the boulder-clay of Ohio as being covered over a considerable area by finely laminated clays, which he believes to have been formed as follows:— "In the retreat of the great ice-sheet across the lake basin (Erie), at first small pools, then larger basins, and, finally, a great inland sea bordered it on the south. In these bodies of water a portion of the material ground up was suspended, and then deposited as the laminated portion of the Erie clay."[‡]

When the ice had finally melted away, and the great inland sea had either vanished or been much reduced in extent, the climate gradually became so genial that a luxuriant forest-growth sprung up over all the area of the North-western States, and, for aught we know to the contrary, these genial conditions may have prevailed even up to the shores of the

---

[*] *Report of the Geol. Surv. of Ohio,* vol. ii. chap. xxx.

[†] I have often tried to conceive how 100 feet of tough till could have been slowly extruded in the form of loose clay and stones from the foot of an ice-sheet so as to cover a wide flat country, but have never been able to realise the process. Let me ask those geologists who hold the opinion that boulder-clay has really been deposited in this way, why it is that along the southern limits of the "Northern Drift" that formation consists almost exclusively of more or less loose accumulations of boulders, gravel, and sand, while to the north boulder-clay is present as the basement drift with boulders, gravel, and sand lying upon it?

[‡] "Erie clay" is the general term applied by Newberry to the boulder-clay and the laminated clay which immediately overlies it.

Arctic Ocean. The plant remains of the old "forest-bed" certainly indicate a climate not less genial than that which now characterizes the regions where it occurs ; and we may reasonably infer, therefore, that when the buried trees grew green under the sun the climatic conditions of North America were much the same as they are at present.

The beds which overlie the forest-bed have already been noticed. They seem to vary a good deal in different regions. Thus, they may consist of heavy beds of sand, gravel, and boulders, or of clay with gravel and boulders, or of true unmodified drift or boulder-clay.

As to the precise succession of events which took place in North America after the forest-bed epoch there is some diversity of opinion. Professor Newberry,* for example, believes that after that epoch there was a very general submergence of the state of Ohio beneath an inland, or even a continental expanse of water, across which floated icebergs and ice-rafts. The succession of changes were, therefore, according to him, as follows :—

1st. A period of a great continental glacier or ice-sheet.

2nd. The retreat of the ice, and the appearance of a vast freshwater lake (covering a large part of Ohio), in which were deposited the finely laminated Erie clays, &c.

3rd. The silting-up of the lake, and the advent of a luxuriant forest-growth.

4th. The submergence of the land below a great inland sea of fresh water, and the deposition from floating ice of blocks and boulders.

Some of these views are controverted by Professor Winchell (State geologist of Minnesota), who surveyed a large portion of north-western Ohio. He writes to me that he found what to him were " satisfactory proofs of the existence of two distinct glacier deposits." The buried soil of Ohio, which extends westwards through Indiana and Illinois, enters Iowa, and even appears in southern Minnesota, " is distinctly intercalated," he says, " between glacier drift clays, and this no more proves an iceberg origin for the upper deposit than it does for the lower. The two deposits cannot be said to

* *Report of Progress* (Ohio Survey), 1870, p. 340 ; *Report of Geol. Surv. of Ohio,* vol. ii. chap. xxx.

differ noticeably wherever I have examined them," the overlying mass being "as *evidently of glacier origin* as the drift that underlies the soil-bed."

These apparently contradictory views are not so irreconcilable as they seem to be. This becomes evident when we take a glance at the distribution of the forest-bed and the varying character of the drift deposits underneath which it lies concealed. We find, in the first place, that the buried forest-bed occurs most abundantly in the southern regions of the North-western States, where it lies covered for the most part with heavy masses of gravel, sand, and erratics of northern origin. Passing north towards the Canadian boundary the soil-bed becomes less conspicuous as a member of the drift series, being represented chiefly by occasional "logs" and "sticks," which occur as boulders in the glacial deposits. Traces of it, however, appear to occur at Grand Sable, on the south shore of Lake Superior, and at Toronto; and it is quite possible that the "hardened peaty bed" of Cape Breton may also be a relic of it. Now in north-western Ohio, in Minnesota, and apparently also in the northern regions of Illinois and Indiana, the forest-bed is overlaid by true till or hardpan —an unstratified mass, packed with striated stones and boulders, while the whole surface of the country is in many places dotted with loose erratics, and sprinkled with gravel and sand, which occasionally rise into hillocks and knolls so as to form conspicuous objects in the flat, treeless prairie lands.*

We must agree with Professor Winchell that if the lower hardpan be the morainic matter of a great ice-sheet, the similar deposit which overlies the forest-bed in Minnesota, &c., must have had a like origin; in other words, there was a return to glacial conditions after the forest-bed period, during which an ice-sheet again invaded New England and the North-western States. How far south this last ice-sheet extended is a point which American geologists have yet to determine. We are not without evidence, however, to show that it did not reach the limits attained by the preceding ice-flow.

* See *Geological Survey of Iowa,* vol. i. p. 99; *Geological Survey of Ohio,* vol. ii.; *Geological and Natural History Survey of Minnesota,* Second Annual Report, 1873, p. 92 *et sqq.*

Professor J. D. Whitney has given some account of a "driftless region" in Wisconsin, Iowa, and Minnesota.* He tells us that a considerable area, forming an elevated plateau, chiefly in Wisconsin and near the Mississippi River, is quite destitute of drift; and this is the more remarkable seeing that the regions to the north, west, east, and south are all more or less deeply covered with such deposits.

Whitney describes the surface of the rock within the driftless region as being uneven and irregular, and bearing the marks of chemical rather than of mechanical erosion. This is especially the case where limestone or dolomite forms the rock in place. No glacial furrows or striæ, no drift-scratches, and no evidence of the rock having been planed down to a level, are anywhere visible. A variable thickness of surface-wash overlies the rocks, which is evidently the result of weathering and chemical action. From these and other facts Whitney concludes that the region under review "must have formed an island at the time when the great currents from the north were bringing down the detrital materials, which are spread over so vast an area in the northern hemisphere."

Now throughout this remarkable region the remains of numerous extinct mammalia have again and again been detected. They occur promiscuously embedded in the surface-wash, or in cracks and crevices of the limestone. The animals mentioned are mastodon, megalonyx, elephant, buffalo, wolf, extinct species of peccary, racoon, and several rodents, &c. Many of these were got in clayey loam at considerable depths from the surface—as much as 40 ft. in some places—indicating the lapse of a long period since the time of their entombment.

Beyond the driftless region, however, in those tracts that are thickly covered with gravel, sand, boulders, and hardpan, no such mammalian remains occur in superficial or postglacial deposits. In such districts, as we have seen, they are only met with in connection with the old forest-bed which occupies an interglacial position.

* *Report of the Geological Survey of Wisconsin,* vol. i. p. 114 *et sqq.*; *Geological Survey of Illinois,* vol. i. p. 160. The driftless region, according to Whitney, is nearly coincident with that of the productive lead region in north-western Illinois, Iowa, and south-western Wisconsin.

From recent observations it would appear that the area described by Whitney is not altogether destitute of glacial drift. Professor Winchell writes me, that "so far as that area enters Minnesota, it cannot be said to be driftless, for isolated patches of drift (remains of the older drift-sheet), which have a general *facies* indicating greater age, are found throughout it. The region, however, is deeply buried under the 'bluff-formation,' or what is supposed to be the equivalent of the loess of Continental Europe—a fine siliceous clay, indistinctly stratified, evidently deposited from waters nearly or quite tranquil. The remains of this old drift-sheet in the 'driftless area' which I refer to in my first Annual Report[*] are supposed to belong to that which lies below the 'soil-bed,' which, whenever penetrated, gives *abundant* evidence of a former vegetable covering for the country which now is a treeless prairie. The deposits which overlie the 'soil-bed,' except where these are loess, are as evidently of glacier origin as those that underlie it."

From all this we gather that there were certain regions over which the older ice-sheet prevailed, but which the last ice-flow did not cover. In such areas, therefore, we meet with only the older morainic débris, lying in isolated patches. During the continuance of the long interglacial period that supervened after the disappearance of the greater ice-sheet, chemical action and the atmospheric forces—rain, frost, and

---

[*] The passage referred to by Professor Winchell is as follows:—"There is an area in the south-eastern part of the State, where very little of it (drift) is found. The rocks stand out prominently in bluffs and terraces caused by their various capacity to withstand the elements, covered with very little besides the decomposed débris of their own beds. Yet in this portion of the State, which seems to be an extension of the so-called 'driftless region' of Iowa, the valleys, on being excavated for cellars and wells, reveal a clay charged with pebbles and sometimes large boulders. This clay is said to contain fragments of wood and leaves half decomposed. Sufficient examination has not yet been made to show the relation of this blue clay in the south-eastern part of the State containing vegetable deposits, with the vast sheet of blue clay containing, so far as known, no vegetable remains, which is spread over a great portion of the entire State. It seems, however, to be of older date, and may consist of the remains of a previous glacial sheet, which under the action of the last glacial epoch was subjected to erosion and wash, but was not replaced by fresh deposits. In that way the vegetable growths of the surface, accumulating between the periods of the two glacial epochs, would be buried in the depressions to various depths beneath the débris from the hill sides, and considerable beds of peat or even an entire soil would be preserved, while toward the north, the movement of the glacier-ice entirely destroyed and removed the ancient soils." *First Ann. Rep. Geol. & Nat. Hist. Surv. of Minnesota*, p. 61. In a forthcoming Report Professor Winchell tells me that he goes more fully into this subject.

running water—did their best to remove all traces of the former glaciation. The general aspect of the so-called driftless region appears indeed to have been so modified, that even so distinguished an observer as Whitney was under the impression that it had never been subjected to glacial influence. Escarpments, bluffs, and terraces of rock stand out as prominently as they do in many of the midland and southern districts of England. And yet there is the tell-tale old hardpan, scattered here and there, to show that, however weathered an appearance the "driftless area" may present, it was nevertheless at one time buried under an ice-sheet. These phenomena, therefore, are precisely analogous to those which the midland part of England presents—a region in which, as we have seen, the glaciated outline, which it must have received during the greatest extension of the ice-sheet (period of great chalky boulder-clay, &c.), has been almost completely obliterated—the hilly districts where a distinctly glaciated contour still exists being those over which the later ice-sheets prevailed.

Now it will no doubt occur to the reader as a difficulty that any old land-surface should have been preserved under the glacial deposits of a great ice-sheet. Why was not the soil-bed with its vegetable débris utterly swept away? This is a difficulty which constantly meets us in every country where drift deposits have been studied with any care. I will not attempt to explain why the great ice-sheets did not always plough out every superficial deposit of gravel, sand, clay, silt, or peat. But to one who believes that till was rolled forward *en masse* under the ice, and that much of the fine polishing and striation received by the rocks below was due not so much to stones and grit frozen into the bottom of the glacier, as to the passage over the rocky surface of a ground-moraine of clay and stones, it does not appear so very wonderful that preglacial and interglacial deposits should sometimes have escaped destruction. Let it be noted, moreover, that such interglacial remains generally appear in best preservation and in greatest abundance where the glacial deposits are thickest, and that they are more especially frequent in the regions which were farthest removed from the centres of glaciation.

From these facts I would infer that in areas where the movement of a great ice-sheet was slowest there would be less erosive action,* and a tendency in the ground-moraine, therefore, to accumulate underneath. We might consequently expect to meet with more frequent traces of preglacial and interglacial land-surfaces in such positions, than in areas where the ice-sheet was moving faster, and where, as a result of this quicker motion, the till or hardpan would not be able to accumulate to any extent. Again, we know that a glacier not only loses in thickness, but begins to slacken its pace as it approaches its termination, and thus its erosive power always lessens in that direction. This is the reason, as it seems to me, that the "forest-bed" appears in greatest force in the southern parts of the North-western States. In Canada and the north, where the glaciation, owing to the greater thickness and quicker motion of the ice, was much more severe, traces of an old land-surface under the drift are few and far between.

Whether the "forest-bed" in the southern portions of Ohio was ever actually covered by the ice-sheet of the last glacial epoch is a point which American geologists will no doubt be able to settle. Dr. Newberry, who has had every opportunity of studying the facts in the field, and whose authority therefore demands our respect, believes that the deposits immediately overlying the forest-bed in southern Ohio have been laid down during a period of submergence when icebergs were floating over the drowned districts. He is of opinion that when the great glacier had retired to the Laurentian highlands of Canada the basin of Lake Erie was filled with such a depth of water that the lake communicated with all the other great sheets of water so as to form one vast inland sea. Ohio, it will be remembered, is bounded on the north by Lake Erie. In the extreme north of the State there is an upland district which forms the divide between waters which flow a long way south to feed the Ohio River, and a number of shorter streams whose course is directly north into Lake Erie. According to Dr. Newberry, the waters of the lake rose upon the northern slopes of the

---

* The reader must distinctly understand that I am not speaking here of local or valley glaciers.

divide until they actually reached the level of certain passes across which the surplus waters rushed, flooding all the country on the southern side of the divide down to the valley of the Ohio River. He thinks "that in the period of the greatest submergence the larger part of the summit of the watershed was under water, and was swept by breakers and shore-waves, by which some of the beds of sand and gravel were formed," which are now met with upon the watershed ; and he believes that the coarser materials (boulders) of which these deposits are composed were " derived from icebergs stranding on the shoals which now form the crest of the divide." At that time the great glacier is supposed to have been shedding its icebergs along the Canadian shores of Lake Erie, and "a sufficient depth of water existed in the passes of the watershed to float icebergs of considerable size, and as currents flowed through these passes, some of the boulders scattered over southern Ohio were probably transported by them. When the water-level had been somewhat depressed by the slow elevation of the continent, these gaps became waste-weirs, through which powerful streams of water continued to flow for a long time, cutting the gaps deeper, and transporting great quantities of gravel and boulders, and depositing them in lines which lead down towards the valley of the Ohio."

In confirmation of his theory Dr. Newberry points to the fact that not only are water-worn materials scattered over the summit of the watershed, but a series of old lake-terraces occur at various heights along the slopes overlooking Lake Erie, which clearly indicate, he thinks, successive levels occupied by the great sheet of water. Besides these lake-terraces, however, there also occur great morainic ridges, which in the same manner run along the northern slopes of the divide. The highest of the lake-terraces does not appear to occur at much more than 200 ft. above the present level of Lake Erie, while the uppermost morainic ridge rises to nearly 500 ft.

The evidence amounts to this, therefore, that while the lower terraces may be, and probably are, of lacustrine origin, the highest ridges are morainic : as, indeed, one of the lower embankments also would appear to be. It is difficult, however, to believe, on the evidence produced, that the waters of Lake Erie ever actually overflowed the summit of the watershed. Dr. Newberry suggests that the natural overflow of the lake may have been dammed up by the great glacier, and the water-level successively lowered as the ice dams melted away. "It is also possible," he thinks, "that warping of the earth's crust may have changed the relative altitudes of different portions of the margin of the lake basin."

The water-worn deposits which are scattered over the summit of the watershed are compared with the Scotch kames, and sections of them are given to show how close the resemblance is. Is it not possible, therefore, that they may have had a similar origin? Are not these just the deposits which would be formed underneath the ice by subglacial streams, and in front of it by the torrents and floods escaping from it as it melted away? If we suppose the ice to have filled up the basin of Lake Erie to such an extent, that its terminal front rested immediately behind the summit of the watershed, then large volumes of water must have been discharged from it, which might well scatter gravelly moraine-matter over the uplands, and sweep it through the passes or "waste weirs"* down to the low grounds. Indeed, the same action must have gone on continuously, although with varying intensity, both during the advance and the retreat of the great glacier; and it is therefore quite possible that much of the clay, sand, and gravel in southern Ohio may have been deposited at a time when the ice-sheet actually reached down to the central portion of that State, or even farther south still. As the level of the ice was reduced, ridges of morainic gravel, sand, and boulders, much of which would be well water-worn, would gather round its margin along the northern slopes of the watershed, and so "kames" would be formed which, when the ice-level had been further reduced, would appear as more or less continuous ridges and linear mounds, dotted here and there with boulders. If some such explanation were admissible, it would relieve us of the necessity for supposing that Lake Erie itself was ever filled with water to such a height as the summit of the watershed in northern Ohio.

* It is quite possible that these "passes" may have been deepened by subglacial streams when the whole region was covered with ice.

But be that as it may, it will hardly be doubted that the melting of the ice-sheet would cause floods enough to account for all the loamy clay, sand, and gravel which are found spread over the forest-bed in southern Ohio, and thus the views held by Dr. Newberry and Professor Winchell are not contradictory, but really complementary the one of the other. In north-western Ohio, Winchell holds the upper drift to be of the same nature as that which underlies the forest-bed ; in the southern districts, again, Newberry finds that the bulk of the drift which covers the forest-bed consists of more or less water-worn morainic débris, erratics, and flood-gravels, sand, and clay. In the one case, we have the ground-moraine of the second ice-sheet, sprinkled here and there with the water-worn materials that were distributed over the country when that ice-sheet was melting away ; in the other case, the upper drift seems entirely composed of the latter kind of detritus. So that one might hold Professor Winchell's view and yet quite agree with Dr. Newberry when he remarks that "the yellow clay, abounding with gravel and containing occasional boulders, which overlies the forest-bed, and is more generally the surface deposit of southern Ohio, is evidently the more immediate and coarser product of the action of the in-coming flood, and copious drainage from the north upon the ancient forest-covered land of which the sub-soil was the boulder-clay."

That, in this short review of the evidence, too much stress has not been laid upon the action of the floods that resulted from the melting of the great glacier, we may learn from a series of remarkable articles which recently appeared from the pen of Professor J. D. Dana.[*] Along the courses of the river-valleys of New England and other regions in the Northern States, occur a number of high-level terraces of detritus, which Professor Hitchcock long ago described as raised sea-beaches. Dana, however, has shown, by a careful examination of many of the New England valleys, that the terraces in question are not marine, but mark on the contrary the height attained by the flood waters that escaped

* "On Southern New England during the Melting of the Great Glacier;" *American Journal of Science & Arts*, Third Series, vol. x. pp. 168, 280, 353, 409, 497.

from the melting ice-sheet. These flood waters left their "mark not only in the structure and degree of coarseness of the deposits along the watercourses, but also in denudations of the drift-covered surface." In certain valleys, the terraces rise more than 150 ft. above the ordinary flood-level* of the present rivers ; and that the ocean took no part in their formation, is evident from the fact that the terraces gradually sink to lower levels as they are followed down the valleys. The "pitch," or fall, of the great flooded rivers, to whose action the "terraces" are due, was very considerable : thus, below Birmingham, in the Housatonic valley, it was as much as eight feet per mile ; while in the highest modern floods in that valley, the pitch is only about two feet below Birmingham. We must remember that there was nothing to interrupt the free course of the flood-waters to the sea ; their outlets were wide and deep, and from this we learn that "the rivers in the lower parts of Housatonic, Connecticut, and Thames valleys, were cataracts on a scale beyond all modern knowledge ;" and these, as Dana remarks, are but examples of a condition that prevailed generally over the glacier-covered lands. He shows further that so great was the flood in the Connecticut valley, that the waters overflowed in at least three places across the divide into adjoining valleys. "The Connecticut, when the glacial flood was at its height, had a depth of 150 ft. or more, all the way from Middletown to Turner's Falls, at Springfield—and to an undetermined distance beyond ; and from Hartford to Turner's Falls it averaged fifteen miles in width. It was a great stream, fed by numerous headlong torrents from either side ; and at the same time feeding other streams from its surplus waters. Its depth and extent were in spite of great losses from overflows into other valleys."

Floods like this seem quite adequate to produce all the phenomena described by Newberry. Clay, sand, gravel, and shingle would be swept along and scattered about the

---

* In the Connecticut Valley "the height of the flood was such that the waters instead of stopping at 24 or 25 feet above low-water mark, as now, continued rising until 175 feet deep ; and from that level they went plunging down the narrow channel to the Sound ; that, at Hartford, the river rose above the modern 30-foot flood-level to 190 feet ; that, at Springfield, they reached a height of more than 200 feet above low-water mark, and 240 feet above mean sea-level."

undulating low grounds, and even occasional ice-floated boulders might be carried far south over the inundated districts.

Passing northwards into the region where the deposits immediately overlying the "forest-bed" are recognised as true hardpan or unmodified drift, we find that this is covered now and again with spreads and heaps of gravel and sand, and dotted with erratics. Farther north still, the hardpan becomes, as we have seen, a much less conspicuous member of the drift; the most prominent drift deposits in the upland districts of the watershed, between the St. Lawrence and Hudson's Bay, being undulating hummocks, &c., of gravel and sand, and sporadic erratics.

Mr. G. M. Dawson, whose observations in the central region of North America have already been referred to, is of opinion that the rock-striations and *roches moutonnées* in the region of Lake Winnipeg and the Lake of the Woods, are clearly due to the grinding action of an ice-sheet which descended in a south-westerly direction from the Laurentian axis ; but he thinks that the drift, consisting of till with striated stones and overlying masses of sand, gravel, shingle, and erratics, which stretches west from the lakes along the 49th parallel of latitude to the base of the Rocky Mountains, has been dropt by icebergs, during a submergence of the land to the depth of upwards of 4,000 ft. He admits, however, that there are "difficulties yet unaccounted for by the theory of the glaciation and deposit of drift on the plains by icebergs." Chief among these, he says, is the entire absence of marine organic remains, the only fossil found being a piece of the common cedar. Another difficulty, however, presents itself which, to my mind at least, is equally, or even more, inexplicable on the iceberg hypothesis, and that is the occurrence at a height of 4,200 feet, and about twenty-five miles from the base of the Rocky Mountains, of boulders derived from the Laurentian axis. When we remember that the maximum height of the latter is only some 1,600 ft., we may well ask how these boulders could possibly have been carried by floating ice ; for, when the sea stood at the level of 4,200 ft., the Laurentian axis, from which the boulders have come, must have been drowned to a depth of 2,400 ft.

at least! There are other difficulties which will occur to any one who keeps in view the nature of the glaciation, which, according to Professor Dana and the States geologists, has affected New England and the North-west. It is hardly conceivable that such a degree of depression as 4,000 ft. and more, could have overtaken the area described by Mr. Dawson, without having been continued at the same time into the regions which have been examined in detail by the geologists of the States. Yet none of these observers has detected any evidence of such extensive submergence in the sea.

If we admit the former presence upon the Laurentian watershed of a sheet of ice 11,000 or 12,000 ft. in thickness, such as Professor Dana has shown must have existed, in order to account for the glaciation of New England, then there can be no difficulty in understanding how the ice should have descended into the valley of the Red River, and thereafter slowly ascended the long slope westwards to near the base of the Rocky Mountains. Of course, such a mass of ice could not have been nourished solely on the Laurentian uplands. It implies the presence to the north of a great confluent ice-sheet deriving from the north. In the region of Lake Winnipeg, the ice moved towards the south-west up and across the valley of the Saskatchewan, and probably became confluent with the local glaciers that descended the valleys of the Rocky Mountains. It was underneath this massive ice-flow that the till described by Mr. Dawson must have been formed. The overlying gravel, sand, and erratics belong to a later stage, and I believe it will yet be quite possible to account for all the phenomena without having recourse to the extreme measure of submerging the continent to a depth of over 4,000 ft. It is worth noting that the succession of the drift deposits, mentioned by Mr. Dawson, is precisely the same as obtains in every highly-glaciated region; at the bottom there is till, the old ground-moraine, and above that come sand, gravel, and erratics, the morainic débris washed out by subglacial streams and rivers, and by floods flowing off the melting ice. In the British Islands, in Scandinavia, in Switzerland, in New England and the North-western States, in Canada, and elsewhere, the same succession constantly recurs.

I shall here make bold to venture a suggestion which may possibly help to explain the drift phenomena described by Mr. Dawson. Let us suppose, then, that the Laurentian ice-sheet has become confluent with the local glaciers of the Rocky Mountains, and that the striation of the rocks and the formation of till have been in active progress for some time. A period arrives when, the climax of glacial cold having been reached, the ice-sheet and the local glaciers no longer increase in thickness, but begin to lose more than they gain. Now we can easily conceive that a time must come when the Laurentian ice-sheet and the local glaciers will cease to be confluent. The space that then intervenes will be swept by torrents of water which, in summer-time, will swell to great floods. Vast quantities of gravel and sand, brought down partly by subglacial streams and partly derived from the denudation of the till, will be scattered broadcast over the deserted beds of the ice-sheet and the glaciers, and it will necessarily happen that as the floods issuing from the ice-sheet will much surpass those deriving from the local glaciers, the débris belonging to the ice-sheet will be swept outwards, and may even invade the territory once covered by the local glaciers. During each returning winter ground-ice will gather on the bottoms of streams and rivers, enclosing stones and boulders, and ever and anon rising to the surface, will float these away. Much ice will also form here and there at the foot of the ice-sheet, and, indeed, wherever there are pools and sheets of water ; and thus boulders and erratics, disgorged from the glacier, and the débris and gravel of its moraine, will be frozen up. When spring and summer return, and the great floods resume their action, ice-rafts, with their rocky freights, will be swept forward and carried whithersoever the currents lead them. Similar ice-rafts, sailing from the base of the Rocky Mountains, will, at the same time, be hurried far east into the ground once occupied by the retreating ice-sheet. Thus we may see how there would be a dovetailing of the upper drift deposits derived from the west with those which had come from the north-east. As each summer returned, the drenching rains and great floods would reappear until the ice-sheet had retired far to the north, and its flood-waters were discharged in some other direction. I do not believe we have at present any proper conception of the amount of water that flowed from the melting ice-sheet. It must have been enormous. According to Dr. Croll's theory, our hemisphere, during a cold phase of the glacial epoch, was much nearer the sun in summer-time than it is now. It is true that the summer was short, but much more heat *per diem* being then received from the sun, great floods must have resulted, even during the climax of glacial cold ; indeed, the floods may have been more excessive then than afterwards. We have also to remember that in the short summer there would be an excessive evaporation and consequently a much heavier rain-fall than is at present experienced in North America. But as the glacial period drew to a close, the summers would become less intense, and the ice would melt more gradually away.

What became of the flood waters which, as I have suggested, must have been discharged in such volumes over the ground that spread between the base of the Rocky Mountains and the edge of the ice-sheet ? It is most probable that at first they swept over the watershed and entered the valley of the River Missouri ; and in confirmation of this I may point to the fact that the great loess or bluff formation of the Mississippi valley is believed, by the geologists of Iowa and Missouri, to have been brought thither by the Missouri River. At a later stage the drainage may have been by the Red River valley. One can have some faint idea of the amount of water flowing from the melting ice when he learns that the Mississippi at that time, " below the mouth of the Ohio, had *an average breadth of fifty miles*, and, along by Tennessee and northern Mississippi, of *seventy-five miles*; so that it was indeed a great stream." (Dana.) Over the whole country to which the flooded waters had access, similar deposits would be formed in the broader and more open valleys—the detritus becoming finer grained the farther the waters flowed.

In this account of American glacial geology I have been led into more detail than I anticipated, but this need not be regretted if the notes here put together should induce some of us in this country to pay more attention to the results obtained by American glacialists than has hitherto been done. Very much has been written on the subject, and I have not attempted even to refer, however briefly, to several points of interest, my chief object being merely to point out the general succession of events which appears to have characterized the American area during the glacial epoch. Before passing on to another part of my subject, however, I ought to mention the fact that many examples of buried river-channels have been described by American geologists. An interesting account of these is given by Dr. Newberry,* from which we learn that some of the old channels occur at depths varying from 50 ft. up to 200 ft. Some of the old courses enter Lake Erie at a depth of more than 200 ft. below the level at which they now enter the lake. They are filled up with alluvial and drift deposits, and, in one case at least, yielded unmistakable relics of interglacial age. This trough was pierced at Bloomington, Illinois, and the succession of the deposits passed through has already been given, see p. 45. It is quite evident that the rivers which cut out these old channels flowed at a time when the land stood relatively higher than now, and probably most of the buried channels date back to preglacial ages. Nevertheless, there is abundant evidence to show that even during interglacial times (the "Forest-bed" era), when a genial climate obtained, the land stood at a considerably higher level than at present.

In reading descriptions of the mounds of gravel and sand which cover large tracts of country in New England and the North-western States, and also in Canada, one cannot fail to notice how closely all the appearances coincide with those we are familiar with in this country. Professor Hitchcock, describing the drifts of New England, says they "form ridges and hills of almost every possible shape. It is not common to find straight ridges for a considerable distance. But the most common and most remarkable aspect assumed by these elevations is that of a collection of tortuous ridges, and rounded and even conical hills, with correspondent depressions between them."† This description would apply

* *Proceedings of Boston Natural History Society,* May, 1862; *Annals of the Lyceum of Nat. Hist.,* New York, June, 1869; "Surface Geology of Ohio," *Rep. of Geol. Surv. of Ohio,* vol. ii. chap. xxx.

† *Trans. of the Assoc. of Amer. Geol. and Natur.,* 1840-1842, p. 191.

word for word to some of the larger areas of kames in Scotland. The American mounds and cones are almost invariably composed of well water-worn materials, usually gravel and sand ; and they are, moreover, not infrequently falsebedded. Occasionally boulders are found inside these mounds ; but this appears to be rather exceptional, and such included stones are usually more or less rounded. Now and again a mound appears to be composed of coarse shingle and rounded boulders. But when boulders occur in mounds of sand and fine gravel, they seem to be confined chiefly to the upper parts of the deposits.*

Immense numbers of large erratics cumber the surface of the ground in many parts of New England, the North-western States, Canada, and Labrador, and are scattered over the tops and slopes of the mounds and ridges of sand and gravel. Even much farther north the same phenomena are so striking as to arrest the attention of the traveller who is not strictly a geologist. Every glacialist must be interested in reading the accounts given of the Barren Grounds of North America by the various writers who have visited these inhospitable regions. Sand-hills and huge erratics appear to be as common there as in the countries farther south. Captain Back gives a very graphic account of the isolated cones and " chains of sand-hills," which he saw in several places stretching far away on either side from the valley of the Great Fish River. He tells us that " the ridges and cones of sand were not only of great height, but singularly crowned with immense boulders, grey with lichen, which assuredly would have been considered as having been placed by design, had not the impossibility of moving such enormous masses proved incontestably that it was Nature's work." This was in 66° N. lat. In another place " the country was formed of gently undulating hills, whose surfaces were covered with large fragments of rock and a coarse gravelly soil." † In the

---

* *Report on the Geology of Lake Superior Land District,* p. 235 ; see also *Geology of New York,* part iii. p. 121, where Lardner Vanuxem says : "With some exceptions, they (erratics) are generally found upon the surface, frequently upon the tops of hills or on their sides, appearing in almost all their localities as if but recently dropped," &c. See further, for an excellent account of the kames of Ohio, *Geol. Surv. of Ohio,* vol. ii. chap. xxx.

† *Narrative of Arctic Land Expedition to the Mouth of the Great Fish River,* &c. pp. 140, 346.

Barren Grounds to the west of the bleak country traversed
by Back, sand-hills and huge erratics are equally abundant,
the erratics being often abundantly dotted over the hillocks
of drift.*   The same appearances have been noted again and
again by explorers.   Between Lake Winnipeg and the
Saskatchewan River, the number of boulders perched on the
sides and summits of ridges and mounds seems to be specially
remarkable.†

From similar appearances connected with the kames of
Scotland, I concluded that the erratics might have been
dropped into their present anomalous positions during a
period of submergence.   But I now feel persuaded that icebergs were not needed to perch the boulders where they are.
Of course it is quite possible that at the lower levels of the
country—in tracts which can be proved to have been submerged during late glacial times—many of the loose erratics
may have been dropped by icebergs.   But in the interior of
the country, and at heights which we have no evidence to
show were covered by the waters of a glacial sea, the scattered erratics and *blocs perchés* have most probably been left
lying on the ground upon the retreat of the last ice-
sheet.   From the descriptions given of the "hogs'-backs,"
"cobble knolls," and other prominent heaps and ridges of
gravel and sand in America, it seems hardly possible to
doubt that these accumulations are of the same nature as the
Swedish åsar, Irish eskers, and Scotch kames, and that they
have been formed in the same way, some being flood-gravels
laid down by the waters issuing from the melting ice-sheet,
while others mark the courses of subglacial streams and
rivers.   The erratics dotted over their surface may have fallen
from the edge of the retreating ice, or they may have been
introduced from above through crevasses and dropped upon
the beds of subglacial rivers : or again they may have melted
out of the ice itself where they lay engorged ; and their
generally rough and non-glaciated aspect agrees with this
view of their origin.

The erratics sometimes show striæ which not infrequently

---

* See Franklin's *Journey to the Shores of the Polar Sea*, and his *Second Journey;*
also Sir J. Richardson's *Journal of a Boat Voyage through Rupert's Land.*
† *Royal Geographical Journal*, vol. xxx. p. 275 (Palisser's Exploration).

are placed parallel to those of the bare rock upon which the blocks rest.   A good example of this appearance is quoted by Mr. J. De Laske.*   He states that "around one of the quarries to the west of Carver's Harbour the ground is literally covered with boulders, some of which are enormous. Many of these turned out of their beds exhibit the polishing and scratching of the common floor-rock of the island (Mount Desert Island).   Furthermore, if carefully turned over, we find some of them left just where they had last been employed in scratching the ledges—the parallel scratches of the boulder being placed parallel to those of the rock beneath."

The general distribution of erratics in North America, so far as that has been carefully studied, indicates transport by land-ice rather than icebergs.   Of course some may have been floated by river-ice, and others may have been carried by icebergs and dropped over such low-lying regions as can be proved, from the presence of sea-shells in undisturbed deposits, to have been submerged.   But erratics by themselves can no longer be taken as evidence of former depression of the land.   It is a fact familiar to American geologists that the "trains of boulders often follow the direction of the grander slopes of the surface, and especially the courses of the larger valleys."   This we can understand if the erratics were carried by a glacier, but how can we suppose that the currents of a sea would always elect to flow along the line of the larger submerged valleys?   It is true that the boulders have often been transported "across valleys and hills without deviation from a right line;" but the striations upon the rock-surfaces show that the great ice-sheet often neglected the minor features of the country in the same way, and there is no need therefore to invoke the aid of icebergs to account for such erratics as have travelled across country—indeed the upper surface of the ice might often be moving in a right line, while its lower portions were flowing in obedience to the contour of the ground.   Another excellent proof that the erratics have been transported by land-ice lies in the fact mentioned by Hitchcock, Dana, and others, that they sometimes occur at heights of 1,000 ft., or even more than

* *Second Ann. Rep. upon Nat. Hist. & Geol. of Maine,* 1862.

3,000 ft. above the rock-masses from which they have been derived.

Amongst the so-called *raised beaches* described by Professor Hitchcock, there is one which occurs in the White Mountains at a height of 2,449 ft. above the sea ; but it seems most likely that these terraces are, as Dr. Packard and other writers have suggested, of freshwater origin—being the relics of glacial lakes like the Parallel Roads of Glen Roy. Many of the terraces in question are strewn with huge boulders, as if these had been stranded by rafts of ice.

It becomes more and more apparent, indeed, that among American geologists the belief in a great submergence of the land below the sea in late glacial and postglacial times is passing away. Thus one of the keenest observers in the States, Professor J. D. Dana, can find no trace of a greater submergence in New England than twenty feet. The old sea-coast terrace, he tells us, "is universally but five to twenty feet in height." But as one goes north the amount of former depression increases until, in the Gulf of St. Lawrence, raised beaches are encountered at an elevation of 500 ft. That these beaches are really marine is proved by their having yielded sea-shells, and remains of whales, seals, &c. Similar old sea-coasts have been met with in the Arctic regions at various levels up to 1,000 ft. During this depression of the low maritime regions, beds of clay accumulated off the coast, and became gradually stocked with shells of an arctic type. These are the "Leda clays" of Labrador and Maine, so ably described by Dr. Dawson, Dr. Packard, and others.[*] It can hardly be doubted that they are the equivalents of the Scottish and Scandinavian shelly clays. The fossils which they contain are very decidedly arctic in the lower beds, but in the upper beds they give evidence of a gradually ameliorating climate.

This period of depression eventually passed away, and the sea once more began to retire until it reached its present limits.

To the era of great flooded rivers succeeded a more placid condition of things, when the modern alluvial flats and terraces which border the streams and valleys were formed.

* See also a paper by G. F. Matthew, *Canadian Naturalist*, vol. viii. p. 104.

Of these, however, no further notice need be taken at present ; all that we are called upon to observe in regard to them is this, that nowhere within the area covered by the glacial débris laid down during the last advance of the ice-sheet have they yielded any remains of the old pachyderms and other extinct animals which, as we have seen, lived in the North-western States during the last interglacial period.

In the valleys of the White Mountains, and in those of the Rocky Mountains and the Sierra Nevada, a number of terminal moraines mark the sites of local glaciers, which gradually dwindled down to insignificance, and even in many cases vanished altogether, as the cold of the glacial epoch passed away.

CHAPTER XXXVI.

GENERAL SUCCESSION OF GLACIAL AND INTERGLACIAL DEPOSITS.

Evidence for a glacial epoch in geographical distribution of plants.—Traces of a glacial epoch in the southern hemisphere.—Mr. Darwin on evidence for alternations of cold and warm periods in the north and south.—Cause of submergence in glacial times.—Tables of succession of glacial and interglacial deposits.

WE have now completed our review of the glacial deposits, and have learned that the succession of changes during the Ice Age was singularly uniform over large areas in the northern hemisphere. All this points unmistakably to the operation of cosmical influences. It is impossible to believe that mere local elevations and depressions of land were the causes that induced that remarkable rotation of cold and mild periods which we term the glacial epoch. What degree of elevation, it might be asked, would be needed to convert almost every mountain range and group in the northern hemisphere into a centre of glaciation, and to cover northern Europe and northern America with great continental ice-sheets? And how, upon this hypothesis of upheaval, are we to explain the occurrence of interglacial deposits, which speak to us of wide land-surfaces clothed with luxuriant vegetation and inhabited by an abundant mammalian fauna? Instead of appealing to movements of the earth's crust as the primary cause of the glacial epoch—movements which are assumed, without any evidence in their favour, to have taken place, and which, even if they did happen, would certainly not account for a very large proportion of the geological phenomena—I prefer to look, for an explanation of the wonderful vicissitudes of glacial times, to that theory which is based upon the fact that there are changes in the eccentricity of the earth's orbit. Dr. Croll's theory harmonizes so closely with the facts, and explains so much that has hitherto been inexplicable, that for the present it seems to me we must accept it as the only reasonable interpretation.

The evidence for intensely cold climatic conditions having obtained in our hemisphere at a period not very remote from the present, rests, as we have seen, to a great extent upon purely geological evidence. Thus we point to ice-marks, to morainic deposits, and to arctic shell-beds, as proofs that the temperate regions in which these occur have experienced at some time in the past a considerably colder climate than they now enjoy. But the geographical distribution of many plants and animals tells the same tale, as Edward Forbes showed long ago. Thus certain alpine plants occur on the tops of Scottish mountains which are evidently related to similar forms that grow in Scandinavia; and analogous facts have been noted in many other regions. The inference is that when the cold of the glacial period was coming on, the northern plants migrated southwards to occupy the territory formerly held by the temperate group, and this in like manner at the same time gradually crept farther south. When the cold began to abate migration would recommence, but this time it would be in the opposite direction, that is to say, from south to north. As the warmth returned the great body of the arctic or northern forms would make for the north, while others would find the requisite climate by merely ascending the mountains. By-and-by the time would come when the northern and temperate groups had returned to their preglacial homes, but the fact of their dispersal during glacial times would be chronicled by the isolated northern forms found living on the tops of the mountains in temperate regions. "These views," says Mr. Darwin, "grounded as they are on the perfectly well-ascertained occurrence of a former glacial period, seem to me to explain in so satisfactory a manner the present distribution of the alpine and arctic productions of Europe and America, that when in other regions we find the same species on distant mountain sum- mits, we may almost conclude, without other evidence, that a colder climate formerly· permitted their migration across the intervening lowlands, now become too warm for their existence." My limits, however, will not allow me to give a digest of the views put forward by Edward Forbes and subsequently extended by Mr. Darwin, and I can only refer those who are not already familiar with the subject to the paper by the former in the "Memoirs of the Geological Survey of Great Britain," and to Chap. XII. of the "Origin of Species."*

The time will come when geologists will endeavour to correlate the drift deposits of the northern with those which are known to occur in the southern hemisphere. At present, however, we are very insufficiently acquainted with the latter. But we shall hardly expect to meet in the south with such striking geological evidence for the former existence of a glacial period as our own hemisphere so abundantly presents. The southern is the great water hemisphere; south of the 40th parallel of S. latitude we find only the extremity of South America (Patagonia), a portion of New Zealand, Tasmania, and a number of more or less barren islands, with the ice-smothered Antarctic continent stretching towards the Pole. Nevertheless, insignificant as these areas are when contrasted with the extent of glaciated land-surface which occurs in our own hemisphere north of the 40th parallel, we shall yet see that many of them yield distinct evidence of having experienced severer climatic conditions than obtain at present. Mr. Darwin, for example, showed many years ago that large glaciers came down, within geologically recent times, to low levels in the Cordillera of South America, and his observations have been supplemented by Mr. D. Forbes, who informed Mr. Darwin that he had seen ice-worn rocks and scratched stones at about the height of 12,000 ft. in various parts of the Cordillera, between lat. 13° and 30° S. Yet no true glaciers, Mr. Darwin says, "now exist even at much more considerable heights along this whole space of the Cordillera. Farther south on both sides of the continent, from lat. 41° to the southernmost extremity, we have the clearest evidence of former glacial action, in numerous immense boulders, transported far from their parent source." A few years ago these observations were extended by Agassiz, who came to the conclusion that vast glaciers had descended from the mountains and overspread extensive areas in the

* See also Mr. Wallace's recent work, *The Geographical Distribution of Animals.*

low grounds. Drs. Haast and Hector have shown also that in New Zealand colossal glaciers at one time descended to low levels in that island; and some traces of glacial action have been observed in the mountains of the south-eastern corner of Australia. Again, traces of considerable glaciation have been noted by Mr. G. W. Stow in Natal, British Kaffraria—the Kaga and Krome mountains; he mentions the occurrence of *roches moutonnées,* erratic blocks, unstratified clays with angular boulders, striated boulders, and other glacial phenomena, all of which he refers to the action of land-ice. According to the theory supported in this volume, glacial and mild climates would alternate in the two hemispheres, and consequently the glacial deposits and ice-markings detected south of the equator will be either a little older or younger than the similar memorials met with in our hemisphere; while all must of course belong to one and the same great epoch. At present, however, the glacial deposits of the south are not sufficiently known, and we cannot tell whether they contain any records of interglacial mild climates; but a study of the distribution of animals and plants throws much light upon the subject. In his "Origin of Species" this interesting question is treated by Mr. Darwin with his usual clearness and breadth, and I must again refer the reader to the chapter already indicated. He remarks that Dr. Croll's theory throws so much light on geographical distribution that he is strongly inclined to trust in it. It accounts, for instance, for the presence on the temperate plains of the north and south, and on the lofty mountains of the tropics in all parts of the world, of either the same species or varieties of the same species. Great migrations from north to south took place, as we have seen, during the climax of glacial cold in our hemisphere. "As the cold became more intense," says Mr. Darwin, "we know that arctic forms invaded the temperate regions; and from the facts just given, there can hardly be a doubt that some of the more vigorous, dominant, and widest-spreading temperate forms invaded the equatorial lowlands. The inhabitants of these hot lowlands would at the same time have migrated to the tropical and subtropical regions of the south, for the southern hemisphere was at this period warmer. On the decline of the glacial period, as both hemispheres gradually recovered their former temperatures, the northern temperate forms living on the lowlands under the equator would have been driven to their former homes or have been destroyed, being replaced by the equatorial forms returning from the south. Some, however, of the northern forms would almost certainly have ascended any adjoining high land, where, if sufficiently lofty, they would have long survived like the arctic forms on the mountains of Europe. . . . In the regular course of events the southern hemisphere would in its turn be subjected to a severe glacial period, with the northern hemisphere rendered warmer; and then the southern forms would invade the equatorial lowlands, the northern forms which had before been left on the mountains would now descend and mingle with the southern forms. These latter, when the warmth returned, would return to their former homes, leaving some few species on the mountains, and carrying southward with them some of the northern temperate forms which had descended from their mountain fastnesses. Thus we should have some few species identically the same in the northern and southern temperate zones and on the mountains of the intermediate tropical regions. But the species left during a long time on these mountains, or in opposite hemispheres, would have to compete with many new forms, and would be exposed to somewhat different physical conditions; hence they would be eminently liable to modification, and would generally now exist as varieties or as representative species; and this is the case."

Thus there are several lines of evidence which all seem to converge and point to one and the same conclusion, namely, that the glacial epoch was not one long continuous period of cold, but consisted rather of a succession of cold and warm eras.

In the course of these pages frequent mention has been made of the submergence of the land in glacial times. In the British Islands, in Scandinavia, in northern Germany, and in North America, we have evidence of very remarkable oscillations of the relative level of sea and land. These changes of level have usually been ascribed by geologists to

movements of elevation and subsidence of the solid crust of
the earth—movements which are well known to have happened frequently in the past history of the globe, and which
are taking place even in our own day. But the sea may rise
upon the land without any movement of the land itself.
M. Adhémar and Dr. Croll have pointed out that a vast ice-
cap (such as that which covered so many northern regions
during the cold periods of the glacial epoch) would of itself
cause a rise of the sea in the glaciated hemisphere by dis-
placing the earth's centre of gravity. But to what extent
this rise would take place is uncertain. According to Dr.
Croll, if the ice now resting on the Antarctic continent,
which he estimates to be at least two miles in thickness,
were transferred to our hemisphere, the result would be a
very considerable submergence in northern and temperate
latitudes. "Suppose," he says, "that during the glacial
epoch, at a time when the cold was gradually increasing on
the northern and the warmth on the southern hemisphere,
the ice should melt more rapidly off the antarctic continent
than it was being formed on the arctic and sub-arctic regions;
suppose also that by the time a quantity of ice, equal to
one-half what exists at present on the antarctic continent,
had accumulated on the northern hemisphere, the whole of
the antarctic ice had been melted away, the sea would then
be fuller than at present by the amount of water resulting
from the one mile of melted ice. The height to which
this would raise the general level of the sea would be as
follows :—

"The antarctic ice-cap is equal in area to $\frac{1}{23\cdot46}$ of that
covered by the ocean. The density of ice to that of water
being taken at ·92 to 1, it follows that 25 ft. 6 in. of ice
melted off the cap would raise the general level of the ocean
1 ft., and the one mile of ice melted off would raise the
level 200 ft. This 200 ft. of rise resulting from the melted
ice we must add to the rise resulting from the displacement
of the earth's centre of gravity. The removal of the two
miles of ice from the antarctic continent would displace the
centre of gravity 190 ft., and the formation of a mass of ice
equal to the one-half of this on the arctic regions would carry
the centre of gravity 95 ft. farther; giving in all a total

displacement of 285 ft., thus producing a rise of sea-level at the North Pole of 285 ft., and in the latitude of Edinburgh of 234 ft. Add to this the rise of 200 ft. resulting from the melted ice, and we have then 485 ft. of submergence at the Pole, and 434 ft. in the latitude of Edinburgh. A rise to a similar extent might probably take place after the period of maximum glaciation, when the ice would be melting on the northern hemisphere more rapidly than it would be forming on the southern."*

There can be little doubt that M. Adhémar and Dr. Croll have indicated a *vera causa* of changes in the relative level of land and sea; and certainly it is remarkable that evidence of submergence should so often accompany marks of strong glaciation, as if the one were somehow dependent upon the other. In reviewing the evidence, one cannot but admit, therefore, that much of the submergence in glacial times may be due to the transference of ice from one hemisphere to the other, in the manner pointed out by Dr. Croll; but in the case of submergence to the extent of upwards of 1,000 ft., as in Wales and Ireland, it seems more likely that we have evidence of an actual subsidence of the land itself— a point which Dr. Croll is quite willing to concede.

In concluding my account of the glacial deposits, it may aid the reader who wishes to follow the argument in my concluding chapters, if I here summarise the general results of our review in a series of short tabular statements. In each table I begin with the oldest deposits.

SCOTTISH GLACIAL DEPOSITS.

1. Lower accumulations of till with subjacent and intercalated interglacial freshwater and marine beds. — Intense glacial conditions, with intervening periods marked by milder conditions.

2. Freshwater and marine deposits of last interglacial period. — Land surface with trees, &c., and mammalia; temperate climate, succeeded by submergence and colder conditions; arctic and northern shells.

3. Upper till (including most of the shelly till of maritime regions and the greater proportion of the till of inland districts). — Re-elevation of the land; intense glacial conditions, but not so excessive as before.

4. Moraine-débris and perched blocks; lake terraces; ancient flood-gravels, &c.; kames, &c. — Ice-sheet or confluent glaciers retreating; glacial lakes; great floods; large local glaciers.

* *Climate and Time*, p. 388.

5. Brick-clays with arctic and boreal shells; erratics. } Further retreat of the ice; land not so extensive as now; floating ice.

6. Valley moraines and glacial gravels. } Final retreat of the glaciers.

ENGLISH GLACIAL DEPOSITS.

1.
  a. Cromer "till and contorted drift."
  b. Gravel, sand, and clay (interglacial).
  c. Great chalky boulder-clay of eastern counties, &c.; "northern drift" of midland and southern counties; unfossiliferous bottom boulder-clay of Cheshire, Somerset, &c.
  d. Gravel, sand, &c.; Bridlington, &c., shell-bed (interglacial).
  e. Purple boulder-clay of Yorkshire; lower shelly boulder-clay of Lancashire, Cheshire, &c.

Period of great oscillations of climate; intense glacial conditions (with confluent glaciers covering the low grounds) interrupted by milder intervals during which the glaciers retired. Cold of the earliest recognisable glacial period (Cromer beds) not so intense as during the deposition of great chalky boulder-clay when the climax of glacial severity was reached. Purple boulder-clay, &c., indicates less severity of climate than during accumulation of chalky boulder-clay, &c.

2. Hessle sand and gravel with mammalian remains, *Cyrena fluminalis*, and marine littoral shells; middle sand, &c., of Lancashire, Cheshire, &c.

Last interglacial period; climate temperate; Yorkshire inhabited by the mammoth, horse, ox, and deer; land becomes submerged eventually to a depth (in Wales) of 1300 feet.

3. Hessle boulder-clay; younger boulder-clay of Durham, Northumberland, &c.; upper shelly boulder-clay of Lancashire, Cheshire, &c.

Re-elevation of the land; return of intense glacial conditions; climate, however, not so severe as during deposition of chalky boulder-clay, &c.

4. Morainic débris and perched blocks on mountain-slopes, &c., at high levels in Wales and Lake country; flood-gravels, &c.; hummocks of gravel and sand = kames.

Confluent glaciers retreating; great floods scouring the drifts of the low grounds; large local glaciers.

5. Nar valley beds. { Climate somewhat colder than at present; partial submergence.

6. Valley moraines. Final retreat of the glaciers.

IRISH GLACIAL DEPOSITS.

1. Till; lower boulder-clay (probably the equivalent of the lower shelly boulder-clay of Lancashire). } Intense glacial conditions (early interglacial beds not certainly known to occur).

2. Middle sand and gravel. { Last interglacial period; climate temperate; land submerged for upwards of 1,200 feet.

3. Upper boulder-clay. { Re-elevation of the land: return of glacial conditions; but climate not so cold probably as during deposition of lower boulder-clay.

4. and 5, Morainic débris and perched blocks at high levels; eskers, &c. } Retreat of confluent glaciers; great floods; large local glaciers.

6. Valley moraines. Final retreat of glaciers.

SCANDINAVIAN GLACIAL DEPOSITS.

1. Till.	Intense glacial conditions.
2. Interglacial freshwater beds	Amelioration of climate. [There would appear to have been more than one interglacial period during the glacial epoch in Sweden.]
3. Till.	Return of intense glacial conditions; glaciation probably not so severe.
4. Morainic débris; perched blocks; åsar, &c.	Confluent glaciers retreating; great floods; local glaciers.
5. Clays, &c., with arctic shells.	Climate still cold; land submerged for 600 feet or so.
6. Moraines.	Retreat of the glaciers.

GLACIAL DEPOSITS OF CENTRAL EUROPE.

1. Grund - moränen or till; perched blocks at high levels, as on the Jura, Mont Salève, &c., in Switzerland; on Ullrichsberg, in Carinthia, &c.	Intense glacial conditions; Alpine glaciers invade the low grounds of France, Baden, Würtemberg, Bavaria, and Upper Austria, and the Valley of the Po.
2. Lignite beds, gravel, &c., of Dürnten, &c., in Switzerland; ancient river-gravels at Klagenfurt in Carinthia; lignite and gravel, &c., of Leffe, &c., in Italy [perhaps, also, some portion of the so-called Pliocene sands of Piedmont, &c.]	Last interglacial period; climate temperate, and somewhat like that of Switzerland now; elephant, rhinoceros, and great bovine and cervine animals inhabit Central Europe; man lives in Switzerland. Climate changes from temperate to cold-temperate and glacial.
3. Moraines overlying the older glacial and interglacial deposits.	Return of glacial conditions; new advance of glaciers; climate not so intense as during formation of older grund-moränen.
4. "Diluvial gravels and sand," and loess in part.	Melting of the glaciers; great floods.
5. and 6, Newer moraines; river gravels and loess in part.	Periodic retreat of the glaciers.

NORTH AMERICAN GLACIAL DEPOSITS.

1. Till or "unmodified drift" or "hardpan;" shelly boulder-clay of Canada; great moraines of Rocky Mountains, &c.	Intense glacial conditions; ice-sheet covering all the north-eastern portion of the continent and becoming confluent in part with local glaciers of Rocky Mountains. Great glacial lakes formed during the subsequent melting of ice-sheet.
2. "Forest - bed" of northwest, &c.; mammalian remains of so-called "driftless area."	Last interglacial period; climate mild or temperate; abundant vegetation and mammalian fauna.
3. Upper till or "hardpan" covering the "Forest-bed;" coarse gravel and sand with erratics, in part.	Return of intense glacial conditions; ice-sheet not quite so extensive as before.
4. Morainic débris and perched blocks; lake terraces; kames and coarse gravel and sand, with erratics; flood-gravels, &c.; loess.	Ice-sheet retreating; glacial lakes; great floods; large local glaciers in Rocky Mountains, &c.

5. Leda clays with arctic } Further retreat of ice; land not so extensive as
   shells; erratics. } now; floating ice.
6. Valley moraines and gla- } Final disappearance of many local glaciers.
   cial gravels. }

A glance at the foregoing tables will show that interglacial deposits occur in Scotland, England, Ireland, Scandinavia, Central Europe, and North America. That interglacial
deposits should not be equally well developed in the glacial
deposits of each country, ought not to surprise us. We
must bear in mind that the preservation of such loose incoherent beds must always be exceptional under the conditions
which are known to have obtained in glacial times. But
as I have already enlarged upon this point while treating of
the Scotch glacial deposits, I need not trouble the reader
with a repetition of the remarks referred to.

There is one important point, however, to which I desire
to call special attention. It is this: that in every country
where the glacial deposits have been studied with any attention to details, we have clear and convincing proof of a mild
interglacial period having supervened in what one may term
the later stage of the glacial epoch. This—the last interglacial period—has left its mark alike in the British Islands,
in Scandinavia and northern Europe, in central Europe, and
in northern America. In Switzerland the climate of the
period referred to was mild and genial, the elephant and the
rhinoceros being at that time denizens of the country. In
North America, during the same period, a widespread forest
covered the North-western States and doubtless other
regions, and the mastodon and elephant roamed over the
land. Turning to the British deposits, we find that after
the disappearance of the great ice-sheet underneath which
the older accumulations of boulder-clay were formed, a land-
surface appeared, with rivers and lakes, and the work of
atmospheric erosion went on. In the fluviatile and lacustrine
deposits of this period in Scotland we find remains of the
mammoth, of cervine and bovine animals, of water-rats and
frogs. In Yorkshire beds of the same age have likewise
yielded mammalian bones, together with the freshwater shell,
Cyrena fluminalis, which occurs commonly in the so-called
postglacial beds of the Thames. The evidence in Scotland
and the north-west of England shows that this land-surface

was eventually submerged in a sea whose waters were colder than those that now lave our shores.

The middle sands of Lancashire, &c., are generally thought to be the only representatives we have in England of this last interglacial period. The Hessle beds, however, which give evidence of terrestrial conditions, must, as I believe, be relegated to the same mild interval in the glacial epoch. Thus it would seem that in England, as in Scotland, dry land appeared after the ice-sheet which deposited the purple boulder-clay of Yorkshire and the lower shelly boulder-clay of Lancashire, &c., had melted away, and that rivers flowed in our valleys and effected great erosion long before the land sank down below the sea to receive its covering of " middle sands." Have we, then, any remains of that old land-surface in England other than those that occur at Hessle ? are there any English river-gravels that can be correlated with the lignite beds of Switzerland ? I believe that such river-gravels do exist, and that these have hitherto been erroneously referred to postglacial times. The consideration of this important point brings us, as we shall presently see, face to face with the question of the antiquity of man ; for it is in these so-called postglacial deposits that the earliest traces of man have been detected.

CHAPTER XXXVII.

CAVE-DEPOSITS AND ANCIENT RIVER-GRAVELS OF ENGLAND.

Prehistoric deposits.—Stone, Bronze, and Iron ages.—Palæolithic or Old Stone period.—Neolithic or New Stone period.— Universal distribution throughout the British Islands of neolithic implements.—Animal remains associated with neolithic relics.—Palæolithic implements.—Absence of intermediate types.— Break between palæolithic and neolithic periods.—Caves and cave-deposits. —Kent's cavern, Torquay.—Succession of deposits.—River-gravels, &c., with mammalian remains and palæolithic implements. — Geographical changes during palæolithic period.—Disturbance and partial reconstruction by river-beds before neolithic times.—Gap between neolithic and palæolithic deposits.

A FASCINATION attaches to the early history of every people. We long to penetrate that mystery which the lapse of ages has drawn like a thick curtain round the cradle of our race. How eagerly do we scan the oldest written records that have any reference to our country and its people ; and how assiduously do we try to shape a coherent story out of those vague myths, legends, and traditions which have come down to us from the long-forgotten past. But there are memorials of man in this, as in other countries, which date back to so remote a period that even the oldest traditions have nothing whatever to say about them. The English historian begins his narrative with the Roman invasion, and the archæologist until recent years could hardly trace the story farther back ; but now he can tell us of a time infinitely far beyond the first dim beginnings of history and tradition, when races of savage men and tribes of wild animals, some of which have long been extinct, were denizens of Britain. Hitherto we had been taught to look upon Stonehenge and the so-called Druid-circles as the oldest memorials of man in this country—mysterious monuments belonging to the shadowy past, about whose age and uses only vague conjectures could be offered. If older races than the builders of Stonehenge ever lived in Britain, we knew nothing, and could hardly hope to know anything, about them. The past was apparently separated from us by a gulf which it was vain to think that any ingenuity would succeed in bridging over.

Now all this is changed. The massive monoliths of Stonehenge, however venerable their antiquity, seem but as structures of yesterday; the standing-stones of Avebury, of Callernish, and Stennis, the so-called vitrified forts, the round towers of Ireland, and all those remains of ancient camps, dwellings, and burial-places so abundantly met with throughout the British Islands, are of immeasurably more recent date than certain rude stone implements which our cave-deposits and ancient river-gravels have yielded. Since Stonehenge rose upon Salisbury plains no great change in the physical geography of Britain has taken place. The destruction of ancient forests and the cultivation of the soil have doubtless in some measure altered the aspect of the land, and influenced the character of the climate. Our hills and valleys, however, we are sure have remained the same, and even the coast-line has experienced probably little change. Changes undoubtedly there have been, yet none so considerable as to invalidate the truth of the statement, that since the days of the builders of Stonehenge no great geological revolution has taken place in Britain. But the rude stone implements to which I have referred date back to a period when the appearance presented by our country differed greatly from that which obtains now ; and for so vast a time did the old tribes who used these rude implements occupy the British area, that the slowly-acting forces of Nature were enabled, during that time, to bring about many geological changes, each of which required long ages for its evolution.

What, then, is the nature of that evidence which has weighed with archæologists and geologists in assigning to man this great antiquity? It would lead me far beyond the limits I have set for myself were I here to attempt anything like a detailed account of the archæological evidence. My object will be sufficiently served if I give only a brief outline of the general results.*

---

* The reader who desires fuller information must consult Sir J. Lubbock's *Prehistoric Times*, and Mr. Evans's *Ancient Stone Implements of Great Britain.*

All those monuments and memorials of man which belong to prehistoric times have been arranged by archæologists under three groups. The classification adopted is based chiefly upon the distinguishing features presented by such objects of workmanship as weapons, implements, and personal ornaments. The oldest group comprises implements of *stone ;* next in order come *bronze* relics ; and these are succeeded by tools and weapons of *iron.* The articles of stone indicate upon the whole a much lower grade of development than those of metal, and hence archæologists have inferred that the races who used stone-knives, hatchets, and hammers preceded in time those to whom the use of metal was known. In like manner they have argued that cutting-tools and weapons of bronze were supplanted by weapons of iron—the use of iron for such purposes evincing more knowledge of the metals and a greater advance in civilisation. Hence it is customary to speak of the Stone Age, the Bronze Age, and the Iron Age.

Geological investigations have strongly supported this classification—deposits containing the stone implements having been proved in many ways to be older than those which have yielded relics of bronze, just as these latter have been shown to belong as a whole to an older period than weapons and tools of iron. But while we speak of these three ages it must be distinctly understood that they are not separated from each other by any hard and fast line. The manufacture of stone tools and weapons did not die out all of a sudden, and the employment of bronze immediately succeed. On the contrary, stone hammers and implements continued in some use long after bronze had been introduced, just as this latter certainly found favour and was extensively employed, especially for ornamental purposes, after the advantages of iron for knives and swords had become recognised.

With the bronze and iron ages, however, the geologist proper has comparatively little to do : although, did space permit, it could be shown that even in regard to the history of these two ages, he might have something not uninteresting to say. But as I have already remarked, the physical changes which have supervened since the beginning of the

bronze age, sink into insignificance before those which can be
shown to have taken place during the preceding stone age.
It is to the relics of this latter age, then, and the lessons
which these seem to teach, that I wish now to direct
attention.

The stone age is subdivided into two periods, which are
termed respectively the Neolithic or New Stone period, and
the Palæolithic or Old Stone period. To the former belong
those implements and weapons which are often more or less
polished and finely finished, and which in variety of form
and frequent elegance of design evince no inconsiderable skill
on the part of the old workmen.

These relics occur, it may be said, throughout the whole
length and breadth of the land—from the extreme north of
Scotland to the south of England, and they are equally
abundant in the sister island. As a rule, they are met with
either at or near the surface of the ground, and they very
frequently appear associated with the remains of such
animals as the dog, the horse, the sheep, the pig, and certain
species of oxen which are believed to have been the precursors
of the present breeds.

The weapons and implements belonging to the older or
palæolithic period are altogether of ruder form and finish.
They are merely chipped into the requisite shape of adze,
hatchet, scraper, or whatever the implement may chance to
be. Although considerable dexterity is shown in the
fashioning of these rude implements, yet they certainly
evince much less skill on the part of the tool-maker than
the relics of the newer or neolithic period. It is somewhat
noteworthy also that while the implements of the neolithic
period are made of various kinds of stones, those of the
palæolithic period consist almost exclusively of flint ; and so
characteristic are the shape and fashion of the latter, that an
experienced archæologist has no difficulty in recognising and
distinguishing them at once from relics of neolithic age.

We find no tools or weapons of intermediate forms which
might indicate a gradual improvement and progress from the
rude types characteristic of palæolithic times to the more
finished implements used by neolithic man. The one set of
relics is sharply marked off from the other. Even a casual

observer cannot fail to notice the marked difference between a collection of neolithic implements and one of palæolithic flint hatchets. Nor can we help thinking that the people who used the latter were far less advanced than, and decidedly inferior in mechanical skill and contrivance to, the race or races by whom the polished implements were fashioned.

A distinct passage can be traced from the new stone period into the age of bronze. We can see plainly how neolithic man continued to improve the shape and fashion of stone implements, until at last he acquired a knowledge of the use of metals. But between the disappearance of palæolithic man and the advent of his neolithic successor occurs a blank which hitherto the ingenuity of archæologists has failed to bridge over. Why is it that while a passage can be traced from the new stone period into the bronze age, the two periods of stone should yet be separated by a clear line of demarcation? The social conditions and degree of advance shadowed forth by the appearance of the rude palæolithic implements belong to a lower grade of civilisation than that which the polished stone implements represent. It is not probable, but in the highest degree unlikely, that men would suddenly and completely abandon the use of rudely-chipped flint-hatchets, and all at once, as by a kind of inspiration, acquire the skill to fashion elegantly-shaped and even finely-polished implements of various kinds of stone. Long years were surely required for such a measure of progress. Had the palæolithic period in Britain merged continuously into neolithic times, it seems certain that the older rude forms would have been gradually improved upon, both as regards shape and finish. Moreover, if one may judge from modern analogies, this improvement would be a very slow process. We know that many savage tribes in building their huts continue repeating the same kind of structure from generation to generation, just as the birds do with their nests. We know also that in the fashioning of their implements and weapons they often show extremely little or even no advance whatever upon their forefathers. But, as just stated, we find no trace of any intermediate age of gradual progress linking on, as it were, the palæolithic to the neolithic period. If such an intermediate stage had obtained in Britain we should long ere this have discovered some evidence of it. Nothing of the kind, however, occurs, and we must explain its absence as best we may. But the fact of this break in the succession—this hiatus or gap in the record—will be rendered more apparent after we have learned something as to the mode and position in which the older stone implements occur.

Implements of palæolithic age are met with in caves and in certain ancient river-gravels under circumstances which we shall presently see argue for these relics a very great antiquity.

In the limestone districts of England caverns more or less abound. These remarkable cavities are formed by the slow percolation through the rock of acidulated water in the following manner. Rain-water absorbs carbonic acid from the atmosphere, and, after passing over and sinking through the soil, always takes up more, which it derives from decaying organic matter. Thus acidulated, it soaks downward through the rock by natural cracks and fissures, the walls of which it gradually dissolves, and eventually makes its exit at some lower level as a spring or springs of *hard* water. In the course of long ages this constant circulation of rain-water and springs, and consequent waste of limestone, result in the formation of caves and winding galleries, through which very frequently considerable streams have found their way as underground rivers. Thus, both by chemical action and by the tear and wear of aqueous erosion, these subterranean galleries and caves have been gradually widened and deepened. When traced from lower to higher levels they prove in not a few cases to have once communicated with the upper surface by wide apertures, formed either by the falling-in of the roof or by the water eating along some natural fissure. Many of these apertures, however, are now closed up with calcareous matter and heterogeneous débris.

After streams had flowed in such underground channels for a longer or shorter time, they were often at last compelled to abandon them, either owing to one or other of the many changes which the subterranean forces have brought about, or to some local shifting of the subaerial part of their course, such as frequently happens during heavy floods. Caves which were in this way deserted naturally became the dens of wild beasts or the abodes of savage men.

Thus in the phenomena of the English caves we have, as Sir Charles Lyell has pointed out, the following succession of changes : 1st, a period when the caves and tortuous galleries were licked out by the percolation of acidulated water ; 2nd, a time when these hollows became the channels of engulphed streams ; and, 3rd, a period when these streams disappeared, and the caves were occupied by wild beasts and men, whose remains are now found commingled upon the floors of the caverns.

Let us now briefly examine the mode in which these remains occur. For this purpose it will be sufficient to select one example, as this may be considered typical of all the others. Our specimen cave is the famous Kent's Cavern near Torquay, which has been systematically ransacked for some years under the direction of a committee of the British Association, the details of the investigation being from time to time communicated by Mr. Pengelly, who has personally superintended the operations.[*]

The deposits met with upon the floor of the cave are given in descending order as follows :—

1. Large blocks of limestone, sometimes cemented together by stalagmite.

2. A layer of black muddy mould, 3 in. to 12 in. in thickness.

3. Stalagmite 16 in. to 20 in. thick, reaching 5 ft. in part, almost continuous, containing large fragments of limestone, a human jaw, and remains of extinct animals.

4. Red cave-earth, varying in thickness, and containing 50 per cent. of angular fragments of limestone, with numerous bones of extinct animals, and implements fashioned by the hand of man. Excavated to a depth of 4 ft.

5. Crystalline stalagmite in places 12 ft. thick, with bones of the cave-bear.

6. Breccia and red loam, with remains of the cave-bear, and some human implements.

[*] Full details are given in Mr. Pengelly's interesting yearly reports, *Brit. Ass. Rep.*, beginning in 1865 ; the same geologist gives an admirable summary of the evidence in a Lecture to the working classes at Manchester ; see also Mr. Evans's *Ancient Stone Implements ;* and Sir C. Lyell's *Antiquity of Man.*

The large blocks of limestone that cumber the floor of the cavern have of course fallen from the roof. The layer of black muddy mould which immediately underlies them has yielded portions of the human skeleton, along with fragments of pottery and articles of stone and bronze. Besides these there also occur bones of deer, oxen, sheep, pig, and other animals which are still indigenous to the country. There is nothing therefore to indicate that this upper deposit is of great antiquity; some of the remains indeed appear to belong to the Romano-British period.

The black mould rests upon a pavement of stalagmite—a deposit which is formed by the drip of water holding carbonate of lime in solution. The accumulation of this deposit must in most cases be a very slow process, nor are we in much danger of over-estimating the time required for the growth of the stalagmite in Kent's Cave. A solid cake of stalagmite, varying in thickness from 1 in. to 5 ft., and almost continuous over the whole floor of this extensive cave, implies the lapse of a very long time. We have to conceive of it forming gradually, as drop after drop of lime-water fell from the roof and evaporated upon the floor. Nor was its accumulation at all likely to have been continuous: sometimes the drip would be in one place, sometimes in another; and indeed portions of the roof and floor might remain dry during lengthened periods. One may gather some notion of the time required to form a layer of stalagmite 5 ft. thick, when he reflects that some two thousand years have elapsed since the Romano-British remains were left upon the floor of the cave, and that in all that time the deposition of stalagmite has been very partial—many parts being quite free from it, while where thickest it does not exceed 6 in.; in fact the deposit occurs only in patches.*

Below the stalagmite comes a mass of red earth or loam, of irregular thickness. It has not been excavated to a greater depth than 4 ft. Both the stalagmite and the underlying

* Of course, the rate at which stalagmite forms depends almost entirely on the quantity of acidulated water passing through the rock. In some caves the rate will be excessive; in others again it will be very slow. Hence, even if we ascertained the rate at which the stalagmite increased in one particular cave, still that would give us no criterion by which to estimate the time required for the growth of stalagmite in any other cave, for the conditions in separate caves are never likely to be precisely the same.

cave-earths have yielded a large quantity of bones and teeth of extinct, or no longer indigenous, mammalia, commingled with which are numerous implements of flint and some of horn, "presenting," as Mr. Pengelly says, "a character so humble and so little varied as to betoken a very low type of civilisation."

Scattered throughout the whole deposit, in stalagmite and earth alike, occur many fragments of limestone, similar to those which overlaid the black mould.

Underneath the cave-earth in certain parts a lower bed of stalagmite appears, which reaches in places the great thickness of 12 ft. This ancient deposit rests upon a second cave-earth or breccia, in which human implements and numerous remains of the cave-bear have been found. When one reflects on the length of time required for the formation of 12 ft. of stalagmite, the great antiquity of these lower deposits cannot fail to astonish him.

There are many interesting questions suggested by the remarkable commingling of mammalian remains in these cave accumulations, but I shall reserve what I have to say upon this subject to a succeeding chapter. Meanwhile the lessons we learn from the English caves would appear to be these:—

1st. That man and certain locally or altogether extinct animals co-existed in England at some remote period.

2nd. That the long duration of this period is shown by the thickness of the stalagmitic pavements, which rest upon and are intercalated with the cave-earth; and by the evidence of drip which is more or less conspicuous all through the cave-earth itself.

3rd. That after having occupied the English caves for untold ages palæolithic man disappeared for ever, and with him vanished many animals now either locally or wholly extinct.

4th. That the deposits immediately overlying the stalagmite and cave-earth contain an almost totally different assemblage of animal remains, along with relics of the neolithic, bronze, iron, and historic periods.

5th. That there is no passage, but on the contrary a sharp and abrupt break, between these later deposits and the underlying palæolithic accumulations.

But if cavern-deposits suggest a high antiquity for our race, still more does the evidence supplied by certain river-deposits, which now fall to be described.

It has long been known to geologists that in the south and south-east of England sheets and beds of gravel frequently occur in positions which are not, and never can be, reached by the present rivers. They rest upon the gentle slopes of the valleys in those regions at a height often of many feet above the streams; nay, they even occur on some hill-tops, and are spread over more or less isolated plateaux, that terminate abruptly at the margin of the sea—in both cases occupying positions which are quite beyond the reach of any possible river-floods. Nevertheless, in many cases there can be no doubt whatever that the deposits referred to are actually the products of river-action, and were accumulated just where we see them by running water. But if this be so

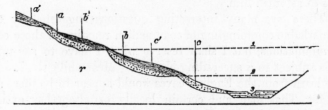

Fig. 67.—Diagram to explain formation of river-gravels and loess or flood-loam : *a b c* river-gravels, *a' b' c'* flood-loam ; 1 2 3 successive levels of river erosion. (After Sir J. Lubbock : *Pre-hist. Times,* p. 381.)

—and it cannot be otherwise—then great changes in the drainage-system of the south of England must have taken place since these old gravels and loams were deposited. The accompanying illustration — a diagrammatic section across a river-valley—will make this intelligible. The horizontal line 1 indicates the level at which the river flowed when the deposits *a* and *a'* were laid down, *a* being gravel and *a'* loam. The former of these deposits marks out the bed of the ancient river at its average flow, while the loam *à* represents the finer material which the water during flood-time spread along the low-lying slopes of the valley. As the river continued to flow it gradually ate into the underlying rock, until at last it reached the level marked 2. The gravel bed *b* was then formed, and the flood-loam *b'* was deposited above the older gravel bed *a*. In the same manner, when the stream had dug down to the lowest level 3, the gravel bed *c* was accumulated, while the flood-loam *c′* overspread the gravel of the higher level 2. Thus the deposits of gravel, sand, and loam that cover the slopes of these valleys mark out the successive levels occupied by the rivers as they slowly excavated the solid rocks to attain their present channels.

That the work of excavation required a long time for its performance no one will doubt. The erosion of solid rocks by running water, and the formation of thick accumulations of well-rounded gravel are necessarily very slow processes. Nor is it difficult to understand that the excavation of a valley thirty or forty miles in length, by some half-mile or more in breadth, to a depth of 50 or 100 ft., must have occupied a very long time indeed.

Now in almost all the old gravels which have just been described as lying quite beyond the reach of the present rivers, and as marking the successive stages of that erosion which eventually succeeded in giving to the valleys their present depth, flint instruments are found in greater or less abundance. And from this it follows, as a matter of course, that man was an occupant of our country many long ages before the valleys in the south of England were hollowed out and made to assume the appearance which they now present. In those early times the rivers did indeed flow, for the most part, in the same general direction as they do now ; but this was at levels, and in positions above the highest points which even the heaviest floods in our day could attain.

But this is not all. The old flood-loams and gravels have also yielded numerous remains of many extinct animals which are associated with the flint implements in such a way as to lead irresistibly to the conclusion that both were deposited contemporaneously. All these implements belong without exception to the palæolithic period. In none of the ancient river deposits do any traces of the neolithic age appear. Had polished implements of stone occurred in any of these old gravels even in small quantities, they could hardly have escaped detection ; but when any such relics do happen to occur in alluvial deposits, these latter are invariably found to occupy positions which prove them to be of much more recent date than even the latest accumulations of what we term the ancient river-gravels. They are, in short, found at or quite close to the surface, and associated with such animals as the pig, the horse, the dog, oxen, &c.

To those who have never pondered over the subject the facts thus briefly stated may possibly not convey any vivid impression of the great antiquity of palæolithic remains. Indeed, an adequate conception of the vast lapse of time implied can only be attained by those who are willing to examine the evidence for themselves. Yet before passing to the next part of my subject, I may roughly indicate some of the geographical conditions that obtained in the south of England during the palæolithic period, in the hope that this may convey a livelier impression of the antiquity of man as an occupant of our country.

When palæolithic man lived in the south of England the Isle of Wight formed part of the mainland—a range of chalk downs, at least 600 ft. in height, running east of the Isle of Purbeck, and joining on to the Needles. The rivers that traverse Dorset, together with the Avon and the Stour, then united in one large river and flowed eastwards along a broad valley which is now occupied by the Solent and Spithead, while Southampton Water at that early period formed merely an affluent of the same great stream.* The gravel that paved the bed of this ancient river before it had cut its way deep down into the older Tertiary deposits, is now found capping the cliffs of the mainland at heights ranging from 50 ft. to 130 ft. above the level of the sea.

Again, so long a time elapsed during the palæolithic age that the Thames at London was able to excavate its valley to a breadth of four miles, and to a depth of not less than 100 ft. Everywhere, indeed, throughout the south of England we have the most clear and convincing evidence that the land was worn away by streams and rivers which, at the beginning

---

* The Rev. W. Fox of Brixton was the first to infer the former existence of this ancient river; see *Geologist*, vol. v. p. 452. The whole subject has been worked out in great detail by Mr. T. Codrington (*Quarterly Journal of the Geological Society*, vol. xxvi. p. 528) ; see also Mr. Evans's *Ancient Stone Implements*, p. 605; the two last-named authors arrived independently at substantially the same conclusion.

of the palæolithic age, flowed at a height of 20, 40, 60, or 100 ft., and more above the present levels ; and the deepening of these valleys was completed before the neolithic age commenced. Everywhere, too, we find convincing proofs that during palæolithic times our shores stretched much farther out to sea. " When we remember," says Mr. Evans, " that the traditions of our mighty and historic capital, now extending across the valley, do not carry us back even to the close of that period of many centuries, when a bronze-using people occupied this island ; when we bear in mind that beyond that period lies another of probably far longer duration, when our barbaric predecessors sometimes polished their stone implements, but were still unacquainted with the use of metallic tools ;—when to the historic, bronze, and neolithic ages we mentally add that long series of years, which must have been required for the old fauna, with the mammoth and rhinoceros, and other to us strange and unaccustomed forms, to be supplanted by a group of animals more closely resembling those of the present day ;—and when, remembering all this, we realise the fact that all these vast periods of years have intervened since the completion of the excavation of the valley, and the close of the palæolithic period, the mind is almost lost in amazement at the vista of antiquity displayed."*

More than this, not only do the palæolithic and ossiferous gravels afford evidence of having been deposited by rivers during a long protracted period of time, which enabled them slowly to erode the valleys of southern England to their present depth, but they also yield unmistakable proof of having been finally subjected to disturbance and reconstruction—a disturbance and reconstruction which were certainly completed before the advent of neolithic man in Britain. Thus we meet with gravels of the age in question scattered over the whole length and breadth of some districts, resting alike on valley-bottom, hill-side, and hill-top — in fact wrapping the country in a more or less continuous mantle. No river-action will account for these appearances. The gravels, no doubt, lie thickest in the valleys, but they sweep up the hill-sides and over the hill-tops into totally different

* *Ancient Stone Implements*, &c., p. 622.

drainage areas ; and, as Mr. J. W. Flower has well remarked,[*] the basins from which the present rivers are fed are altogether insufficient to supply the requisite amount of water. I recently was fortunate enough to visit the district round Brandon, under the guidance of my colleague, Mr. Skertchly, who was at that time engaged in examining the ground for the Geological Survey. After we had gone over a considerable area, and noted the wide distribution of the gravels and their anomalous positions, it became evident that, as my friend said, if the gravels owed their distribution to river-action, then the river which scattered them must have been broad enough to cover the whole country like a wide sea.

Then, again, no mere river-action will account for the coarse and tumultuous aspect so often presented by the palæolithic gravels. One frequently sees sand, clay, grit, well-rounded stones, angular blocks, and sharp-edged débris all huddled together in the direst confusion—the larger stones often standing on end, and not lying in the position they must have assumed under ordinary river-action. I might enter into further details here for the purpose of showing that the ancient ossiferous river-gravels of southern England have been subjected to some powerful disturbing force since the time of their formation, but as my friend Mr. Skertchly, whose acquaintance with the phenomena is much more intimate and extensive than mine, has been good enough to furnish me with some notes on the implement-bearing gravels of the districts examined by him, I gladly refer the reader to Chapter XL., where my friend tells his own tale. The cause of the great disturbances referred to I shall point out when I come to consider in detail the geological position of the palæolithic deposits.

In fine, then, whether we have reference to the evidence furnished by the cave-deposits or to that supplied by the river-gravels, we are alike assured that after the disappearance of palæolithic man, and before the advent of his neolithic successor, there supervened a period of unknown but neces-

---

[*] *Quart. Jour. Geol. Soc.*, vol. xxv. p. 458. Mr. Flower mentions the fact that at Brandon he saw palæolithic gravels at a height of 80 feet above the source of the river (Little Ouse), where they were not commanded by any higher grounds, from which a river capable of leaving such a deposit could possibly have been supplied.

sarily of great duration. There is no direct passage from the older into the newer deposits—the latter overlie the former *unconformably*. It now becomes our task to ascertain, if possible, what it was which interrupted the sequence—to discover what is meant by the break or hiatus that separates palæolithic from neolithic times.

CHAPTER XXXVIII.

CLIMATE OF THE PALÆOLITHIC PERIOD.

Groups of mammalian remains associated together in palæolithic deposits.—
Southern, arctic, and temperate species.—Theory of annual migrations.—
Condition of this country during palæolithic period.—Cause of extreme
climate of Siberia.—Supposed elevation of Mediterranean area in palæolithic times.—Probable climatic effects of such an elevation.—Climate of
western Europe during palæolithic period not "continental" but "insular."
—Conclusions.

REFERENCE has been made in the preceding chapter to
the fact that both in cave-deposits and river-gravels
human implements are found associated with numerous mammalian remains belonging to species many of which are either
now locally or wholly extinct. The appearance of these
remains suggests many interesting inquiries, but at present
I shall confine attention to one question—namely, what were
the climatic conditions under which these animals occupied
our country ?

The species naturally arrange themselves in three groups : *
the first embracing those animals which are either at present
living in warm climates, or which have in southern regions
their nearest representatives ; the second comprising animals
of arctic and northern habitats ; and the third containing such
species as inhabit temperate latitudes.

In the first or southern group we meet with the lion, the
tiger, the spotted hyæna, two extinct species of elephant, and
two of rhinoceros, *Felis caffer, Maichairodus latidens*—an
extinct species of tiger furnished with terrible sabre-like
teeth, and the hippopotamus.

In the second or northern group occur the glutton, the
reindeer, the musk-sheep, the pouched marmot, the alpine

---

* In these notes I have availed myself of the lists given by Mr. Boyd
Dawkins in several papers; see *Quarterly Journal of the Geological Society*, vol.
xxv. p. 192 ; *Popular Science Review*, 1871, p. 388 ; *Quart. Jour. Geol. Soc.*, 1872,
p. 410. See also the same author's *Cave-Hunting.*

hare, the lemming, and the extinct woolly rhinoceros and mammoth; the latter animal, however, probably ranged far into temperate regions.

The third or temperate group comprises the bison, the great urus, the grisly bear, the cave-bear, the Irish elk, and Brown's deer (the last three being extinct species). Besides these we find also the lynx, wild cat, ermine, stoat, weasel, martin cat, otter, wild boar, horse, beaver, and other smaller animals which are still indigenous to Britain.

The panther, the fox, and the wolf also occur in British palæolithic deposits; but since these animals are capable of bearing great vicissitudes of climate, it is evident, as Mr. Dawkins remarks, that they can tell us nothing definite about the climate of our country during palæolithic times.

Now what does this very remarkable assemblage of animals indicate? How are we to explain the occurrence in our caves and river-deposits of species belonging to such widely-separated zones? In what manner have the hippopotamus, the reindeer, and the musk-sheep become entombed in our ancient superficial deposits? I need hardly say it is quite impossible that these animals could have lived side by side. The musk-sheep, like the reindeer, feeds chiefly on lichens and grasses. In the warm months it ranges to Melville Island, and its remains were found by Dr. Kane as far north as the dreary regions of Smith's Sound. Even during the coldest season of the year it does not wander farther south than the southern borders of the Barren Grounds. In Europe, the reindeer, as every one knows, is confined to Lapland and Norway. The hippopotamus, on the other hand, is restricted to the rivers of middle and southern Africa. At the same time it is highly probable that it may have ranged within comparatively recent times as far north as Nubia. Nay, we may even admit that the physical condition of Egypt is such as would be quite suited to the wants of the great river-horse, and that the present restricted range of that animal is due to other than climatic causes. But although we thus widen the limits within which the hippopotamus might live and flourish, there still intervenes a vast region up to the mountains of Norway, throughout which the conditions are equally unsuited to the reindeer and the hippopotamus.

These two animals, in short, belong to distinct and widely-separated zones.

Various theories have been proposed to account for the intermingling in our superficial deposits of such discordant species. Some have held that the hippopotamus may have been covered, like the mammoth, with a thick woolly coat, to enable it to brave the severe winters of the north ; but it is impossible to believe that an animal the greater part of whose time is spent in the water could have lived in a country that was occupied at the same time by musk-sheep, reindeer, and gluttons—the presence of such characteristic arctic species clearly implying that during winter at least our rivers were frozen over.

Another view which has been largely adopted attempts to get over the difficulty by assuming that during the accumulation of our river-deposits Britain was marked by a kind of Siberian climate—by strongly contrasted summers and winters. The summers are supposed to have been so warm and genial that they wooed to the latitude of Britain the elephant and hippopotamus, which upon the approach of winter beat a rapid retreat to the south—the country they had just vacated being next invaded from the north by the arctic mammalia. A parallel to this state of things was thought to be found in Siberia, where at the present day, as is well known, great annual migrations of the fauna take place. During the intense cold of winter the reindeer roam in vast herds towards the south to gain the shelter of the forest-lands, and thus encroach upon the province of the moose-deer, or elk, where they become the prey of the tiger. As the cold of winter disappears the reindeer again pass to the north, whither they are followed by foxes, wolves, and bears. Similar migrations characterize the fauna of the northern latitudes of North America. In both cases, however, the migrations are between arctic and temperate zones, and are therefore hardly comparable to the migrations which (if this theory be true) must have characterized Europe during palæolithic times. The invasion by the reindeer of the province occupied by the elk does not astonish us, for their territories border and overlap. But it is extremely difficult, or even impossible, to believe that the musk-sheep and the hippopotamus could ever have traversed the same country in the same year; at all events, we know of no annual migration so astounding as this. Furthermore, it cannot be said that the hippopotamus, the rhinoceros, or the elephant are migratory animals. The tiger, as we know, will travel far from his usual head-quarters in pursuit of prey, but we cannot say as much for the lion and the spotted hyæna. The frequency with which remains of these animals, more especially the hyæna, occur in our caves, shows clearly that they were not mere summer visitors, but actual denizens of the country throughout the year. Looking therefore simply to the character of those species that make up the southern group, there appear to be strong grounds for rejecting the "migration theory." And we are inclined still more strongly to this opinion when we come to consider the climatic conditions under which, according to that theory, these animals inhabited Britain.

It is inferred that the southern and northern groups oscillated to and fro with the seasons at a time when the British Islands were joined to themselves and the Continent, and when the conditions were such that snow and ice still covered large areas in Wales, the north of England, Scotland, and Ireland; it is held, in short, that the palæolithic age corresponds to the latest period of glaciation in our country.

Now it would not be difficult to show that, with the presence of perennial snow and ice in the high grounds of Great Britain, our rivers would remain frozen over for a great part of the year. During the summer they would sometimes burst their icy bonds, and, swollen with heavy rains and the torrents derived from the melting of the snow-fields and glaciers, would overflow the low grounds and carry devastation far and wide. Over broad areas in our valleys, therefore, there could be little vegetation.* Such areas as were not covered with snow might perhaps support scraggy birch and pine, and here and there tall grasses and dwarf willows might nestle in sheltered hollows; but mosses and lichens

---

* Those who are familiar with the glacier-valleys of Switzerland and Scandinavia will understand what I mean. If even in such valleys the rivers escaping from the glaciers cover wide areas with barren heaps of gravel and shingle, how much more must this have been the case in Britain, where, according to the migration theory, each intense winter was succeeded by an excessive summer temperature.

would most probably form the prevailing growths. If the pleistocene hippopotamus could live on such fare, he must have been a more easily satisfied animal than his modern representative. It is true that in arctic regions the short summer brings into bloom a number of pretty flowerets, and causes the grasses to shoot up with surprising rapidity; but this is due to the influence of a sun that keeps above the horizon during the greater part of summer. A glacial period in England, however, would not be tempered by the presence of a midnight sun in summer-time. With the poor and meagre vegetation therefore which a country of this kind would be able to support, the herbivora could not have been abundant. Indeed, only a very few mammalia could possibly have existed under the conditions supposed; and probably none of these would belong to that group which consists of such species as still inhabit the temperate zones of Europe and America. If, therefore, we eliminate the whole of this group, we have left only the true arctic mammalia—the glutton, the reindeer, the musk-sheep, the pouched marmot, the tailless hare, and the lemming—to form food for the lion and his congeners, the tiger and the hyæna. But how can we suppose it possible that these carnivora would leave the temperate zone (which, when arctic conditions supervened in Britain, must have shifted to more southern regions of Europe, where no doubt it was characterized by the presence of an abundant mammalian fauna), to prey upon the few reindeer and smaller animals that were likely to be found so far north as the frozen barrens of England? Yet we know that the hyæna at least was a regular denizen of our caves, and found matters so comfortable, that, according to Mr. Dawkins, its large size, as compared with that of the living animal, was probably due to "the abundance of food which it obtained."

Such considerations as these have led me to conclude that this theory of annual migrations is untenable. With glacial conditions in Scotland and the hilly grounds of England and Ireland, neither temperate flora nor fauna could have existed in our country. There could be nothing in such an arctic England, therefore, to tempt the herbivora away from the rich feeding-grounds of the then temperate zone, and just as little to wile the carnivora so far from their wonted haunts. And to suppose the hippopotamus, the elephant, and the rhinoceros capable of migrating for enormous distances, and to such a country too, is to suppose that these animals differed entirely from their present representatives.

But it has been objected that we have no right to infer, from the fact of glaciers having existed in Britain, that the summer temperature during that period was ungenial. Large glaciers exist in the Alps, and much greater ones fill the upper valleys of the Himalaya; yet, as every one knows, the low grounds at the base of these mountains enjoy warm and genial climates. Is not it possible, therefore, that the same conditions may have obtained in Britain during palæolithic times, and that while glaciers filled all our mountain-valleys, the lowlands of England may have basked in summer warmth and sunshine?

Now it can hardly fail to occur to the reader that these are not cases in point. Britain is not in the latitude of northern India, neither is it in that of Lombardy or Provence, while in comparison with the Alps and the Himalaya our mountains sink into utter insignificance. Those who speculate upon the possibility of something like a Siberian climate having obtained in Britain during palæolithic times, completely ignore geographical and physical considerations. They find northern and southern mammalia in our caves and river-gravels, and jump at once to the conclusion that a period of strongly contrasted summers and winters must have characterized Britain at the time it was in the occupation of such discordant groups of animals. Yet a little consideration will serve to show that this hasty conclusion is entirely opposed to and directly contradicted by all that we know of the causes to which the various climates of the globe are owing.

It is admitted by geologists that during palæolithic times the physical features of our continent were much the same as they are now—all the great high grounds, all the great drainage-systems, were even then in existence. Denudation, or the wearing away of the earth's surface by rains, frosts, and rivers, no doubt helped during palæolithic times to modify the features of the land, and valleys, as we have seen, were scooped out to some depth; nevertheless, when viewed on the large scale, such minor modifications of the surface may be disregarded. Then, if this be so,—if the changes referred to were so inconsiderable—we may be very sure that since the disappearance of palæolithic man, there has been even less change in the physical features of Europe. This is one important fact to remember.

Again, we know that under the present condition of things, our continent owes the equableness of its climate in great measure to the influence of the Atlantic. This is another important fact that we cannot lose sight of. Were an extensive land-surface to be substituted for that great ocean, there is good reason to believe that our summers and winters would be as excessive as those in similar latitudes of Asia and North America.

But at the present day what is the fact? why, simply this, that as we recede from the western shores of Europe, and approach the interior of that continent, the colder do the winters become, while the difference between summer and winter constantly tends to increase. In England the thermometer rarely sinks 18° below freezing-point, but in the interior of the continent, and under almost equal latitudes, we find a mean of $+ 14°$; and "it is not uncommon to see the mercury freeze at Kasan. In the interior of Siberia it often remains solid for several weeks together."[*] To show the contrast between the climate of western Europe and that of northern Asia, we may compare the summer and winter temperatures of Aalesund, in Norway, and Jakutsk, on the Lena. These two places are as near as may be under the same latitudes—the former being in 62°·24 N. lat., and the latter in 62°·5 N. lat. At Aalesund the summer temperature is 57° F., and in winter the thermometer registers 35° F. At Jakutsk, on the other hand, the temperature of summer reaches 62°·2 F., while that of winter sinks to 43°·8 below zero.

Now what are the causes that induce such widely divergent climates? Why is it that places situated under the same or nearly similar latitudes do not experience the same climatic conditions? If the reader will examine the charts of isotheral and isochimenal lines, he will have no difficulty in

* Kaemtz's *Complete Course of Meteorology*, p. 173.

perceiving that Europe is beholden to the presence of the Atlantic for its insular climate. Our winters are ameliorated and our summers rendered less excessive by the moist winds that are almost continually passing from west and south-west across our continent. That is a fact as well ascertained as any fact can be.

In northern Asia the conditions could hardly be more strongly contrasted. There no mild and genial ocean tempers the severity of winter. During that season every wind that blows across Siberia, no matter whence it comes, is bitingly cold. The west winds, that temper our winters with the warmth of the Gulf-stream, are robbed of their moisture and cooled down before they cross the snows of the Ural Mountains to pour into Siberia. The gales from the Arctic Ocean are still colder ; nor is much warmth derived from the winds that sweep northwards from the high Mongolian plateau, while at the same time the serenity of the sky favours the radiation of the ground. In summer-time the conditions are reversed. Dry and scorching winds reach Siberia from the west, and the heat of the Mongolian deserts is wafted from the south ; while owing to the great clearness of the atmosphere the northern plains are soon warmed by the continuous shining of the arctic sun : and thus the temperature rises rapidly all over Siberia. In North America the seasons are also more marked than with us, and the causes for this are somewhat similar to those which induce the more strongly-contrasted summers and winters of northern Asia.

If the present climate of Europe departs so very widely from that of other regions in similar latitudes of the northern hemisphere, upon what grounds can it be supposed that a totally different state of matters existed during palæolithic times ? Let it be remembered that the physical features of the land were much the same then as they are now, and that the Atlantic Ocean also was certainly in existence. No great range of mountains existed then which does not exist now, nor have any mountains been formed in Europe since palæolithic man vanished for ever. It is true that the British Islands have been separated from themselves and the continent, and that a narrow strip of land that once extended along the western borders of these islands and the mainland has been submerged; but it is idle to imagine that such changes could have had the effect which some have supposed. Nay, even if we conceived that a large part of the Mediterranean existed in the condition of dry land during palæolithic times, still, that would not produce anything approaching to a Siberian climate in Europe.[*]

We know that in the present economy of things the climatic influence of the Mediterranean in summer-time extends but a very short distance north into Europe. It certainly does not cross either the Alps or the Pyrenees. A line drawn from Bayonne by Viviers and Turin to the head of the Adriatic, corresponds to the July isothermal line of 72°·5 F. When the same line is continued towards the north-east into Hungary, it suddenly sweeps down to Constantinople; and, circling round the Black Sea, returns upon itself at Odessa, after which it continues for some distance in the normal north-easterly direction. That sudden curve to the south-east is, of course, due to the presence of the Black Sea, and seeing that the Mediterranean does not influence the same isothermal line in either France, Italy, or Austria, it is quite clear that the modifying effect of this large inland sea has nothing whatever to do with the climate of central Europe. South of the line referred to, however, we find the July isotherms violently disturbed. That of 77° F. runs along the shores of the Mediterranean from Barcelona by Perpignan and Montpellier to Toulon. From this place it

---

[*] Mr. Dawkins believes that it would (*Quart. Jour. Geol. Soc.*, vol. xxviii. p. 410); but, as I have endeavoured to show elsewhere (*Geological Magazine*, vol. x. p. 49), there is no evidence to show that in *late glacial times* the Mediterranean was of less extent than it is now. Of course I do not deny that during warm interglacial periods Europe and Africa were connected. They must have been joined to have allowed the southern mammals to migrate northwards. In his recent work (*Cave-Hunting*, p. 390) Mr. Dawkins reiterates his belief that a kind of Siberian climate would result in Europe if the area of dry land within the Mediterranean basin were to be increased in extent so as to convert that sea into two landlocked sheets of water, while at the same time by some compensating earth-movement the region of the Sahara was submerged below the sea. Such changes may quite well have taken place during the glacial epoch, but we have no evidence to show that they happened in late glacial and postglacial times. And even if they did, they would not induce the kind of climate which Mr. Dawkins desiderates. It is the belief of some continental geologists that the great size attained by the old glaciers of Northern Italy was due to the existence of a Sahara Sea: and doubtless the winds sweeping north under such conditions would be cooler and more humid than they are now. But I fail to see how a submerged Sahara and a reduced Mediterranean would bring about a Siberian climate in Europe. All they could do would be to render the summers in Southern Europe colder and the winters probably more severe.

strikes directly south-south-east to Cape Spartivento, then curves gently on to Palermo, after which it sweeps round by Messina and the Gulf of Taranto, across Italy, and more than half-way up the Adriatic. It then doubles suddenly back upon itself, skirts the eastern shores of the Adriatic, and crosses the south of Turkey and the Ægean Sea to Mytelene and Asia Minor. This irregularity is just as surely caused by the presence of the Mediterranean as the abrupt curving of the July isothermal line of 72°·5 is due to that of the Black Sea. In short, it is perfectly apparent that the isothermal lines in the south of Europe are deflected by the inland seas from their normal direction, this deflection being confined to the immediate proximity of these basins. But in central and northern Europe, all the isotheral lines are pushed south by the overwhelming influence of the Atlantic; while in the opposite season, all the isochimenal lines are swept boldly north and north-east. (See charts at end of volume.)

Were the Mediterranean to be converted into two land-locked seas, the isotheral lines in that area would then be less disturbed, and would preserve the general south-west and north-east trend which they follow in central Europe. The summers in Italy, Turkey, and Greece would thus be some-what hotter and drier, but the general summer temperature of Europe would remain unaffected. The winds flowing from the south would no doubt be warmer, but they would also carry less moisture. When they reached the Alps, they would part with their warmth and moisture, just as they do now; but since they would bring more of the one and less of the other than at present, the snow-fields and glaciers on the south side of the Alps would tend to shrink back. Again, the isothermal chart shows that the supposed increase of land would not produce any appreciable climatic effect beyond a short distance into Spain and France, while not a trace of its influence would reach England. The Continent, laved along its entire western borders by a wide ocean, would be cooled over an immense area by the winds blowing from west and south-west; such is the case now,[*] and it must have been

---

[*] See the late Professor Coffin's treatise on the "Winds of the Northern Hemisphere," *Smithsonian Contributions* for 1853.

equally so in palæolithic times. Thus, even had the warmth derived from the Mediterranean area been much greater than we can conceive it to have been, its effect would, nevertheless, be counterbalanced, and far more than counterbalanced, by the influence of the Atlantic.

The consideration of this subject brings us back to the point which, as I think, has already been sufficiently proved, namely, that during our latest glacial period, there could be no great annual migrations of the mammalia in western Europe. For, since the climate required for such migrations does not exist in Europe now, and seeing that it would not obtain even if Britain were to become part of the Continent, and a large portion of the Mediterranean to be converted into land, how can we suppose it possible, that, with snow-fields and glaciers in Britain, the climate could have been other than cold and ungenial. Surely, under such geographical and physical conditions as did actually supervene in north-western Europe during our latest glacial period, the summers must of necessity have been cold, and the vegetation poor and scanty. In winter-time, supposing the Gulf-stream to have flowed then as it flows now, the cold would be ameliorated over all western Europe. But should it be supposed, that, during the last cold period, the Gulf-stream flowed in some other direction, then, in the absence of this great heat-bringer, our winters would indeed be excessive, and our summers dreary in the extreme.

In short, we may conclude, that, so long as Europe exposes a vast line of coast to the Atlantic, and so long as her physical features endure, just so long will her climate continue to differ from that of either Asia or North America, no matter whether or not the British Islands become continental or the area of land in the Mediterranean basin be increased. And as it is in the present, so also it must have been in the past. No mere obliteration of our inland seas could neutralise the influence of the outlying ocean. If the summers of Europe are at present rendered less excessive by the presence of the Atlantic, the same must have been the case during the last continental condition of our islands, and that to a much greater degree, owing to the presence of more numerous and larger snow-fields. For this, if for no other reason, it seems to me that the theory of annual migrations during that period in western Europe must be abandoned.

I have discussed this theory at some length, because, as we shall presently see, the question of palæolithic climate has a direct bearing upon that of the antiquity of man. In order, therefore, that I may carry the reader along with me, I shall here briefly summarise the points which I have attempted to establish in this chapter :—

1. The migrations of land animals in northern Asia and equivalent latitudes in North America, take place between arctic and temperate regions. This is simply the case of adjacent provinces overlapping one another. Inasmuch, therefore, as the migration theory asks us to believe that widely-separated zones overlapped across the whole breadth of the temperate provinces, it is unreasonable, and not supported by our knowledge of what actually occurs in nature.

2. The general character of the southern group of mammalia, as exhibited in cave-deposits and river-gravels, is nonmigratory.

3. The union of Britain and Ireland to the Continent, across the up-raised beds of the English Channel and the Irish Sea, and a great increase of land within the area of the Mediterranean, could not confer upon Europe a climate in any degree approaching to that of Siberia or British America. The climate of our continent would still be *insular*, and consequently great migrations could not take place.

4. During the last continental condition of our islands, snow-fields and glaciers existed in our country—betokening a climate quite unsuited to the needs of the southern mammalia. The winters at that period must have been excessive, and the summers cold and ungenial.

5. Lastly, so long as the Atlantic continues to wash the coasts of Europe, and so long as the present configuration of the land endures, our continent must continue to enjoy an insular climate, and there is not the slightest physical evidence to show that it possessed any other kind of climate during the period that the southern mammalia inhabited Britain.

CHAPTER XXXIX.

GEOLOGICAL AGE OF THE PALÆOLITHIC DEPOSITS.

Oscillations of climate.—Cold and warm periods.—Evidence of the river-deposits.—Character of the evidence cumulative in favour of former climatic changes.—No evidence of warm postglacial climate.—Southern mammalia not of postglacial age.—Age of cave-deposits.—No proof that they are postglacial.—Relation of river-gravels to glacial deposits.—Age of the boulder-clay at Hoxne, &c.—Boulder-clay upon which palæolithic deposits sometimes rest belongs to the older glacial series.—Distribution of palæolithic gravels.—Comparison between palæolithic gravels of South England and river-deposits of the north.—Palæolithic deposits not met with in districts that are covered with accumulations belonging to the later glacial series, but confined to regions which we cannot prove to have been glaciated during the latest period of glacial cold.—Palæolithic deposits of interglacial, not postglacial age.—Most of them probably belong to last interglacial period.—Recapitulation.

THE theory of annual migrations being, as I have tried to show, untenable, we can now only explain the remarkable commingling of northern, southern, and temperate groups in our superficial deposits, by assuming that certain great oscillations of climate characterized the accumulation of our cave-earths and river-gravels. We must admit, in short, that

Fig. 68.—Generalised diagram-section across the valley of the Thames below London, greatly exaggerated vertically. (W. Whitaker): 1. Pebble-gravel (preglacial); 2. boulder-clay; 3. valley-gravel (highest terrace); 4. valley-gravel and brick-earth (lower terraces); 5. the Thames and its marshes; X sea level; r Tertiary beds and Chalk.

the northern mammalia occupied Britain during a cold and arctic condition of things, and that on the other hand the southern forms prevailed over the same area at a time when our winters were mild and genial.

This result derives strong confirmation from a study of the deposits themselves. In the first place it has been shown by

Professor Prestwich and others that the ancient river-gravels and loams which occur at the highest levels above the present streams possess certain broad characters that serve to distinguish them in a rough way from the gravels and loams that occupy the lower levels of the valleys. As a rule the former are the coarser of the two, and frequently contain large blocks of stone which could only have been transported by river-ice. Add to this that the beds often give evidence of having been subjected to a violent "push," which has tumbled them up and thrown them into confusion — phenomena which, as Professor Prestwich has pointed out, could hardly have been produced otherwise than by the grounding of heavy ice-rafts. The general absence of these appearances, and the usually finer-grained character of the ingredients in the low-level gravels, would seem to point to a milder condition of things—to a time when the rivers were less liable to flood, and ice-rafts were uncommon.

According to Professor Prestwich,[*] the shells met with in the high-level beds have a northerly range, and the absence of southern species tends still more to distinguish these beds from those of lower levels. In the latter there occur in great abundance two species of shells (*Cyrena fluminalis* and *Unio littoralis*), neither of which is now found living in England, but tenanting the rivers of more southerly latitudes,[†] a fact that seemingly corroborates the inference deduced from the appearance of the beds themselves.

Again, it cannot be denied that the northern group of mammalia is most characteristic of the high-level gravels, and the southern group of those at the lower levels. And notwithstanding that remains of both northern and southern species are not uncommonly commingled, still it is a fact, although, as Sir J. Lubbock remarks,[‡] "too much importance must not be attached to the observation, that our ancient hippopotamus has been less frequently found in association with the mammoth and the hairy rhinoceros, than with *Elephas antiquus* and *Rhinoceros hemitœchus* (Falc.)," two species which had a more southerly range.

[*] *Philosophical Transactions*, 1864, p. 279.
[†] *Cyrena fluminalis* is now extinct in Europe, but it still inhabits the Nile and abounds in Cashmere; *Unio littoralis* lives in the Seine and the Loire.
[‡] *Pre-historic Times*, third edition, p. 299.

If the high- and low-level gravels were deposited during different climatic conditions, this "might have produced," as Mr. Evans says,[*] "some effect on the method of living, and on the implements of the men of the two periods." And he thought it at one time "probable that a marked distinction might eventually be drawn between the high and low-level implements; but so far as Britain is concerned," he is now of opinion that "this can hardly be done. Still the *facies* of a collection from two different spots is rarely quite the same, and," he thinks, "there is generally a preponderance of the ruder pointed implements in the high-level gravels, and of the flat, ovate, sharp-rimmed implements in the low-level."

Now it may be admitted that none of these facts taken separately and alone is quite convincing. The character of the evidence, however, is cumulative, and when we perceive that the whole points in one and the same direction, it is impossible not to feel its weight and cogency. Under the assumption that considerable changes of climate accompanied the deposition of the palæolithic beds, the facts enumerated above have a distinct and definite meaning, but they are utterly meaningless, and must even be quite ignored, if we are to accept the theory of annual migrations.

The fact that the remains of northern and southern forms occur mingled in our river-deposits, is only what one might have expected. Those who study the formation of fluviatile sediments will readily understand how fossils, entombed at widely separate intervals, may come to occupy the same level. Rivers are constantly cutting down through their own deposits, and again filling up the excavations they make. In this way gravel and sand are banked against similar beds, which may belong to a much greater antiquity; and the line of junction it is often impossible to determine, the one deposit seeming to shade into the other. And thus beds which appear to be continuous and of contemporaneous origin may, and in point of fact do, frequently deceive us in these respects.

There is nothing, therefore, abnormal or extraordinary in the intermingling in our palæolithic beds of mammalian remains

---

[*] *Ancient Stone Implements of Great Britain,* p. 616.

belonging to widely separated provinces. It would have been surprising indeed had it been otherwise.*

So, far, therefore, as the direct evidence of the beds themselves is concerned, there seems to be nothing against, but a good deal in favour of, the theory of changes of climate. That theory not only explains appearances which are left unsolved by any other hypothesis, but when we come to take a wider view of matters, and to consider the relation of the palæolithic deposits to the glacial drifts, we shall find that no little light is cast upon the interesting question of the antiquity of man in Britain.

From the discussion in our last chapter it would be gathered that the palæolithic deposits are believed by certain geologists to belong to late glacial and postglacial times : that is to say, that man and his congeners, the mammals of the caves and rivers, did not enter Britain until the Ice Age was passing away. Now if this were so we should be forced to admit that at least one warm period had supervened after the disappearance of the last confluent glaciers, and before the advent of the present temperate condition of things ; such a period of mild and genial winters being necessary to

---

* Although this appears so obvious, yet Mr. Boyd Dawkins thinks that the remains of the southern, temperate, and northern mammalia could not have been so commingled, "as they are generally preserved in the same mineral state. It would have been impossible for this (commingling) to have taken place without leaving decided traces behind in the rolled and water-worn condition of the older series, such as may be seen in the case of the Eocene and Miocene fossils in the Red Crag of Suffolk." (*Cave-Hunting*, p. 397.) Mr. Dawkins, I am sure, does not believe that he can distinguish any difference in the state of preservation of a bone say 50,000 years old and that of another say 55,000 years. And yet that is just what his argument amounts to, for, according to the views supported in this volume a large proportion of the northern, temperate, and southern mammalia, whose relics occur in the English valley-gravels, belong to one and the same interglacial period—a period which could have lasted for only a few thousand years. The time during which the arctic forms lived in Britain is not separated by any lengthened interval from the era which introduced the temperate group—but the former period merged gradually with the latter, just as that again passed by insensible gradations into the still milder era that followed. When at last cold conditions once more ensued and great bodies of water derived from the ice-sheet that re-appeared in the northern districts were sweeping over the low grounds of England, there would necessarily be very considerable denudation and reassortment of old river-deposits, and a commingling of mammalian remains which had been buried at "widely separated intervals." It is absurd, however, to suppose that these intervals were as prolonged as the period that intervened between the entombment of Eocene and Miocene fossils in Eocene and Miocene strata and their subsequent disinterment and final reburial in the Red Crag of Suffolk. The ossiferous gravels of England belong to one and the same formation—indeed they constitute only one subdivision of that formation : the Eocene, Miocene, and Pliocene deposits, on the other hand, are separate and distinct formations, distinguished by very dissimilar suites of organic remains.

account for the presence of the hippopotami, elephants, and rhinoceroses of the caves and river-gravels.

Have we any evidence, then, for the former existence of a warm postglacial period ? It may be confidently answered— none whatever.   There are few points we can be more sure of than this, that since the close of the glacial epoch—since the deposition of the shelly clays, and the disappearance of the latest local glaciers—there have been no great oscillations but only a gradual amelioration of climate.   It is impossible that any warm period could have intervened after the last cold, and before the present temperate conditions, without leaving some notable evidence in the superficial deposits of Scotland, the north of England, Scandinavia, and North America —these being the countries in which, as we have seen, the passage from the later glacial beds to recent accumulations can be most distinctly traced.   The climate of Britain is milder now than at any other period subsequent to the re-elevation of our country after the last great submergence and the melting of the latest ice-sheet ; our winters have gradually become less intense ; Britain has slowly passed from an arctic to a temperate condition of things : and Scandinavian, Swiss, and American geologists tell the same tale as regards their countries.   From all this, then, it follows that the southern mammalia could not have lived in Britain during postglacial times.   They must belong either to preglacial or interglacial ages, or to both.

When we come to ask why our cave-deposits have so frequently been relegated to postglacial times, we get no satisfactory answer.   If we put out of consideration the upper layers in certain cave-deposits, there is really nothing in the bone-earths and breccias to limit the age of these accumulations to such a recent period.   Accordingly, many geologists have been of opinion that the mammalian remains occurring in the caverns were introduced at various epochs, and may belong to preglacial equally with postglacial times.   Buckland thought that the great mammals existed in Britain before the period of the diluvium or drift ; and his belief is shared by Mr. Godwin-Austen and some of our leading geologists.   Professor Ramsay is decidedly of opinion that " caves such as those in which mammalian remains occur must have existed in preglacial times ; and therefore it would be strange," he adds, " if none of those explored contained preglacial remains." But between preglacial and postglacial times there intervened several mild interglacial periods, during which, as I have shown, the climate in Scotland and in Yorkshire was suited to the wants of the mammoth, the reindeer, the Irish deer, the urus, and the horse ; and I have also pointed out that, so far as geological evidence is concerned, there is nothing to show that some interglacial periods may not have been warm enough to cause all the snow and ice to vanish from Britain. If such was the case as regards Scotland and the north of England, surely the southern districts must have been characterized by similar climatic conditions. It is, therefore, not necessary to suppose that any large portion of the bone-deposits was preglacial ; for during interglacial periods the caves would form dens for wild beasts, just as they must have done in preglacial times. To some such mild and genial interglacial period or periods I would refer the hippopotamus and the other southern forms met with in English caves. The conditions under which these animals lived need not have been comparable to those that characterize the tropics. All that we are entitled to infer is that the winter temperature of Britain during certain interglacial periods must have been mild and genial. It is by no means necessary to suppose, however, that the summers were much warmer than they are now. An equable and genial climate, with no great difference between the seasons, would nourish an abundant vegetation, and render the country capable of sustaining a prolific mammalian fauna.

Now let us turn our attenion to the river-gravels, for the purpose of ascertaining what relation they bear to the glacial deposits. It has been shown that, in some valleys at least, the river-gravels are of more recent date than certain accumulations of glacial age. Thus, for example, at Hoxne, in Suffolk, freshwater beds containing flint implements were seen by Mr. Prestwich to overlie boulder-clay. From this it has been inferred that these beds, and indeed all palæolithic deposits, are of postglacial age—a conclusion which was reasonable and indeed inevitable, so long as the existence of only one deposit of boulder-clay was known. But in order to prove the postglacial age of the Hoxne river-beds, it now becomes necessary to show that the boulder-clay at that place can only belong to the close of the glacial epoch : for as we have seen boulder-clay may be of various ages. In Yorkshire there are three boulder-clays with intervening deposits ; there are two boulder-clays with interglacial sands and gravels in East Anglia ; in Lancashire and the north-west a similar succession occurs, and the same is the case in Ireland. In Scotland, again, we find several deposits of till with intervening freshwater and marine beds. Finally, distinct breaks representing mild periods occur in the glacial formations of Scandinavia, of Switzerland, and America.

To what age, then, does the boulder-clay at Hoxne belong ? There can be no doubt whatever that it is older than the purple and Hessle boulder-clays of Yorkshire, or the shelly boulder-clays of Lancashire and the north-west of England, and certainly dates back to a much earlier period than the upper till, the shelly clays, and local moraines of Scotland. Indeed, judging from its position, so far removed from the great centres of glaciation, I had no hesitation in correlating it with the chalky boulder-clay of Mr. Searles V. Wood—a correlation with which my friend and colleague Mr. Whitaker agrees. There can be no doubt, he says, that the boulder-clay at Hoxne forms part of the widespread sheet that covers Essex, Herts, Beds, Cambridge, Suffolk, Norfolk, &c. Now this chalky boulder-clay was laid down, as we have seen, during the climax of glacial cold, when the ice-sheet covered not only all Scotland and the north of England, but even the midland and southern counties as well, down to the valley of the Thames at least. After the ice-sheet which deposited that boulder-clay had melted away, another cold period with its ice-sheet supervened, and the purple boulder-clay of Yorkshire was next accumulated. This latter ice-sheet in like manner disappeared and was succeeded by the last interglacial period, when the climate became suited to the mammoth and to certain cervine and bovine animals, while in the rivers lived the *Cyrena fluminalis*—that freshwater shell which occurs so frequently in the ancient river-gravels of the Thames and elsewhere. So that we have what appears to be positive evidence enough, that the climatic conditions in Yorkshire, during some part of the last interglacial period, did not differ from those which accompanied the deposition of many ossiferous and palæolithic gravels in southern England.

It is evident, then, that the occurrence of the ancient river-gravels at Hoxne, superposed on the chalky boulder-clay, is no proof whatever that these gravels are of postglacial age. We know that after the deposition of the chalky boulder-clay there were at least two great advances of the confluent glaciers, and the consequent formation of younger deposits of till or boulder-clay. This, then, is a case in which mere superposition fails to tell us all that is necessary to be known, before we can conclude that the overlying beds are of postglacial age.

Before we can make up our minds as to the geological age of the river-gravels in question, it is evident that we must consider the distribution of similar accumulations throughout the country, and their relation to the drift-deposits belonging to the last cold period. When we have done so, the first noteworthy fact that we shall remark is that palæolithic river-gravels are exclusively confined to the south and south-east of England. They occur in the valleys of the Ouse, the Waveney, the Thames, the Avon, and their numerous tributaries, and at various places along the southern coast of England. North of the Ouse and west of the valley of the Axe, no river-gravels have yielded any palæolithic implements.* Nor has a single trace of gravels belonging to this age been anywhere recognised in Wales, the northern counties of England, Scotland, or Ireland. The tool-bearing drifts are thus singularly confined to a somewhat narrow and circumscribed area.

North of this area we find river-gravels of undoubted postglacial age lying in the bottoms of the valleys, and occupying positions that seldom rise more than a few feet or yards above the present levels of the streams. They are also, as far as bulk is concerned, of inconsiderable importance. The palæolithic gravels of the south, however, not only attain a great thickness, but from their position we can see that since the time of their formation very considerable

---

* *Ancient Stone Implements of Great Britain*, p. 477 et sqq.

derangement of the drainage-systems has taken place. Mr. Prestwich remarks : " One feature of these deposits is, that although closely related to the present configuration of the surface, yet they are always more or less independent of it. They are often near present lines of drainage, yet could not as a whole possibly have been formed under their operation." In short, it holds generally true that while the palæolithic gravels of the south began to be laid down at a time when the streams were commencing to hollow out their valleys, the gravels of the north were for the most part not deposited until after the valleys in which they occur had come to assume much of their present appearance. This is very significant, but I shall come to that presently ; meanwhile let us glance at the distribution of the old mammalia with which palæolithic man was contemporaneous.

Not for the moment taking account of cave-deposits, we find that beds containing remains of the fauna characteristic of palæolithic times do not occur at the actual surface in any district that lies beyond the limits reached by the implement-bearing beds. To this rule there are very few exceptions, nevertheless it is true that remains of the hippopotamus were obtained from an ancient river accumulation near Leeds ; and some of the northern forms have been occasionally met with here and there in different parts of the country. Underneath the glacial deposits of Norfolk the old mammalia occur in great abundance ; and, as we have seen, similar fossils appear in the interglacial beds of Yorkshire and Scotland. But in the superficial river-gravels north of the palæolithic area, they are conspicuous by their absence, and this is specially the case with the southern forms.

How then are we to explain this anomalous distribution ? It cannot be said that the mammalia may never have occupied the midland and northern districts. The fact that their bones occur abundantly in caves that lie far north of the limits reached by the palæolithic beds, shows that the animals were by no means confined to a narrow area in the south-east of England, and the occurrence of the hippopotamus near Leeds is further proof in the same direction. If the climate was suited to the mammalia that swarmed in the south—to elephants, rhinoceroses, and hippopotami, to lions, hyænas, and tigers—it surely could not have been other than genial in the north of England and in Scotland. Yet in neither region do any of these animals occur in the superficial or unquestionably postglacial river-gravels.

Now, take in connection with all this the remarkable fact that the south-east of England, where palæolithic and ossiferous river-gravels and loams are so well developed, is precisely that part of the country over which the sea did not prevail during the last great submergence of the British area, and in which we find no traces of the later glaciation. We have seen that some of the palæolithic gravels rest upon a boulder-clay which we can recognise as a deposit of land-ice laid down during the climax of glacial cold, when the ice-sheet extended as far south as the valley of the Thames. After this great ice-sheet had melted away, there is reason to believe that a wide land-surface appeared, and that a mild climate ensued, during the continuance of which the old boulder-clay was subjected to great erosion. Again, however, the climate became intensely cold and the ice-sheet re-advanced as far south at least as the middle of Lincolnshire ; this re-advance of the glaciers gave rise to the purple boulder-clay of Yorkshire, which, as Mr. S. V. Wood and his confrères have pointed out, rests on the highly-denuded surface of the chalky boulder-clay. Once more the ice-sheet melted away, and mild climatic conditions returned, when the mammoth, the urus, the Irish deer, and the horse lived in Scotland, and when various species of deer and oxen, together with the mammoth, were denizens of Yorkshire. It is more than probable that our island was joined to the continent in the early stages of this last interglacial period. But while mild and genial conditions still prevailed, the sea gradually encroached upon the land, until the latter became submerged in Wales, to a depth of more than 1,000 feet. The shells of the middle sands, &c., of Lancashire indicate a somewhat colder temperature than now prevails in our seas, and the evidence furnished by the marine interglacial clays of Scotland tell a similar tale. The climate was evidently again becoming cold and arctic. To what depth the land was submerged we cannot tell, but ere long re-elevation ensued ; and, the climate increasing in severity, great glaciers once more covered all Scotland and the north of England, reaching down into Lincolnshire. The interglacial deposits were then subjected to intense erosion, and the whole face of the country within the glaciated area was scoured and polished. South of that area, however, the river-gravels with their mammalian remains and palæolithic implements were preserved. So that, were we to colour on a map that portion of the British Islands which the last ice-sheet overwhelmed, the colour would also serve to indicate the regions in which no palæolithic implements have occurred, and where the old fauna characteristic of palæolithic times is either entirely absent from the river-gravels, or represented by only a few scattered examples, all with one exception (that of the Leeds hippopotamus) consisting of northern and temperate forms. On the other hand, that part of the map left uncoloured would be co-extensive with the districts in which palæolithic implements have been discovered, and where, in the ancient river-gravels, remains of the old mammalia often occur in great abundance.

If palæolithic deposits have a very limited range, such is not the case with those of neolithic age. Implements belonging to this later age, occur everywhere throughout the British Islands. From Caithness to Cornwall, and from the east coast of England to the western borders of Ireland, they are being continually picked up. Even in the bleak Orkney and Shetland Islands, and all over the Inner and Outer Hebrides, relics of neolithic times have been met with. So that the wide distribution of these implements is in striking contrast to the limited range of palæolithic remains.

We know that neolithic man was accompanied by a mammalian fauna that differed very much from that with which palæolithic man was associated. Dogs, horses, pigs, several breeds of oxen, the bison, the red deer, the Irish elk, and such like were the characteristic forms of neolithic times. Remains of these animals have occurred again and again in recent river- and lake-deposits in almost every part of England, Scotland, and Ireland. It is doubtful, however, whether the mammoth and the woolly rhinoceros lived in Britain down to neolithic times. Further evidence on this head is most desirable. It seems, however, to be beyond all reasonable doubt, that the southern group of animals had, as far as Britain is concerned, utterly vanished before the advent of the neolithic period.

How, then, are all these facts to be accounted for ? Why are palæolithic river-gravels restricted to the south-east of England, while neolithic remains occur broadcast throughout these islands ? What is the reason for the limitation of the southern mammalia to one small area in the south-east, and why should the mammoth and woolly rhinoceros occur so abundantly in the valley-gravels of that district, while they appear so seldom, and that only at wide intervals, in the valley-gravels of the north ? Beyond the palæolithic area, the great store-houses of mammalian remains, both of southern and northern forms, are caves, and certain beds which, from their position, we can recognize as being of preglacial and inter-glacial age.

The answer which I give to all these queries is simply this—the palæolithic deposits are of preglacial and inter-glacial age, and do not, in any part, belong to postglacial times. They are either entirely wanting or very sparingly represented in the midland and northern counties, in Wales, Scotland, and Ireland, because all those regions have again and again been subjected to the grinding action of land-ice, and the destructive influence of the sea. But in those dis-tricts which were not submerged during the last great depression of the land, and in such regions as were never overwhelmed by the confluent ice-masses, the valley-gravels form a continuous series of records from preglacial times to the present day. In short, the palæolithic beds dovetail into the glacial drifts, and are overlapped (as in Yorkshire) by the deposits thrown down during the final cold period. To the last interglacial period, then, we must refer the great bulk of the palæolithic river-gravels of the south-east of England. They are contemporaneous with those ancient freshwater deposits which in Scotland and in Yorkshire underlie the most recent accumulations of till or boulder-clay, and some of which have been partially re-arranged and covered with marine deposits belonging to the time of great submergence that preceded the latest glaciation. No doubt, however, por-tions of the ancient tool-bearing gravels, especially in the

valley of the Thames and the districts to the south, may
date back to the earlier warm periods of the glacial epoch,
and thus be contemporaneous with the oldest freshwater beds
in the Scottish till; while some may go back to even preglacial ages.   All that we can say for certain is, that no
palæolithic bed can be shown to belong to a more recent
date than the mild era that preceded the last great submergence and the final period of confluent glaciers.

When this view of the succession is accepted, many apparent anomalies receive a simple, and, as it seems to me, a
satisfactory explanation.   After the great chalky boulder-
clay of the eastern counties of England and the "northern
drift" of the midland districts had been laid down, the ice
melted away, and never again extended so far south.   An
interglacial period of unknown duration separated the deposition of the chalky boulder-clay from the accumulation of the
purple boulder-clay of Yorkshire.   The latter indicates another
invasion of the ice-sheet, but the spoor of the confluent
glaciers, underneath which it accumulated, has not been
followed farther south than Lincolnshire.   During all these
changes the southern districts not only escaped glaciation, but,
under the influence of subaerial denudation, were gradually
losing that ice-worn aspect which they must have presented
after the disappearance of the great ice-sheet which had formerly overwhelmed them.   The glacial conditions under which
the purple boulder-clay of Yorkshire was accumulated eventually passed away, and the last interglacial period ensued.   It
is highly probable, as I have said, that in the early stages of
this period, Britain was continental, and that the climate was
at first cold.   This is shown by the appearances presented by
the high-level or older valley-gravels of the palæolithic area
which contain a predominance of northern forms, and afford
other indications of a cold climate having prevailed at the time
of their formation.   It is evident, indeed, that as the land-ice
retired into the deep mountain glens, the country would be
invaded first by the arctic mammalia ; the rivers would be
liable to be frozen over, and, upon the breaking-up of the
frost in summer time, ice-rafts would run aground and thrust
the fluviatile deposits into confused heaps.   As the climate
ameliorated, and the rivers ceased to flood their valleys to so

great a depth, the arctic mammalia would gradually retire, and
be succeeded by animals belonging to more temperate zones.
The southern mammalia would thus come later in time than
the northern forms ; and in accordance with this we find that
the valley-gravels at the lower levels are characterized by the
prevalence of southern forms, and otherwise yield proof of
having been deposited under mild conditions of climate.*
By-and-by a process of submergence ensued, and this drowning
of the land would seem to have commenced at a time when a
temperate climate still obtained in Britain. The evidence, however, shows that colder conditions supervened and that arctic
species of shells lived in the submerged districts of Scotland.
Step by step the land, as far south, probably, as the middle of
England, was largely encroached upon by the sea. Re-elevation
now ensued and the climate becoming still more arctic, great
glaciers once more coalesced upon the Lowlands of Scotland,
and united with those of Scandinavia, England, and Ireland to
form the last great ice-sheet. Extensive as this ice-sheet was,
however, it does not seem to have gone farther south than the
valley of the Humber in the east, and the neighbourhood of
Chester in the west. Over all the area covered by the ice
there would necessarily be much erosion. The marine interglacial beds would be highly denuded, and such valley-gravels,
&c., as the sea had spared would likewise be subjected to the
grind of the ice. In the most highly glaciated districts, therefore, as in Scotland and the north of England, very few traces
of the old freshwater deposits would be spared. But towards
the southern limits reached by the ice, as in the maritime districts of South Lancashire, Cheshire, and Yorkshire, there
would be less erosive action and consequently a greater chance
of interglacial beds being preserved.

I have already referred to the remarkable fact that within
the region covered by ice during the latest cold period, rock-
escarpments are as a rule of infrequent occurrence, such as do

* Of course the process of excavating their valleys must have been continued
by the rivers of southern England during the whole of the glacial epoch; and
the succession of changes described above as having taken place in the last interglacial epoch would therefore only be a repetition of what must have happened
in previous interglacial periods. It must also be obvious that the recurrence of
flood-periods towards the beginning and the close of each mild interglacial
era would give rise to much redistribution of river-deposits, and tend to obscure
and obliterate those more or less regular terraces of gravel, sand, &c., which
rivers ordinarily form along the sides of their valleys.

appear being generally of little importance in the landscape. It is quite otherwise, however, in the districts beyond. There magnificent rock-escarpments are common, and the scenic features of the country that lay out of the reach of the last ice-sheet are in strongest contrast to those presented by the region over which the confluent glaciers prevailed. So long a time, indeed, has elapsed since the period of greatest glaciation, when the ice-sheet advanced into the south of England, that the atmospheric forces since then have been able to obliterate almost all traces of an ice-worn outline in the midland and southern districts of the country ; and, but for the presence of the " northern drift," the much-eroded and patchy chalky boulder-clay, and its so-called " denudation gravels," we should probably never have known that an ice-sheet ever extended farther south than a line drawn between Chester and the Humber.

While the last ice-sheet was disappearing great floods from the melting ice swept over the low grounds of England. To this period must be attributed those tumultuous deposits with occasional palæolithic implements and mammalian remains which are scattered over hill and valley alike, in the east-midland districts especially. No mere river-action can possibly account for the appearance presented by these confused accumulations, or for the anomalous positions in which they so often occur. They clearly indicate the flow of immense bodies of water, such as must have been set free during summer-time from the ice-sheet that lay to the north, even before the latter had begun its retreat; nor can we forget that under the climatic conditions which then obtained there must have been excessive evaporation and, as a consequence of that, drenching rains. When the final melting ensued the floods probably increased still more, so as to inundate wide regions with torrential waters. Thus not only would new accumulations of clay, silt, sand, gravel, and shingle be formed, but the ancient river-gravels of the last interglacial period would be much eroded and their materials reconstructed and huddled together, while whatever lay loose at the surface, whether on hill-top, hill-side, or valley-bottom, would be swept on so as to mingle with the heterogeneous detritus carried forward by the floods. In short, the flood-gravels of the midland districts are precisely of the same origin as much of the gravelly drift that overlies the upper boulder-clay in the low grounds of Scotland and other glaciated regions.

Gradually the ice melted away until it had disappeared from all the low grounds, and was represented by large local glaciers in the mountain-valleys of the north. Britain was at this time an island, and arctic shells lived round the Scottish shores. Eventually, however, our country again became continental, and although valley-glaciers still lingered amongst our mountains, yet the land was clothed and peopled with plants and animals. Reindeer at first roamed over the country, but ere long an abundant mammalian fauna stocked our plains and valleys—consisting of oxen, red deer, Irish elks, horses, and other animals characteristic of temperate zones. It is extremely uncertain, however, whether the mammoth and the woolly rhinoceros returned to their old haunts. Certainly none of the southern mammalia ever did; these had vanished for ever, and with them palæolithic man had also disappeared—his neolithic successor being now the lord of the soil.

It is thus, then, that I would explain the anomalous distribution of the palæolithic deposits, and that remarkable gap or hiatus which separates the neolithic from the palæolithic age.

CHAPTER XL.

GEOLOGICAL AGE OF THE PALÆOLITHIC DEPOSITS—*Continued*.

Mr. Skertchly on interglacial age of palæolithic gravels, — Physical features, &c., of the Fenland.—Section across Fenland showing succession of beds.— —Boulder-clay.—Old river-gravels.—Flood-gravels.—Beach-gravels and floor-gravels.—Fen-beds, &c.—General summary of results.

THE views concerning the geological age of our palæolithic gravels, which are set forth in the preceding pages, have lately received strong support from the results obtained by Mr. S. B. J. Skertchly in a detailed examination of the Fenland and adjoining districts. It is extremely gratifying to me to find that the conclusions I have formed should have been arrived at independently by a geologist who has examined the evidence from quite a different standpoint. It was my inability to correlate the palæolithic and ossiferous gravels and cave-deposits of England with the true postglacial beds of Scotland and the north of England, which first led me to suspect that English geologists were mistaken in relegating the former accumulations to postglacial times. Knowing that the cold climatic conditions of the glacial epoch had been more than once interrupted by warm intervals, during which certain of the old mammalia lived in Scotland, and being well assured that no warm period had supervened between the close of the last cold period and the present, I could not resist the conclusion that our ossiferous and palæolithic deposits must be of preglacial and interglacial age. Mr. Skertchly, as will be seen presently, obtained substantially the same results by a careful scrutiny of the old gravel-beds themselves. That two geologists working at a subject from totally different points of view should nevertheless arrive at one and the same conclusion, affords pretty strong presumptive evidence in favour of their explanation of the phenomena being the true one.

Mr. Skertchly has been good enough to furnish me with the following outline of his work, which the reader will find much more fully displayed in the official memoir* descriptive of the region which my colleague has surveyed :—

"It was during five years' study of the sands, gravels, and clays which overlie the great chalky boulder-clay, that I independently arrived at similar conclusions to those so much more fully developed by yourself. The convictions came very slowly—indeed, they were forced upon me ; but so opposed were they to the general belief of geologists, that it was not without considerable trepidation that I allowed them to become part of my geological creed. The publication of your work, however, in which my surmises received such bold confirmation, left no further room for doubt, and since then every day's fieldwork has only strengthened my belief in the interglacial age of palæolithic man.

"The first key to the relation borne by the Fen-beds to the glacial period was the recognition of the antiquity of the chalky boulder-clay, the peculiar distribution of certain gravels, and the singular dissemination of their fossils, including palæolithic implements. But the remarks which I have to make will be more easily followed after I have first briefly described the features of the Fenland.

"The Fenland is a great alluvial plain, comprising an area of more than 1,300 square miles, and averaging in height about 15 ft. above the level of the sea. The fen-basin is, for the most part, hollowed out of the Oxford and Kimeridge clays ; but boulder-clay overlies these rocks over a great portion of the district. Fringing the western shore of this basin we find a series of gravels which I call the *Beach-gravels*, and which are generally continued over the floor of the basin, in which position I call them *Floor-gravels*. Above these gravels comes a series of peat-beds and marine silts and clays, all of which are very variable—peat, for instance, in some places occurring from the surface down to the gravels, and at others being entirely absent. The beach- and floor-gravels contain no fossils, save now and then a rolled bone, which seldom belongs to a member of the old 'palæolithic fauna.' Other gravels occur in patches near to the former

* "The Geology of the Fenland," *Mem. of Geol. Surv. of Great Brit.*

courses of the old Fen rivers. These are fossiliferous, and have yielded bones of the mammoth, &c. Covering the high land in Lincolnshire on the northern boundary of the Fenland, and in Norfolk and Suffolk the eastern and southern boundaries, are widespread sands and gravels, to which I have given the name of *Flood-gravels.* The general lie of the beds is shown in the following distorted diagram-section.

"I must premise that all these gravels are quite distinct from those associated with the boulder-clay, although there have been attempts to show that they are preglacial in the old sense of the term—that is to say, older than the chalky boulder-clay. Wherever that clay occurs, however, they repose unconformably upon it. The gravels have never before been distinguished, and it was not until I succeeded in unravelling their complexity that their relations to the glacial period appeared.

"The gravels marked *b* occur solely along the courses of the Fen rivers Ouse, Nene, and Welland, generally as isolated patches, but sometimes connected with the true valley-gravels of those rivers. They differ from the gravels marked *d* in several important features; namely, they contain

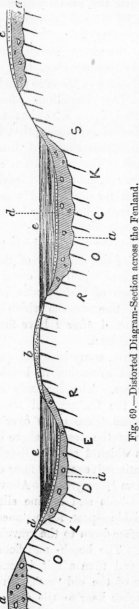

Fig. 69.—Distorted Diagram-Section across the Fenland.

a, Boulder-clay; *b*, Old river-gravel; *c*, Flood-gravel; *d*, Beach-gravel passing downwards into Floor-gravel; *e*, Fen-beds, the dark parts indicating peat.

numerous shells, sometimes whole, sometimes fragmentary; they are very often much contorted; they never form beaches or pass into the floor-gravels; and, lastly, the mammalian remains yielded by them belong to the old 'cave fauna,' and not to that of the more recent period. It is furthermore significant that, with the exception of the Welland patches, they belong to rivers farther up whose valleys palæolithic implements are found, and it is probable that ere long that river will be added to the list of those whose valleys afford evidence of the (as yet) earliest known human occupation of our land.

"These gravels are older than any of the true fen-beds, younger than the boulder-clay, and older, in all probability, than the formation of the Fenland basin, for they seem to have suffered denudation at that time equally with the glacial and other beds. The marine shells indicate a moderately cold sea, *Cyprina Islandica* and other northern forms being the predominant species; but the presence of *Cyrena fluminalis* seems to prove that the climate was not excessive. I may here remark that the latter shell has never been found in any valley in England opening westward or southward, nor in any deposit containing the modern mammalian fauna, and that being extinct, as far as this country is concerned, it tends to prove the antiquity of the gravel. *Cyprina Islandica* still lives in the Wash, but the associated shells in the gravel, although British, yet do not live along this coast, so that the molluscan fauna is as foreign to the locality as the mammalian. In all these points these gravels differ from the others in the Fenland, and I am anxious to impress the fact because upon it turns a great deal of the argument for the correlation of the gravels.

"Many circumstances incontestably prove that during the palæolithic period the British Isles were connected with each other and with the Continent. It does not, however, seem to have been so much insisted upon that other facts as certainly point to a restriction of British soil. Yet the fact that the estuaries of the Nene, Ouse, and Welland in palæolithic times were twenty-five miles farther inland than at present, and the water-level forty feet higher, not merely proves that England was not then joined to the Continent, but that the land stood relatively at least forty feet lower than at present. To what period, then, can these gravels be assigned? It seems to me only to one, and that the time of the.great submergence, when the Welsh mountains were depressed some 1,300 ft. Hitherto the shores of that old sea have been unknown; but here in the Fenland, that land of mystery, we find them preserved to us.

" But the evidence of the continental condition of Great Britain in palæolithic times is equally incontestable. How, then, can these antagonistic views be reconciled? Clearly by ascribing to that epoch a much greater length of time than has hitherto been granted. *Part* of the palæolithic epoch—and that the earliest part—occurred while England was joined to the Continent; but it did not end until that connection was severed even to a greater extent than at present. The length of that period cannot yet be estimated, nor can we tell how many migrations the Old Stone folk had to undertake owing to changing climatic conditions; but we may be sure that if this view of the prolonged duration of the palæolithic age be correct, we should find evidence of the advance of civilisation. And accordingly we do, for many of the palæolithic implements in the neighbourhood of Brandon are more highly finished than is known elsewhere, and, moreover, we get there the first evidence of the use in England of more intractable material than flint. These considerations long since led me to look upon palæolithic deposits as belonging to widely separated eras—a view which you have so boldly advanced, and that from the study of a more limited area of palæolithic beds than it has been my good fortune to investigate.

" I must now turn to the palæozoic gravels and sands of Suffolk. They have been described by many previous writers as confined to the river-valleys, and to be, consequently, river-gravels. This is no otherwise true than that being (naturally) thicker in valleys than elsewhere they are there worked and the implements brought to light. In point of fact, however, they spread all over the country quite irrespective of the drainage-system, crossing watersheds, occupying the highest ground and running down to the lowest; and at points as widely distant as possible from any

water-course I have found implements. These gravels and
sands are, for the most part, quite unstratified, and only
show signs of stratification in limited areas. They form
wide sandy heaths, which are only useful for rabbit-warrens.
Every phase of their character shows that they are the effect
of great floods sweeping across the face of the country. They
have naturally accumulated in greatest force in the valleys, and
as it would be impossible but that streams were locally formed
so we find portions showing stratification and false-bedding,
but these appearances are by no means confined to the river-
channels. They are older than much of the present river-
valley, for the river has cut through them, and the waste so
derived has been re-arranged as true river-gravel, and in
both palæolithic implements are found, although in the latter
case they are often more rolled.

"It seems clear to me that man could not possibly have
lived at the time when these great floods swept across the
country, but must have been a prior occupant, whose dis-
carded relics were swept up with other surface-matter to form
the sandy deposit, and these floods I believe to have originated in the melting back of an ice-sheet, probably that
which formed the purple boulder-clay of Yorkshire and
Lincolnshire. There must have been several such recessions,
each giving rise to floods, both directly from the dissolution
of the ice, and indirectly from the increased rainfall, consequent upon the enhanced humidity of the atmosphere, owing
to the rapid evaporation of that ice. When, then, could
palæolithic man have lived? The answer is, in the mild
period between the recession of the great ice-sheet and its
resultant floods, on the one hand, and the floods produced
by the dissolution of another and subsequent ice-sheet, on
the other hand. Each succeeding flood-period would sweep
away or incorporate the material (if any) left by the preceding
one. Hence the complication of these implement-bearing
beds. Those of the non-glaciated south of England may
represent almost the whole of the glacial period, and, it
may be, some portion of preglacial time also. The partially glaciated east of England presents less complication,
and in the Victoria Cave are preserved deposits belonging to
different stages of the palæolithic period, and separated by

true glacial beds.   To me one of the most striking facts connected with the palæolithic beds of Suffolk is this—that the
ruder implements seem to be so much older than the mass of
the material composing the beds in which they are found;
yet it has been taken for granted that these *terrestrial* implements are as much contemporaneous with the gravel-beds as
the *aquatic* shells which the latter contain.   I believe that
many of the ruder implements from the valley of the Little
Ouse and Lark are much older than the better-worked ones
—they differ as much in petralogical texture as in workmanship—they are more weathered and more rolled.   That their
separation is a very difficult task is certain; but it should be
recognised as a difficulty, and not ignored by grouping all
things together.

"Very similar flood-gravels to those of Norfolk and
Suffolk are found in Lincolnshire around Spilsby.   They
have not yet yielded palæolithic implements and perhaps
will not do so, for there probably will be found some area to
the north beyond which man did not then penetrate; but as
the deposits are in every sense similar to those under consideration they may be looked upon as of the same age.

"We now come to the first of the true fen-beds—the
beach- and floor-gravels.   These form, as their names imply,
beaches (as along the Lincolnshire border of the Fenland),
and cover the bottom of the basin almost uninterruptedly.
The Wash is often spoken of as the estuary of the Fen rivers,
and the alluvial beds of the Fens as estuarine deposits.   The
Wash, however, is a true *bay*, and is no more an estuary than
the North Sea is the estuary of the Thames and Humber;
neither are the fen-beds estuarine, but marine or freshwater.   The beach-gravels occupy much the same relative
levels as the old fossiliferous river-gravels before described;
and hence they have been confounded with them.   But they
possess important differences—to wit, they are regularly
stratified and not contorted, and they pass downwards into
the floor-gravels, while the fossiliferous beds do not.   Moreover they never contain marine or other shells, notwithstanding that their physical aspect at once proclaims them to
be true beaches.   Occasionally they enclose a few rolled
bones, but these belong to the neolithic fauna; or if a frag-

ment of older date occur, its condition at once stamps it as having been derived from some older bed. Implements of any kind are entirely wanting in them, but in some few cases thin beds of peat and marine silt are found—deposits which, coming on in force subsequently, are, as it were, foreshadowed in these gravels which are thus at once marked as belonging to what we may for convenience call the Fen period. The only marine organism I have found is a stone with a small patch of *Flustra* adhering to it. Bearing in mind the absence of palæolithic implements and fossils it seems probable that these gravels belong to the interval between the emigration of the Old and the immigration of the Newer Stone folk, and that they represent in time some of the latest glacial deposits of northern Britain.

"The Nar Valley beds are older than these gravels and newer than the old fossiliferous river-gravels.

"Reposing upon the beach and floor-gravels are the peat-beds and marine silt of the Fens. The peat, speaking generally, occupies a surface-area of about 500 square miles, and attains a thickness of 20 feet. It occupies most of the ground along the west, south, and south-east. Sometimes it forms one great bed extending from the surface to the gravels, at others it is entirely wanting; but, as a rule, there are several layers, some of which extend far eastwards under the marine silt. Three layers of peat can be determined with some degree of certainty, but the whole of these fen-beds indicate a struggle for supremacy by the fresh water on the one hand, and the sea upon the other. Wherever the former obtained the mastery, peat grew; wherever the latter triumphed, silt was deposited, and the alternations were sometimes very rapid. The peat, as we have said, began to grow during the formation of the floor-gravels, but climatic conditions ceased to be favourable to its development before the Roman invasion, and peat now only grows in a few dank sheltered valleys, and in a few stagnant shallow trenches. In this respect it is different from much of the Scottish peat, which is certainly of post-Roman date.* The climate is now too dry for peat to form in force, and this, amongst other

---

* See *ante*, p. 319, where it is shown that while some Scottish peat is of post-Roman age, much belongs to an older period.—J. G.

things, shows that a gradual desiccation has taken place since postglacial times. Another peculiarity in fen peat is the almost entire absence of *Sphagnum,* a strong growing *Hypnum* supplying its place.

"Interspersed through the peat are several buried forests, which hitherto have been classed as one, but which are certainly as many as five in number. The only tree found therein which is not indigenous to the district is the Scotch fir, *Pinus sylvestris,* which attained colossal dimensions, and possessed remarkably thick bark—a certain indication of the greater severity of the then climate.

"The marine silts are of two kinds, clay and warp. They call for no special mention here, being very similar to the deposits to which the name of *Scrobicularia clay* has been given. As, however, that term applies only to one phase of the deposit, I prefer to call it merely *Fen silt.* The area occupied by this silt is about 600 square miles, but it is gradually increasing, about 64,000 acres having accreted since the second century, the mean rate of deposition being about 11 feet per annum. The mammals of the peat and silt belong to the newer fauna. Neolithic, bronze, and iron implements occur in the upper part and on the surface.

"A few words may now be said respecting the physical history of the Fens. The first important event was the breaching of the great Chalk barrier between Lincolnshire and Norfolk, which let the sea into the low-lying plains of the Oxford and Kimeridge clays and resulted in the scooping out of the great basin, part of which is now occupied by the Fens and the rest by the Wash. This important event occurred in late Tertiary times. Then the Ice Age came on, and glacial clay was deposited along the coast (Cromer till). Next succeeded a mild period, during which the "middle glacial" sands of Mr. S. V. Wood were deposited, which range in elevation from 300 feet above the sea to 600 feet below it (at Boston). These are said to be marine, and in some places they may be so, but I am inclined to doubt whether this is always the case. Then came a return of intense glacial conditions (broken by mild intervals) during which the great boulder-clays of the eastern and north-eastern counties were deposited. After the ice-sheet vanished Britain was united to the continent. The next event was the great sub-mergence, the most southern traces of which we find in the fossiliferous valley-gravels of the Fens at a height of 40 feet above the sea-level. Then we have the floods from the ice, which again formed to the north, and, finally, as the glacial epoch came to a close, the beach- and floor-gravels were formed. The boulder-clay filled up the basin of the Fens, which was re-excavated during the great submergence. The after history of the fens is one of deposition—first of gravels, then of peat and silt. The climate was colder and wetter than at present, but long intervals of dryness intervened during which forests slowly crept down from the high land as the peat temporarily ceased to grow : of these dry intervals we know at least five.*

"The following table shows the deposits treated of, in their natural sequence :—"

TABLE OF FENLAND BEDS.

(By Sydney B. J. Skertchly.)

Deposits.	Fossils.	Physical Conditions.	Remarks.
9. Blown sand	None	As at present.	
8. Peat	*Bos longifrons, B. primigenius, Megaceros Hibernicus, Castor fiber.* Buried forests; iron, bronze, and neolithic implements	Similar to present, but rather colder, rainfall heavier, with dry intervals	Does not now grow under natural conditions.
7. Shell marl	Recent shells	As above	Intercalated in upper part of peat.
Silt	Mammals as above. Whale, grampus. *Scrobicularia piperata* and other recent shells. Neolithic implements	As above	Forming simultaneously with peat at all times. Still forming.
6. Beach and floor gravels	Deer. *Bos longifrons*	Land submerged 50 feet ; climate cold	
5. Nar Valley beds	Recent marine shells many not now living in the Wash	As above	In Nar Valley only.

* When Mr. Skertchly penned these notes he was not aware that Mr. Axel Blytt, of Christiania University, had come to similar conclusions regarding the climatic conditions under which the peat-mosses and buried forests of Norway have been formed. [J. G.] See page 417.

N N

TABLE OF FENLAND BEDS—*continued.*

Deposits.	Fossils.	Physical Conditions.	Remarks.
4. Old valley and flood-gravels	Shells, with *Cyrena fluminalis* and *Cyprina Islandica,* Old "cave fauna," palæolithic implements	Land at first continental, afterwards submerged 40 feet. The great submergence of Wales, &c.	
3. Boulder-clay .	None . . .	Land 500 ft. higher than now. Icesheet. England continental.	
2. Sands, gravels, and clays	Unknown . .	?	Only reached at Boston. They correspond to S. V. Wood's middle glacial.
1. Glacial deposits	None . . .	Land relatively much as at present	Till and contorted beds of Norfolk coast.

Late Tertiary (Pliocene ?)—Chalk barrier breached.

CHAPTER XLI.

GEOLOGICAL POSITION OF NEOLITHIC, PALÆOLITHIC, AND OSSIFEROUS DEPOSITS OF FOREIGN COUNTRIES.

Palæolithic deposits wanting in Switzerland.—Mammalia of interglacial beds.— Swiss postglacial deposits belong to neolithic, bronze, and more recent periods.—Postglacial deposits of northern Italy of neolithic or more recent age.—Mammalian remains of Piedmont.—Palæolithic tools and remains of southern mammalia nowhere found in superficial deposits overlying the great northern drift.—Wide distribution of neolithic implements over northern Europe.—Inferences.—Palæolithic man and the southern mammalia not postglacial.—Distribution of the old mammalia over Siberia and North America.—Proofs of mild climates within Arctic Circle.—Trees in Greenland.—Mammalia absent from districts covered with the later glacial deposits, but abound in the districts beyond.—General conclusions.

IF the conclusions now arrived at in regard to the preglacial and interglacial position of palæolithic remains and the old mammalia be reasonable, they ought not to contradict, but, on the contrary, should receive confirmation from the evidence supplied by other regions. I propose, therefore, to discuss very briefly the relation borne by the mammaliferous beds of Switzerland, Italy, and North America to the glacial deposits of those countries.

In Chapter XXXII. it will be remembered that some account is given of certain lignite beds which rest upon the ancient ground-moraine of the Swiss lowlands, and are covered by accumulations belonging to the last great advance of the glaciers in that country. With those lignites are associated human relics, the remains of elephant and rhinoceros—both southern forms—and other mammalia, none of which is northern. There is no doubt that the underlying ground-moraine corresponds to our older deposits of till, and just as little that the overlying glacial débris is the Swiss equivalent of our upper boulder-clays and shelly clays; in other words, the Swiss lignites occupy exactly the horizon of our most recent palæolithic deposits.

With this singular notable exception, nowhere in the Swiss low grounds do any remains of the southern mammalia occur. Relics of the neolithic and bronze ages are plentiful —bones of dogs, pigs, deer, sheep, horses, &c., turn up in every recent alluvium—but not a single trace of any of the southern mammalia or of palæolithic man has ever been discovered.* The mammoth and the woolly rhinoceros have been disinterred from the old loams of the Rhine and other rivers, but lions, tigers, hippopotami, elephants, and hyænas are nowhere visible. Now, on the assumption that these animals and palæolithic man did not live in Europe after the last great increase of the Swiss glaciers, their absence from the surface alluvia and gravels is precisely what we should have anticipated. The deposits which may once have contained them have been well-nigh obliterated—the only fragments left being the lignite beds of Dürnten and Wetzikon. It may be, however, that underneath the vast deposits of loess belonging to the last cold period, palæolithic deposits lie concealed.†

The same facts meet us on the Italian side of the Alps. Marl-beds and peat-bogs occur in many places, particularly in Piedmont, where the latter occupy depressions in the surface of the ancient glacial moraines. Traces of lake-dwellings (*Palafitte*) are found beneath these old peat-mosses, and answer in every respect to the similar relics met with in Switzerland (*Pfahlbauten*). The animal remains associated with the *palafitte* are the dog, horse, ox, goat, sheep, stag, roebuck, boar, bear (*Ursus arctos*), &c.‡ Nowhere have the mosses, alluvia or marl-beds (which are all clearly of later date than the moraines belonging to the last extension of the Alpine glaciers) yielded any trace of the old southern

* Professor Fraas describes the occurrence of palæolithic remains at Schussenried in Würtemberg. They rest upon the old moraine of the extinct glacier of the Rhine, and lie far beyond the limits reached by the glaciers in what the Swiss geologists call the second ice period. (The moraines of the first and greatest extension of the glaciers extend for some five miles beyond Schussenried.) The Schussenried palæolithic deposit therefore occupies precisely the same position as the gravel beds that overlie the boulder-clay at Hoxne, and is not more entitled than these to be classified as postglacial.

† To the last interglacial period probably belong the lignites at Steinbach near Baden-Baden, and at Imberg near Sonthofen in Bavaria. These beds occur in ancient river-gravels which are covered with the loess of the last cold period.

‡ Gastaldi, *Lake Habitations and Pre-historic Remains in Italy.*

mammalia or of palæolithic man. The human relics all belong to neolithic, bronze, or still more recent times.

It is well known, however, that beds of lignite and river accumulations containing remains of the mastodon, the elephant, the rhinoceros, the hippopotamus, &c., occur in Piedmont. These deposits are older than the moraines of Ivrea and the great heaps of similar débris lying at the mouths of the lake-valleys of northern Italy. According to the Italian geologists, they must be correlated with the lignite beds of Dürnten and Wetzikon in Switzerland, and hence are not of preglacial or postglacial, but of interglacial age.

Palæolithic implements are said to occur in the gravels of the Tiber,* but they have not been discovered in fluviatile deposits in any other part of Italy. So also in beds of sand near Megalopolis, in Greece, palæolithic implements are associated with bones of the great pachyderms;† and palæolithic valley-gravels containing remains of the African elephant occur near Madrid.‡ It is in France, however, in the valleys of the Somme and the Seine, where such deposits are most typically represented.

In Scandinavia, Denmark, Holland, northern Germany, and Russia no palæolithic gravels have been detected, neither have the remains of the more characteristic southern genera —*Hippopotamus, Elephas antiquus, Rhinoceros megarhinus,* and *R. leptorhinus* (Owen)—ever occurred in any superficial river deposit throughout that vast area. The lion and hyæna, however, have left their traces in the caves of Germany, and in the ancient river-gravels of the Main and the Rhine numerous mammalian remains have been detected. Among these are elephant (*E. antiquus*), hippopotamus, rhinoceros, mammoth, Irish elk, reindeer, urus, cave-bear, &c. The river-gravels and sands that contain these remains occur at a considerable height on the slopes that overlook the present valleys, and although they have not as yet yielded any trace of man or his works, yet, according to Dr. Sandberger, there can be no doubt that they belong to the same age as the palæolithic gravels of England and France. Overlying the

---

* *Ancient Stone Implements*, &c., p. 571.   † *Op. et loc. cit.*

‡ *Op. et loc. cit.*; see also Casiano de Prado's *Descripcion física y geológica de la Provincia de Madrid*, p. 186.

gravels in question comes the great deposit of loess or diluvial mud which the rivers carried down during the last considerable extension of the Alpine glaciers. There can be no question that this loess, which covers such vast areas in the low grounds of Europe, is simply the flood-loam laid down by the vast inundations that took place during the melting of the great glaciers.* Such inundations would occur not only when the climax of glacial cold was past and the glaciers had begun to retreat, but even during the very climax of the glacial epoch ; each summer (when the heat received from the sun was probably greater than it is now in central Europe) would liberate vast quantities of water, which would form rivers of a depth and breadth of which we have nowadays no conception. According to Dr. Sandberger, in these times the Rhine at Strasburg carried forty-eight times as much water as it now does at its highest.

Now when one thinks of it, this distribution of palæolithic and mammalian remains is very remarkable. For when we put aside the caves we find that no palæolithic implements and none of the southern mammalia occur in those regions, which are more or less thickly covered with the sand, gravel, and erratics belonging to the northern drift. Holland, Denmark, northern Russia, and the whole of northern Germany, from the borders of the Baltic down to near the base of the Hartz mountains and the Riesengebirge, are abundantly covered with plateaux and heaps of drift, in the hollows of which occur numerous lakelets and pools. These deposits form what has long been known as the Northern Drift, and no doubt they belong in large measure to the climax of the glacial epoch, when the Scandinavian ice-sheet reached its farthest limits. How far south the last ice-sheet extended has not yet been ascertained ; it is most likely, however, that it actually invaded northern Germany. We know, at

---

* My brother has suggested that the loess may owe its origin to the blocking-up of the North Sea by the *mer de glace* of Scandinavia and Britain, which by damming up the exit of the great rivers flowing north would cause them to inundate all the low grounds to the south. It is not improbable, I think, that this may have happened; but wide-spread deposits of flood-loam would have taken place even had there been no damming back of the waters, just as we have seen was the case in North America. The great "Bluff formation" of the Mississippi evidently could not have resulted from a damming-back of that river, but simply marks the depth and breadth reached by the inundations during the melting of the great ice-sheet.

all events, that it was confluent with the Scotch ice, and
that, owing to its pressure, the latter was forced to trespass
upon the north-eastern districts of England.   There is reason
to believe, also, that in late glacial times the northern drift
of Germany was modified to some extent during a period of
submergence, as is proved by the presence of sea-shells in
the drift both of East and West Prussia.   But the extent of
that submergence is not known ; a very slight degree of
depression, however, must have brought the sea over a wide
region in northern Germany.   Now over all the broad area
occupied by the northern drift the superficial river-deposits
have yielded only remains of the present temperate fauna,
with human implements belonging to neolithic or still more
recent times.   Of the earlier palæolithic age they contain no
trace whatever.   Similarly, in the great valleys that drain
down from the Central Alps—the Rhine, the Rhone, the
Danube, and the Po—we find immense accumulations of
flood-loam or loess, the upper portions of which at least
must belong to that last cold period during which the glaciers
advanced upon the lowlands of Switzerland and overwhelmed
the forest-lands of Zurich.   Now it is a fact that hitherto
the only human relics found resting upon these deposits
appertain to neolithic and more recent times.   Neither
palæolithic implements nor bones of the southern mammalia
have there been detected.   It is only when we get fairly
beyond the limits of the " Alpine diluvium " belonging to the
latest era of great glaciers, that palæolithic deposits come on
in force, as in the north-east of France.

No one will be inclined to believe that, at a time when
the hippopotamus and the southern forms of elephant and
rhinoceros were joint tenants of England and the north-east
of France, these animals never strayed into similar latitudes
of Germany.   During the palæolithic period Britain was
united to the Continent, and it is in the highest degree
unlikely that man and his southern congeners were then
restricted to the few river-basins in western Europe, where
their remains are now met with.   Besides, as we know from
the evidence of the caves and the old refuse-heap at Schussenried, palæolithic man was a denizen of Germany, and the lion
and the hyæna were his congeners there.

No sooner, however, do we admit the interglacial age of the palæolithic river-deposits than all our difficulties vanish, and the manner in which the gravels are distributed becomes full of meaning.

After the great *mer de glace* that extended from Scandinavia to the plains of Germany had retired, and the massive Rhone glacier had retreated from the low grounds of France and once more shrunk into its mountain-valley, and when the mighty ice-streams that invaded the plains of Piedmont had melted away, vegetation followed the retreating steps of the ice, and palæolithic man, accompanied by the arctic mammalia, wandered over Europe. As the climate grew milder these latter gradually migrated northwards, and were succeeded by the temperate and southern groups; and, seeing that the hippopotamus ranged as far at least as Leeds in England, there is no reason why it should not have followed some of the great European rivers down to the shores of the Northern Ocean. The Elbe, the Weser, the Rhine, and the Meuse were surely as likely to tempt the old river-horse to a bath as the smaller rivers of England. Nor were such waters as the Rhone and the Po likely to be despised.

This period of mild and genial winters eventually passed away, but before it did so certain great changes in the geography of Europe took place. A large part of the British Islands disappeared below the sea. But as this submergence continued, the last cold period of the glacial epoch began. The land again rose and great confluent glaciers covered Scandinavia and a large part of the British Islands, uniting to form one great *mer de glace* which reached down to and even beyond the valley of the Humber. At the same time huge glaciers descended all the valleys of the Alps, and, advancing upon the low grounds of Switzerland, overwhelmed the forests, and here and there buried beneath their débris deposits containing remains of the southern and temperate mammalia. The rivers, greatly swollen, swept down vast quantities of fine glacial silt, underneath which were concealed such of the ossiferous beds as the rivers themselves had not demolished and re-arranged. The southern mammalia had left Europe, and in their place came the northern forms—mammoths and woolly rhinoceroses, the mammoth ranging into southern Italy—and at a still later date herds of reindeer, which lived south as far as the slopes of the Pyrenees. Glaciers then existed in the Vosges and the Black Forest, and those of the Pyrenees exceeded in size their present puny descendants.

After this glacial condition of things had lasted for a long time, the climate began to ameliorate. In the north of Europe the ice again melted away, but the old freshwater deposits which had been laid down in palæolithic times, and which in the previous interval of depression had doubtless suffered extensive denudation, had been well-nigh completely demolished under the grinding of the ice-sheet. In Scotland, Ireland, Wales, and the north of England little or no trace of them remained. Even the marine deposits which were laid down towards the close of the last interglacial period had been extensively eroded, although, as might have been expected, they have been more abundantly preserved than the freshwater accumulations. In the great valleys of the Alps, the interglacial beds had almost entirely disappeared—the only traces of them preserved being the lignites of Dürnten, and the bone-beds and lignites of northern Italy. In the lower reaches of the valleys that drain from the Alps, vast sheets of loess had been distributed—obscuring and concealing any palæolithic beds which may have existed at the surface before the last cold period commenced. But beyond the glaciated regions, and south of the area which had been submerged, the old valley-gravels, with their interesting memorials of man and his associates, the southern mammalia, remained. These, however, had been greatly denuded, and to a large extent re-arranged and scattered about by the floods that ensued during the melting of the glaciers.

When the last ice-sheet had retired from the low grounds, it was followed by the sea to a certain extent, and arctic shells then lived round the Scottish coasts. Eventually, however, Britain again became continental, while the climate still continued cold and ungenial. The mammoth and its associate, the woolly rhinoceros, seem to have lived down to this time in central Europe, for their remains occur in the loess of the Rhine; it is very doubtful, however, whether they ever revisited Britain. But palæolithic man and the southern mammalia not only did not re-enter Britain, but would even appear to have become extinct in Europe.

During palæolithic times more than one land-passage existed between Europe and Africa, across which doubtless the southern mammalia had entered our continent. At what particular time these land-passages became submerged there is no unequivocal evidence to show; but it is probable that they disappeared during the last cold period. Whether Europe was again united to Africa in postglacial and neolithic times we cannot tell; but we do know that the immigration of the southern mammalia ceased with the close of the last interglacial period.

It was neolithic man who, after the last ice period had passed away, became the sole occupant of Europe—his relics being found everywhere throughout the continent, accompanied by the remains of that group of mammalia which is still characteristic of these latitudes.

We must now glance at the distribution of the old mammalia in the higher latitudes of Asia and North America. The great plains of Siberia, extending from the base of the Ural Mountains to Behring's Straits, are traversed by several large rivers, which in many places have exposed fine sections of those extensive alluvial beds that almost everywhere throughout this vast region form the subsoils. These alluvial deposits are often literally packed with the remains of mammoth, woolly rhinoceros, bison, and horse. So abundant, indeed, are remains of the mammoth, that for many years they have actually been quarried for the sake of the ivory—in 1821, no less a quantity than 20,000 lbs. of this product having been obtained from New Siberia alone. The Liakhov Islands and New Siberia have evidently formed at one time a portion of the Asiatic continent; indeed, they appear to be chiefly composed of ancient river alluvia, which are scarped into a series of low cliffs along the coast—the resort of the ivory hunters, where they may be seen every summer digging the mammoth-tusks out of the frozen soil which has partially thawed. The fossils are usually well-preserved. Indeed, on one occasion, the actual carcass of a mammoth was exposed in one of the cliffs in so fresh a state, that the dogs ate the flesh.

The presence of these numerous animal remains indicates the former prevalence of a milder climate in Siberia than now. For we can hardly doubt that the animals actually occupied the low-lying tracts through which the rivers of northern Asia flow. At the same time it is evident, that, during winter, carcasses would frequently be frozen into the ice in the upper reaches of the rivers, and, when summer returned, would often be floated down for long distances before they became finally entombed.* It is impossible to believe, however, that all the remains which occur so abundantly along the whole borders of the Arctic Sea, have been floated down in this way from lower latitudes. By far the larger proportion must belong to creatures that lived and died in the latitudes where their bones are now found.

It is remarkable that, nowhere in the great plains of Siberia do any traces of glacial action appear to have been observed. If cones and mounds of gravel and great erratics like those that sprinkle so wide an area in northern America and northern Europe had occurred, they would hardly have failed to arrest the attention of explorers. Middendorff does indeed mention the occurrence of trains of large erratics which he observed along the banks of some of the rivers, but these, he has no doubt, were carried down by river-ice.† The general character of the tundras is that of wide flat plains, covered for the most part with a grassy and mossy vegetation, but here and there bare and sandy. Frequently nothing intervenes to break the monotony of the landscape. The eye wanders over a sealike expanse that stretches far away until it seems to blend with the blue distance. Here and there, perhaps, a slight roll of the ground makes a faint low arch against the pale horizon, and serves as a landmark to Samojede and Ostjak, but otherwise the ocean of the

---

* Dr. Rae suggests that the animals might have been drowned far up the rivers and afterwards floated down stream for perhaps "hundreds of miles, until they reached the shallows at the mouth, where the heads, loaded with a great weight of bone and tusks, would get aground in three or four feet of water." In this position they would be frozen up as soon as the winter set in; and as the ice would remain solidly frozen to the muddy bottom, it would eventually be buried under new deposits of mud when the next spring with its floods came round.—*Philosophical Magazine*, vol. xlviii. (1874), p. 60.

† *Reisen in den äussersten norden und osten Sibiriens*, Band iv. Theil i. p. 269.

tundra extends without interruption — an interminable plain.*

It would appear, then, that in northern Asia representatives of the glacial deposits which are met with in similar latitudes in Europe and America do not occur. The northern drift of Russia and Germany ; the upper till and åsar of Sweden ; the younger deposits of till, the kames, eskers, and erratics of Britain ; and the equivalent accumulations of northern America have apparently no representatives in Siberia.† Consequently we find the great river-deposits with their mammalian remains, which tell of a milder climate than now obtains in those high latitudes, still lying undisturbed at the surface.‡

We must now take a rapid glance at the distribution of mammalian remains in North America.

In the regions lying to the west of the Rocky Mountains (Alaska), we have a continuation of the same physical conditions that characterize the more northerly latitudes of Asia, namely, great plains intersected by large rivers. Along the banks of these rivers, north of Mount St. Elias, numerous mammalian remains (especially the mammoth) have been detected. In Kotzebue Sound, Captain Beechey found that the wasting of the frozen cliffs was continually exposing the bones and tusks of mammoths and other quadrupeds—among which were urus, reindeer, musk-ox, a large deer (perhaps the moose), and others. But in the northern latitudes east of the Rocky Mountains, no such mammalian remains have been detected. According to Sir J. Richardson, "none have hitherto been found in Rupert's Land, though the annual waste of the banks of the large rivers and the frequent landslips would have revealed them to the natives or fur-traders

---

* Schrenck's *Reise durch die Tundren der Samojeden*, Theil i. p. 271. Some good descriptions of tundra landscapes will be found in G. Kennan's *Tent Life in Siberia*.

† Mr. T. Belt has proposed an explanation of the great plains of Siberia similar to that suggested by my brother in reference to the loess of Europe. He thinks that the rivers flowing north were dammed back by an ice-sheet extending from the polar regions, and that thus an immense sea of fresh water was formed in which the silt and sand of the tundras were accumulated. It seems to me, however, that great inundations caused by the floods of the ice period would account for all the phenomena fully better—more especially for the entombment of the mammalian remains.

‡ It is by no means improbable that the mammoth and woolly rhinoceros may have survived in northern Asia down to a comparatively recent date.

had they existed even in small numbers.   They are rare also,
or altogether wanting, in Canada."*

Nevertheless, proofs are not wanting of a former mild condition of things having prevailed within comparatively recent
times in the far north of British America.   Sir Edward
Belcher brought away from the dreary shores of Wellington
Channel (lat. 75° 32′ N.) portions of a tree which there can
be no doubt whatever had actually grown where he found it.
The spot where it was found lay about a mile and a half
inland.   I give the account in Sir Edward's own words.   He
says : "I at once perceived that it was no spar, and not
placed there by human agency : it was the trunk and root of
a tree, which had apparently grown there and flourished, but
at what date who will venture to say ?   It is, indeed, one of
the questions involved in the change of this climate.   As the
men proceeded with the removal of the frozen clay surrounding the roots, which were completely cemented, as it were,
into the frozen mass, breaking off short like earthenware,
they gradually developed the roots, as well as what appeared
to be portions of leaves and other parts of the tree, which
had become embedded where they fell, and now were barely
distinguishable—at least, not so much as some impressions
on coal—to the casual observer. . . . When a warmer climate
prevailed here, this tree possibly put forth its leaves and
afforded shade from the sun : most fervently did I just now
wish for its return. . . . Two neighbouring mounds were
also dug into, but they proved to be peat—doubtless other
stumps and vegetable matter, the only remaining traces of
what might at some distant period have been a forest.   All
the surrounding earth and tufts of grass indicated this spot
to have been the bottom of some lake or marsh."†   Dr.
Hooker, who carefully examined the piece of wood brought
by Sir Edward, pronounced it to belong to a species of pine,
probably to *Pinus* (*Abies*) *alba*, the most northern conifer,
which advances as far north as the sixty-eighth parallel.
The structure of the wood was found to differ remarkably in
its anatomical characters from that of any other conifer with
which Dr. Hooker was acquainted, and the peculiar conditions

* *Journal of a Boat Voyage through Rupert's Land*, vol. ii. p. 210.
† *The Last of the Arctic Voyages*, vol. i. p. 380.

of an arctic climate seemed to him to afford an adequate explanation of the appearances presented.*

With the exception of this discovery of Sir Edward Belcher's, and possibly also of those mentioned in the note below, we have no direct evidence which seems to prove that any milder climate than the present has prevailed in British America since glacial times.† The whole surface of the country, from the shores of the Arctic Ocean down to the latitudes of the great lakes, and even considerably farther south, is more or less abundantly sprinkled with drift deposits—with till, and heaps and hummocks of sand and gravel, and numerous erratics. Yet nowhere over this wide area, down to the borders of the United States, do the extinct mammalia appear in any postglacial deposits. In the neighbourhood of the great lakes they occur in fresh-water clays, along with abundant vegetable remains, and these clays are clearly overlaid by glacial deposits. It is only when the southern limits of the northern drift are approached, that the extinct mammalia begin to be found in any numbers at the very surface ; and their remains occur in greatest profusion in the regions which have not been reached by the drift of the last cold period. In proof of this I need only remind the reader of the account which has already been given of the "forest-bed" of the North-western States, and

* *Op. cit.* p. 381; *British Association Report* for 1855, p. 101. Captain McClure discovered in Banks's Land, in lat. 74° 48', many fossil-trees, as well as fragments not fossilised, lying over a wide extent of ground (*Discovery of a North-West Passage*, p. 208). Again, trunks of trees, which had evidently grown *in situ*, were detected in Prince Patrick's Island, in lat. 76° 12' N. long. 122° W., by Lieutenant Mecham. Two of these measured respectively 4 ft. in circumference, and a third 2 ft. 10 in. ; one of the former reached 30 ft. in length. Unfortunately the species was not determined, but according to the ship carpenter it resembled larch. "When comparatively dry, it was tried as fuel, but its virtue had gone; it threw out little or no flame, but smouldered rather than burnt, like so much tinder" (*Voyage of H.M.S. Resolute*, McDougall, pp. 292, 293). It is highly probable that all these trees belong to the same period as the pine described by Sir Edward Belcher, but without a geological examination of the ground it would be hazardous at once to conclude that they do. The remains of trees, &c., of Miocene age occur so plentifully within the Arctic Circle, that it is just possible that the trees discovered by McClure and Lieutenant Mecham may be referable to Miocene times.

† I am aware that several arctic explorers are of opinion that the climate of Greenland has altered for the worse within quite recent times. The huts of Esquimaux have been met with in places which are not now visited by the natives. And this, taken in connection with other evidence, points as some think to a somewhat milder climate having prevailed in those regions within even historical times. But the succession of a few unusually mild years would possibly explain all the appearances referred to.

the abundant mammalian remains of the so-called "driftless area" of Iowa, Wisconsin, and Minnesota.

Thus in the western as in the eastern hemisphere, we are confronted with precisely the same phenomena. In districts which give no evidence of submergence during the latest period of glacial cold, and in regions which can be proved never to have been over-ridden by the last great continental glaciers, the extinct mammalia occur in less or greater abundance at the very surface. In Britain and central Europe, the old ossiferous alluvia, when traced from the low grounds to the mountains, disappear as soon as the morainic débris and Alpine diluvium of the last cold period are reached. Nowhere in morainic turbaries or alluvium which can be demonstrated to be of postglacial age, do any of the extinct southern mammalia or palæolithic implements appear. But when the hippopotamus, the elephant, and their congeners do occur, in regions that are covered by the latest glacial deposits, they invariably occupy interglacial or infraglacial positions. The great plains of Siberia never could have nourished glaciers. We cannot conceive that even during the most intense cold of the glacial epoch, conditions similar to those which characterized Britain, Scandinavia, Switzerland, and North America, could have existed in northern Siberia; the absence of high grounds, and the comparative dryness of the climate, must have prevented any accumulation of glacier-ice. If morainic débris, mounds and cones of sand, and large erratics, like those of North America, occurred in Siberia, travellers would hardly have failed to notice them. Nor can I learn that marine deposits similar to our shelly marine clays and associated deposits cover any portion of northern Asia. Siberia would thus appear to have escaped the glacial and marine erosion which overtook certain regions in Europe and North America, and consequently river-deposits belonging to mild interglacial and preglacial ages have been preserved. Hence the great bone accumulations of northern Asia appear only where we might have anticipated they would. It is otherwise, as we have seen, with the corresponding latitudes in British America. Over all that vast region the evidences of glacial action are most conspicuous, and nowhere do the extinct mammalia occur. The trees discovered by Sir E. Belcher and others belong in all probability to the last interglacial period.

The anomalous distribution of the extinct mammalia appears inexplicable on the assumption that the ossiferous beds are all of postglacial age ; but if they belong for the most part to interglacial times, the mode of their occurrence is precisely what might have been expected. It seems, indeed, impossible to resist the conclusion that—at the time palæolithic man and the southern mammalia frequented the lower latitudes of Europe (where their remains occur so abundantly in river-gravels and cave-deposits), and while mammoths, horses, buffaloes, and oxen roamed over northern Siberia—Scotland, Ireland, Denmark, Scandinavia, and other regions of northern Europe also supported an abundant mammalian fauna, and that the mastodon and its congeners likewise occupied what are now the wooded regions and barrens of North America. And the remains of these creatures seldom or never occur in the regions referred to, because the deposits which once contained them have either been obliterated by the action of ice and the sea, or lie concealed below drift accumulations that gathered above them in the last cold period of the glacial epoch.

CHAPTER XLII.

CONCLUSION.

SO many diverse threads of evidence have now been followed, that it may be well rapidly to catch these up, and so weave them into one connected whole. Hitherto we have followed the analytical method, we must now in conclusion pursue the synthetical, and endeavour to build up the story of that chequered past, whose records we have just been perusing.

Upwards of 200,000 years ago the earth, as we know from the calculations of astronomers, was so placed in regard to the sun that a series of physical changes was induced, which eventually resulted in conferring upon our hemisphere a most intensely severe climate. All northern Europe and northern America disappeared beneath a thick crust of ice and snow, and the glaciers of such regions as Switzerland assumed gigantic proportions. This great sheet of land-ice levelled up the valleys of Britain, and stretched across our mountains and hills down to low latitudes in England. Being only one connected or confluent series of mighty glaciers, the ice crept ever downwards and outwards from the mountains, following the direction of the principal valleys, and pushing far out to sea, where it terminated at last in deep water, many miles away from what now forms the coast-line of our country. This sea of ice was of such extent that the glaciers of Scandinavia coalesced with those of Scotland, and the north-eastern districts of England, upon what is now the floor of the shallow North Sea, while a mighty stream of ice flowing outwards from the western seaboard obliterated the Hebrides, and sent its icebergs adrift in the deep waters of the Atlantic. In like manner massive glaciers, born in the Welsh and Cumbrian mountains, swept over the low grounds of England, and united with the Scotch and Irish ice upon the bottom of the Irish sea. At the same period the Scandinavian mountains shed vast icebergs into the northern ocean, and sent southward a sheet of ice that not only filled up the basin of the Baltic but overflowed Finland, and advanced upon the plains of northern Germany ; while from every mountain-region in Europe great glaciers descended, sometimes for almost inconceivable distances, into the low countries beyond.

Ere long this wonderful scene of arctic sterility passed away. Gradually the snow and ice melted and drew back to the mountains, and plants and animals appeared as the climate ameliorated. The mammoth and the woolly-coated rhinoceros roamed in our valleys, the great bear haunted our caves, and pine-trees grew in the south of England ; but the seasons were still well marked. In winter-time frost often covered the rivers with a thick coat of ice, which the summer again tore away, when the rivers, swollen with the tribute of such receding glaciers as still lingered in our deeper glens, rushed along the valleys and spread devastation far and wide. By slow degrees, however, the cold of winter abated, while the heat of summer increased. As the warmth of summer waxed, the arctic mammalia gradually disappeared from our valleys, and sought out northern and more congenial homes. Step by step the climate continued to grow milder, and the difference between the seasons to be less distinctly marked, until eventually something like perpetual summer reigned in Britain. Then it was that the hippopotamus wallowed in our rivers, and the elephant crashed through our forests ; then, too, the lion, the tiger, and the hyæna became denizens of the English caves.

Such scenes as these continued for a long time ; but again the climate began to change. The summers grew less genial, the winters more severe. Gradually the southern mammalia disappeared, and were succeeded by arctic animals. Even these, however, as the temperature became too severe, migrated southward, until all life deserted Britain, and snow and ice were left in undisputed possession. Once more the confluent glaciers overflowed the land, and desolation and sterility were everywhere.

During these oscillations of climate there would seem to have been not infrequent mutations of land and sea, but such vicissitudes, although doubtless producing local effects, certainly do not seem to have been the causes of the chief climatic changes. It is much more likely that the mild interglacial periods were induced by eccentricity of the earth's orbit, combined with precession of the equinoxes.

We cannot yet say how often such alternations of cold and warm periods were repeated; nor can we be sure that palæolithic man lived in Britain during the earlier warm intervals of the glacial epoch. But since his implements are met with at the bottom of the very oldest palæolithic deposits, and since we know that the animals with which he was certainly contemporaneous did occupy Britain in early interglacial ages, and even in times anterior to the glacial epoch itself, it is in the highest degree likely that man arrived here as early at least as the mammoth and the hippopotamus.

Be this, however, as it may, the evidence appears to be decisive as to the presence of man in Britain during the last mild interglacial period. And this being so, it is startling to recall in imagination those grand geological revolutions of which he must have been a witness.

During the last interglacial period he entered Britain at a time when our country was joined to Europe across the bed of the German Ocean; at a time when the winters were still severe enough to freeze over the rivers in the south of England; at a time when glaciers nestled in our upland- and mountain-valleys, and the arctic mammalia occupied the land. He lived here long enough to witness a complete change of climate—to see the arctic mammalia vanish from England, and the hippopotamus and its congeners take their place. At a later date, and while a mild and genial climate still continued, he beheld the sea slowly gain upon the land, until little by little, step by step, a large portion of our country was submerged—a submergence which, as we know, reached in Wales to the extent of some 1,300 ft. or thereabout.

Once more, however, the land re-emerged, and glaciers yet again thickened in our mountain-valleys, and advanced to coalesce upon the low grounds. Gradually the confluent ice-streams continued to increase, until eventually the British and Scandinavian *mers de glace* became confluent for the last time. All Scotland, save the higher mountain-tops, lay buried, and one and the same overwhelming mantle of ice wrapped the northern part of England, Wales, and Ireland in its folds. The sea between Scotland and the Hebrides was filled up, the Irish Sea was in like manner obliterated, while the united Scandinavian and British *mer de glace* flowed south in our island as far as middle Lincolnshire at least, and perhaps to a yet more southerly latitude in Germany. It is not improbable, indeed, that at this time a considerable part of the low grounds of northern Prussia were covered by the sea, and that ice-rafts and bergs floated over the drowned districts; while we know that in Switzerland the Alpine glaciers crept out upon the low grounds and overwhelmed the forest-lands of Zurich and Constance.

A similar succession of changes characterized North America. After a great continental ice-sheet had retired, wide inland seas of fresh water appeared, and a luxuriant forest-growth overspread the land, which became the resort of a prolific mammalian fauna—mastodons, elephants, buffaloes, peccaries, and other animals. By-and-by, however, the last cold period ensued, and another great ice-sheet streamed over the continent, ploughing up the old forest-land, or burying it under heaps of rubbish and erratic blocks.

During this latest cold period of the glacial epoch, palæolithic man, for aught that we can say, may have occupied the south of Europe; but it is in the highest degree unlikely that he lived so far north as the unsubmerged and non-glaciated areas of southern England.

Another great change now ensued. The climate again became less arctic, and great floods descending from the melting ice spread devastation far and wide over the low grounds to which the ice itself had not extended. Step by step the glaciers retired, and were followed by the sea, until the area of land was reduced to somewhat less than its present dimensions. Eventually the ice retired to the deep mountain dales and glens, and then Britain for the last time became continental. The treeless land was now invaded by the reindeer, the moose-deer, the arctic fox, the lemming, and the marmot, and neolithic man likewise entered upon the scene : his palæolithic predecessor had, as far as Britain and northern Europe are concerned, vanished for ever.

Thus the palæolithic and neolithic ages are separated by a vast lapse of time—by a time sufficient for the submergence and re-elevation of a large part of our country, and the slow growth and decay of a great ice-sheet.

In early neolithic times the climate was somewhat excessive, but as ages passed away it gradually became ameliorated. A strong forest-growth by-and-by covered the country, and herds of oxen wandered in its grassy glades ; but the southern mammalia never returned to their old haunts, and it is even doubtful whether the mammoth and the woolly rhinoceros again appeared in Britain. They seem, however, to have still lingered on for a time in central Europe.

As years rolled on the sea again stole in between our islands and the Continent, until a final severance was effected. It is beyond my purpose, however, to trace the later changes. From early neolithic times a gradual improvement and progress attended the efforts of our barbaric predecessors, until at length a period arrived when men began to abandon the use of stone implements and weapons, and for these to substitute bronze. And so, passing on through the age of bronze and the days of the builders of Stonehenge, we are at last brought face to face with the age of iron and the dawn of history.

[POSTSCRIPT.—While these pages are passing through the press, my friend Mr. Skertchly writes me to say that he has just made a very notable discovery. This is no less than the occurrence, near Brandon, of brick-earth, containing " bones, shells, and human implements," which is clearly overlaid by a mass of true chalky boulder-clay. It is difficult to overestimate the importance of this discovery. Amongst other points, for which I have contended above and which are now demonstrated by Mr. Skertchly's "find," is this, that man was an occupant of British soil as early at least as that interglacial period which preceded the climax of glacial cold, and the deposition of the great chalky boulder-clay of East Anglia.] .

APPENDIX.

NOTE A.

Table of British Sedimentary Strata.

POST-TERTIARY	PLEISTOCENE* or QUATERNARY	Recent and prehistoric.
		Postglacial.
		Late glacial.
		Middle glacial.
		Early glacial.
		Preglacial.
TERTIARY OR **CAINOZOIC**	PLIOCENE*	Crag.
	MIOCENE*	Bovey beds, Mull leaf-beds, &c.
	EOCENE*	Hempstead beds.
		Bembridge beds.
		Osborne beds.
		Headon beds.
		Bagshot beds.
		London tertiaries.
SECONDARY OR **MESOZOIC**	CRETACEOUS* ..	Chalk and upper greensand.
		Lower greensand, or upper Neocomian.
		Wealden clay and Hastings sand.
	JURASSIC*	Purbeck.
		Portland (includes Kimeridge clay).
		Coralline oolite (with coral rag).
		Oxford clay.
		Forest marble.
		Great oolite.
		Fuller's earth.
		Inferior oolite.
		Upper lias.
		Middle lias.
		Lower lias.
	TRIASSIC* or NEW RED SANDSTONE	Rhætic or Penarth beds.
		Keuper.
		Dolomitic conglomerate.
		Bunter.
PRIMARY OR	PERMIAN*	Magnesian limestone.
		Rothliegende.
	CARBONIFEROUS*	Coal-measures.
		Carboniferous limestone.
		Lower limestone shale and calciferous sandstone series.
	DEVONIAN and OLD RED SANDSTONE*	Devonian beds and old red sandstone.

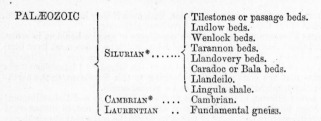

PALÆOZOIC

SILURIAN* ...... {
Tilestones or passage beds.
Ludlow beds.
Wenlock beds.
Tarannon beds.
Llandovery beds.
Caradoc or Bala beds.
Llandeilo.
Lingula shale.
}

CAMBRIAN* .... Cambrian.

LAURENTIAN .. Fundamental gneiss.

THE Formations marked with an asterisk have all been considered to yield evidence, more or less satisfactory, of the former action of ice. But in some cases the proofs are hardly convincing. It must be remembered that the records of mild and genial climates are more likely to be preserved than are traces of cold and glacial conditions. The former will usually be represented by abundantly fossiliferous marine and fresh-water deposits. In the case of the latter, a few ice-floated stones and boulders are all the relics that are likely to be handed down. The ice-markings on the rocks, and the morainic accumulations of mountain-valley and lowland, are almost certain sooner or later to be obliterated. Take, for example, the Glacial or Drift Formation of Quaternary times. Even now, the action of the weather, of frost, and rain, and rivers, is slowly but surely effacing the marks left by the old glaciers. In the midland and southern districts of England, as I have shown in the text (see p. 385), so long a period has elasped since the period of greatest glaciation that all superficial ice-markings have been obliterated, and we only know that these regions were once covered by glaciers from the presence of boulder-clay and erratics. Should our islands eventually become submerged, it might well be that, as the land sank down, what the atmospheric forces had failed to obliterate would succumb to the action of the sea. Should the land be afterwards re-elevated, it is very doubtful indeed if a single recognisable trace of former glacial work would remain. The farther back we go in time, therefore, the more difficult must it become to detect evidence of ice-action. The older formations consist for the most part of deposits which gathered on the floors of ancient oceans. Very few land-surfaces have been preserved. Consequently, if we are to find in the older formations any traces of former glacial cold, it will consist for the most part of scattered stones and boulders embedded in the heart of oceanic accumulations. Nevertheless, there are not wanting, even in some of the palæozoic formations, deposits which bear the strongest resemblance to morainic débris. Of course, when we are dealing with formations so far removed from us in time, and in which the animal and plant remains depart so widely from existing forms of life, we can hardly expect to derive much aid from the fossils in our attempts to detect traces of cold climatic conditions. The arctic shells in our post-tertiary clays are convincing proofs of the former existence in our latitude of a severe climate; but when we go so far back as palæozoic ages, we have no such clear evidence to guide us. All that palæontologists can say regarding the fossils belonging to these old times is simply this, that they seem to indicate, generally speaking, mild, temperate, or genial, and even sometimes tropical, conditions of climate. Many of the fossils, indeed, if we are to reason from analogy at all, could not possibly have lived in cold seas. But, for aught that we know, there may have been alternations of climate during the deposition of each particular formation; and these changes may be marked by the presence or absence, or by the greater or less abundant development of certain organisms at various horizons in the strata. Notwithstanding all that has been done, our knowledge of the natural history of these ancient seas is still very imperfect; and therefore, in the present state of our information, we are not entitled to argue, from the general aspect of the fossils in our older formations, that the temperature of the ancient seas was never other than mild and genial.

It is beyond my purpose in this Note to do more than jot down a few instances of what have been considered as indications of former ice-action.

The oldest, or Laurentian, formation consists of rocks which have been so highly altered from their original condition, that, even if they had ever contained any evidence of old ice-action, it must have been obliterated.

Mr. James Thomson has described the occurrence of granite boulders in schist of supposed Cambrian age, in the island of Islay, which he infers must have been transported by ice. The beds in which the boulders lie show very little trace of stratification, and no granite occurs *in situ* in the island.[*] I have sometimes thought also that the conglomerates belonging to this formation, in the north-west of Scotland, might possibly have had a glacial origin.

In the Lower Silurian of the south of Scotland (Glen App and Dalmellington) we find large blocks and boulders (from one foot to five feet in diameter) of gneiss, syenite, granite, &c., none of which belong to the rocks of that neighbourhood. Indeed, no such rocks, of older age than the Silurian, occur nearer than the Laurentian rocks of the north-western Highlands and islands. Possibly the boulders may have come from some ancient Atlantis; and, considering the great size of the blocks, and the considerable distance they may have travelled, it is not unreasonable to conjecture that ice may have had something to do with their transport. No ice-markings, however, have been observed upon any of the stones; nor, when we reflect upon the vast age of this deposit, could these be expected to have resisted the long-continued action of percolating water.[†] Similar boulder-beds have been found in Ireland. Professor Dawson records a somewhat similar instance in the Lower Silurian of Maimanse, Lake Superior, where a conglomerate occurs with boulders two feet in diameter. Again, in the Upper Silurian of Nova Scotia, the same author has detected beds of angular stones and chips, "the materials of which seem precisely similar to that which is at present produced by the disintegrating action of frost on hard, and especially schistose and jointed rocks."[‡]

The conglomerates belonging to the Old Red Sandstone formation in the north of England and in Scotland have appeared to several competent observers closely to resemble a consolidated boulder-drift. Among other instances, mention may be made of the conglomerates of Kirkby Lonsdale and Sedburgh.[§] My colleague, Mr. R. Etheridge, jun., informs me that in certain localities in Victoria, Australia, he and his colleagues observed a conglomerate which in some places reached at least one hundred feet in thickness, and which Mr. Selwyn was inclined to regard as probably of glacial origin. The latter author says: "The character of the conglomerate beds is such as almost to preclude the supposition of their being due to purely aqueous transport and deposition. It is, however, very suggestive of the results likely to be produced by marine glacial transport; and the mixture of coarse and fine, angular and water-worn material, much of which has clearly been derived from distant sources, would also favour this supposition."[∥] The deposit occurs, Mr. Etheridge informs me, at many localities throughout the colony, with a slightly varying matrix. Grooved and scratched stones have not been observed, but from similar deposits on the [Lerderderg River, Victoria, Mr. Daintree obtained a few grooved stones.[¶] Mr. Selwyn classed the deposit provisionally as Devonian. Great beds of conglomerate occur at the base of the Carboniferous, in various parts of Scotland, which it is difficult to believe are other than ancient morainic débris. They are frequently quite unstratified, and the stones often show that peculiar blunted form which is so characteristic of glacial work. These are confusedly huddled together in a dull, tough arenaceous matrix; and the whole deposit will sometimes continue to exhibit these appearances over a wide area. Ever and anon, however, we detect traces of water-action; the stones become more rounded, and are spread out in more or less regular layers or beds. The coarse, unstratified portions so closely resemble till, that only a practised eye can distinguish the difference at a glance; and many geologists who had not previously tried their hammers on the deposit, might well mistake it for a post-tertiary glacial accumulation. It is typically developed in the Lammermuir Hills district, and appears also in Ayrshire, Arran,

---

[*] *British Association Reports*, 1870, p. 88.
[†] *Explanation of Sheet 7, Ayrshire* (Geological Survey of Scotland), p. 8.
[‡] *Canadian Naturalist*, vol. ii. p. 6; and vol. vi. p. 416.
[§] *The Reader* for August 12, 1865; *History of the Isle of Man* (Cumming), p. 86; *Trans. Geol. Soc. Edin.*, vol. ii. part 3.
[∥] *Physical Geology and Geography of Victoria*, p. 16.
[¶] *Report on the Geology of the District of Ballan, Victoria*, 1866, p. 11.

and other regions in the west of Scotland. Amongst these conglomerates my brother has noticed many striated stones. Erratic blocks have occurred in certain French Carboniferous strata, and Mr. Godwin-Austen has attributed the transport of these to floating ice.* In North America the Carboniferous deposits appear also to have yielded what seems to be evidence in the same direction. Thus, in Ohio for example, a boulder of quartzite, 17 in. by 12 in. in diameter, was found embedded in a seam of coal and overlying shale ; and Professor Newberry has suggested† that it may have been transported by ice down some ancient Carboniferous river, and so dropt into its present position, where eventually the sediment covered it up. Similar boulders in coal have been met with elsewhere in America. Professor Dawson‡ also mentions the occurrence, in the Lower Carboniferous of Nova Scotia, of angular fragments and chips of various hard rocks cemented together, which he thinks may fairly be regarded as evidence of somewhat intense winter cold, in the same way as the angular débris detected by him in the Upper Silurian of Nova Scotia. But he cites a still more remarkable example from the coal formation of that colony. This he describes as a gigantic esker of Carboniferous age, "on the outside of which large travelled boulders were deposited, probably by drift-ice ; while, in the swamps within, the coal-flora flourished, and fine mud and coaly matter were accumulated." At the meeting of the British Association at Bradford (September, 1873), Mr. Blandford described what he took to be evidence of ice-action in certain Carboniferous deposits in India.

Professor Ramsay has given a detailed account§ of the occurrence, in Permian conglomerate, of blunted and well-scratched stones, which seems conclusively to prove the existence of glaciers and icebergs in England at some time during that far-distant age. The same author has further suggested that similar accumulations in Germany, belonging to the Permian, betray like traces of old ice-action. Professor Hull has also noticed traces of ice-action in deposits of the same age in Ireland.‖ A boulder deposit, supposed to be of Permian or Jurassic age, occurs extensively in Natal. It contains huge erratics, some of which have been transported sixty or eighty miles from their parent rocks, and rest upon a smoothed and grooved surface of sandstone.¶

The New Red Sandstone (Triassic) of Devonshire has yielded scattered blocks or erratics, which Mr. Godwin-Austen was the first to attribute to the action of floating ice. Mr. Pengelly, however, thinks that the blocks need not have travelled far, but might have been moved along an ancient shore-line by breakers.

In the north of Scotland, a coarse boulder conglomerate is associated with the Jurassic strata in the east of Sutherland, the possibly glacial origin of which long ago suggested itself to Professor Ramsay** and other observers. Recently, Mr. Judd has come to the conclusion that the boulders were floated down by ice from the highland mountains at the time the Jurassic strata were accumulating.††

The Cretaceous formation has likewise yielded what Mr. Godwin-Asten has suggested‡‡ are ice-borne stones and boulders. These erratics have been detected not only in the chalk of England, but also in the Cretaceous strata of the Alps. It is possible, however, that some of these may have been carried seawards, attached to the roots of drifted trees ; and others, again, may have been floated away by some of the larger sea-weeds. But according to Mr. Godwin-Austen, with whom Sir C. Lyell agrees, only coast-ice could have transported the blocks and stones got in the white chalk near Croydon.

In the Eocene strata of Switzerland erratics have been met with, some of them angular and others rounded. They often attain a large size ; blocks 10 feet long being not uncommon, and one even measured 105 ft. in length, 90 ft. in breadth, and 45 ft. in height. Some of the blocks consist of a kind of granite, which is not known to occur anywhere in the Alps.§§

* *Quart. Jour. Geol. Soc.*, vol. xii. p. 58.   † *Report Geol. Surv. of Ohio*, 1870.
‡ *Acadian Geology*, p. 324; *American Naturalist*, vol. vi. p. 416.
§ *Quart. Jour. Geol. Soc.*, vol. xi. p. 197 ; *Philosophical Magazine*, vol. xxix. p. 290.
‖ *Explanation of Sheet* 47 (Geol. Surv. of Ireland).
¶ *Quart. Jour. Geol. Soc.*, vol. xxvi. p. 514 ; xxvii. p. 544.
** *Phil. Mag.*, vol. xxix. p. 290.   †† *Quart. Jour. Geol. Soc.*, vol. xxix. p. 195.
‡‡ *Quart. Jour. Geol. Soc.*, vol. xiv. p. 262 ; xvi. p. 327 ; *Geologist*, 1860, p. 38; *Brit. Assoc. Rep.*, 1857, p. 62.
§§ *Petrifakten und erratische Jurablöcke im Flysch* (Bachmann).

The Miocene of the Moncalieri-Valenza hills, in the north of Italy, has been shown by Professor Gastaldi to contain enormous blocks of Alpine rocks, which require us to call in the agency of floating ice to account for their presence.*

The Quarternary embraces, of course, the glacial and associated deposits which form the subject of this volume.

Now, if we were to judge only from the general aspect presented by their organic contents, we should be forced to admit that none of these formations, from the Silurian down to the Miocene, afforded any trace whatever of cold or glacial conditions. Yet that very cold conditions did supervene during the continuance of some of these formations, seems indisputable. Geologists are staggered by the appearance of glacial deposits in the Permian—a formation whose fossils indicate mild and genial rather than cold climatic conditions. The occurrence in the Eocene, also, of huge ice-carried blocks seems incomprehensible, when the general character of the Eocene fossils is taken into account, for these have a somewhat tropical aspect. So likewise the appearance of ice-transported blocks in the Miocene is a sore puzzle. The fossils embedded in this formation speak to us of tropical and sub-tropical climates having prevailed in Central Europe; nay, more, Miocene deposits have been detected in high arctic latitudes. Species of sequoia, coniferæ, poplar, willow, beech, oak, plane-tree, walnut, plum or prunus, buckthorn, Andromeda, Daphnogene, and several other evergreens, grew during Miocene times in North Greenland! Even in Spitzbergen, abundant traces of the same kind of vegetation have been preserved. Yet it was precisely during the continuance of this period or age that the great erratics were carried down from the Alps, and dropped on what was then the sea-bottom in the North of Italy. These apparently contradictory appearances may, however, be satisfactorily accounted for by inferring a former alternation of cold and warm climates, like that which I have tried to show prevailed during Quaternary times. It is singular, to say the least of it, that the beds which contain those great erratics (Eocene and Miocene) are wonderfully barren of fossils; and there is nothing, therefore, in the palæontological evidence that need cause us to hesitate in attributing the presence of the large erratics in the Eocene and Miocene to former severe conditions of climate. Indeed, the very fact that evergreens found during Miocene times a congenial habitat in North Greenland and Spitzbergen shows, on the principles explained in Chapters viii., ix., and x., that the eccentricity of the earth's orbit had then attained a high value, and that a series of genial and glacial climates must consequently have alternated in our hemisphere at that time. For the same reason, I see nothing contradictory in concluding, with Professor Ramsay, that glaciers existed in England during the Permian period, even although the plants and shells, &c., usually met with in Permian strata seem to indicate mild climatic conditions. The more characteristic Permian conglomerates are unfossiliferous; so also are those coarse boulder-beds belonging to the Carboniferous, the Old Red Sandstone, and the Lower Silurian. It might quite well be that during the continuance of each and all of those periods cold and mild climates alternated. Silurian, Carboniferous, Permian, Oolitic, and Cretaceous fossils are obtained in high arctic latitudes, and we should not therefore feel surprised if those formations in our own or analogous latitudes should occasionally exhibit traces of severe climatic conditions.

[In addition to the papers, &c., referred to in the footnotes, the reader should consult also Lyell's " Principles of Geology," vol. i. chap. x. and xi. ; and Dr. Croll's " Climate and Time," chap. xviii., in which he will find a fuller digest of the evidence bearing on former glacial epochs than I have been able to make room for.]

---

* *Sugli Elementi che compongono i Conglomerati Miocent del Piemonte* (B. Gastaldi).

NOTE C.

List of the Fossil Organic Remains of the Glacial Deposits of Scotland.

(By Robert Etheridge, Jun., F.G.S.)

THE succeeding list of fossils of the glacial deposits of Scotland has been prepared with a view of demonstrating how far such deposits have proved fossiliferous.

The list does not pretend to be other than it is : a compilation from the published results of those workers who have devoted much time and energy to the elucidation of the subject, a list of whose papers and publications is appended.

The present compilation does not, perhaps, contain every species recorded from the glacial deposits of Scotland ; it is hardly possible indeed that it could, for, notwithstanding the great strides made of late towards the reconciliation of the various names used by some of the earlier writers, yet so much doubt exists regarding the correctness of some of their determinations, that it is almost impossible to avoid here and there, either on the one hand an omission, or, on the other, a recapitulation, under a different designation, of a previously expressed species.

It was at first contemplated to arrange the species under the various divisions of Till, Boulder-clay, brick-clays, &c., but for reasons similar to those just expressed in regard to species this idea was abandoned, and the present general arrangement substituted.

The first column of the list is devoted to the name of the genus and species ; the second to the principal localities at which each species has been found, together with a few of the better synonyms.

The terminology of the Mollusca followed is that of Jeffreys' "British Conchology."

Succeeding the list of fossils will be found a few short notes bearing on the principal localities, with the conditions under which the organic remains were found.

List of papers and publications consulted in the compilation of the succeeding list :—

1839. Smith, J. On the Last Changes in the relative Levels of Land and Sea in the British Islands. *Mems. Wern. Nat. Hist. Soc.*, vol. viii. part 1. pp. 49—107.

1841. Landsborough, Rev. D. Description of a Newer Pliocene Deposit at Stevenston. *Proc. Geol. Soc.*, vol. iii. p. 444.

1846. Forbes, E. The Fauna and Flora of the British Islands, &c. *Mem. Geol. Surv.*, vol. i. pp. 406—432.

1850. Cleghorn, J., & J. Smith. On the Till near Wick, in Caithness. *Quart. Jour. Geol. Soc.*, vol. vi. p. 385.

1853. Forbes and Hanley. A History of British Mollusca. 4 vols., 8vo. London, 1853.

1857. Smith, J. A. Horns of *Cervus tarandus* in Dumbartonshire. *Proc. R. Phys. Soc. Edin.*, vol. i. p. 247.

1858. Jamieson, T. F. On the Pleistocene Deposits of Aberdeenshire *Quart. Jour. Geol. Soc.*, vol. xiv. p. 509.

1862. Smith, J. Researches in Newer Pliocene and Post Tertiary Geology. Glasgow, 1862, 8vo.

1863. Jeffreys, J. Gwyn. Notice of an Ancient Sea-Bed and Beach near Fort William, Invernesshire. *Brit. Assoc. Report*, 1862, t. s. p. 73.

Geikie, A. The Glacial Drift of Scotland. *Trans. Geol. Soc. Glas.*, vol. i. Appendix.

Allman, Prof. On a New Fossil Ophiuridan, from Post-Pliocene Strata of the Valley of the Forth. *Proc. R. Soc. Edin.*, vol. v. p. 101.

Walker, R. On the Skeleton of a Seal (*Phoca Grœnlandica ?*) and the Cranium of a Duck from the Pliocene Beds of Fifeshire. *Annals & Mag. Nat. Hist.*, vol. xii. p. 382.

1864. Walker, R. On Clays containing Fossils near St. Andrews ; with Remarks on some of the latter. *Annals & Mag. Nat. Hist.* vol. xiv. p. 200.

Watson, Rev. J. Boog. On the Great Drift Beds with Shells in the South of Arran. *Trans. R. Soc. Edin.*, vol. xxiii. pp. 523—546.

1866. Haswell, J. Glacial Clay at Cornton, near Bridge of Allan. *Geol. Mag.*, vol. ii. p. 182.

Bryce, J. Order of Succession of the Drift Beds in Arran. *Quart. Jour. Geol. Soc.*, xxi. pp. 204—213.

Crosskey, Rev. H. W. On the *Tellina calcarea* bed at Chapelhall, near Airdrie. *Quart. Jour. Geol. Soc.*, vol. xxi. p. 219.

Jamieson, T. F. History of the last Geological Changes in Scotland. *Quart. Jour. Geol. Soc.*, vol. xxi. pp. 161—203.

Brown, Rev. T. Glacial Beds at Elie, Fifeshire. *Trans. R. Soc. Edin.*, vol. xxiv. p. 617.

1867. Crosskey, Rev. H. W. Fossils Collected at Windmillcroft. *Trans. Geol. Soc. Glas.*, vol. iii. p. 115.

Bennie, J. *Bos longifrons* and *B. primigenius*, in the Ancient Drift of the Clyde. *Trans. Geol. Soc. Glas.*, vol. ii. p. 152.

Crosskey, Rev. H. W. and D. Robertson. The Post-Tertiary Fossiliferous Beds of Scotland. *Trans. Geol. Soc. Glas.*, vol. ii. (Introduction; Dalmuir), pp. 267—282.

Peach, C. W. Fossils of the Boulder-clay of Caithness. *Proc. R. Phys. Soc. Edin.*, vol. iii. pp. 38 and 396.

1868. Howden, J. C. Superficial Deposits of the South Esk. *Trans. Geol. Soc. Edin.*, vol. i. p. 141.

Geikie, J. Discovery of *Bos primigenius* in the Lower Boulder-clay. *Geol. Mag.*, vol. v. p. 393.

Woodward, S. P. Manual of Mollusca. 2nd Edition. London. 1868.

1869. Mahony, J. A. Organic Remains found in Clay near Crofthead, Renfrewshire. *Geol. Mag.*, vol. vi. pp. 390—393.

Dawkins, W. B. Distribution of the British Post-Glacial Mammalia. *Quart. Jour. Geol. Soc.*, vol. xxv. p. 192.

Turner, Prof. On the Bones of a Seal found in Red Clay near Grangemouth. *Proc. R. Soc. Edin.*, 1869—70, p. 105.

Norman, Rev. A. M. Shetland Final Dredging Report, part ii. On the Crustacea, Tunicata, Polyzoa, Echinodermata, Actinozoa, Hydrozoa, and Porifera. *Brit. Assoc. Report*, 1868, pp. 247—336.

1870. Coutts, J. On the Post-Tertiary Clay-beds at Kilchattan Bay, Isle of Bute. 8vo., Glasgow. (A paper read before the *Nat. Hist. Soc. Glas.*)

1871. Crosskey, Rev. H. W., and D. Robertson. On the Post-Tertiary Fossiliferous Beds of Scotland—*Trans. Geol. Soc. Glas.*, vol. iii. Cumbrae College; Loch Gilp; Caithness; Lucknow Pit;—pp. 113—129. East Tarbert; West Tarbert; Crinan; Duntroon; Old Mains, Renfrew; Paisley—pp. 321—341.

Crosskey, Rev. H. W. On Boulder Clay. *Trans. Geol. Soc., Glas.* vol. iii. p. 149.

Young, J., and R. Craig. On the Occurrence of Seeds of Freshwater Plants and Arctic Shells, &c., in Beds under the Boulder-clay at Kilmaurs. *Trans. Geol. Soc. Glas.*, vol. iii. p. 310.

Craig, R. Section in Cowdon Glen, &c. *Trans. Geol. Soc. Glas.*, vol. iv. p. 17.

Crosskey, Rev. H. W. and D. Robertson. On the Post-Tertiary Fossiliferous Beds of Scotland. *Trans. Geol. Soc. Glas.*, vol. iv. pt. 1. (Garvel Park New Dock, Greenock, pp. 32—45.)

1873. Robertson, D., and Rev. H. W. Crosskey. On the Post-Tertiary Fossiliferous Beds of Scotland. *Trans. Geol. Soc. Glas.*, vol. iv. pt. 2. (Kilchattan Tile-work, Bute; Tangy Glen, near Campbeltown, pp. 128—137.)

Smith, Dr. J. A. Notes on the Ancient Cattle of Scotland. *Proc. Soc. Antiq. Scot.*, vol. ix. pp. 588—674.

1874. Brady, Prof. G. S., Rev. H. W. Crosskey, and D. Robertson. A Monograph of the Post-Tertiary Entomostraca of Scotland, &c. *Pal. Soc.*, pp. v and 232, pls. 16. 4to., London.

Robertson, D., and Rev. H. W. Crosskey. On the Post-Tertiary Fossiliferous Beds of Scotland (Jordanhill Brick-works; Stobcross; Fairfield,

near Govan; Paisley Canal; Dipple Tile-works). *Trans. Geol. Soc.
Glas.*, vol. iv. pt. 3. pp. 241—256.

1875. Jack, R. L. Notes on a Till or Boulder-clay, with Broken Shells in the
Lower Valley of the River Endrick, near Loch Lomond. *Trans. Geol.
Soc. Glas.*, vol. v. pt. 1. pp. 1—25.

Robertson, D., and Rev. H. W. Crosskey. On the Post-Tertiary Fossiliferous Beds of Scotland. (Kyles of Bute.) *Trans. Geol. Soc. Glas.*,
vol. v. pt. 1. pp. 29—35.

The compiler has also to acknowledge very material assistance kindly rendered
by the following gentlemen :—Messrs. Gwyn Jeffreys, F.R.S., David Robertson,
F.G.S., H. B. Brady, F.R.S., James Bennie, C. W. Peach, A.L.S., and R.
Etheridge, F.R.S.

PLANTÆ.

CRYPTOGAMIA.

Thallogens.

Diatomaceæ and Desmidaceæ.

In the Cowdon Glen interglacial beds, Renfrewshire, eighteen genera, comprising thirty-one species, of *Diatomaceæ*, and three genera and species of *Desmi-
daceæ*, have been recorded by Mr. Mahony.[*]

Algales.

Nullipora (Melobesia) poly-morpha. *Linn.*	Caithness, in boulder-clay; Dalmuir; West Tarbert; Paisley; Garvel Park New Dock, Greenock; Houston Clay-field.
Corallina officinalis. *Linn.*	Paisley.
Jania rubens. *Lamx.*	Paisley.

Acrogens.

Musci.

Accompanying the Diatoms of the Cowdon Glen deposit are six genera and
eleven species of Mosses. Further information regarding these will be found in
Mr. Mahony's paper previously cited, and also in another by the same author
" On the Botany of the Windmillcroft Beds."[†]

PHANEROGAMIA.

Exogens.

Amongst various remains of Phanerogamous plants recorded from Scotch
Glacial Deposits the following appear to be the more worthy of notice :—

Corylus Avellana. *Linn.*	Roots and stems in the interglacial beds of Cow-don Glen, Renfrewshire.
,, sp. ind.	In brick-clay at Portobello.
Cratægus Oxycanthus. *Linn.*	Do. Do.
Betula alba. *Linn.*	Interglacial beds of Cowdon Glen.
,, sp. ind.	In brick-clay at Portobello.
Galium palustre. *Linn.*	Interglacial beds of Cowdon Glen.
Hippuris, sp. ind.	Kilmaurs, in an interglacial peaty deposit with the remains of *Elephas primigenius.*
Myriophyllum spicatum. *Linn.*	Interglacial beds of Cowdon Glen.
Pedicularis palustris. *Linn.*	Do. do. do.

[*] *Geo'. Mag.*, vol. v. p. 391.   [†] *Proc. Nat. Hist. Soc. Glasgow*, vol. i. p. 159.

Pinus sylvestris. *Linn.*	Bark in the interglacial beds of Cowdon Glen; brick-clay at Portobello.
Potamogeton lucens. *Linn.*	Interglacial beds of Cowdon Glen.
,, sp. ind.	Seeds at Kilmaurs, in an interglacial peaty deposit with remains of *Elephas primigenius.*
Quercus, sp. ind.	In brick-clay at Portobello.
Ranunculus aquatilis. *Linn.*	Interglacial beds of Cowdon Glen.
Salix alba. *Linn.*	Leaves in the beds of Cowdon Glen.
? Scutellaria galericulata. *Linn.*	Interglacial beds of Cowdon Glen.
Taxus baccata. *Linn.*	In brick-clay at Portobello.
Vaccinum Myrtillus. *Linn.*	Twigs in the Cowdon Glen interglacial beds.

Endogens.

Hordeum distichum.	A cereal, apparently closely allied to this species, was found by Dr. Howden at Montrose, in a bed of peat resting on glacial marine clay beneath estuary beds.*
Scirpus lacustris. *Linn.*	Interglacial beds of Cowdon Glen.

ANIMALIA.

INVERTEBRATA.

Sub-kingdom: PROTOZOA.

Class: Rhizopoda.

Foraminifera.

Genus BILOCULINA. *D'Orbigny.*	
B. elongata. *D'Orb.*	Dalmuir; Tangy Glen, near Campbeltown, in laminated clay overlaid by boulder clay; Kilmaurs; Jordanhill Brick-work.
B. depressa. *D'Orb.*	Lochgilp; Duntroon; Kilchattan Tile-work, Bute; Kyles of Bute; Jordanhill Brick-work.
B. ringens. *Lamk.*	Caithness, in boulder-clay; Lochgilp; Duntroon; Paisley; Garvel Park New Dock, Greenock; Kilchattan Tile-work, Bute; Tangy Glen, near Campbeltown; Paisley Canal.
Genus BOLIVINA. *D'Orb.*	
B. punctata. *D'Orb.*	Duntroon; West Tarbert.
Genus BULIMINA. *D'Orb.*	
B. marginata. *D'Orb.*	Caithness, in boulder clay; Lochgilp; Cumbrae College; Duntroon; East and West Tarbert; Garvel Park New Dock, Greenock; Crinan; Kyles of Bute.
B. pupoides. *D'Orb.*	Duntroon; Garvel Park New Dock, Greenock; Caithness, in boulder clay; Kilchattan Tile-work, Bute.
Genus CASSIDULINA. *D'Orb.*	
C. crassa. *D'Orb.*	Lochgilp; Cumbrae College.
C. lævigata. *D'Orb.*	Caithness, in boulder clay; Lochgilp; Kilchattan Tile-work, Bute; Tangy Glen.

* *Trans. Geol. Soc. Edinburgh*, vol. i. p. 144.

Genus CORNUSPIRA. *Schultze.*
C. foliacea. *Philippi.*
Lochgilp; East Tarbert; Duntroon; Garvel Park New Dock, Greenock; Tangy Glen, near Campbeltown; Annochie, in brick clay.

Genus CRISTELLARIA. *Lamarck.*
C. rotulata. *Lamk.*
Caithness, in boulder clay; Crinan; Garvel Park New Dock, Greenock; Kilchattan Tile-work, Bute; Kyles of Bute.

Genus DENTALINA. *D'Orb.*
D. communis. *D'Orb.*
Caithness, in boulder clay; Cumbrae College; Crinan; Duntroon; Old Mains, Renfrew; Garvel Park New Dock, Greenock; Kilchattan Tile-work, Bute; Kyles of Bute; Lewis, in laminated beds (*R.E.*)

D. guttifera. *D'Orb.*
Duntroon.

Genus DISCORBINA. *Parker & Jones.*
D. globularis. *D'Orb.*
Duntroon; Tangy Glen, near Campbeltown, in laminated clay overlaid by boulder clay; Stobcross; Paisley Canal.

D. rosacea. *D'Orb.*
Caithness, in boulder clay; Lochgilp; Paisley.

Genus GLOBIGERINA. *D'Orb.*
G. bulloides. *D'Orb.*
Caithness, in boulder clay; Lochgilp; Duntroon; Tangy Glen, near Campbeltown, in laminated clay overlaid by boulder clay; ? Loch Lomond beds, in shelly-boulder clay.

Genus LAGENA. *Walker & Jacob.*
L. apiculata. *Reuss.*
Garvel Park New Dock, Greenock.

L. biconica. *Brady, M.S.*
Lochgilp; Duntroon.

L. caudata. *D'Orb.*
West Tarbert.

L. distoma. *P. & J.*
West Tarbert; Crinan; Duntroon; Paisley; Garvel Park New Dock, Greenock; Kilchattan Tile-work Bute; Kyles of Bute.

L. globosa. *Montg.*
Caithness, in boulder clay; Lochgilp; Cumbrae College; East Tarbert; Duntroon; Old Mains, Renfrew; Paisley; Garvel Park New Dock, Greenock; Kilchattan Tile-work, Bute; Tangy Glen, near Campbeltown; Kyles of Bute; ? Loch Lomond beds, in shelly boulder clay.

L. gracillima. *Seg.* var.
Garvel Park New Dock, Greenock; Tangy glen, near Campbeltown.

L. Jeffreysii. *Brady.*
East Tarbert; Tangy Glen, near Campbeltown; Caithness, in boulder clay.

L. lævis. *Montg.*
Cumbrae College; West Tarbert; Crinan; Duntroon: Old Mains, Renfrew; Garvel Park New Dock, Greenock; Kilchattan Tile-work, Bute; Tangy Glen, near Campbeltown; Paisley; Kyles of Bute.

L. Lyelli. *Sequenza.*
Duntroon.

L. marginata. *Montg.*
Caithness, in boulder clay; Cumbrae College; Duntroon; Old Mains, Renfrew; Paisley; Tangy Glen, near Campbeltown; Killchattan Tile-work, Bute.

L. semistriata. *Will.*
Caithness, in boulder clay; Lochgilp; West Tarbert; Old Mains, Renfrew; Kyles of Bute.

L. squamosa. *Montg.*
Caithness, in boulder clay; Lochgilp; Duntroon; Tangy Glen, near Campbeltown.

L. squamosa, var hexagona.
Paisley Canal.

L. striata. *Montg.*
Cumbrae College; Lochgilp; West Tarbert; Duntroon; Paisley; Garvel Park New Dock,

L. sulcata. *W. & J.*

Greenock; Kilchattan Tile-work, Bute; Kyles of Bute.

Caithness, in boulder clay; Cumbrae College; Lochgilp; E. Tarbert; Duntroon; Garvel Park New Dock, Greenock; Tangy Glen, near Campbeltown; Kyles of Bute; ? Loch Lomond Beds, in shelly-boulder clay. Synonym: *L. costata,* Williamson.

Genus LITUOLA. *Lamarck.*
  L. Canariensis. *D'Orb.*

Stobcross; Dipple Tile-works.

  L. ornata. *Brady.*

Lochgilp.

  L. scorpiurus. *Montf.*

Paisley; Kilchattan Tile-work, Bute.

Genus NODOSARIA. *Lamarck.*
  N. humilis. *Roemer.*

Monreith Tile-works, Wigtownshire (*Geol. Surv.*)

  N. raphanus. *Linn.*

Caithness, in boulder clay.

  N. scalaris. *Batsch.*

Duntroon.

Genus NONIONINA. *D'Orb.*
  N. asterizans. *F. & M.*

Caithness, in boulder clay; Cumbrae College; Tangy Glen, near Campbeltown; Jordanhill Brick-work; Stobcross; Dipple Tile-works; Kyles of Bute; Lewis, in laminated beds (*R.E.*); Towncroft Farm, near Grangemouth, in red clay with seal bones.

  N. depressula. *W. & J.*

Caithness, in boulder clay; Dalmuir; Crinan; Paisley; Garvel Park New Dock; Kilchattan Tile-work, Bute; Tangy Glen, near Campbeltown; Monreith Tile-work, Wigtownshire (*Geol. Survey*); Stobcross; Paisley Canal; Dipple Tile-works; ? Loch Lomond Beds, in shelly-boulder clay; Kyles of Bute; Lewis, in laminated beds (*R.E.*)

  N. turgida. *Will.*

Lochgilp; Kilchattan Tile-work, Bute; Duntroon; Kyles of Bute; Houston Clay-field.

  N. umbilicatula. *Montg.*

Stobcross.

Genus ORBULINA. *D'Orb.*
  O. universa. *D'Orb.*

Jordanhill Brick-work; ? Paisley Canal.

Genus PATELLINA. *Williamson.*
  P. corrugata. *Will.*

Paisley; Garvel Park New Dock, Greenock.

Genus PLANORBULINA. *D'Orbigny.*
  P. Mediterranensis. *D'Orb.*

Caithness, in boulder clay.

Genus POLYMORPHINA. *D'Orbigny.*
  P. communis. *W. & J.*

Cumbrae College.

  P. gibba. *D'Orb.*

East Tarbert; Kyles of Bute.

  P. lactea. *W. & J.*

Caithness, in boulder clay; Dalmuir; Lochgilp; Kilchattan Tile-work, Bute; Tangy Glen; Kyles of Bute.

  P. oblonga. *Will.*

East Tarbert; Kyles of Bute.

  P. compressa. *D'Orb.*

Caithness, in boulder clay; Dalmuir; Cumbrae College; East and West Tarbert; Duntroon; Old Mains, Renfrew; Paisley; Garvel Park New Dock, Greenock; Kilchattan Tile-work, Bute; Tangy Glen, near Campbeltown; Towncroft Farm, near Grangemouth, in red clay with seal bones.

Genus POLYSTOMELLA. *Lamarck.*
  P. arctica. *P. & J.*

Caithness, in boulder-clay; East and West Tarbert; Kilmaurs; Kyles of Bute.

  P. crispa. *Linn.*

Caithness, in boulder clay; Lochgilp; West Tar-

APPENDIX.

577

	bert; Duntroon; Tangy Glen, near Campbeltown, in laminated clay below boulder clay. Lewis, in laminated beds (*R.E.*)
P. striato-punctata. *F. & M.*	Caithness, in boulder clay; Arran; Dalmuir; Lochgilp; Bucklivie; Annochie, in brick clay; East and West Tarbert; Crinan; Duntroon; Old Mains, Renfrew; Paisley, in laminated clay under a true glacial clay; Kilchattan Tilework, Bute; Kyles of Bute; Tangy Glen, near Campbeltown; Windmillcroft; Terally Brickwork, near Drummore; Monreith Tile-work, Wigtownshire (*Geol. Surv.*); Jordanhill Brickworks; Stobcross; Paisley Canal; Dipple Tileworks; Loch Lomond beds, in shelly-boulder clay; Houston Clay-field.
Genus PULVINULINA. *Parker & Jones.*	
? P. Caracalla. *Roemer.*	Caithness, in boulder clay.
Genus QUINQUELOCULINA. *D'Orbigny.*	
Q. agglutinans. *D'Orb.*	Paisley; Garvel Park New Dock, Greenock; Kyles of Bute.
Q. bicornis. *W. & J.*	Duntroon.
Q. Gualteriana. *D'Orb.*	Paisley Canal.
Q. seminulum. *Linn.*	Caithness, in boulder clay; Dalmuir; Cumbrae College; Lochgilp; East and West Tarbert; Duntroon; Paisley; Garvel Park New Dock; Kilchattan Tile-work, Bute; Tangy Glen, near Campbeltown, in laminated clay below boulder clay; Windmillcroft; Kyles of Bute; Lewis, in laminated beds (*R.E.*); Jordanhill Brickwork; Stobcross; Paisley Canal; Dipple Tileworks; Fort William; Houston Clay Field.
Q. subrotunda. *Montg.*	Caithness, in boulder clay; Dalmuir; Cumbrae College; Lochgilp; East Tarbert; Duntroon; Paisley; Garvel Park New Dock, Greenock; Kilchattan Tile-work, Bute; Tangy Glen, near Campbeltown; Jordanhill Brick-works; Stobcross; Paisley Canal; Dipple Tile-works.
Genus ROTALIA. *Lamarck.*	
R. Beccarii. *Linn.*	Caithness, in boulder clay; Paisley; Kilchattan Tile-work, Bute; Tangy Glen, near Campbeltown; Arran; Kyles of Bute.
R. orbicularis. *D'Orb.*	Lochgilp.
R. Soldarii. *D'Orb.*	Caithness, in boulder clay.
Genus SPIROLOCULINA. *D'Orbigny.*	
S. limbata. *D'Orb.*	Duntroon.
S. planulata. *Lamk.*	Dalmuir.
Genus TEXTULARIA. *Defrance.*	
T. difformis. *Will.*	Caithness, in boulder clay.
T. sagittula. *Defrance.*	Lochgilp.
T. variabilis. *Will.*	West Tarbert; Duntroon.
Genus TRILOCULINA. *D'Orb.*	
T. oblonga. *Montg.*	Caithness, in boulder clay; Lochgilp; Garvel Park New Dock, Greenock; near Paisley; Kyles of Bute; Lewis, in laminated beds (*R.E.*)
T. tricarinata. *D'Orb.*	Garvel Park New Dock, Greenock.
Genus TROCHAMMINA. *Parker & Jones.*	
T. incerta. *D'Orb.*	Caithness, in boulder clay.

P P

T. inflata. *Montg.*	Caithness, in boulder clay ; Duntroon ; Stobcross ; Dipple Tile-works.
Genus TRUNCATULINA. *D'Orb*	
T. lobatula. *W. & J.*	Caithness, in boulder clay ; Dalmuir ; Cumbrae College ; Lochgilp ; West Tarbert ; Crinan ; Duntroon ; Old Mains, Renfrew. ; Paisley ; Garvel Park New Dock, Greenock ; Kilchattan Tile-work, Bute ; Tangy Glen, near Campbeltown ; Fort William ; Lewis, in laminated beds (*R.E.*)
T. refulgens. *Montf.*	Lewis, in boulder clay (*R.E.*)
Genus UVIGERINA. *D'Orb.*	
U. pygmæa. *D'Orb.*	Kyles of Bute.
Genus VAGINULINA. *D'Orb.*	
V. legumen. *Linn.*	Caithness, in boulder clay ; Tangy Glen, near Campbeltown.
V. linearis. *Montg.*	Caithness, in boulder clay.
Genus VERNEUILINA. *D'Orb.*	
V. polystropha. *Reuss.*	Garvel Park New Dock, Greenock ; Kilchattan Tile-work, Bute.

Spongida.

Genus CLIONA. *Grant.*	
C. cælata. *Grant.*	Caithness, in boulder clay ; Dalmuir ; Old Mains, Renfrew ; Paisley ; Garvel Park New Dock ; Kilchattan Tile-work, Bute ; Lochgilp ; Fort William ; Houston Clay-field.
Genus GEODIA. *Lamarck.*	
G., sp. ind.	Caithness (*C. W. Peach*).
Genus SPONGILLA. *Lamarck.*	
S. fluviatilis. *Pallas.*	Interglacial beds at Cowden Glen, Renfrewshire.

Sub-kingdom: CŒLENTERATA.

Class: Actinoza.

Order : Zoantharia (Z. sclerodermata).

Genus SPHENOTROCHUS. *Edwards & Haime.*	
S. Wrightii. *Gosse.*	Old Mains, Renfrew.

Sub-kingdom: ANNULOIDA.

Class: Echinodermata.

Ophiuroidea.

Genus HOPLOASTER.	
H. gracilis. *Allman.*	Coast two miles W. of Dunbar, in brick clay ; Montrose. Synonym: *Ophiolepis gracilis*, Allman.
Genus OPHIOPHOLIS. *Müller & Troschel.*	
O. aculeata. *Müller.*	Dalmuir ; Paisley ; Garvel Park New Dock ; the remains of this species consist for the most part of spines and plates. Synonym: *Ophiocoma bellis*, Forbes.
Genus OPHIOTHRIX. *Müller & Troschel.*	
O. fragilis. *Muller.*	Caithness, spines in boulder clay. Synonym: *Ophiocoma rosula*, Forbes.

Genus OPHIURA. *Lamarck.*
  O. albida. *Forbes.*

West Tarbert; Duntroon; Garvel Park New Dock, Greenock: Kilchattan Tile-work, Bute.

  O. lacertosa. *Pennant.*

Garvel Park New Dock. Synonym: *O. texturata,* Forbes.

Echinoidea.

Genus AMPHIDOTUS.
  Agassiz.
  A., sp. ind.

Kilchattan Tile-work, Bute.

Genus ECHINUS. *Linnæus.*
  E. esculentus. *Linn.*

Lochgilp; Garvel Park New Dock; Kilchattan Tile-work, Bute; Houston Clay-field. Synonym: *E. sphæra,* Müller.

  ? E. lividus. *Lamk.*

Langbank (*J. Young*).

  E. Norvegicus. *Sars.*

Fort William.

Genus TOXOPNEUSTES.
  Agassiz.
  T. Dröbachiensis. *Müller.*

Dalmuir; Cumbrae College; Lochgilp; E. & W. Tarbert; Crinan; Duntroon; Old Mains, Renfrew; Paisley; Garvel Park New Dock; Kilchattan Tile-work; Caithness (spines); Fort William. Synonym: *Echinus neglectus,* Lamk.

Holothuroidea.

Genus PSOLUS. *Oken.*
  P. phantapus. *Linn.*

Houston, near Glasgow, in brick clay;* Bute (*Prof. Geikie*).

Genus SIPUNCULUS. *Linnæus.*
  S. Bernhardus. *Forbes.*

Caithness; Dalmuir, remains in *Trophon clathratus;* Garvel Park New Dock, Greenock.

Sub-kingdom: ANNULOSA.
Class: Annelida.

Hirudinea.

Genus HÆMOPIS. *Savigny.*
  H. sanguisorba.

Jaws and teeth of the "Horse Leech" have been detected in the interglacial beds at Cowdon Glen, Renfrewshire (*Mahony*).

Tubicola.

Genus FILIGRANA. *Berkeley.*
  F. implexa. *Berkeley.*

Garvel Park New Dock, Greenock.

Genus PECTINARIA. *Lamarck.*
  ? P., sp. ind.

Caithness, in boulder clay (*C. W. Peach*).

Genus SERPULA. *Linnæus.*
  S. triquetra. *Martin.*

Dalmuir; Stevenston (*Landsborough,* fide *Smith*); Lochgilp.

  S. vermicularis. *Linn.*

Caithness, in boulder clay; Dalmuir; Lochgilp; West Tarbert; Garvel Park New Dock; Kilchattan Tile-work, Bute; Jordanhill Brickworks; Fort William; Houston Clay-field.

Genus SPIRORBIS. *Lamarck.*
  S. carinatus. *Flem.*

Paisley; Houston Clay-field.

  S. corrugatus. *Montg.*

Bute (*Smith*).

  S. granulatus. *Montg.*

Caithness, in boulder clay.

---

* Owen, *Palæontology,* 1861, p. 41.

S. nautiloides. *Lam.* — Dalmuir; Stevenston (*Landsborough,* fide *Smith*). Synonym : *Serpula spirorbis,* Lin.

S. spirillum. *Linn.* — East Tarbert; Duntroon; Paisley; Garvel Park New Dock, Greenock; Arran; Jordanhill Brick-works.

Class: Crustacea.

Cirripedia.

Genus BALANUS. *Lister.*

B. balanoides. *Linn.* — Paisley; Windmillcroft; Dalmuir (*Smith*). Lewis, in boulder clay (*R.E.*)

B. cariosus. *Darwin.* — Kyles of Bute (*R. & C.*)

B. concavus. *Bronn.* — Aberdeenshire (*Jamieson,* fide *Smith*).

B. crenatus. *Brug.* — Caithness, in boulder clay; Dalmuir; Paisley; Cumbrae College; East and West Tarbert; Crinan; Old Mains, Renfrew; Garvel Park New Dock, Greenock; Kilchattan Tile-work, Bute; Duntroon; Arran; Jordanhill Brick-work; Stobcross; Fairfield; Paisley Canal; Dipple Tile-works; Fort William; Kyles of Bute; Houston Clay-field.

B. Hameri. *Ascanius.* — Lochgilp; Old Mains, Renfrew; Garvel Park New Dock, Greenock; Kyles of Bute; this is the prevailing Cirripede at Uddevalla. ? Synonym : *B. uddevalensis,* Linn.

B. porcatus. *Da Costa.* — Caithness, in boulder clay; Dalmuir; Cumbrae College; Lochgilp; West Tarbert; Crinan; Old Mains, Renfrew; Duntroon; Paisley, attached to large boulders; Garvel Park New Dock, Greenock; Kilchattan Tile-work, Bute; Kyles of Bute, Fort William; Elie and Errol, Fife; Houston Clay-field. Synonyms : *B. Scoticus* (Brown); ? *B. Costatus* (Smith, *Researches,* p. 48).

Genus VERRUCA. *Schumacher.*

V. Strömia. *Müller.* — Caithness, in boulder clay; Dalmuir; Cumbrae College; Lochgilp; West Tarbert; Crinan; Duntroon; Old Mains, Renfrew; Paisley; Garvel Park, New Dock; Kilchattan Tile-work, Bute; Tangy Glen, near Campbeltown; Kyles of Bute; Fort William; Houston Clay-field. Synonym : *Creusia verruca* (Lam.)

Ostracoda.

Genus ARGILLÆCIA. *G. O. Sars.*

A. cylindrica. *G. O. Sars.* — Duntroon; Cartsdyke; Paisley; Dalmuir; Dumbarton; Garvel Park New Dock; Kilchattan Tile-work, Bute.

Genus ASTEROPE. *Philippi.*

A. teres. *Norman.* — Jordanhill.

Genus BOSQUETIA. *Brady, Crosskey, & Robertson.*

B. robusta. *B. C. & R.* — Paisley.

Genus BYTHOCYTHERE. *G. O. Sars.*

B. constricta. *G. O. Sars.* — Tangy Burn; Duntroon; Dumbarton; Govan.

B. simplex. *Norman.* — Duntroon; Lochgilp; West Tarbert; Cartsdyke; Paisley; Dalmuir; Govan; Jordanhill; Garvel Park, New Dock.

Genus CANDONA. *Baird.*
  C. albicans. *Brady.* — Crofthead (Cowdon Glen).
  C. lactea. *Baird.* — Crofthead (Cowdon Glen).
Genus CYPRIS. *Müller.*
  C. cinerea. *Brady.* — Crofthead (Cowdon Glen).
  C. compressa. *Baird.* — Dipple.
  C. gibba. *Ramdohr.* — Crofthead (Cowdon Glen); Dipple; Terally Brick-works.

  C. lævis. *Müller.* — Dipple.
  C. ovum. *Jurine.* — Dipple Tile-works.
  C. salina. *Brady.* — Crofthead (Cowdon Glen).
  C. virens. *Jurine.* — Crofthead (Cowdon Glen).
Genus CYTHERE. *Müller.*
  C. albomaculata. *Baird.* — Cumbrae; West Tarbert; Dipple.
  C. angulata. *G. O. Sars.* — Paisley; Old Mains, Renfrew; Dalmuir; Dumbarton; Inchlonaig; Garvel Park New Dock, Greenock; Cumbrae College; Kilchattan Tile-work; Kyles of Bute; East and West Tarbert; Lochgilp; Crinan; Dumbarton; Dipple Tile-works.

  C. castanea. *G. O. Sars.* — Tangy Burn; Duntroon; Kilchattan Tile-work; Dipple Tile-work; Cumbrae College; Dumbarton; Paisley; Dalmuir; Old Mains, Renfrew; Fairfield, near Govan; East Tarbert.

  C. Cluthæ. *B. C. & R.* — Cumbrae; Cartsdyke; Govan; Arran; Garvel Park New Dock; Kilchattan Tile-work, Bute.

  C. concinna. *Jones.* — Paisley Canal; Stobcross; Jordanhill; Govan; Old Mains, Renfrew; Dalmuir; Crinan; Duntroon; Elie; Errol; Fort William; Dryleys; Dipple Tile-works; Dumbarton; Inchlonaig; Garvel Park New Dock, Greenock; Cumbrae College; Kilchatan Tile-work, Bute; Kyles of Bute; East and West Tarbert; Lochgilp; Arran; Houston Clay-field.

  C. convexa. *Baird.* — Cumbrae College; Lochgilp; Errol.
  C. costata. *Brady.* — Paisley.
  C. crispata. *Brady.* — Cumbrae College; Paisley.
  C. deflexa. *B. C. & R.* — Jordanhill.
  C. Dunelmensis. *Norman.* — Paisley Canal; Stobcross; Jordanhill; Old Mains, Renfrew; Dumbarton; Inchlonaig; Duntroon; Errol; Elie; Dryleys; Barry; Govan; Dalmuir; Kilchattan Tile-work, Bute; Kyles of Bute; West Tarbert; Lochgilp; Wick; Arran; King-Edward; Clashmahew Tile-work; Annochie.

  C. emarginata. *G. O. Sars.* — Barrie; Elie; Errol; Arran; East Tarbert.
  C. Finmarchica. *G.O. Sars.* — Gamrie; Wick; Lochgilp.
  C. globulifera. *Brady.* — Paisley; Govan; Barry; Elie; Dryleys; Annochie; Errol.

  C. limicola. *Norman.* — Duntroon; Kyles of Bute; Kilchattan Tile-work, Bute; Cumbrae College; Dumbarton; Cartsdyke; Inchlonaig; Tangy Burn; Terally Brick-work; Garvel Park New Dock; Gamrie.

  C. Logani. *B. & C.* — Elie.
  C. lutea. *Müller.* — Paisley Canal; Jordanhill; Old Mains, Renfrew; Dalmuir; Dumbarton; Inchlonaig; Garvel Park New Dock, Greenock; Cumbrae College; Kilchattan Tile-work, Bute; Kyles of Bute; East and West Tarbert; Lochgilp; Wick; Crinan; Duntroon; Fort William; Dipple Tile-work; Errol; Gamrie; Clashmahew Tile-work.

  C. Macallana. *B. & R.* — Kilchattan; Cumbrae.

C. mirabilis. *Brady.* — Barrie; Elie; Dryleys; Errol; Wick.

C. pellucida. *Baird.* — Paisley; Stobcross; Jordanhill; Old Mains, Renfrew; Dalmuir; Inchlonaig; Garvel Park New Dock; Kyles of Bute; East and West Tarbert; Lochgilp; Arran; Gamrie; Paisley Canal.

C. porcellanea. *Brady.* — Kilchattan Tile-work; Cumbrae College; Cartsdyke; Dalmuir; West Tarbert; Garvel Park New Dock.

C. pulchella. *Brady.* — Duntroon; Lochgilp; Kilchattan Tile-work, Bute; Dumbarton; Dipple Tile-work.

C. quadridentata. *Baird.* — Lochgilp.

C. Robertsoni. *Brady.* — Lochgilp.

C. tenera. *Brady.* — Wick; Dipple, &c.

C. tuberculata. *G. O. Sars.* — Paisley; Old Mains, Renfrew; Dalmuir; Dumbarton; Inchlonaig; Garvel Park, New Dock; Cumbrae College; Kilchattan Tile-work, Bute; Kyles of Bute; East and West Tarbert; Lochgilp, &c.; Gamrie; Annochie; King-Edward; Wick; Errol; Crinan; Duntroon; Dipple Tileworks.

C. villosa. *G. O. Sars.* — Paisley Canal; Stobcross; Jordanhill; Govan; Old Mains, Renfrew; Dalmuir; Dumbarton; Inchlonaig; Garvel Park New Dock; Cumbrae College; Kilchattan Tile-work; Kyles of Bute; East and West Tarbert; Lochgilp; Crinan; Errol; Duntroon; Barry; Gamrie; Clashmahew Tile-work; Dipple Tilework.

C. viridis. *Müller.* — Paisley Canal; Stobcross; Jordanhill; Govan; Old Mains, Renfrew; Dalmuir; Dumbarton; Inchlonaig; Garvel Park New Dock; Cumbrae College; Kilchattan Tile-work; Kyles of Bute; East and West Tarbert; Lochgilp; Wick; Duntroon; Errol.

Genus CYTHERIDEA. *Bosquet.*

C. ? inornata. *B. C. & R.* — Annochie.

C. lacustris. *G. O Sars.* — Crofthead; Dipple Tile-work.

C. papillosa. *Bosquet.* — Paisley; Stobcross; Jordanhill; Old Mains, Renfrew; Dumbarton; Inchlonaig; Garvel Park New Dock; Cumbrae College; Kilchattan; Kyles of Bute; East and West Tarbert; Lochgilp; Wick; Arran; Duntroon; Dipple Tile-work; Elie; Errol; Gamrie; King-Edward; Terally Brick-works.

C. punctillata. *Brady.* — Paisley; Stobcross; Jordanhill; Govan; Old Mains, Renfrew; Dalmuir; Dumbarton; Inchlonaig; Garvel Park New Dock; Cumbrae College; Kilchattan Tile-work, Bute; Kyles of Bute; East and West Tarbert; Lochgilp; Wick; Arran; King-Edward; Crinan; Elie; Duntroon; Fort William; Terally Brick-work; Clashmahew Tile-works; Port Logan Cliffs; Dipple Tile-works; Errol; Dryleys; Barry; Houston Clay-field.

C. Sorbyana. *Jones.* — Elie; Dryleys; Errol; King Edward; Tangy Burn.

C. torosa. *Jones.* — Crofthead (Cowdon Glen).

Genus CYTHERIDEIS. *T. R. Jones.*

C. subspiralis. *B. C. & R.* — Wick.

Genus CYTHEROPTERON. *G. O. Sars.*

C. angulatum. *B. & R.* — Duntroon; Crinan; West Tarbert; Kyles of Bute; Kilchattan Tile-work; Cumbrae College; Dumbarton; Dalmuir; Inchlonaig; Garvel Park New Dock; Fort William.

C. arcuatum. *B. C. & R.* — Tangy Burn, near Campbeltown; Elie; Dryleys; Errol.

C. inflectum. *B. C. & R.* — Errol; Dryleys.

C. latissimum. *Norman.* — Paisley; Windmillcroft; Jordanhill; Govan; Old Mains, Renfrew; Dalmuir; Dumbarton; Inchlonaig; Garvel Park New Dock; Cumbrae College; Kilchattan Tile-work; Kyles of Bute; East and West Tarbert; Wick; Elie; Errol; Duntroon; Fort William; Crinan: Dryleys; Barry; Gamrie; Annochie.

C. Montrosiense. *C. B. & R.* — Tangy Burn; Govan; Barrie; Elie; Dryleys; Errol; Annochie; King-Edward.

C. nodosum. *Brady.* — Duntroon; Crinan; Kyles of Bute; Cumbrae College; Cartsdyke; Dalmuir; Old Mains, Renfrew; Errol; Arran; Garvel Park New Dock.

C. rectum. *Brady.* — Crofthead.

Genus CYTHERURA. *G. O. Sars.*

C. cellulosa. *Norman.* — Gamrie; Duntroon; West Tarbert.

C. clathrata. *G. O. Sars.* — Tangy Burn, near Campbeltown; Crinan; Duntroon; Lochgilp; Cumbrae College; Dumbarton; Cartsdyke; Paisley; Dalmuir; Old Mains, Renfrew; Inchlonaig; East Tarbert; Garvel Park New Dock; Gamrie.

C.? complanta. *B. C. & R.* — Annochie.

C. compressa. *B. C. & R.* — Gamrie.

C. concentrica. *B. C. & R.* — Paisley; Barry; Elie; Dryleys; Errol.

C. cuneata. *Brady.* — West Tarbert.

C. flavescens. *Brady.* — Kyles of Bute.

C. gibba. *Müller.* — West Tarbert; Lochgilp; Fort William; Errol.

C. nigrescens. *Baird.* — Stobcross; Jordanhill; Govan; Paisley Canal; Old Mains, Renfrew; Dalmuir; Dumbarton; Inchlonaig; Cumbrae College; Kilchattan Tile-work; Kyles of Bute; East and West Tarbert; Arran; Duntroon; Dipple Tile-work; Elie.

C. pumila. *B. C. & R.* — Duntroon; Cartsdyke; Garvel Park New Dock.

C. Sarsii. *Brady.* — Duntroon; Lochgilp; Kyles of Bute; Cumbrae College; Cartsdyke; Paisley; Dalmuir; Barry; Gamrie; Garvel Park New Dock; East Tarbert.

C. similis. *G. O. Sars.* — Duntroon; Lochgilp; Kyles of Bute; Kilchattan; Cumbrae; Dumbarton; Cartsdye; Dalmuir; Barry; Garvel Park New Dock; East Tarbert.

C. striata. *G. O. Sars.* — Lochgilp; West Tarbert; Kyles of Bute; Cumbrae College; Cartsdyke; Garvel Park New Dock.

C. undata. *G. O. Sars.* — Paisley Canal; Jordanhill; Govan; Old Mains, Renfrew; Dalmuir; Dumbarton; Inchlonaig; Garvel Park New Dock; Cumbrae College; Kilchattan Tile-work; Kyles of Bute; East and West Tarbert; Wick; Arran; Lochgilp; Crinan: Duntroon; Terally Brick-works; Gamrie.

Genus EUCYTHERE. *Brady.*
  E. argus. *G. O. Sars.*
    Duntroon ; Lochgilp ; Kyles of Bute ; Kilchattan Tile-work ; Cumbrae College ; Dumbarton ; Cartsdyke ; Paisley ; Dalmuir ; Old Mains ; Elie, &c.

Genus KRITHE. *B. C. & R.*
  K. Bartonensis. *Jones.*
    Crinan ; Duntroon ; Elie.
  K. glacialis. *B. C. & R.*
    Errol.
Genus LIMNICYTHERE. *Brady.*
  L. ? antiquata. *B. C. & R.*
    Crofthead ; Dipple Tile-works ; Terally Brick-works.
  L. inopinata. *Baird.*
    Crofthead ; Dipple Tile-works.
Genus LOXOCONCHA. *G. O. Sars.*
  L. elliptica. *Brady.*
    Govan.
  L. fragilis. *G. O. Sars.*
    Cartsdyke ; Paisley : Garvel Park New Dock.
  L. impressa. *Baird.*
    Duntroon ; Crinan ; West Tarbert ; Cumbrae College ; Wick ; Gamrie.
  L. tamarindus. *Jones.*
    Paisley ; Dalmuir ; Dumbarton ; Inchlonaig ; Garvel Park New Dock ; Cumbrae College ; Kilchattan Tile-work ; Kyles of Bute ; West Tarbert ; Lochgilp ; Elie ; Crinan ; Duntroon ; Clashmahew Tile-works ; Dipple Tile-works.

Genus PARADOXOSTOMA. *Fischer.*
  P. abbreviatum. *G. O. Sars.*
    Lochgilp.
  P. ensiforme. *Brady.*
    Kyles of Bute.
  P. flexuosum. *Brady.*
    Lochgilp.
  P. Fischeri. *G. O. Sars.*
    Lochgilp ; Cartsdyke ; West Tarbert ; Garvel Park New Dock.
  P. tenerum. *B. C. & R.*
    Dumbarton ; Cartsdyke ; Dalmuir ; Garvel Park New Dock.
  P. variabile. *Baird.*
    Tangy Burn ; Duntroon ; Lochgilp ; Kyles of Bute ; Cumbrae College ; Dumbarton ; Cartsdyke ; Paisley ; Govan ; East Tarbert ; Garvel Park New Dock.

Genus POLYCOPE. *G. O. Sars.*
  P. orbicularis. *G. O. Sars.*
    Duntroon ; Dumbarton ; Paisley ; Cartsdyke ; Old Mains, Renfrew ; Govan ; Dalmuir ; Garvel Park New Dock.

Genus PONTOCYPRIS. *G. O. Sars.*
  P. mytiloides. *Norman.*
    Dumbarton ; Cartsdyke ; Paisley ; Dipple ; Garvel Park New Dock.
  P. trigonella. *G. O. Sars.*
    Lochgilp ; Paisley ; Cartsdyke ; Dipple ; Garvel Park New Dock ; Duntroon.

Genus POTAMOCYPRIS. *Brady.*
  P. fulva. *Brady.*
    Dalmuir ; Crofthead (Cowdon Glen).
Genus PSEUDOCYTHERE. *G. O. Sars.*
  P. caudata. *G. O. Sars.*
    Dalmuir ; East Tarbert.
Genus SCLEROCHILUS. *G. O. Sars.*
  S. contortus. *Norman.*
    Paisley ; Windmillcroft ; Jordanhill ; Govan ; Old Mains, Renfrew ; Dalmuir ; Dumbarton ; Garvel Park New Dock ; Cumbrae College ; Kyles of Bute ; East and West Tarbert ; Tangy Burn. ; Lochgilp ; Crinan ; Duntroon ; Fort William ; Elie ; Errol ; Dryleys ; Gamrie.

Genus XESTOLEBERIS. *G.*
    O. Sars.
    X. aurantia.   *Baird.* | Lochgilp.
    X. depressa.   *G. O. Sars.* | Lochgilp; Paisley; Wick; West Tarbert.

Decapoda.

Genus CARCINUS. *Leach.*
  ? C. mænas.   *Linn.*   Bridge of Johnstone, near Paisley (fragments of the carapace, &c., *Prof. Geikie*); Oban (*Prof. Geikie*).

Genus PAGURUS. *Fabricius.*
  P. Bernhardus. *Linn.*   Dalmuir (fragments); Cumbrae College (a claw)

Sub-kingdom; MOLLUSCA.

SECTION: MOLLUSCOIDA.

Class: Polyzoa.

Genus CABEREA. *D'Orbigny.*
  C. Ellisii. *Flem.*   Garvel Park New Dock, Greenock.
Genus CANDA. *Lamouroux.*
  C. reptans. *Linn.*   Duntroon; Paisley; Houston Clay-field.
Genus CELLEPORA. *Fabricius.*
  C. pumicosa. *Linn.*   Caithness, in boulder clay.
Genus CELLULARIA. *Pallas.*
  C. scruposa. *Linn.*   West Tarbert.
Genus CRISIA. *Lamouroux.*
  C. denticulata. *Lamk.*   Caithness, in boulder clay.
  C. eburnea. *Linn.*   Dalmuir; Lochgilp; Crinan; Duntroon; Paisley; Garvel Park New Dock; Kilchattan Tile-work, Bute; Tangy Glen, near Campbeltown; Stobcross.

Genus DISCOPORELLA. *D'Orb.*
  D. Grignoniensis. *Busk.*   Dalmuir; Duntroon; Houston Clay-field. A Crag form.
  D. hispida. *Fleming.*   Paisley.
Genus FLUSTRA. *Linnæus.*
  F. avicularia. *Mont.*   Duntroon.
Genus HIPPOTHOA. *Lamouroux.*
  H. catenularia. *Jamieson.*   Caithness, in boulder clay; Dalmuir; Duntroon.
  H. divaricata. *Lamx.*   Caithness, in boulder clay.
Genus IDMONEA. *Lamouroux.*
  I. fenestrata. *Busk.*   Garvel Park New Dock, Greenock.
Genus LEPRALIA. *Johnston.*
  L. annulata. *Fabr.*   Do.   do.   do.
  L. concinna. *Busk.*   Garvel Park New Dock, Greenock; Lochgilp.
  L. cruenta. *Norman.*   Garvel Park New Dock, Greenock.
  L. crystallina. *Norman.*   Do.   do.   do.
  L. hyalina. *Linn.*   Do.   do.   do.
  L. Peachii. *Johnston.*   Caithness, in boulder clay; Cumbrae College Lochgilp; Dalmuir; Garvel Park New Dock.
  L. Peachii var labiosa. *Johnston.*   Caithness, in boulder clay.
  L. pertusa. *Esper.*   Dalmuir.
  L. simplex. *Johnston.*   Caithness, in boulder clay.
  L. tubulosa. *Norman.*   Garvel Park New Dock, Greenock.
  L. unicornis. *Johnston.*   Caithness, in boulder clay; Dalmuir, with the central mucro preserved (*Crosskey & Robertson*).
  L. ventricosa. *Hass.*   Fort William.

L. verrucosa. *Esper.* — Dalmuir; Duntroon; Garvel Park New Dock, Greenock.

Genus MEMBRANIPORA. *Blainville.*

M. craticula. *Alder.* — Paisley.

M. Flemingii. *Busk.* — Lochgilp; Garvel Park New Dock, Greenock; Stobcross; Houston Clay-field.

M. unicornis. *Fleming.* — Paisley; Dalmuir; Duntroon.

M., sp. ind. — Caithness, in boulder clay (*C. W. Peach*).

Genus SALICORNARIA. *Cuvier.*

S., sp. ind. — Caithness, in boulder clay (*C. W. Peach*). Lewis, in laminated beds (*R.E.*)

Genus TUBULIPORA. *Lamarck.*

T. flabellaris. *Fabr.* — Dalmuir.

T. hispida. *Fleming.* — Dalmuir; Caithness, in boulder clay.

T. patina. *Linn.* — Garvel Park New Dock, Greenock.

T. phalangea. *Couch.* — Dalmuir; Duntroon.

T. serpens. *Linn.* — Dalmuir.

? T. verrucaria. *M. Edw.* — Largs (*Landsborough,* fide *Forbes*). This is probably a synonym of *T. phalangea,* Couch.

Class: Brachiopoda.

Genus RHYNCHONELLA. *Fischer.*

R. (Terebratula) psittacea. *Linn.* — Ayrshire (*Forbes*);* Caithness (*C. W. Peach*).

Genus TEREBRATULA. *Lhwyd.*

T. caput-serpentis. *Linn.* — Ayrshire (*Smith*).†

Section: MOLLUSCA PROPER.

Class: Lamellibranchiata.

Monomyaria.

Genus ANOMIA. *Linnæus.*

A. ephippium. *Linn.* — Caithness, in boulder clay; Dalmuir; Lucknow Pit, Ayrshire; Paisley; Lochgilp; Garvel Park, New Dock, Greenock; West Tarbert; Duntroon; Old Mains, Renfrew; Kilchattan Tile-work, Bute; Gamrie; Cumbrae College; Jordanhill Brick-work; Partick; Paisley Canal; Kyles of Bute; Gartness, in gravel; Houston Clay-field.

A. ephippium var aculeata. *Linn.* — Dalmuir; Lochgilp; Paisley; Stevenston (*Smith*); Cumbrae College; Garvel Park New Dock, Greenock; Kilchattan (*Jamieson*); Kyles of Bute.

A. ephippium var squamula. *Linn.* — Paisley; Caithness, in boulder clay; Lochgilp; Garvel Park New Dock, Greenock; Fort William.

A. patelliformis. *Linn.* — Stevenston (*Smith*); a Tertiary fossil of the Clyde Beds (*Jeffreys*); Fort William; Synonym: *A. undulata,* Gmelin.

Genus OSTREA. *Linnæus.*

O. edulis. *Linn.* — Lucknow Pit, Ayrshire; Kyles of Bute (*Prof. Geikie*); Gourock (*Prof. Geikie*); Cornton (*Haswell*); Caithness (*Peach*). [Messrs. Robert-

---

son and Crosskey have failed to discover this species in any of the older glacial beds of the Clyde. They state that at the Kyles of Bute it occurs in a bed resting on the true glacial shell bed, but not in the latter.]

Genus Pecten. *Pliny.*

P. Groenlandicus. *Sow.* — Elie; Errol; Tangy Glen, near Campbeltown; Montrose, at a depth of from 30 to 40 feet below the surface. Synonym: *P. vitreus.* Gray [non Chem.]

P. Islandicus. *Müller.* — Dalmuir; Cumbrae College; Paisley; West Tarbert; Duntroon; Old Mains, Renfrew; Kilchattan Tile-work, Bute; Kyles of Bute, *in situ* and often covered with large *Balani;* Inchlonaig; Garvel Park New Dock, Greenock; Caithness, in boulder clay; Fort William; Kilmaurs (*J. Young*); Belhelvie; Ellishill; Arran; Langbank; Lochgilp; Gartness, in gravel; Lewis, in laminated beds (*R.E.*); Houston Clay-field.

P. maximus. *Linn.* — Kyles of Bute (*Prof. Geikie*). Fairlie (*Prof. Geikie*); Caithness, in boulder clay; Garvel Park New Dock, Greenock; Fort William. [Messrs. Robertson & Crosskey state that at the Kyles of Bute this species occurs in a bed resting on the true glacial shell bed, but not in the latter.].

P. opercularis. *Linn.* — Caithness, in boulder clay; Lucknow Pit, Ayrshire; Kyles of Bute (*Prof. Geikie*); Arran; Cruden (*Jamieson*).

P. pusio. *Linn.* — Dalmuir (*Smith*). Synonym: *P. sinuosus,* Turton.

P. septemradiatus. *Müller.* — Loch Lomond Beds (*Smith*); Clyde deposits (*Jeffreys*); Fort William (*Jeffreys*); Synonym: *P. Danicus,* Chem.

P. similis. *Laskey.* — Fifeshire (*Fleming,* fide *Smith*). A Coralline Crag fossil (*S. Wood*).

P. tigrinus. *Müller.* — Loch Lomond Beds (*Smith*). Synonym: *P. obsoletus,* Pennant.

P. varius. *Linn.* — Dalmuir (*Smith*).

Dimyaria.

Genus Artemis. *Poli.*

A. lævigata. *Forbes.* — Stevenston (*Landsborough*).

Genus Astarte. *G. Sowerby.*

A. borealis. *Chem.* — Caithness, in boulder clay; Arran; Dalmuir; Lucknow Pit, Ayrshire; Crinan; Stevenston (*Landsborough*); Gamrie; Kyles of Bute; Lochgilp; Gourock (*Prof. Geikie*); Errol; Holy Loch (*Prof. Geikie*); a true arctic form. Synonyms: *A. arctica; A. islandica.*

A. borealis var semisulcata, *Leach.* — Bute; Wick (*Smith*). Synonym: *Crassina Withami,* Smith.

A. compressa. *Montg.* — Caithness, in boulder clay; Arran, Dalmuir; Lochgilp; Gourock; West Tarbert; Duntroon; Old Mains, Renfrew; Garvel Park New Dock, Greenock; Kilchattan Tile-works, Bute; Kyles of Bute; Croftamie, in blue clay; Gamrie; Elie; Paisley; Stevenston (*Landsborough*). Loch Lomond Beds, in shelly-boulder clay; Gartness, in gravel; Houston Clay-field. Synonyms: *A. propinqua,* Landsborough; *A. multicostata,* Smith; *A. Uddevallensis,* Smith.

A. compressa var globosa.
　Müller.
　　Paisley ; Garvel Park New Dock, Greenock.

A. compressa var striata.
　Müller.
　　Paisley ; Fort William ; Arran ; Lewis in boulder-
　　clay (*R.E.*).

A. depressa. *Brown.*
　　Dalmuir and Bute (*Smith*). Lewis (*R.E.*). An
　　arctic form. Synonym : *A. crebricostata,* Forbes.

A. sulcata. *Da Costa.*
　　Lochgilp ; West Tarbert ; Old Mains, Renfrew ;
　　Garvel Park New Dock, Greenock ; Caithness,
　　in boulder clay ; Paisley ; Loch Lomond beds,
　　in shelly boulder clay ; Westergateside, near
　　Drymen, in gravel ; Kyles of Bute ; Port Lo-
　　gan Cliffs, Wigtownshire ; Lewis (*R.E.*) Hous-
　　ton Clay-field.

A. sulcata var elliptica.
　Brown.
　　Dalmuir ; Lochgilp ; Loch Long (*Prof. Geikie*) ;
　　Paisley ; Bute ; Croftamie ; Belhelvie ; Arran ;
　　Gartness, in gravel ; Fort William ; Lewis, in
　　boulder clay (*R. E.*) Synonyms : *A. Gairensis,*
　　Smith ; *Crassina elliptica,* Brown ; *Crassina
　　ovata,* Brown ; *A. semisulcata,* Jeffreys [non
　　Leach].

A. sulcata var Danmo-
　niensis.
　　Stevenston (*Smith*) ; Banff (*Smith*).

A. sulcata var Scotica. *M.
　& R.*
　　Gamrie (*Prestwich*) ; Caithness ; Clyde Beds
　　(*Smith*).

A. triangularis. *Montg.*
　　Fort William.

Genus AXINUS. *J. Sowerby.*

A. ferruginosus. *Forbes.*
　　Annochie (*Jamieson*). Synonym : *Lucina ferru-
　　ginosa,* Forbes.

A. flexuosus. *Montg.*
　　Dalmuir ; Lochgilp ; East and West Tarbert ;
　　Crinan ; Duntroon ; Cumbrae College ; Dipple
　　Tile-works ; Kyles of Bute ; Annochie ; Old
　　Mains, Renfrew, specimens with united valves ;
　　Houston Clay-field.

A. flexuosus var Gouldii.
　Phil.
　　Lochgilp ; Paisley ; Kilchattan Tile-work, Bute ;
　　Garvel Park New Dock, Greenock ; Kyles of
　　Bute. Synonym : *Lucina Gouldii,* Philippi.

A. flexuosus var Sarsii.
　Phil.
　　Annochie (*Jamieson*) ; Arran (*Bryce*). Synonym :
　　Axinus Sarsii, Philippi.

Genus CARDIUM. *Linnæus.*

C. aculeatum. *Linn.*
　　Stevenston (*Landsborough*).

C. echinatum. *Linn.*
　　Caithness, in boulder clay ; Paisley ; Kilchattan
　　Tile-work, Bute ; Lochgilp ; Gamrie ; Corn-
　　ton, near Bridge of Allan ; Belhelvie ; Luck-
　　now Pit, Ayrshire ; Gartness, in gravel ; Lewis,
　　in laminated beds (*R. E.*)

C. edule. *Linn.*
　　Caithness, in boulder clay ; Dalmuir ; Old Mains,
　　Renfrew ; Garvel Park New Dock, Greenock ;
　　Kilchattan Tile-works, Bute ; Cornton, near
　　Bridge of Allan ; Lochgilp ; Lucknow Pit,
　　Ayrshire ; Kinness Burn, St. Andrews, in blue
　　clay ; Lewis, in laminated beds (*R.E.*)

C. exiguum. *Gmelin.*
　　Caithness, in boulder clay ; Paisley ; Lochgilp ;
　　Dalmuir (*Smith*) ; Bute (*Smith*) ; Garvel Park
　　New Dock, Greenock. Synonym : *C. pygmæum,*
　　F. & H.

C. fasciatum. *Montg.*
　　Caithness, in boulder clay ; Cumbrae College ;
　　West Tarbert ; Paisley ; Garvel Park New
　　Dock, Greenock ; Arran ; Lochgilp ; Kyles of
　　Bute ; Houston Clay-field.

C. Grœnlandicum. *Chem.*
　　Gamrie (*Jamieson*) ; King-Edward (*Jamieson*).

C. minimum. *Phil.*
　　Bute (*Smith*). Synonym : *C. Suecicum,* F. & H.

C. Norvegicum. *Spengler.*
　　Caithness, in boulder clay ; Cruden ; Cumbrae

College; Stevenston (*Landsborough*); Lucknow Pitt, Ayrshire. Synonym: *C. lævigatum*, Penn et auct. [non Linn.].

Genus CORBULA. *Bruguière.*
C. gibba. *Olivi.*

East Tarbert; Tangy Glen, near Campbeltown. Synonym: *C. nucleus*, F. & H.

Genus CRENELLA. *Brown.*
C. decussata *Montg.*
C. faba. *Müller.*

Caithness, in boulder clay; Elie.
Errol (*Jamieson*).

Genus CYAMIUM. *Philippi.*
C. minutum. *Fabr.*

West Tarbert; Fort William. Synonym: *Turtonia minuta*, F. & H.

Genus CYPRINA. *Lamarck.*
C. Islandica. *Linn.*

Caithness, in boulder clay; Dalmuir; Cumbrae College; Lochgilp; Lucknow Pitt, Ayrshire; Paisley; West Tarbert; Duntroon; Old Mains, Renfrew; Garvel Park New Dock, Greenock; Kilchattan Tile-work, Bute; Kyles of Bute; Gamrie; Elie; Chapelhall; Ellishill; Langbank; Croftamie, Dumbartonshire, in blue clay; Arran; Jordanhill Brick-work; Stobcross; Fairfield; Paisley Canal; Loch Lomond beds, in shelly-boulder clay; Westergateside, near Drymen, in gravel; Gartness, in gravel; Lewis, in boulder clay (*R.E.*); Houston Clay-field. Synonym; *Venus Islandicus*, Linn.

Genus DONAX. *Linnæus.*
D. vittatus. *Da Costa.*

Caithness, in boulder clay; Ayr (*Smith*). Synonym: *D. anatinus*, F. & H.

D. trunculus. *Linn.*

This shell is recorded by Smith* from Stevenston, [*fide* Landsborough].

Genus GLYCIMERIS. *Lamarck.*
G. siliqua. *Lamk.*

Caithness, in boulder clay.

Genus KELLIA. *Turton.*
K. suborbicularis. *Montg.*

St. Fergus (*Jamieson*); a very doubtful determination.

Genus LEDA. *Schumacher.*
[L. antiqua. *Smith.*]

This is mentioned by Smith in his list, but without any locality; a very doubtful form.

L. arctica. *Gray.*

Elie and Errol; Lucknow Pitt, Ayrshire; Clashmahew Tile-works, Wigtownshire, with the epidermis preserved; Terally Brick-works, near Stranraer; Montrose; Tyrie. Synonyms: *Leda (Nucula) truncata*, Brown; *Nucula Portlandica*, Hitchcock. Essentially an arctic species; occurs in the "Leda clay" of Montreal.

L. limatula. *Say.*

King-Edward (*Jamieson*).

L. lucida. *Lovén.*

Do. do.

L. minuta. *Müller.*

Caithness, in boulder clay; Elie; Errol; Barry; Bute. Synonyms: *Nucula minuta*, Smith; *Leda candata*, F. & H.

L. pernula. *Müller.*

Dalmuir; Lochgilp; Duntroon; West Tarbert; Old Mains, Renfrew; Paisley; Crinan; Garvel Park New Dock, Greenock; Tangy Glen, near Campbeltown; Arran; Windmillcroft; Kilmaurs; Jordanhill Brick-work; Paisley Canal; Kyles of Bute; Inchlonaig; Clashmahew Tileworks; Port Logan Cliffs, Wigtownshire; Barry; Lewis, in laminated beds (*R.E.*); Hous-

---

* *Researches*, p. 49.

L. pernula var baccata.
Steenst.

L. pernula var mucilenta.
Steenst.

L. pygmæa. *Münster.*

ton Clay-field. Synonyms: *Nucula oblonga,* Brown. [Forbes placed *Leda rostrata,* Lamk., recorded from Dalmuir by Smith, as a synonym of *N. oblonga,* Brown.]

Caithness, in boulder clay.

Paisley; Garvel Park New Dock; Kilchattan Tile-work, Bute.

Dalmuir; Lochgilp; West Tarbert; Crinan; Duntroon; Old Mains, Renfrew; Paisley; Montrose; Annochie, in brick clay; Caithness, in boulder clay; Tangy Glen, near Campbeltown; Elie and Errol; Windmillcroft; Cumbrae College; Arran; Jordanhill Brick-work; Partick; Paisley Canal; Dipple Tile-works; Kyles of Bute; Inchlonaig; Clasmahew Tileworks; Port Logan Cliffs; Fort William; Houston Clay-field.

L. pygmæa var gibbosa.
Smith.

L. pygmæa var lenticula.
Müller.

Genus LEPTON. *Turton.*
L. nitidum. *Turton.*

Genus LUCINA. *Bruguière.*
L. borealis. *Linn.*

Cumbrae College.

Paisley; Garvel Park New Dock; Kilchattan Tile-work, Bute.

Lochgilp. Occurs in the post-glacial beds of Christiana (*Sars*).

Kyles of Bute, and Gourock (*Prof. Geikie*); Caithness, in boulder clay. Synonym: *Venus borealis.* Linn.

L. spinifera. *Montg.*
Genus LUCINOPSIS. *Forbes & Hanley.*
L. undata. *Pennant.*

Caithness, in boulder clay.

Ayr (*Smith*); Kyles of Bute (*Crosskey*). [Messrs. Robertson and Crosskey state that at the Kyles of Bute this shell occurs in a bed resting on the true glacial shell-bed, but not in the latter.]

Genus LUTRARIA. *Lamarck.*
L. elliptica. *Lamk.*

Kyles of Bute; Lucknow Pit, Ayrshire. Fossil in all our upper Tertiaries from the Scotch glacial beds to the Coralline Crag (*Jeffreys*). [Messrs. Robertson and Crosskey state that at the Kyles of Bute this shell occurs in a bed resting on the true glacial shell-bed, but not in the latter.]

Genus MACTRA. *Linnæus.*
M. solida. *Linn.*

Kyles of Bute (*Prof. Geikie*); Stevenston (*Landsborough*); Forth Beds (*Smith*); Lewis (*R. E.*)

M. solida var elliptica.
Brown.
M. solida var truncata.
Montg.
M. subtruncata. *Da Costa.*

Stevenston (*Landsborough*); Duntroon; Gamrie.

Forth beds (*Smith*). This appears to be a very doubtful determination.

Cumbrae College; Kilchattan Tile-work, Bute; Forth beds (*Smith*). Synonym: *M. cuneata,* Sow.

M. subtruncata var striata.
Brown.
M. stultorum. *Linn.*

Dalmuir; Ayrshire (*Smith*)?

Jeffreys remarks that this shell occurs, "but not commonly, in all our upper Tertiary strata, from the Scotch glacial beds (*Smith*) to the Coralline Crag (*S. Wood*)."*

---

* *British Conchology,* vol. ii. p. 423.

Genus MODIOLARIA. *Beck.*
M. albicostata. *Sow.*

Dalmuir (*Smith*). Perhaps a variety of *M. discors*, Linn.

M. discors. *Linn.*
M. discors var lævigata. *Gray.*
M. nigra. *Gray.*

Paisley. Synonym: *Crenella discors*, F. & H.

Dalmuir; Lochgilp; Elie; Errol.
Kyles of Bute; Errol; Garvel Park New Dock, Greenock. Synonyms: *Crenella nigra*, F. & H.; *Modiola nigra*, Gray.

Genus MONTACUTA. *Turton.*
M. bidentata. *Montg.*
M. elevata. *Stimpson.*
M. ferruginosa. *Montg.*

Dalmuir. Synonym: *Mya bidentata*, Montagu.
Lochgilp; Tangy Glen, near Campbeltown.
Kilchattan Tile-work, Bute. Synonym: *Mya ferruginosa*, Montagu.

Genus MYA. *Linnæus.*
M. arenaria. *Linn.*
M. truncata. *Linn.*

Bute (*Smith*); Lochgilp, a single valve only.
Windmillcroft; Dalmuir; Cumbrae College; Lochgilp; East Tarbert; Duntroon; Old Mains, Renfrew; Paisley; Kilchattan Tile-work, Bute; Garvel Park New Dock, Greenock; Wick; Rothesay; King-Edward; Elie; Kyles of Bute; Jordanhill Brick-work; Stobcross; Paisley Canal; Dipple Tile-works; Gartness, in gravel; Barry; Fort William; Lewis (*R.E.*); Houston Clay-field.

M. truncata var Uddevallensis. *Forbes.*
Genus MYTILUS. *Linnæus.*
M. edulis. *Linn.*

Dalmuir; Lochgilp, *in situ;* Rothesay; Kyles of Bute, *in situ.*

Dalmuir; Cumbrae College; Lochgilp; Old Mains, Renfrew; Paisley; Garvel Park New Dock, Greenock; Caithness, in boulder clay; Gamrie; Cornton, near Bridge of Allan; Ellishill; Jordanhill Brick-work; Partick; Stobcross; Fairfield; Paisley Canal; Dipple Tile-work; Kyles of Bute; Fort William; Houston Clay-field.

M. modiolus. *Linn.*

Dalmuir; Cumbrae College; Lochgilp: West Tarbert; Old Mains, Renfrew; Paisley; Kilchattan Tile-work, Bute; Caithness, in boulder clay; Crinan; Garvel Park New Dock, Greenock; Arran; Paisley Canal; Kyles of Bute; Fort William; Houston Clay-field.

Genus NUCULA. *Lamarck.*
N. nitida. *G. B. Sow.*
N. nucleus. *Linn.*

Paisley (*Crosskey*).
Caithness, in boulder clay; Lochgilp; Paisley; Rothesay. Synonym: *Arca nuclea*, Linn.

N. nucleus var tumidula. *Malm.*
N. sulcata. *Brown.*

Paisley.
Caithness (*Peach*). This appears to be of very doubtful stability.

N. tenuis. *Montg.*

Lochgilp; West Tarbert; Duntroon; Paisley; Garvel Park New Dock, Greenock; Kilchattan Tile-work, Bute; Annochie; Montrose; Cumbrae College; Jordanhill Brick-work; Partick; Barrie; Houston Clay-field.

N. tenuis var expansa. *Reeve.*
N. tenuis var inflata. *Mörch.*
N. proxima. *Say.*

Cumbrae College.
Paisley; Elie and Errol. A decidedly arctic shell.
Recorded from Aberdeenshire by Smith,[*] [*fide* Jamieson.] According to Gould this shell is closely allied to, if not identical with, *N. nitida*, Sow.[†]

---

[*] *Researches*, p. 54.

[†] Jeffreys, *British Conchology*, vol. ii. p. 150.

Genus PHOLAS. *Lister.*
  P. crispata. *Linn.*

Stevenston (*Landsborough*); Cumbrae College; Gamrie; King-Edward; Kilchattan Tile-work, Bute; Houston Clay-field.

  P. dactylus. *Linn.*
Genus PSAMMOBIA. *Lamarck.*
  P. Ferroënsis. *Chem.*

Stevenston (*Landsborough*); Ayr (*Smith*).

Kyles of Bute (*Crosskey*). [Messrs. Robertson and Crosskey state that at this locality this shell occurs in a bed resting on the true glacial shell-bed, but not in the latter.]

Genus SAXICAVA. *Fleurian de Bellvue.*
  S. Norvegica. *Spengler.*

Caithness, in boulder clay; Arran; Belhelvie; Gourock; Fairlie; Kyles of Bute, *in situ;* Langbank; Lewis, in boulder clay (*R.E.*) Synonyms: *Panopæa arctica*, Gould; *P. Bivonæ*, Smith; *Panopæa Norvegica*, F. and H.

  S. rugosa *Linn.*

Caithness, in boulder clay; Elie and Errol; Dalmuir; Lochgilp; Cumbrae College; East and West Tarbert; Old Mains, Renfrew; Garvel Park New Dock, Greenock; Paisley; Kilchattan Tile-work, Bute; Rothesay; Stobcross; Paisley Canal; Kyles of Bute; Kinness Burn, St. Andrews; Lewis, in boulder clay (*R.E.*); Houston Clay-field. Synonym: *S. pholadis*, Linn.

  S. rugosa var arctica, *Linn.*

Lochgilp; Dalmuir; East Tarbert; Garvel Park New Dock, Greenock; Kyles of Bute; Jordanhill Brick-work; Dryleys, near Montrose. Synonym: *Mya arctica*, Linn.

  S. rugosa var precisa. *Montg.*

Lochgilp, one valve only.

  S. sulcata. *Smith.*

Paisley; Montrose; Annochie; Kyles of Bute; Ellishill; Belhelvie; Rothesay.

Genus SCROBICULARIA. *Schumacher.*
  S. alba. *S. Wood.*

Dalmuir; Lochgilp; West Tarbert; Duntroon; Garvel Park New Dock, Greenock. Synonyms: *Ligula Boysii*, Montg.; *Abra fabilis*, S. Wood; *Syndosmya alba*, F. & H.

  S. prismatica. *Montg.*

Lochgilp; Kilchattan Tile-work, Bute; Kyles of Bute; Greenock (*Smith*). Synonyms: *Ligula prismatica*, Montg.; *Syndosmya prismatica*, F. & H.

Genus SOLECURTUS. *De Blainville.*
  S. candidus. *Renier.*

Caithness (*Peach*).

Genus SOLEN. *Linnæus.*
  S. siliqua. *Linn.*

Fragments in Clyde beds (*Prof. Geikie*); Kilchattan Tile-work, Bute, in fragments.

Genus TAPES. *Mühlfeldt.*
  T. decussatus. *Linn.*

Scotch and Irish beds (*Forbes*); Lucknow Pit, Ayrshire.

  T. pullastra. *Montg.*

Clyde beds (*Smith*); Lucknow Pit, Ayrshire. Synonym: *Venus pullastra*, Smith.

  T. virgineus. *Linn.*
Genus TELLINA. *Linnæus.*
  T. Balthica. *Linn.*

Kyles of Bute (*Prof. Geikie*).

Caithness, in boulder clay; Arran; Dalmuir; Old Mains, Renfrew; Paisley; Gamrie; King-Edward; Belhelvie; Lewis (*R.E.*). Towncroft Farm, near Grangemouth, in muddy sand above a red clay containing seals' bones. This

	form occurs in the Bridlington and Mammaliferous Crags, Cromer beds, Isle of Man beds, and Scandinavian deposits, &c. Synonym: *T. solidala*, F. & H.
T. calcarea. *Chem.*	Caithness, in boulder clay; Elie; Dalmuir; Lochgilp; Lucknow Pit, Ayrshire; Windmillcroft; Cumbrae College; East Tarbert; Crinan; Duntroon; Old Mains, Renfrew; Paisley; Kilchattan Tile-work, Bute; Cornton, near Bridge of Allan; Chapelhall; Gamrie; Belhelvie; Rothesay; Jordanhill Brick-work; Stobcross; Fairfield; Paisley Canal; Kyles of Bute; Kinness Burn, St. Andrew's, in blue clay (as *T. proxima*); Inchlonaig; Garvel Park New Dock; Houston Clay-field. Synonyms: *T. proxima*, Brown; *T. sordida*, Couthouy.
T. crassa. *Linn. (Gmelin).*	Ayr (*Smith*).
T. donacina. *Linn.*	Banff (*Smith*).
T. fabula. *Gronovius.*	Lochgilp.
T. Grœnlandica. *Beck.*	Bute (*Forbes*).
T. squalida. *Pulteney.*	Kyles of Bute (*Crosskey*); Dalmuir. Synonym: *T. incarnata*, F. & H.
T. tenuis. *Da Costa.*	Kyles of Bute (*Crosskey*); Gamrie.
Genus THRACIA. *Leach.*	
T. myopsis. *Beck.*	Elie; Errol; Greenock (*Jeffreys*). Markedly arctic.
T. papyracea. *Poli.*	Kyles of Bute and Lochgilp (*Prof. Geikie*).
Genus VENUS. *Linnæus.*	
V. Casina. *Linn.*	Caithness, in boulder clay. From the Clyde beds to the Coralline Crag (*Jeffreys*).
V. exoleta. *Linn.*	Lucknow Pit, Ayrshire; Clyde beds (*Smith*). Synonyms: *Cythere exoleta*, Lam.; *Artemis exoleta*, Forbes.
V. fasciata. *Da Costa.*	Lucknow Pit, Ayrshire.
V. gallina. *Linn.*	Caithness, in boulder clay. Synonym: *V. striatula*, Donovan.
V. lincta. *Pulteney.*	Caithness, in boulder clay; Dalmuir; Kyles of Bute (*Prof. Geikie*); Clyde beds (*Smith*). Synonym: *Artemis lincta*, F. & H.
V. ovata. *Pennant.*	Caithness, in boulder clay; Tangy Glen, near Campbeltown.
Genus YOLDIA. *Möller.*	
Y. hyperborea. *Lovén.*	Errol. [? the young of *Leda arctica*.]
Y., sp. ind.	Elie. This is identical with a species found by Dr. Törell at Spitzbergen, in 80° N. Lat. (*Brown*).

Class: Gasteropoda.

Prosobranchiata.

Genus APORRHAÏS. *Da Costa.*	
A. pes-pelicani. *Linn.*	Caithness, in boulder clay; Kilchattan Tile-work, Bute; Gourock; King-Edward; Fort William; Lewis (*R.E.*); Houston Clay-field. [Messrs. Robertson and Crosskey state that at the Kyles of Bute this species occurs in a bed resting on the true glacial shell-bed, but not in the latter.]
Genus BUCCINUM. *Linnæus.*	
B. ciliatum. *Fabr.*	Bute (*Forbes*).
B. Grœnlandicum. *Chem.*	West Tarbert; Old Mains, Renfrew; Paisley; Dalmuir; Errol. The shells recorded by Prof. Geikie from the Clyde beds as *B. Humphrey-*

B. undatum. *Linn.*

sianum, appear to be this species (*Jeffreys*).*
According to Messrs. Crosskey and Robertson,
this species was recorded in Dr. Thomson's
Dalmuir list as *B. striatum,*† Sow. Synonym:
B. Cyaneum, Beck.

Dalmuir; Cumbrae College; Lochgilp; Paisley;
Caithness, in boulder clay; West Tarbert;
Duntroon; Gourock; Old Mains, Renfrew;
Garvel Park New Dock; Kilchattan Tile-
work, Bute; Gamrie; Cornton, near Bridge
of Allan; Jordanhill Brick-work; Fairfield;
Paisley Canal; Kyles of Bute; Gartness, in
gravel; Drymen, in gravel; Fort William;
Lewis (*R.E.*); Houston Clay-field. Synonyms:
B. vulgare, Da Costa; *B. porcatum,* Gmelin.

B. undatum var carinatum.
Turton.
Genus CERITHIUM. *Adanson.*
C. reticulatum. *Da Costa.*
Genus CERITHIOPSIS. *Forbes
& Hanley.*
C. costulata. *Müller.*
C. tubercularis. *Montg.*

Bute (*Smith* fide *Jeffreys*). This is a monstrosity.

Cumbrae College; Lochgilp; Duntroon.

Wick. Synonym: *C. nivea,* Jeffreys.
Jeffreys records this as fossil from the Clyde beds
[*fide* Smith].

Genus CHITON. *Linnæus.*
C. albus. *Linn.*
C. cinereus. *Linn.*

Fort William (*Jeffreys*).
Lochgilp; Garvel Park New Dock, Greenock;
Caithness, in boulder clay; Fort William.
Synonym: *C. asellus,* F. & H.

C. marmoreus. *Fabr.*

Dalmuir; Lochgilp; Old Mains, Renfrew; Garvel
Park New Dock, Greenock; Fort William
(*Jeffreys*).

C. ruber. *Linn.*

Dalmuir; Lochgilp; Garvel Park New Dock,
Greenock; Fort William (*Jeffreys*).

Genus COLUMBELLA. *La-
marck.*
C. Holböllii. *Müller.*
Genus CYCLOSTREMA. *Mar-
ryat.*
C.? costulatum. *Müller.*

Fort William (*Jeffreys*).

Paisley (*Crosskey*); Fort William (*Jeffreys*).
Synonym: *Margarita? costulata,* Müller.

Genus DEFRANCIA. *Millet.*
D. Leufroyii. *Michaud.*

Wick, in boulder clay. Synonyms: *Pleurotoma
Leufroyi,* Mich.; *Mangelia Leufroyi,* F. & H.

Genus DENTALIUM. *Linnæus.*
D. abyssorum. *Sars.*
D. entalis. *Linn.*

Wick, in boulder clay.
Wick, in boulder clay; Belhelvie; King-Edward,
Gamrie; Lewis (*R.E.*).

D. tarentinum. *Lamk.*

Gamrie. Smith makes *D. tarentinum* and *D.
dentale,* Linn., synonymous; it is therefore
doubtful which of the two has been found at
this locality.

Genus FISSURELLA. *Bru-
guière.*
F. Græca. *Linn.*

Clyde beds (*Forbes*). Synonym: *F. reticulata,*
F. & H.

Genus FUSUS. *Bruguière.*
F. antiquus. *Linn.*

Cumbrae College; West Tarbert; Lochgilp;
Paisley (*Prof. Geikie*); Garvel Park New
Dock, Greenock; Gourock; Kilchattan Tile-

work, Bute; Croftamie, Dumbartonshire, in blue clay; Caithness, in boulder clay; Paisley Canal; Kyles of Bute; Houston Clay-field.

F. curtus. *Smith.*
Stevenston (*Landsborough*).* Probably a very doubtful species.

F. despectus. *Linn.*
Dalmuir (*Forbes*); Kippet Hills, Loch of Slains, Aberdeenshire (*Jamieson*): Synonyms: *Murex carinatus*, Pen.; *Fusus carinatus*, Lamk.; *F. tornatus*, Gould; *F. carinatus*, Smith.

F. gracilis. *Da Costa.*
Dalmuir; Lewis (*R.E.*).

F. propinquus. *Alder.*
Lochgilp (*Prof. Geikie*); Gamrie; Kind-Edward.

Genus HELCION. *De Montfort.*

H. pellucidum. *Linn.*
Dalmuir; Lochgilp; Ayr. Synonym: *Patella pellucida*, Lin.

H. pellucidum var lævis. *Pennant.*
Dalmuir; Banffshire (*Forbes*).

Genus HELIX. *Linnæus.*

H. hispida. *Linn.*
Kinness Burn, St. Andrews.

Genus HOMALOGYRA. *Jeffreys.*

H. atomus. *Phil.*
Dalmuir; Cumbrae College; Lochgilp; West Tarbert; Duntroon; Garvel Park New Dock, Greenock; Old Mains, Renfrew; Paisley; Kilchattan Tile-work, Bute; Fort William; Jordanhill Brick-work; Stobcross; Dipple Tile-works; Houston Clay-field. Synonym: *Skenea nitidissima*, F. & H.

Genus HYDROBIA. *Hartmann.*

H. ulvæ. *Pennant.*
Paisley; Dalmuir; Kinness Burn, St. Andrews. Synonym: *Rissoa ulvæ*, F. & H. Jeffreys says that the males of this species are probably the *Rissoa subumbilicata*, Montg., which under this name is recorded by Smith from Dalmuir.

Genus LACUNA. *Turton.*

L. divaricata. *Fabr.*
Dalmuir; Cumbrae College; Lochgilp; West Tarbert; Duntroon; Old Mains, Renfrew; Paisley; Garvel Park New Dock, Greenock; Kilchattan Tile-work, Bute; Caithness; Gamrie; King-Edward; Fort William; Jordanhill Brick-work; Stobcross; Paisley Canal; Kyles of Bute; Houston Clay-field. Synonym: *L. vincta*, F. & H.

L. divaricata var quadrifasciata. *Montf.*
Dalmuir. Synonym: *Turbo quadrifasciatus*, Montf.

L. pallidula. *Da Costa.*
Dalmuir; Lochgilp; Fort William. Synonyms: *Turbo pallidulus*, Turton; *Nerita pallidula*, Da Costa.

L. pallidula var neritoidea. *Gould.*
Dalmuir; Fort William.

L. puteola. *Turton.*
Dalmuir; Cumbrae College; Paisley; Garvel Park New Dock, Greenock; Fort William. Synonym: *Turbo puteolus*, Turton.

Genus LITTORINA. *Ferussac.*

L. limata. *Lovén.*
Dalmuir; Cumbrae College; Lochgilp; Paisley; East and West Tarbert; Garvel Park New Dock; Jordanhill Brick-work. Synonyms: *T. palliatus*, Say; *L. arctica*, Müller; *Turbo expansus*, Brown.

L. litorea. *Linn.*
Dalmuir; Cumbrae College; East and West Tar-

[L. neritoides. *Linn.*]

bert; Paisley; Crinan; Old Mains, Renfrew; Kilchattan Tile-works, Bute; Caithness; Cornton, near Bridge of Allan; Croftamie, Dumbartonshire, in blue clay; Windmillcroft; Lochgilp; Lucknow Pit; Arran; Jordanhill Brick-work; Paisley Canal; Kyles of Bute; Kinness Burn, St. Andrews; Gartness, in gravel; Fort William; Houston Clay-field. Recorded by Prof. Geikie from certain of the Clyde beds. Some doubt regarding the correctness of this is expressed by Jeffreys.*

L. obtusata. *Linn.*

Dalmuir; Cumbrae College; Lochgilp; East and West Tarbert; Duntroon; Paisley; Old Mains, Renfrew; Garvel Park New Dock, Greenock; Kilchattan Tile-work, Bute; Caithness, in boulder clay; Lucknow Pit, Ayrshire; Paisley Canal; Kyles of Bute; Houston Clay-field. Synonym: *L. litoralis*, F. & H.

L. obtusata var neritiforme. *Brown.*

East Tarbert.

L. rudis. *Maton.*

Dalmuir; Lochgilp; Paisley; Garvel Park New Dock, Greenock; Kilchattan Tile-work, Bute; Cornton, near Bridge of Allan; Rothesay; Jordanhill Brick-work; Stobcross; Paisley Canal; Fort William.

L. rudis var patula. *Jeffreys.*

Dalmuir; Bute (*Smith*).

L. rudis var saxatilis. *Johnston.*

Garvel Park New Dock, Greenock; Jordanhill Brick-work.

L. squalida. *B. & S.*

Fort William; Ellishill; Invernettie; Railway cutting between Drymen and Gartness, Stirlingshire, in gravel, with other arctic shells (*Jamieson*); Paisley.

Genus MARGARITA. *Leach.*
M. cinerea. *Couthouy.*
M. olivacea. *Brown.*

Bute (*Prof. Geikie*); Rothesay (*Smith*).
Clyde Beds (*Jeffreys*).

Genus MENESTHO. *Müller.*
M. albula. *Fabr.*

Paisley.

Genus MÖLLERIA. *Jeffreys.*
M. costulata. *Müller.*

Old Mains, Renfrew; Paisley; Fort William.

Genus MUREX. *Linnæus.*
M. erinaceus. *Linn.*

Dalmuir (*Smith*).

Genus NASSA. *Lamarck.*
N. incrassata. *Ström.*

Caithness, in boulder clay; King-Edward; Kyles of Bute (*Prof. Geikie*); Dalmuir (*Smith*); Lochgilp; Kinness Burn, St. Andrews. Synonym: *N. macula*, Montg.

N. reticulata. *Linn.*

Duntroon.

Genus NATICA. *Adanson.*
N. affinis. *Gmelin.*

Dalmuir; Cumbrae College; Lochgilp; West Tarbert; Duntroon; Old Mains, Renfrew; Paisley: Garvel Park New Dock, Greenock; Caithness, in boulder clay; Kilchattan Tile-work, Bute; Gamrie (*Chambers*); Gourock; King-Edward; Rothesay; Paisley Canal; Kyles of Bute; Gartness, in gravel; Fort William; Lucknow Pit, Ayrshire; Houston Clay-field. Synonym: *N. clausa*, B. & S.

N. Alderi. *Forbes.*

Caithness, in boulder clay; King-Edward; Lewis

---

* *Brit. Conchology*, vol. iii. p. 362.

(*R.E.*). Synonyms: *N. intermedia* et *Maro-chiensis*, Philippi; *N. nitida*, F. & H.

N. catena. *Da Costa.*
Paisley; Bute; Gourock. This species is mentioned in Dr. Thomson's Dalmuir list as *N. glaucinoides*, Sow.* Synonyms: *N. monilifera*, F. & H.; *N. glaucina.*

[**N. fragilis.** *Smith.*]
Dalmuir. [Considered by E. Forbes to be a much decayed *N. monilifera.*]

[**N. glaucinoides.** *Sow.*]
Recorded from King-Edward by Smith in Jamieson's list of Aberdeenshire glacial shells,† and also by Landsborough from Stevenston.‡ It is a crag-fossil. Forbes also regarded this fossil as identical with *N. monilifera.*

N. Grœnlandica. *Beck.*
Elie and Errol; Old Mains, Renfrew; Garvel Park New Dock, Greenock, Kilchattan Tile-work, Bute; Jordanhill Brick-work; Paisley Canal; Kilmaurs (*J. Young*). Houston Clay-field. Synonym: *N. pusilla*, F. & H.

N. Islandica. *Gmelin.*
Bute; Caithness, in boulder clay; Gamrie; Fort William; Paisley; Elie and Errol; Gamrie; King-Edward; Kilchattan Tile-work (*Jamieson*); Caithness. Synonyms: *N. helicoides*, F. & H.; *N. pallida*, B. & S. [Jeffreys remarks that it is difficult to determine whether *N. pallida*, B. & S., is a synonym of *N. Grœnlandica* or *N. Islandica.*§ Under the designation of *N. pallida* a species is recorded from Dalmuir.]

N. Montacuti. *Forbes.*
Bute, Clyde beds (*Smith*); Lewis (*R.E.*) Synonym: *Natica Montagui*, Forbes.

N. Smithii. *Brown.*
Ardincaple, near Helensburgh (*Smith*). Synonyms: *Bulbus Smithii*, Brown; also probably *N. flava*, Gould; *N. aperta*, Lovén.

N. sordida. *Phil.*
Caithness, in boulder clay (*Peach*).

Genus ODOSTOMIA. *Fleming.*

O. acicula. *Phil.*
Caithness, in boulder clay.

O. albella. *Lovén.*
Do.   do.

O. conoidea. *Brocchi.*
Lochgilp.

O. pallida. *Montg.*
Do.

O. Lukisi. *Jeffreys.*
Garvel Park New Dock, Greenock.

O. spiralis. *Montg.*
Lochgilp; Dalmuir; Kyles of Bute.

O. turrita. *Hanley.*
Lochgilp.

O. unidentata. *Montg.*
Lochgilp; Garvel Park New Dock; Kilchattan Tile-work, Bute; Kyles of Bute.

Genus PATELLA. *Lister.*

P. vulgata. *Linn.*
Paisley; Caithness, in boulder clay; Fort William (*Jeffreys*); Lucknow Pit, Ayrshire; Houston Clay-field.

Genus PLEUROTOMA. *Lamarck.*

P. nebula. *Montg.*
Caithness (*Jamieson*). Synonym: *Mangelia nebula*, F. & H.; *P. ginnaniana*, Phil.

P. pyramidalis. *Ström.*
Caithness; Gamrie; King-Edward; Kilchattan Tile-work, Bute; Dalmuir; Cumbrae College; Lochgilp; West Tarbert; Crinan; Duntroon; Paisley; Kyles of Bute; Inchlonaig; Fort William. Synonyms: *Defrancia Vahlii*, Beck; *Mangelia pyramidalis*, Ström.

[**P. rufa.** *Montg.*]
Recorded from Kyles of Bute (*Prof. Geikie*); King-Edward and Gamrie (*Jamieson*). Jeffreys

---

* Robertson and Crosskey, *Trans. Geol. Soc. Glasgow*, vol. ii. p. 273.
† *Researches*, p. 57.   ‡ *Proc. Geol. Soc.*, vol. iii. p. 444.   § *Brit. Con.*, vol. iv. p. 218.

P. Trevelyana. *Turton.*

P. turricula. *Montg.*

P. violacea. *Migh. & Ad.*

Genus PUNCTURELLA. *R. T. Lowe.*
P. Noachina. *Linn.*

Genus PURPURA. *Bruguière.*
P. lapillus. *Linn.*

Genus RISSOA. *Fréminville.*
R. cancellata. *Da Costa.*
R. costata. *Adams.*
R. inconspicua. *Alder.*
R. inconspicua var ventrosa. *Montg.*
R. membranacea. *Adams.*
R. parva. *Da Costa.*

R. parva var interrupta. *Adams.*

R. proxima. *Alder.*
R. reticulata. *Adams.*
R. soluta. *Phil.*
R. striata. *Adams.*

R. striata var arctica. *Lovén.*

---

has only recognised this species as a glacial shell from the Belfast deposit,[*] those from the localities just quoted probably being the preceding form, *P. pyramidalis.*

Wick (*Peach*); West Tarbert; King-Edward and Gamrie (*Jamieson*); Kilchattan Tile-work, Bute; Hebrides (*Jeffreys*). Synonyms: *Mangelia Trevelyana*, F. and H.; *Fusus decussatus*, Couthouy.

Cumbrae College; West Tarbert; Duntroon; Paisley; Dalmuir (*Smith*); Garvel Park New Dock, Greenock; Lochgilp; Oban (*Prof. Geikie*); Kilchattan Tile-work, Bute; Caithness; Gamrie; King-Edward; Kyles of Bute; Fort William. Synonyms: *Mangelia turricula*, F. & H.; *Fusus discrepans*, Brown.

Dalmuir; Cumbrae College; Lochgilp; Old Mains, Renfrew; Garvel Park New Dock, Greenock; Kilchattan Tile-work, Bute.

Dalmuir; Lochgilp; Cumbrae College; Old Mains, Renfrew; Garvel Park New Dock, Greenock; Fort William; Houston Clay-field. Synonym: *Cremoria Flemingiana*, Leach.

Dalmuir; Cumbrae College; East and West Tarbert; Crinan; Paisley; Kilchattan Tile-work, Bute; Loch Long (*Prof. Geikie*); Caithness; Lochgilp; Lucknow Pit, Ayrshire; Jordanhill Brick-work; Fort William.

Lochgilp. Synonymn: *R. crenulata*, F. & H.
Largs (*Landsborough*).
Crinan; Jordanhill Brick-work.

Dalmuir (*Smith*).
Bute (*Smith*). Synonym: *R. labiosa*, F. & H.
West Tarbert; Duntroon; Paisley (*Jamieson*); Garvel Park New Dock, Greenock; Houston Clay-field.
Dalmuir; Caithness; Cumbrae College; Lochgilp; West Tarbert; Duntroon; Old Mains, Renfrew; Paisley; Garvel Park New Dock, Greenock; Kilchattan Tile-work, Bute; Kyles of Bute; Jordanhill Brick-work; Fort William; Houston Clay-field. Synonym: *Turbo interruptus*, Adams.
Lochgilp. Synonym: *R. striatula*, Jeffreys.
Lochgilp.
Paisley. Synonym: *R. globosa*, Martin.
Dalmuir; Cumbrae College; Lochgilp; West Tarbert; Duntroon; Old Mains; Garvel Park New Dock, Greenock; Kilchattan Tile-work, Bute; Kyles of Bute; Jordanhill Brick-work; Dipple Tile-work; Fort William; Houston Clay-field. Synonym: *Turbo semicostatus*, Montg.

Garvel Park New Dock, Greenock.

---

* *Loc. cit.*, p. 494.

R. striata var saxitilis. *Möller.*
Paisley.

R. violacea. *Desmarets.*
Lochgilp.

Genus SCALARIA. *Lamarck.*
S. Grœnlandica. *Chem.*
Fairlie; King-Edward (*Jamieson*).

Genus SKENEA. *Fleming.*
S. planorbis. *Fabr.*
Dalmuir; Windmillcroft; Cumbrae College; Lochgilp; West Tarbert; Duntroon; Old Mains, Renfrew; Paisley; Kilchattan Tile-work, Bute; Garvel Park New Dock; Jordanhill Brick-work; Dipple Tile-work; Kyles of Bute; Fort William; Houston Clay-field.

Genus TECTURA. *Cuvier.*
T. virginea. *Müller.*
Dalmuir; Cumbrae College; Lochgilp; Old Mains, Renfrew; Paisley; Garvel Park New Dock, Greenock; Kilchattan Tile-work, Bute; Gamrie; Kyles of Bute; Gartness, in gravel; Houston Clay-field. Synonyms: *Acmœa virginea*, F. & H.; *Lottia virginea*, Alder; *Patella virginea*, Müller.

Genus TRICHOTROPIS. *Broderip & Sowerby.*
T. borealis. *Brod. & Sow.*
Garvel Park New Dock, Greenock; Kyles of Bute.

Genus TROCHUS. *Rondeletius.*
T. cinerarius. *Linn.*
Stevenston (*Landsborough*); Garvel Park New Dock; Kilchattan Tile-work, Bute; Lochgilp; (*Prof. Geikie*); Lucknow Pit, Ayrshire; Fort William.

T. cinereus. *Couthouy.*
Clyde beds (*Jeffreys*). Synonym: *Margarita striata*, B. & S.

T. Grœnlandicus. *Chem.*
Dalmuir; Cumbrae College; Lochgilp; East Tarbert; Old Mains, Renfrew; Paisley; Garvel Park New Dock, Greenock; Caithness; Fort William; Rothesay; Errol; Jordanhill Brick-work; Inchlonaig; Houston Clay-field. Synonyms: *Margarita undulata*, G. B. Sow.; *Turbo incarnatus*, Couthouy; *Trochus inflatus*, Brown.

T. helicinus. *Fabr.*
Dalmuir; Cumbrae College; East Tarbert; Paisley; Garvel Park New Dock, Greenock; Fort William; Jordanhill Brick-work.

[T. lineatus. *Da Costa.*]
Paisley (*Smith*). Jeffreys doubts the correctness of this determination.*

T. magus. *Linn.*
T. millegranus. *Phil.*
Clyde beds (*Smith*); Lucknow Pit, Ayrshire.
Fort William (*Jeffreys*). Synonym: *T. Martini*, Smith.

T. tumidus. *Montg.*
Dalmuir; Lochgilp; Old Mains, Renfrew; Garvel Park New Dock, Greenock; Kilchattan Tile-work, Bute; Fort William; Kyles of Bute.

T. Vahlii. *Möller.*
T. Zizyphinus. *Linn.*
Paisley; Caithness. Synonym; *Margarita Vahlii.*
Caithness, in boulder clay.

Genus TROPHON. *De Montfort.*
T. clathratus. *Linn.*
Dalmuir; Lochgilp; West Tarbert; Duntroon; Old Mains, Renfrew; Paisley; Garvel Park New Dock; Kilchattan Tile-work, Bute; Caithness; Gamrie; Belhelvie; King-Edward; Rothesay; Kyles of Bute; Loch Lomond beds, in shelly boulder clay; Gartness, in gravel;

* *Brit. Con.*, vol. iii. p. 319.

T. clathratus var Gunneri. *Lovén.*

Fort William. Synonyms: *Fusus imbricatus*, Smith; *Fusus scalariformis*, Gould; *F. Peruvianus*, Sow.
Dalmuir; Duntroon; Old Mains, Renfrew; Paisley; Garvel Park New Dock, Greenock; Gamrie; King-Edward; Kyles of Bute; Houston Clay-field.

T. truncatus. *Ström.*

Dalmuir; Cumbrae College; Lochgilp; West Tarbert; Duntroon; Garvel Park New Dock; Old Mains, Renfrew; Paisley; Kilchattan Tile-work, Bute; Caithness; Gamrie; King-Edward; Paisley Canal; Kyles of Bute; Gartness, in gravel; Lewis (*R.E.*). Synonym: *Murex Bamffius*, Donovan.

Genus TURRITELLA. *Lamk.*
T. erosa. *Couthouy.*

Elie. Synonym: *T. polaris*, Beck. A markedly arctic form.

T. reticulata. *Migh. & Ad.*

King-Edward (*Jamieson*). Synonyms: *Mesalia reticulata*, Migh and Ad.; *T. lactea*, Möller.

T. terebra. *Linn.*

Caithness, in boulder clay; Arran; Lewis (*R.E.*); Gourock (*Prof. Geikie*); King-Edward and Auchleuchries (*Jamieson*). Synonym: *T. communis*, F. & H.

Genus VELUTINA. *Fleming.*
V. lævigata. *Pennant.*

Dalmuir; Crinan; Garvel Park New Dock, Greenock; Kilchattan Tile-work, Bute; Houston Clay-field.

V. undata. *Smith.*

Old Mains, Renfrew; Dalmuir; Garvel Park New Dock, Greenock; Paisley (*Jamieson*). Synonym: *V. zonata*, Gould.

Opisthobranchiata.

Genus ACTÆON. *De Montfort.*
A. tornatilis. *Linn.*

Caithness, in boulder clay; Lochgilp. Synonym: *Tornatella fasciata*, F. & H.

Genus CYLICHNA. *Lovén.*
C. alba. *Brown.*

Dalmuir; Lochgilp; Duntroon; Paisley; Garvel Park New Dock, Greenock; Annochie; Gamrie; Kyles of Bute. Synonym: *Volvaria alba*, Brown.

C. cylindracea. *Pennant.*

Lochgilp; Paisley; ? Bute; ? St. Fergus. Synonym: *Bulla cylindracea*, Pen.

C. obstricta. *Gould.*

Dalmuir; Lochgilp.

Genus SCAPHANDER. *De Montfort.*
S. lignarius. *Linn.*

Greenock (*Robertson*, fide *Jeffreys*).

Genus TORNATELLA. *Lamk.*
[T. pyramidata.]

Aberdeenshire (*Smith*, fide *Jamieson*).

Genus UTRICULUS. *Brown.*
U. hyalinus. *Turton.*

Dalmuir; Cumbrae College; Duntroon; Paisley; Garvel Park New Dock; Kilchattan Tile-work, Bute. Synonym: *Bulla hyalina*, Turton.

U. mammillatus. *Phil.*

Dalmuir. Synonym: *Cylichna mammillata*, F. & H.

U. obtusus. *Montg.*

Cumbrae College; Lochgilp; West Tarbert; Duntroon; Paisley; Garvel Park New Dock, Greenock; Kilchattan Tile-work, Bute; ? St. Fergus; Kyles of Bute; Dipple Tile-works; Houston Clay-field. Synonym: *Cylichna obtusa*, F. & H.

U. truncatulus. *Brug.*

Duntroon. Synonym: *Cylichna truncatula*, F. & H.

Note.—In a paper on the " Palæontology of the Post-glacial Drifts of Ireland,"

(*Geol. Mag.* vol. x., 1873., p, 447), Mr. A. Bell mentions having obtained the fry of living Mediterranean forms from glacial clay got near Greenock, viz., *Conus Mediterraneus* and *Cardita trapezia.*

VERTEBRATA.

Class: Pisces.

Fish bones have been found in the brick-clay of Invernettie, near Aberdeen,[*] and in the boulder clay of Caithness.[†] Fish vertebræ are recorded by Messrs. Robertson and Crosskey from the following localities:—Paisley; Kilchattan Tile-work, Bute; Garvel Park New Dock, Greenock;[‡] &c. From the last-named locality *Otolites* have also been obtained. Mr. J. Coutts found small fish vertebræ in the deposit at Houston, near Paisley.

Class: Aves.

The skeleton of a bird is recorded by Jamieson from brick-clay on the side of the river Dee near Aberdeen,[§] and bones from the Paisley deposit by Messrs. Robertson and Crosskey. The same authors notice the occurrence of bird bones in the deposit at Jordanhill Brick-work, Patrick.[‖] In the Appendix to his paper "On the Glacial Drift of Scotland,"[¶] Prof. Geikie mentions the fact that the furculum of a gull was found in brick-clay at the Bridge of Johnston, near Paisley. Smith describes this as the "fourchette of a diver" (*Researches*, p. 14), and adds that the bed was 54 feet above sea-level. Mr. Walker states that the remains of two genera were found in red boulder clay at Strathbeden, Fife.[**]

Class: Mammalia.

SECTION: PLACENTALIA.

Ungulata.

Genus Bos. *Linnæus.* B. longifrons. *Owen.*	Frontal bone and horn cores in blue clay at Kinness Burn, St. Andrew's, with *Tellina calcarea* (= *T. proxima*).
B. primigenius. *Boj.*	In clay forming the bed of the Clyde opposite Jordanhill (*Scouler*);[††] in clay in Rothesay Bay (*Prof. Geikie*); in the interglacial beds of Cowdon Glen, Renfrewshire."[‡‡]
Genus CERVUS. *Linnæus.* C. alces. *Linn.*	Recorded by the late Mr. Smith, of Jordanhill, from the marl beds of Perthshire; the exact locality, according to Dr. J. A. Smith, is Airley-wight, in marl underlying moss. [Dr. Smith likewise records numerous other instances of the occurrence of this species in the post-tertiary beds of Scotland, the most important of which are—a marl pit in Forfarshire; in clay and gravel at Strath Halladale, Sutherlandshire; in a peat-moss on the edge of Williestruther Loch, valley of the river Slitrig, Roxburghshire, with the skull of *Bos longifrons;* in a peat-bog at Oakwood, near Selkirk.] Syno-

* Jamieson, *Quart. Journ.*, vol. xiv. p. 518.
† Peach, *Proc. Roy. Phys. Soc. Ed..* vol. iii. p. 403.
‡ *Trans. Geol. Soc. Glasgow*, vols. iii. and iv.
‖ *Trans. Geol. Soc. Glasgow*, vol. iv. p. 244.
¶ *Trans. Geol. Soc. Glasgow*, vol. i.
** *Annals Mag. N. Hist.* 1863, vol. xii. p. 387.
‡‡ J. Geikie, *Geol. Mag.*, vol. v. p. 393.

§ *Loc. cit.*, p. 510.

†† *Ed. New Phil. Journ.*, vol. iii. p. 135.

? C. dama.   *Linn.*

? C. elaphus.   *Linn.*
C. tarandus.   *Linn.*

Genus EQUUS.   *Linnæus.*
E. caballus.   *Linn.*

E. *sp.*

Genus MEGACEROS.   *Owen.*
M. Hibernicus.   *Owen.*

Genus ELEPHAS.   *Linnæus.*
E. primigenius.   *Blum.*

Genus PAGOMYS.
P. fœtidus.   *Gray.*

nym: *Alces malchis*, Gray. (J. A. Smith, *Pro. Soc. Ant. Scotland*, 1871.)
Recorded by James Smith from Kilmaurs, in boulder clay.
    Do.   do.   do.
Bed of the Clyde opposite Jordanhill (*Scouler*); Croftamie, Dumbartonshire, with shells in blue clay, about 18 feet from the surface.

At Cowdon Glen, with the remains of *Bos primigenius*.*
An almost complete skeleton, with the remains of *Bos longifrons* and *Tellina calcarea*, at Kinness Burn, St. Andrew's, in blue clay.

Interglacial beds at Cowdon Glen, Renfrewshire.† Synonym: *Cervus Megaceros*, Hart. (The remains of this extinct elk were found in the shell marl of an old silted-up loch in the parish of Maybole, Ayrshire,‡ with those of *Cervus elaphus* and *Bos primigenius;* with the antlers of *Cervus capreolus*, in a deposit of gravel, earth, and large boulders, probably a river accumulation, at Coldingham, Berwickshire. § It seems most likely, however, that in the latter instance the remains were those of the true elk, *Cervus alces.* ‖)

Proboscoidea.

At Chapelhall, near Airdrie, the bone of an elephant was found at a height of 350 feet above the sea in laminated sand underlying till; Woodhill Quarry, Kilmaurs, in a peaty deposit underlying sand, in which were glacial shells, and overlaid by about 40 or 50 feet of till; a tusk was discovered during the excavation of the line of the Union Canal between Edinburgh and Falkirk; remains found at Cliftonhall 15 to 20 feet from the surface, in boulder clay; Bishopbriggs, near Glasgow.

Carnivora.

Remains of seals have been found in red clay at Westfield of Auchmacoy, near Aberdeen (*Jamieson*); ¶ in laminated clay at Montrose; in brick-clay at Springfield, near Stratheden, Fife,** 150 feet above sea level, and about 16 feet from surface; a pelvis of a seal was obtained from brick-clay at Tyrie, 30 feet above high-water mark; and at a depth of about 19 feet; †† at Portobello the remains of a seal were likewise found in brick-clay, 20 feet above high-water mark, at a depth of 15 feet from the surface. ‡‡ At Camelon, in a bed of clay 90 feet

---

* R. Craig, *Trans. Geol. Soc. Glasg.*, vol. iv. p. 18.   † *Loc. cit.*
‡ *New Statistical Acc. Scot.*, 1845, vol. v. p. 353.
§ J. Hardy, *Trans. Berwicksh. Nat. Hist. Soc.*, vol. i. p. 247.
‖ Dr. J. A. Smith, *Proc. Soc. Ant. Scot.*, 1871, p. 325.
¶ *Quart. Journ. Geol. Soc.*, vol. xiv. p. 514.   ** Page, *Geologist*, vol. i. p. 538.
†† Allman, *Ed. New Phil. Journ.*, 1858, vol. viii. p. 147.   ‡‡ *Loc. cit.*, 1859, vol. x.

above the level of the Frith of Forth; portions
of a skeleton were found in a brick deposit at
Errol; lastly, in sinking a pit on Towncroft
Farm, Grangemouth, seal bones were found in
a red clay, 80 feet from the surface, and about
68 feet below sea level. From mud adhering
to these bones, Messrs. Robertson and Crosskey obtained *Polymorphina compressa, Nonionina
asterizans*, and *Cytheropteron Montrosiense*. The
majority of the remains mentioned in this list
have been examined by Prof. Turner, who pronounced them to belong to the small arctic seal
(*Pagomys fœtidus*, Gray), and not, as has usually
been stated, to *Phoca vitulina*, Linn. (Turner,
Proc. Roy. Soc. Ed., 1869-70, pp. 105—114.)

Note.—The remains of *Bos longifrons* and *Bos primigenius* were obtained in an
old river-gravel in Glasgow; the first in Rutherglen Loan, the latter in Green-
dyke Street. (J. Bennie, *Trans. Geol. Soc. Glasgow*, vol. ii. p. 152.)

EXPLANATORY NOTES REGARDING CERTAIN OF THE LOCALITIES MENTIONED IN THE FOREGOING LIST.

Windmillcroft.—When compared with glacial deposits at other localities in the
Clyde district the clay at Windmillcroft is peculiar from the very scanty proportion of animal remains found in it, no doubt arising from the fact, that the conditions of deposition were less favourable than those of some other localities.
The deposit consists of a clay bed with arctic mollusca, underlying river gravel,
and resting on a thick bed of white sand containing polished and striated boulders.[*]

Dalmuir, Dumbartonshire.—On the banks of the Dalmuir burn, about eight and
a half miles from Glasgow. This locality was extensively explored and described
by Dr. T. Thomson, Mr. James Smith, and again by Messrs. Robertson and
Crosskey. From the examination of the latter investigators, it appears there are
two shell beds, an upper clay bed containing the mass of the shells, and a lower
more sandy deposit, in which the shells are found in the best state of preservation, and of larger size. The sandy bed is underlaid by stiff blue boulder clay
without shells, and the whole capped by water-worn gravel; 30 feet above sea-
level.[†]

Cumbrae College.—A shell-bearing sand bed near the College, Isle of Cumbrae,
described by Messrs. Robertson and Crosskey, who consider that it appertains to
the older glacial deposits of the West of Scotland. It is peculiarly remarkable
for the very large proportion of sand which enters into its composition; 32 feet
above sea-level.[‡]

Lochgilp.—Near the bridge crossing the Crinan Road to Lochgilphead. At
this locality the boulder clay is immediately overlaid by the shell clay, the usual
laminated clay of the Clyde beds being absent. There is no transition from one
to the other, the line of demarcation between the boulder clay and shell clay
being sharp and distinct. The former does not contain any organic remains.
The shell bed in addition to its fauna, which is very abundant, contains a few
boulders, less striated, and smaller in size than those in the underlying boulder
clay, and often with *Serpulæ* attached. At one part of the deposit *Mya truncata*,
and its variety *M. Uddevalensis*, occur in their natural position, with the valves
united.[§]

Lucknow Pit.—Ardeer Ironworks, Ayrshire. There is evidence to show that
here there was either a shell bed containing an admixture of true arctic and
temperate shells, or else two beds, one with purely arctic forms, the other with
temperate. Messrs. Robertson and Crosskey point out that a commingling of
arctic and temperate forms occur in several Norwegian post-tertiary beds. This
was the first locality in the west of Scotland at which *Leda arctica* was found.[‖]

---

[*] Rev. C. H. Crosskey, *Trans. Geol. Soc. Glasgow*, vol. ii. p. 115.
[†] Robertson and Crosskey, *Trans. Geol. Soc. Glasgow*, vol. ii. p. 267.
[‡] *Ibid.*, vol. iii. p. 113.   [§] *Ibid.*, p. 118.   [‖] *Ibid.*, p. 127.

East Tarbert.—A bed of clay containing arctic shells in the Black burn, at the north-east corner of Tarbert Loch, 12 or 15 feet above high-water mark. The mollusca are few in number both specifically and numerically. From the water-worn condition of many of the remains, it would appear that this deposit contains a large percentage of transported organisms. *Trochus helicinus* is very characteristic.[*]

West Tarbert.—A shell clay on the south side of Tarbert Loch, near its head. Many of the shells in this bed, such as *Buccinum undatum*, and *Pecten Islandicus*, attain a considerable size.[†]

Crinan.—A thin shell-bearing stratum occurs on a small plateau on a promontory at the north side of No. 11 Lock, on the Crinan Canal, 30 feet above high-water mark. The shells are scarce and very fragmentary.[‡]

Duntroon.—A stiff brown clay exposed at high-water mark a little to the south of Duntroon Castle. Amongst an abundant fauna, *Pleurotoma pyramidalis* is very characteristic.[§]

Old Mains.—A shell bed, 30 feet above sea-level, exposed in a tramway cutting, between the Houston Pit, No. 5, and Old Mains Farm, Renfrew. The deposit consists of brown sand and earth with a large number of stones covered with *Balani.*[||]

Paisley.—Throughout the Paisley beds, the organic remains are chiefly confined to the lower half of the deposit, but they may occur in any part of the section from the boulder clay to the summit. *Mytilus edulis* occurs in considerable abundance near the bottom of the section. Messrs. Robertson and Crosskey remark that hitherto the boulder clay of the Paisley district has not yielded any vestiges of life, but occasionally beds containing arctic shells have been found beneath the boulder clay. The same writers observe "that the laminated clay, which has been regarded as the unfossiliferous base of the shell clay, is not unfossiliferous, but contains Foraminifera," such as *Polystomella striato-punctata*, &c.[¶]

Garvel Park New Dock, Greenock.—The fossiliferous clay here lies in a trough in boulder clay, and besides the usual shells of arctic type, characteristic of the Clyde beds, contains one or two additional forms of mollusca, not hitherto plentifully found in similar beds of the neighbourhood. Much speculation has been caused by the very confused appearance presented by this deposit generally. Unfavourable opinions as to its genuineness have been advanced, but Messrs. Robertson and Crosskey have arrived at the conclusion that the conditions of the deposit, both as regards the matrix and organic contents, are perfectly reconcilable with established facts.[**]

Kilchattan Tile-work, Bute.—A deposit of muddy sand, 15 to 20 feet above sea-level, containing shells, is here superimposed on the usual laminated clay resting on reddish boulder clay, at the north-west side of Kilchattan Bay. The characteristic shells are *Tellina calcarea*, *Axinus flexuosus*, *Scrobicularia prismatica*, *Cyprina Islandica*, *Mya truncata*, and *Utriculus obtusus*. In the interior of many of the *Mya* valves, thick patches of the muddy sand have become so firmly indurated, as to be scarcely removable. These patches appear to consist of a strong calcareous base. This deposit has been well described both by Mr. Jamieson and Professor Geikie.[††]

Tangy Glen.—About six miles from Campbeltown, on the Tarbert road. At this locality may be seen the rarer phenomenon of the fossiliferous clay *overlaid* by boulder clay of a dark reddish brown. Organic remains are rare, especially the Mollusca. Both the latter and the Ostracoda more nearly resemble those found in the fossiliferous beds of the east than of the west of Scotland, the former of which are generally considered to be much more arctic in character, The prevailing shell is *Leda pygmæa*. Two other forms rare in Scotch glacial beds are met with here, *Pecten Grœnlandicus* and *Montacuta elevata*.[§§]

Caithness.—The boulder clay of Caithness rises in many places to a height of 200 feet above the sea level, and varies in thickness from 60 to 80 feet. It is a tough and compact mass, with numerous striated and polished boulders, and resembles in general appearance the till which contains no shells. The frag-

---

[*] *Trans. Geol. Soc. Glasgow*, vol. iii. p. 321. [†] *Ibid.*, p. 324. [‡] *Ibid.*, p. 327.
[§] *Ibid.*, p. 328. [||] *Ibid.*, p. 331. [¶] *Ibid.*, pp. 334-341.
[**] *Ibid.*, vol. iv. pp. 32-45. [††] *Ibid.*, pp. 128-133.
[§§] *Trans. Geol. Soc. Glasgow*, vol. iv. pp. 134-137.

mentary remains of mollusca are scattered without order through the general mass, many of them striated, some few with portions of the epidermis still remaining and hardly any in a good state of preservation, certainly in the case of bivalves, never with the valves united. Here and there nests and pockets of sand are met with.*

Montrose.—In a dull red to greenish grey laminated clay, forty feet above the sea-level, occupying the estuary valley of the South Esk, arctic shells, many pieces of chalk, and the bones of a seal have been found.†

Cowdon Glen.—In a section on the Crofthead and Kilmarnock Railway, in Cowdon Glen, Neilston, Renfrewshire, are exposed a series of clay, sand, gravel and peaty beds, in hollows between two beds of till. From these beds, evidently of lacustrine origin, have been obtained numerous genera and species of *Diatomaceæ, Desmideæ, Entomostraca*, mosses, and the remains of many plants. In addition to the foregoing, a portion of the skull of *Bos primigenius*, bones of the great Irish elk and the horse have also been obtained from these beds.

Kilmaurs.—Sandstone quarry of Woodhill, near Kilmaurs. At various times during the past half century, the remains of the mammoth and reindeer have been found in a peaty layer between two thin beds of sand and gravel, overlaid by till or boulder clay, and resting directly on the sandstone rock of the quarry. From their position, it has been contended by some writers, that these remains are of preglacial origin, but an extended examination of the neighbourhood does not bear out this view. It appears that the bed of sand and gravel in which the remains were found, is only one of numerous similar intercalated deposits. The bed rock rises up here and there into prominences, giving it a very irregular surface, and it was probably against one of these that the remains were washed, a lower boulder clay or till appearing in the deeper irregularities of the rocky bed.‡

Chapelhall.—Near Airdrie. In a laminated sand underlying till, a bone of the mammoth was found about three hundred and fifty feet above the sea-level. Professor Geikie remarks that the ground has been so altered in mining operations, that it is impossible to fix the exact condition under which this bone was found.§ *Tellina calcarea* was found at this locality in brick clay between two beds of till, at a height of 510 feet above sea-level. (Smith, *Researches*, p. 141.)

Stevenston.—The shells recorded from this locality were obtained from a bed of blue clay 9 feet thick, underlying 30 to 40 feet of sand.‖

Cornton.—Near Bridge of Allan. A clay was discovered in a burn behind Christie's Brick-work, from which were obtained some years ago the bones of a whale, at a depth of 9 feet from the surface, together with pieces of the bark of the alder and nuts of the hazel. This deposit is most probably a post-glacial or recent accumulation.¶

Croftamie.—Dumbartonshire. At about one hundred feet above the level of the sea the horn of a reindeer was discovered in blue clay, 7 feet in thickness under till, accompanied by arctic shells, in all about eighteen feet from the surface.**

Annochie.—Five miles north of Peterhead, on the Aberdeenshire coast. The shells occur in a bed of fine clay a few feet above the sea-level, passing underneath the beach; they are entire, with the epidermis preserved, but very much decayed.††

Belhelvie.—A clay pit five miles north of Aberdeen, and from 30 to 40 feet above high-water mark. The shells are fragmentary and occur in a black stratum in laminated clay which rests on boulder clay.‡‡

Ellishill.—Railway cutting three miles west of Peterhead. The shells are found in a red clay at an elevation of 120 feet above the sea.§§

Gamrie.—Seven miles east of Banff. Shells occur in a thin sand bed at an elevation of about one hundred and fifty feet. The mass of the deposit, consisting of fine sand and clay, extends to a height of 300 feet.‖‖ The fauna is not so intensely arctic as that of Elie and Errol.

* C. W. Peach, *Proc. Roy. Phys. Soc. Ed.*, vol. iii. pp. 38, 396.
† J. C. Howden, *Trans. Geol. Soc. Ed.*, vol. i. p. 141.
‡ Geikie, *Mems. Geol. Survey, Expl.* 22, Scotland.
§ *Glacial Drift of Scotland. Trans. Geol. Soc. Glasgow*, vol. i.
‖ Landsborough, *Proc. Geol. Soc.*, vol iii. p. 444.
¶ J. Haswell, *Geol. Mag.*, vol. ii. p. 182.
** Dr. J. A. Smith, *Proc. R. Phys. Ed.* vol. i. p. 247.
†† Jamieson, *Quart. Journ. Geol. Soc.*, vol. xxi. p. 196.　　　　‡‡ *Ibid.*, p. 196.
§§ *Ibid.*, p. 196.　　　　‖‖ *Ibid.*, p. 196.

King-Edward.—Five miles south-south-east of Banff. Shells found in silt and gravel at an elevation of from 150 to 200 feet, and overlaid by boulder clay; some of them entire and *in situ.*

Tyrie.—Near Kinghorn, Fife. The shells at this locality were first made known by the late Dr. Fleming.

Invernettie.—A brick-work, one mile south of Peterhead.*

Auchleuchries.—Twenty miles north of Aberdeen. Shells occur as broken fragments in a thick mass of gravel, about three hundred feet above the sea-level.†

Portobello.—At the brick and tile works near Portobello, brick-clays are well exhibited, constantly containing *Foraminifera, Entomostraca,* and occasionally shells. Hugh Miller and Prof. Geikie record the occurrence of *Scrobicularia piperata,* nuts of the hazel, branches of the oak, beech, thorn, and other trees.‡ In Abercorn brick-field *S. piperata* occurs in its natural position. Pebbles of chalk and flint and nests of sand are frequently met with. The latter also contain pieces of chalk, flint, grit, together with *Foraminifera, Entomostraca,* and shelly débris, which appear to be different from those in the clay itself. These deposits are probably in part postglacial.

Elie.—On the Fife coast, eleven miles south of St. Andrews. Shells are contained in a bed of sandy-clay passing out to sea, and are not in a good state of preservation. The fauna of this bed is decidedly arctic in character, more so in fact than in most other localities.§ The bed varies in position from high-water mark to 4 feet above it.

Errol.—Clay pit on the north side of the river Tay, eight miles east of Perth. The clay from which the shells are obtained is about forty-five feet above the sea-level, and is remarkable for the intensely arctic character of its fossils. It lies in a trough of boulder clay, and is distinctly laminated in the lower part, where the shells are also more abundant. *Leda arctica* is obtained here.‖

Towncroft Farm.—Near Grangemouth. At this place a shaft was sunk through alternating beds of sand, mud, gravel, clay, and till, to a depth of 150 feet. At a depth of about eigthy feet, the bones of the small arctic seal (*Pagomys fœtidus,* Gray) were found, accompanied by two species of *Foraminifera: Polymorphina compressa,* D'Orb., and *Nonionina asterizans,* F. and M. In the same shaft, at a depth of only 4 feet from the surface, a portion of a horn of a large red deer was met with in blue mud and sand.

Rothesay.—In the course of an excavation for a gasometer in the town of Rothesay, a shelly clay was cut, underlying a bed of stratified sea-sand, which was again overlaid by a stratum of moss.

Arran.—The boulder clay of the south of Arran is a coarse red sandy clay, full of stones, and at times loose and gravelly, but at others dense and hard, occasionally traversed by beds of sand and clay or bands of stones. Shells are found both in the boulder clay and in the laminated beds; when in the former they are usually much broken. In two places vegetable remains were found in the boulder clay, apparently heather stalks. Mollusca, sixteen species, and one doubtful.¶ The *Entomostraca* were obtained in a shell-bearing clay on the banks of the Cloined Burn, near Lag Arran.**

Jordanhill Brick-work.—One mile north-west of Partick, Glasgow; an arctic shell bed overlying laminated clay or mud, not rich in shells or other animal remains, and those present even in a bad state of preservation. The deposit is 63 feet above sea-level. *Mytilus edulis* abundant.††

Stobcross.—Railway cutting between Galbraith Street and Sandyford Street, Glasgow—nearly parallel to and north of the Clyde. A laminated clay, usually of a sandy character, of later date than the neighbouring boulder clay, and containing a purely marine fauna.‡‡

Fairfield, near Govan.—Two sets of deposits are present at this locality, an upper and lower. The former is probably not of glacial origin; the latter contains a species of *Cytheropteron Montrosiense* met with in certain clays of

* Jamieson, *Quart. Journ. Geol. Soc.,* vol. xxi. p. 197. † *Ibid.,* p. 196.
‡ Geikie, *Mems. Geol. Survey, Memoir 32, Scotland,* p. 128.
§ Jamieson, *Quart. Journ. Geol. Soc.,* vol. xxi. p. 196. ‖ *Ibid.*
¶ Rev. J. B. Watson, *Trans. Roy. Soc. Ed.,* 1864, xxiii., pp. 523-546.
** *Id. Ibid.,* pp. 255-56. †† Robertson and Crosskey, *Mon. Post.-Ter. Ostracoda,* p. 8.
‡‡ R. and C., *Trans. Geol. Soc. Glasgow,* iv. pp. 241-245.

the east of Scotland, which are usually considered to be of a more arctic character than those of the west. The lower deposit consisted of a dark grey clay.*

Paisley Canal (Rowan Bridge).—A grey clay with *Mytilus edulis* abundantly dispersed, and associated with *Tellina calcarea.*†

Dipple Tile-works.—Three miles east of Girvan. There are at this locality three beds showing a direct passage from marine through brackish to fresh-water conditions, viz.—1. Clay with marine shells ; 2. Grey clay with chiefly fresh and brackish water forms, and a few marine ; 3. Laminated clay with fresh-water forms.‡

Kyles of Bute.—General sequence of the beds appears to be from below upwards, viz.—1. Unfossiliferous boulder clay; 2. Laminated clay with *Polystomella striato-punctata* (occupying a similar position at Paisley, &c.) ; 3. Arctic shell bed. At some localities there is, resting on the last, another shell bed, exposed at low water, and containing *Pecten maximus, Ostrea edulis, Aporrhais pes-pelicani*, which is distinct from the arctic shell bed, and must not be confounded with it.§

Kinness Burn.—Near St. Andrews. A bed of bluish brown clay near the mouth of this burn contains shells and mammalian remains, and portions of the oak and birch, apparently deposited in a hollow scooped out of red boulder clay, and underlaid by brick clay. Mr. Walker supposes the deposit to have accumulated towards the close of the glacial period.||

Garnock Water.—At a meeting of the Glasgow Geological Society, on the 30th March, 1876, Mr. D. Robertson read a paper, " Notes on a Post-Tertiary Deposit on the Banks of Garnock Water," 200 yards to the south-east of Kilwinning Iron-works. The exposed section, which is 22 feet above sea-level, shows, going downwards, 2 feet of stratified sand and gravel ; shell layer about 10 inches thick ; and boulder clay upon which it rests. In all 150 species were obtained, amongst them being *Velutina undata* (Smith), a high northern form rarely met with in the Clyde beds. The shells in general agree with the Dalmuir and Old Mains deposits.

Dumbarton.—A bed of glacial clay occurs at the south end of the bridge, crossing Leven Water, 15 to 18 feet above sea-level. The same clay occurs in patches a few feet above high-water mark all along the bay on which Helensburgh stands.¶

Inchlonaig Islands.—Loch Lomond. A bed of dark grey clay, exposed when the lake is low, thickly interspersed with shells.**

Barry.—Forfarshire. The clay here has the same general character as at Dryleys, and is decidedly arctic in character. It lies along the estuary of the Tay in a gully in the most recent of the raised sea-margins.††

Dryleys.—Near Montrose. Thick mass of clay at a brick-works, 40 feet above sea-level.‡‡

Clashmahew Tile-works.—One mile south of Stranraer, Wigtownshire. A bed of brown and another of blue clay (brick clays), with, as a rule, ill-preserved shells ; *Leda arctica*, however, has its epidermis preserved, and may be obtained tolerably whole.§§

Terally Brick-works.—Three miles north of Drummore, Wigtownshire. A small patch of greyish-brown, stiff, fine clay, containing few stones, and imperfectly laminated ; fauna highly arctic.||||

Port Logan Cliffs.—Four miles north-west of Drummore, Wigtownshire. A sandy patch in the boulder clay at the south end of the bay.¶¶ Messrs. Robertson and Crosskey mention a stiff clay, with fragmentary and water-worn shells resting immediately on the rock.***

Monreith Tile-works.—About five miles west of Whithorn, Wigtownshire. There

* R. and C., *Trans. Geol. Soc. Glasgow*, iv. pp. 245-51. † *Id. Ibid.*, pp 251-52.
‡ *Id. Ibid.*, pp. 252-54.
§ Robertson and Crosskey, *Trans. Geol. Soc. Glasgow*, v. pp. 29-3⁵.
|| Annal's *Nat. Hist.*, 1864, xiv. pp. 200-209.
¶ Robertson and Crosskey, *Mon. Post.-Tert. Ostracoda*, p. 41.
** *Id. Ibid.*, p. 42. †† *Id. Ibid.*, p. 75. ‡‡ *Id. Ibid.*, p. 75.
§§ Irvine, *Mems. Geol. Survey, Scot. Expl.* 3, p. 23 ; and R. and C., *Monograph*, p. 86.
|||| Irvine, *Ibid.*, *Expl.* i. p. 9 ; and R. and C., *loc. cit.*, p. 69.
¶¶ D. R. Irvine, *Mems. Geol. Survey, Scot. Expl.* i. p. 8.
*** Robertson and Crosskey, *Mon. Post.-Tert. Ostracoda*, p. 69.

is here an upper reddish-brown rather friable clay, with scratched stones, and a lower stiff blue clay, with few stones, and shell fragments.*

Fort William.—The deposits underlie other strata which may belong to the boulder clay series. A few of the species live now in northern Caithness. The assemblage is regarded as Scandinavian.†

Houston Clay Field.—Two and a half miles north-west of Paisley. Two shell beds were investigated by Mr. J. Coutts, one at ten feet, the other at twenty feet, from the surface. The organisms in the lower clay are dwarfed. The clays probably lie in hollows of the boulder clay. *Proc. Nat. Hist. Soc. Glasgow*, 1876, pp. 336—342.

NOTE D.

MAP AND SECTIONS OF LOCH LOMOND.

This map and the accompanying sections are the work of my friend, Mr. R. L. Jack. The sections are drawn on a true scale (same as the map), and are designed to give a clear idea of what is meant by a true rock-basin. It will be observed that the lake is deepest in its narrow upper reaches, where, half way between Inverness and Tarbet, it attains a depth of 100 to 105 fathoms. In its lower and wider reaches it shallows to 20, 12, 5, and 1 fathom. But so gradual is this shallowing, that were the lake to be drained of all its water, we should hardly be able to discover, without levelling, which was the deepest part of the hollow. The horizontal section brings out this feature in a striking manner. When, therefore, mention is made of a rock-basin 100 fathoms deep, we are not to think of a profound hole like a huge pit, but of an elongated cavity, overlooked it may be on both sides with more or less steep mountains or hills, and sloping in from both ends at a degree of inclination so slight, as to be imperceptible to the eye. Were the Lake of Geneva to be drained, its bed would have merely the appearance of a great plain (yet that lake reaches a depth of 980 feet), and the cavity occupied by Loch Lomond would not be more conspicuous.

Loch Lomond is a very interesting and satisfactory example of a rock-basin. We are quite sure of its depth, because it has been sounded all over by the officers of our navy, and we know that it does not lie in a line of dislocation or gaping fissure, neither is it crossed by any such fractures or displacements, still less does it owe its origin to an unequal movement of elevation or depression. It is as excellent a specimen of an excavated basin as the heart of a glacialist could desire.

NOTE E.

MAP SHOWING THE PRINCIPAL DIRECTION OF THE GLACIATION OF SCOTLAND.

The earliest general sketch-map of Scotland, showing the direction of the glaciation, is that which accompanies my brother's paper "On the Glacial Phenomena of Scotland," published in the *Transactions of the Glasgow Geological Society*. Since the date of that publication our knowledge has greatly increased. A large part of the midland and southern districts of the country has been surveyed by the Geological Survey, and to their maps I must refer those who desire detailed information. I have not found it possible on the present small map to indicate all the places where striæ have been observed by the Survey, for in many cases they are so closely set that a very large scale would be required for the purpose. Those who have been engaged on the work of the Survey in the districts referred to are Professor Geikie, Dr. (now Professor) Young, and Messrs. B. N. Peach, H. M. Skae, R. L. Jack, J. Horne, D. R. Irvine, and myself. Another observer, Mr. Jolly, has also published a short account of some part of

* J. Craik, *Mems. Geol. Survey, Scot. Expl.* ii. p. 9.
† J. G. Jeffreys, *Brit. Assoc. Report.*, 1863, *t. s. p.* 73.

the Merrick district in Galloway. In the north of Scotland the chief additions
to our knowledge have been made by Mr. Jamieson, who has traced the glaciation
of Caithness, and noted a number of localities on the borders of the Moray Frith,
and along the coasts of the north-west Highlands. Mr. C. W. Peach has
described the glaciation of the Shetlands; Dr. Howden has ascertained the
direction of the glaciation in the Montrose district; Mr. J. F. Campbell has indicated the direction of the striæ in some of the islands of the outer Hebrides,*
and I have given an account of the glaciation of Lewis, and have mapped the
striæ in a number of the western sea-lochs, in certain highland valleys, and
along the borders of several of the highland lakes. I append here a few notes
supplementary to the general account of the glaciation of Scotland given in
chapters vi. and vii.

The direction of the glaciation in the basin of the Clyde is very striking.
From a study of the map it will be observed that the ice which streamed down
the vale of the Leven and the Gareloch, instead of flowing out to sea by the
Frith of Clyde, was forced away to south-east and east, eventually crossing the
whole breadth of Scotland, and doubtless coalescing at last with the Scandinavian
ice-sheet. From this we may imagine how great must have been the accumulation of glacier-ice that filled up the lower reaches of the Frith of Clyde, and
poured southwards over the bed of the Atlantic towards the south-west coast of
Scotland and the north of Ireland. It will be noticed, moreover, that at various
places the striæ cross and recross, and there is sometimes an apparent confusion,
especially on the high grounds that extend from Renfrewshire into Lanarkshire.
These curious appearances are due—first, to the meeting of the two great
opposing streams from north and south; and second to the removal of obstructions to the natural flow of the ice during the retreat of the great *mer de glace.*
The two colossal ice-streams met somewhere above Hamilton. Certain appearances would even lead one to infer that the highland stream sometimes reached
as far south as Lesmahagow; for Mr. B. N. Peach got scattered fragments of
mica-schist, gneiss, and other typical highland rocks in the till of that district.
But it is evident that the region between Lesmahagow and Cambuslang was a
kind of debatable ground upon which the rival ice-streams were liable to occasional deflections. The general trend of the striæ west and south-west of
Strathavon, however, clearly indicates that the high grounds in that district
were glaciated by the ice that streamed outwards from the Highlands. If we
draw an undulating line from the sea-coast near Ayr, north-east to the valley of
the Irvine, and thence across the watershed into the Avon, and east to Lesmahagow, then down the valley of the Clyde to Carluke, sweeping it away to the east
by Wilsontown, and thereafter continuing it along the crest of the Pentlands
and the northern slopes of the Lammermuir Hills, by Reston and Ayton to the
sea, we shall roughly indicate the meeting-place of the two great ice-streams.
All along this line we have a "debatable ground" of variable breadth, throughout which we find a commingling in the till of stones which have come from the
north and south. South of it characteristic highland stones do not occur, and
north of it stones derived from the south are similarly absent. When the ice-
sheets were melting back, and so breaking up into a series of gigantic local
glaciers, the direction of flow occasionally became modified. The highland
glaciers, no longer hampered in their course by the ice piled up upon the low
grounds, were enabled to follow the natural slope of their beds; and this gave
rise to another set of striæ. Examples of such cross-hatching of striæ occur, as
my colleague, Mr. Jack, has proved, very abundantly in the basin of the Clyde.
During the climax of glacial cold the lower reaches of the Frith of Clyde were
choked with ice descending from the mountain glens of Argyleshire, and hence
the ice that streamed down the Gareloch and the valley of the Leven was forced
to overflow the high grounds behind Greenock, and so to continue on its way *up*
the valley of the Clyde towards Glasgow. Hereabouts the pressure of the ice-
sheet advancing from the south began to be felt, and a portion of the highland

* Mr. Campbell considers that these islands have been glaciated by sea-ice coming from the
north-west, while on the other hand, my observations in Lewis compel me to believe that the
glaciating agent was land-ice streaming outwards from the mainland. My colleague, Mr.
R. Etheridge, Jun., who accompanied me during my last visit to the Long Island, also concluded that the glaciation had been effected by land-ice coming from the south-east.

ice-stream became deflected, flowing first south-east, then south, and last south-west, while another portion continued on its easterly course across the whole breadth of the country to the North Sea.

In chapter xxiv. I have spoken of the "undertow" of the ice-sheet, and endeavoured to show how the lower strata of the massive ice-sheet might be deflected, while the upper portions of the stream flowed on in one continuous direction. There is abundant proof to show that this was the case in a less or greater degree in almost every part of the country. The striæ are deflected by isolated hills and projecting bosses, while the general direction of glaciation remains unchanged. Nor is there wanting evidence that would lead one to infer that here and there the lower strata of ice followed one route, while the upper strata were moving in a direction nearly at right angles to the course of the ice below.

INDEX.

{ dinavian ice, 80; condition of, during interglacial times, 155, 263; ditto, during deposition of upper boulder-clay, 194; ditto, during transportation of erratics, 201; ditto, during formation of kames, 224, 238; ditto, during deposition of, upper drifts, 247; *mer de glace* of abuts upon Irish coast, 293; general summary of changes in, during glacial and postglacial times, 328

Schimper, M., cited, 401

Schussenried, palæolithic refuse-heap at, 548, 551

Seal, 265, 301

Sea-lochs of Scotland, 279; rock-basins in, 280; eroded by ice, 282

Sedgwick, Prof., cited, 364

Sheep, 548

Shelly clays (aqueous) below till, 162, 163, 164, 166, 174, 176, 181; between two deposits of till, 163, 168; of maritime districts, 253

Shelly till, of Endrick valley, 164, 176; of Invernettie, 164; of King-Edward, 164; of Berwick, 164; of Caithness, 165, 178; of Ballantrae, 167; of Clanyard Bay, 167; of Port Logan, 167; at Monreith, Port William, Cleshmahew, Lady Bay, Innermessan, Sandhead, Cloined Burn, Lewis, 168; origin of, 176; of Lancashire, &c., 336; of Canada, 450

Siberia, winter temperature in, 89; ossiferous beds of, 554

Sidlaw Hills, glaciated rocks of, 63; erratics of, 200

Sierra Guadarrama, ancient glaciers of, 401

Sierra Nevada, ancient glaciers of, 401

Sierra Nevada of California, 403

Skae, Mr. H. M., on glacial lakes in Nithsdale, 231

Skertchly, Mr. S. B. J., on great chalky till, 354; on palæolithic gravels at Brandon, 506; on superficial deposits of the Fenland, 536; on palæolithic brick-earth below chalky boulder-clay, 565

Slains, preglacial beds of, 162

Sleat Sound, rock basin in, 287, 291

Sleswig, sunk forests of, 309

Slitrig Water, interglacial beds of, 123

Smith, Mr., of Jordanhill, cited, 163, 253

Snow-line, 25

Solent, ancient river-valley of the, 504

Solinus, his description of the Orkneys, 314

Solstices, 97

Solway Frith, glacier-ice in, 66; raised beach of, 300

Somerset, former ice-action in, 362

Sordelli, Sig., on shells in morainic deposits of Italy, 443

Sound of Mull, 292

Sound of Jura, rock-basin in, 287, 292, 294

South America, traces of former glacial action in, 484

Southern Hemisphere, why it has a cooler mean annual temperature than the Northern, 109

Southern Uplands of Scotland, till of, 13; direction of striæ in, 17, 63, 66, 75; erratics of, 199

Sowbacks of till, 13, 76

Spey, kame-gravels of the valley of the, 220

Spithead occupies an ancient river-valley, 504

Sponge, freshwater, 127

Spreafico, Sig., cited, 441

Stag, 424, 548

Stainmoor, passage of ice-sheet across, 336

Stalagmite, formation of, 500

Steinbach, lignite of, 458

Steinbock, 426

Stevenston, shelly clay at, 254; blown sand at, 303

Stinchar valley, drift in, 190; morainic débris of, 197; raised beaches at mouth of, 288

Stirling, 151

Stoat, 509

Stoddard, Prof., on a striated pavement in till, 450

Stone Age, 495

Stone implements in postglacial deposits, 301, 326, 398, 427, 548; in Kent's Cave, 499, 501; distribution of palæolithic, 527

Stones carried by ice-bergs, 48, 56; by ice-rafts, 55, 236, 416, 474, 480; in shelly clays, 257

Stones in till or boulder-clay, character of, 9, 60; local distribution of, 12, 73, 355; occasional bedded arrangement of, 18; lines of, 18; whence derived, 67; curled or involved arrangement of, 69

Stopanni, Sig., cited, 430, 441

Stosseite, 71

Stow, Mr., cited, 485

Stranraer, shelly till near, 168

Straths Affrick and Monar, 276

Strath Bran, glacial deposits of, 217

Striæ, on rock-surfaces, 15; direction of, in Scotland, 16, 63; crossing sets of, 64, 72, 194, 248, 456, 609; below glacier, 64; height reached by, in Scotland, 65; direction of, in Scotch Lowlands, 66; deflection of, 74; direction of, in Caithness, in Fraser-

PRINTED BY VIRTUE AND CO., LIMITED, CITY ROAD, LONDON.